FUNCTIONAL APPROACH TO PRECALCULUS

FUNCTIONAL APPROACH

TO PRECALCULUS

MUSTAFA A. MUNEM

JAMES P. YIZZE

MACOMB COUNTY COMMUNITY COLLEGE

WORTH PUBLISHERS, INC.

FUNCTIONAL APPROACH TO PRECALCULUS

COPYRIGHT © 1970 BY WORTH PUBLISHERS, INC.

70 FIFTH AVENUE, NEW YORK, NEW YORK 10011

PRINTED IN THE UNITED STATES OF AMERICA

LIBRARY OF CONGRESS CATALOG CARD NO. 70-115768

DESIGN BY MALCOLM GREAR DESIGNERS, INC.

PREFACE

PURPOSE: This text provides the preparation necessary for students who intend to take calculus or other specialized freshman-sophomore courses in college mathematics. It also gives students in general education an opportunity to fulfill their desire for a mature investigation and understanding of that level of mathematics usually referred to as "precalculus" mathematics.

PREREQUISITES: It is assumed that the students who use this text have had the equivalent of at least one year of plane geometry as taught in high schools and that they have the manipulatory skills which are usually acquired in one and a half years of high school algebra.

GOALS AND EXPOSITION: The text was written with three goals in mind: first, that the student be able to learn from the text itself; second, that he be led to reason carefully and write precisely; and third, that he gain the ability to apply to specific situations the ideas he has learned. To accomplish these goals, the exposition has been interspersed with many examples. Geometric interpretations supplement explanations whenever possible. Definitions and theorems have been carefully stated, and there is a reasonable balance between theory on one hand, and technique, drill, and application, on the other. Review problem sets at the end of each chapter will help students to understand the material covered in each chapter.

Our primary goal, that the presentation be clear and accessible to students, has led us to write some passages in ways that will be (and have been!) questioned by some mathematicians. Aware of these dilemmas we have nonetheless chosen to be guided by what our experience in the classroom has taught us is most appropriate for students.

CONTENT: Although the recommendations for Math O and Math A made by the Committee on the Undergraduate Program in Mathematics (CUPM) of the Mathematical Association of America have greatly influenced the content of this text, they have been tempered by the actual experience gained in two years of class testing preliminary editions of the book at Macomb County Community College. The function concept serves as the central theme.

Chapter 1 sets forth some important preliminary material dealing with real number sets. Set interval notation is introduced here and used throughout the text.

Chapter 2 presents some general notions dealing with the concept of a function. Included here is a discussion of domains, ranges, graphs, symmetry, properties of functions, composite functions, and inverse functions. Sequences are also introduced.

Chapters 3 and 4 deal with polynomial functions, exponential functions, and logarithmic functions. Chapter 3 includes a brief discussion of the solution of linear systems. In Chapter 4, mathematical induction is introduced, then used to prove the binomial theorem; finite sums and geometric series are also covered here.

Chapters 5 and 6, which deal with circular functions and trigonometric functions in the spirit of the previous chapters, include the study of periodic functions, of analytic trigonometry, and the traditional topics of triangle trigonometry.

In Chapter 7, vectors in the plane and elementary properties of rotations are used for geometric and trigonometric applications.

Chapter 8 covers complex numbers, DeMoivre's theorem, and the fundamental theorem of algebra.

Chapter 9 deals with the standard topics of analytic geometry recommended by CUPM.

PACE: The pace of a course, as well as the choice of topics, depends on the particular teacher, on the curriculum, and on the academic calendar. Hence the following suggested pace, which was used under a semester plan, is meant only as a general guide:

Chapter 1: 5 lectures

Chapter 2: 11 lectures

Chapter 3: 8 lectures (Sections 3, 4, and 6 are optional)

Chapter 4: 8 lectures (Sections 2, 6, 7, and 8 are optional)

Chapters 5 and 6: 20 lectures

Chapter 8: 4 lectures (Section 6 is optional)

Other options are possible. For example, if the students are well enough prepared, Chapter 1 can be reviewed briefly in one lecture so that topics in Chapters 7 and 9 can be covered.

This text can also be used in a trigonometry course that meets for 40 hours. The following schedule could be employed:

Chapter 1: 5 lectures

Chapter 2: 8 lectures

Chapters 5 and 6: 20 lectures

Chapter 8: 4 lectures

Chapter 7: 3 lectures

ACKNOWLEDGEMENTS: This text owes a great deal to the special assistance of Professors Jerald T. Ball of Chabot College, Douglas W. Hall of Michigan State University, Frank Prokop of Bradley University, David J. Foulis of the University of Massachusetts, and Sister M. Ferrer McFarland of California State College at Hayward. In addition the following teachers provided advice and criticisms for which we are indebted: Thomas F. Banchoff of Brown University, Karl W. Folley of the University of Detriot, Robert J. Kosanovich of Ferris State College, Richard T. Kuechle of Foothill College, Donald J. Lewis of the University of Michigan, James L. Murphy of Michigan State University, Joseph Murray of the State University of New York at Farmingdale, Henry F. Navarro of Henry Ford Community College, Anthony J. Nespole of Queensborough Community College, Joseph H. Oppenheim of San Francisco State College, David L. Outcalt of the University of California at Santa Barbara, George C. Ragland of Florissant Valley Community College, Franz Schnitzer of Wayne State University, and Norman Wheeler of Schoolcraft College.

Mr. Robert C. Andrews of Worth Publishers, who coordinated this project, merits special thanks. Finally, we thank our colleagues at Macomb, especially Professors William Tschirhart and George Gorte, for their helpful suggestions and criticisms.

Mustafa A. Munem

James P. Yizze

Warren, Michigan

April, 1970

CONTENTS

CHAPTER 1   **Sets and Numbers**   1

Section   1   Sets   3

Section   2   Real Numbers   14

Section   3   Order   24

Section   4   Absolute Value   38

Section   5   Cartesian Coordinate System and
                 Distance Formula   50

CHAPTER 2   **Relations and Functions**   65

Section   1   Relations   67

Section   2   Functions   74

Section   3   Symmetry   89

Section   4   Types of Functions   95

Section   5   Composite Functions   104

Section   6   Inverse Functions   109

CHAPTER 3   **Polynomial Functions**   121

Section   1   Introduction   123

Section   2   Linear Functions   124

Section   3   Systems of Linear Equations   139

Section   4   Determinants   152

Section   5   Quadratic Functions   163

Section   6   Polynomial Functions
                 of Degree Greater Than 2   178

CHAPTER 4   Exponential and Logarithmic Functions   193

Section   1   Introduction   195

Section   2   Properties of Exponents   195

Section   3   Exponential Functions and Their Properties   202

Section   4   Logarithmic Functions and Their Properties   205

Section   5   Properties of Logarithms   209

Section   6   Computation of Logarithms   212

Section   7   Mathematical Induction   221

Section   8   Finite Sums and Series   231

CHAPTER 5   Circular Functions   241

Section   1   Introduction   243

Section   2   The Wrapping Function — a Periodic
             Function   244

Section   3   Circular Functions — Sine and Cosine   255

Section   4   Evaluation of Sine and Cosine   263

Section   5   Graphs of the Sine and Cosine   272

Section   6   Inverses of the Sine and Cosine   283

Section   7   Other Circular Functions   289

CHAPTER 6   Trigonometric Functions   307

Section   1   Introduction   309

Section   2   Angles   309

Section   3   Trigonometric and Circular Functions   322

Section   4   Trigonometric and Circular Function
             Identities   328

Section   5   Trigonometric Equations   337

Section   6   Triangle Trigonometry   342

CHAPTER 7 Vectors in the Plane 359

Section 1 Introduction 361

Section 2 Geometric Approach to Vectors in the Plane 361

Section 3 Analytic Representation of Vectors
in the Plane 368

Section 4 Inner Product 377

Section 5 Applications 382

CHAPTER 8 Complex Numbers and Theory of Equations 397

Section 1 Introduction 399

Section 2 Complex Numbers 399

Section 3 Geometric Representation of Complex
Numbers 406

Section 4 Polar Coordinates 409

Section 5 Roots of Complex Numbers 426

Section 6 Complex Zeros of Polynomial Functions 431

CHAPTER 9 Analytic Geometry 437

Section 1 Introduction 439

Section 2 Circle 440

Section 3 Translations 445

Section 4 Ellipse 451

Section 5 Hyperbola 463

Section 6 Parabola 471

Section 7 Conics 480

APPENDIXES   489

Appendix A   Tables   491

Appendix B   Field Axioms for Real Numbers   507

Appendix C   Trigonometric and Circular Identities   509

ANSWERS TO SELECTED PROBLEMS   511

INDEX   545

CHAPTER 1

Sets and Numbers

1 SETS AND NUMBERS

1 Sets

The primary objective in this section is to present enough about set theory so that the language of sets can be used later to describe mathematical concepts. *Sets* are collections of objects. For example, we can speak of the set of students in a particular course or the set of automobiles in the parking lot or the set of all books in the school library or the set of all letters in the word Florida. In geometry, we speak of a set of lines passing through a fixed point P in the plane (Figure 1) or we may refer to the set of all points that are equidistant from a fixed point C (Figure 2) or to the set of points of intersection of two circles in a plane (Figure 3). We also speak of sets of numbers, such as the set of all count-

Figure 1   *Figure 2*   *Figure 3*

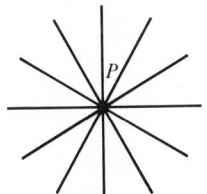

A set of
lines passing
through P

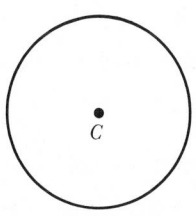

Set of all points
equidistant from
the point C

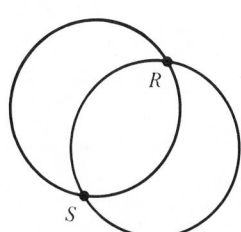

R and S are the points
of intersection of
the two circles

ing numbers (1,2,3, . . . ,etc.) or the set of prime numbers greater than 2 and less than 75.

The set which has no members is called the *null set* or *empty set* and is denoted by $\emptyset$ or by $\{\ \}$. For example, the set of all women presidents in the United States is the empty set, since no woman has been elected to the presidency of the United States. It is important to keep in mind that 0 and $\emptyset$ are not the same.

A set is said to be *finite* if it is possible to list or enumerate *all* the members of the set; a set which is neither finite nor empty is an *infinite* set. For example, if A is the set of all twenty students in a particular class, A is a finite set since its elements can be enumerated. If we use "$N(A)$" to denote "number of elements in A," then $N(A) = 20$. On the other hand, if C is the set of all counting numbers, C is an infinite set since enumeration is impossible in this case.

Set descriptions are usually included between braces. Finite sets can be described by enumeration. For example, $A = \{a,b,c,d\}$ denotes that A is a finite set containing elements a, b, c, and d and no others. We use the notation "$a \in A$" to indicate that "a is an element of set A."

It is important to realize that $\emptyset$ is different from $\{0\}$, since $\{0\}$ is a set with one element, 0, whereas $\emptyset$ is a set that contains no elements.

Besides enumeration, another set description, *set builder notation*, takes the form $A = \{x|x$ has property $P\}$ which is read "A is the set of all elements x such that x has property P." For example, $E = \{x|x$ is an even counting number$\}$ is read "E is the set of all x such that x is an even counting number." Notice that in this case, $2 \in E$, $4 \in E$, $6 \in E$, etc. Since E is an infinite set, it is impossible to enumerate all the elements of E; however, we can use the fact that the members of E form a generally known pattern to write E as $E = \{2,4,6, \ldots\}$, where the three dots mean the same as "etc." We use the symbol $\notin$ to mean "is not a member of"; hence, $1 \notin E$, $3 \notin E$, $5 \notin E$.

EXAMPLE

Use set notation to describe each of the following sets.

a) A, the set of all counting numbers less than 7
b) B, the set of all counting numbers greater than 3
c) C, the set of all students less than 2 inches tall

SOLUTION

a) $A = \{x|x$ is a counting number less than 7$\}$
     or, equivalently, $A = \{1,2,3,4,5,6\}$
     Note that $7 \notin A$.
b) $B = \{x|x$ is a counting number greater than 3$\}$.
     B cannot be described by enumeration because B is an infinite set; however, the known pattern of the elements of B suggests that B can be written as $B = \{4,5,6,7, \ldots\}$.
c)   Since C has no members, $C = \emptyset$.

1.1 Set Relations

Suppose that F is the set of all Ford automobiles and that M is the set of all motor vehicles. Clearly, all the members of F are also found in M. We say that F is a subset of M or, symbolically, $F \subseteq M$, which is read "F is contained in M." The set of all girls in a biology class is a subset of the set of all students in the class. In general, set A is a *subset* of set B, written $A \subseteq B$, if every element of A is an element of B. *The empty set is considered to be a subset of every set.*

EXAMPLES

1   Let $A = \{1,2,3,4,5,6\}$ and $B = \{2,5,3\}$; then $B \subseteq A$.

2   If $A = \{1,2,3\}$ and $B = \{x \mid x$ is a counting number less than $4\}$, then $A \subseteq B$ and $B \subseteq A$.

Example 2 motivates the definition of *equality of sets;* for, if $A \subseteq B$ and $B \subseteq A$, we consider A and B to be different names for the same sets and we write $A = B$.

In Example 1, we have $B \subseteq A$, but $B \neq A$. B is an example of a proper subset of A. In general, B is said to be a *proper subset* of a set A, written $B \subset A$ (notice that the horizontal bar is left off), if all members of B are in A and A has at least one member not in B, that is, $B \subseteq A$ but $B \neq A$.

EXAMPLES

1   If $A = \{1,2,3\}$; $B = \{2,3,1,7,9\}$; and $C = \{2,3,1\}$, then $A \subseteq B$, $C \subseteq B$, $A \subseteq C$, and $C \subseteq A$. More precisely, $A \subset B$, $C \subset B$, and $A = C$.

2   List all subsets of $\{a,b,c\}$.

SOLUTION. $\{a\}$, $\{b\}$, $\{c\}$, $\{a,b\}$, $\{a,c\}$, $\{b,c\}$, $\{a,b,c\}$ and $\emptyset$ are the subsets of $\{a,b,c\}$. Note that all the subsets, with the exception of $\{a,b,c\}$ itself, are proper subsets.

3   If $A = \{2,3,4\}$, $B = \{1,2,3,4,7,8\}$, and $C = \{7,8\}$, then $A \subset B$ and $C \subset B$.

In Example 3, we see that A and C have no members in common. The set of all girls taking biology has no member in common with the set of all boys taking the same class. Such sets are called disjoint sets. In general, two sets which have no members in common are *disjoint*. For example, the sets $\{1,2,3\}$ and $\{4,8,10\}$ are disjoint sets.

Suppose that $A = \{1,2,3\}$ and $B = \{2,8,9\}$. Clearly, $A \nsubseteq B$ and $B \nsubseteq A$. (Why?) Also, A and B are *not* disjoint because $2 \in A$ and $2 \in B$. We say that A and B are overlapping. In general, sets A and B *overlap* if there is at least one member common to A and B and if each set contains at least one member not found in the other. For example, if $A = \{2,3,5,9\}$ and $B = \{3,5,10,11,12\}$, A and B overlap because $3 \in A$ and $3 \in B$, $2 \in A$ and $2 \notin B$, and $11 \in B$ but $11 \notin A$.

When the selection of elements of subsets is limited to some fixed set, the limiting set is called a *universal* set or a *universe*. A universal set represents the complete set or the largest set from which all other sets in that same discussion are formed. The choice of the universal set is dependent upon the problem being considered. For example, in one case it may be the set of all people in the United States, and in another, it may be the set of all people in Michigan.

EXAMPLE

Describe set A where $A = \{x|x$ is a number greater than 2 and x is a member of universal set $U\}$.

a) $U = \{1,2,3,\frac{4}{3},\frac{1}{8}\}$
b) U is the set of all counting numbers.
c) $U = \{0,1,2\}$

SOLUTION

a) $A = \{3\}$
b) $A = \{x|x$ is a counting number greater than 2$\}$

or, equivalently,

$A = \{3,4,5, \ldots\}$
c) $A = \emptyset$

Subsets can be represented pictorially by drawings called *Venn diagrams*. These diagrams often help in understanding set concepts. If we let U be the universal set, an arbitrary set $A \subseteq U$ can be represented as another closed region within the closed region representing U (Figure 4). Each of the four set relations discussed above can be represented by one of four Venn diagrams (Figure 5a, b, c, and d).

Figure 4

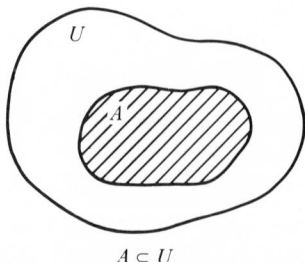

$A \subseteq U$

Figure 5

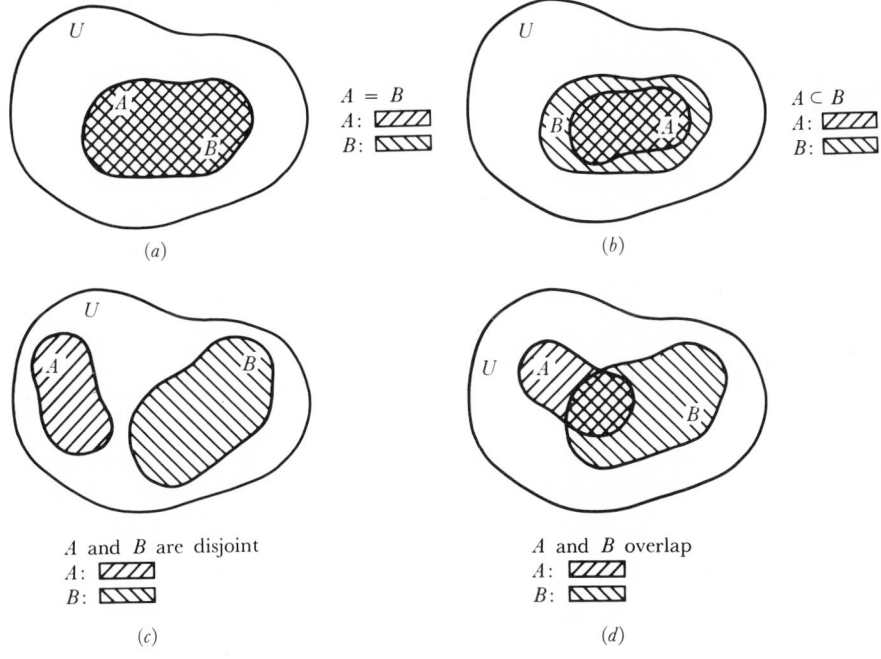

(a)

(b)

$A = B$
A: ▨
B: ▧

$A \subset B$
A: ▨
B: ▧

A and B are disjoint
A: ▨
B: ▧

A and B overlap
A: ▨
B: ▧

(c)

(d)

EXAMPLE

Let N be the set of counting numbers and assume that
$A = \{x | x = 3n, n \in N\}$ and $B = \{y | y = 4m, m \in N\}$.
Use a Venn diagram to illustrate the set relationship between A
and B.

SOLUTION. $A = \{3,6,9,12, \ldots\}$ and $B = \{4,8,12,16, \ldots\}$ are infinite
sets. $3 \in A$ but $3 \notin B$; $4 \in B$ but $4 \notin A$; however, $12 \in A$ and $12 \in B$.
Hence, A and B are overlapping subsets of N (Figure 6).

Figure 6

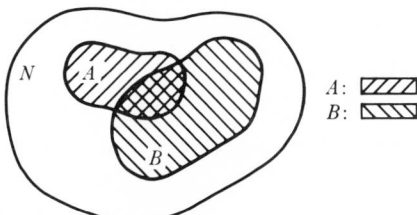

A: ▨
B: ▧

1.2   Set Operations

Consider a universal set $U = \{1,2,3,4,5,6,7,8\}$. From U, we can form
$A = \{1,2,3,4\}$ and $B = \{1,3,7\}$. How can sets A and B be used to form
other sets? One way is simply to combine all the elements of A and B

to form $\{1,2,3,4,7\}$. The operation suggested by this example is that of *set union*.

A union B, written $A \cup B$, and represented by the entire shaded region in Figure 7, is defined as

$$\{x|x \in A \ \text{ or } \ x \in B \ (\text{or both})\}.$$

Figure 7

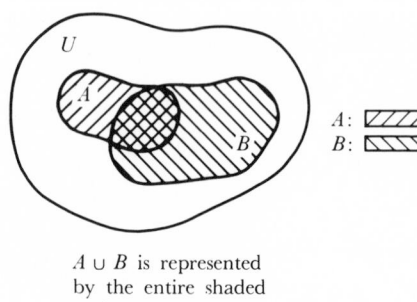

A:
B:

$A \cup B$ is represented by the entire shaded region.

Hence, in the example,

$$\{1,2,3,4\} \cup \{1,3,7\} = \{1,2,3,4,7\}$$

Another way to use A and B to form another set is to form set $\{1,3\}$, the set of all elements common to A and B. This is an example of *set intersection*.

A intersect B, written $A \cap B$, and represented by the shaded region in Figure 8, is defined as

$$\{x|x \in A \ \text{and} \ \ (\text{simultaneously}) \ \ x \in B\}$$

Figure 8

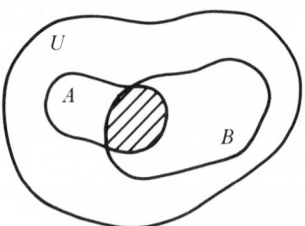

$A \cap B$ is represented by the shaded region.

For example,

$$\{1,2,3,4\} \cap \{1,3,7\} = \{1,3\}$$

If $A = \{1,2,3,4\}$ and $B = \{5,6,7\}$, then $A \cap B = \emptyset$ and A and B are disjoint sets. In general, A and B are disjoint sets whenever $A \cap B = \emptyset$.

The union of two sets, then, is simply the set which results when all the elements of the two sets are combined; the intersection is merely the set of all elements common to the two sets. Note that when the union of two sets containing common elements is described, the common elements are *not* listed twice; hence, $\{2,3,4\} \cup \{1,4,8\}$ is *not* written as $\{2,3,4,1,4,8\}$ but rather as $\{2,3,4,1,8\}$, since the listing of 4 twice is superfluous.

EXAMPLES

1 Determine $A \cup B$ and $A \cap B$ if $A = \{1,2,3,4,5\}$ and $B = \{2,5,6,7\}$.

SOLUTION

$$A \cup B = \{1,2,3,4,5,6,7\} \qquad \text{and} \qquad A \cap B = \{2,5\}$$

2 Let $A = \{x|x$ is a counting number$\}$ and let $B = \{x|x$ is an even counting number$\}$, that is, $B = \{2,4,6,8, \ldots\}$. Form $A \cup B$ and $A \cap B$.

SOLUTION. Note that $B \subset A$ and U is the set of all counting numbers (Figure 9).

Figure 9

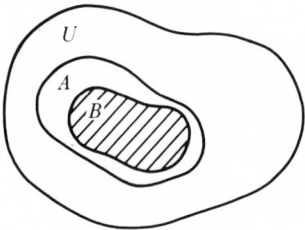

$A \cup B = \{x|x$ is a counting number or x is an even counting number (or both)$\}$

therefore,
$A \cup B = \{x|x$ is a counting number$\} = A$

$A \cap B = \{x|x$ is a counting number and (simultaneously) x is an even counting number$\}$

therefore,
$A \cap B = \{x|x$ is an even counting number$\} = B$

3 Use Venn diagrams to illustrate that $A \cap (B \cup C)$ and $(A \cap B) \cup (A \cap C)$ are equal sets.

SOLUTION. The shaded area of Figure 10a represents $B \cup C$, and the shaded area of Figure 10b represents $A \cap (B \cup C)$. The shaded areas of

Figure 10c and d represent $A \cap B$ and $A \cap C$, respectively, and the shaded area of Figure 10e represents $(A \cap B) \cup (A \cap C)$. Clearly, Figures 10$b$ and e have the same shaded areas, so that the Venn diagrams illustrate the fact that

$$A \cap (B \cup C) = (A \cap B) \cup (A \cap C)$$

Figure 10

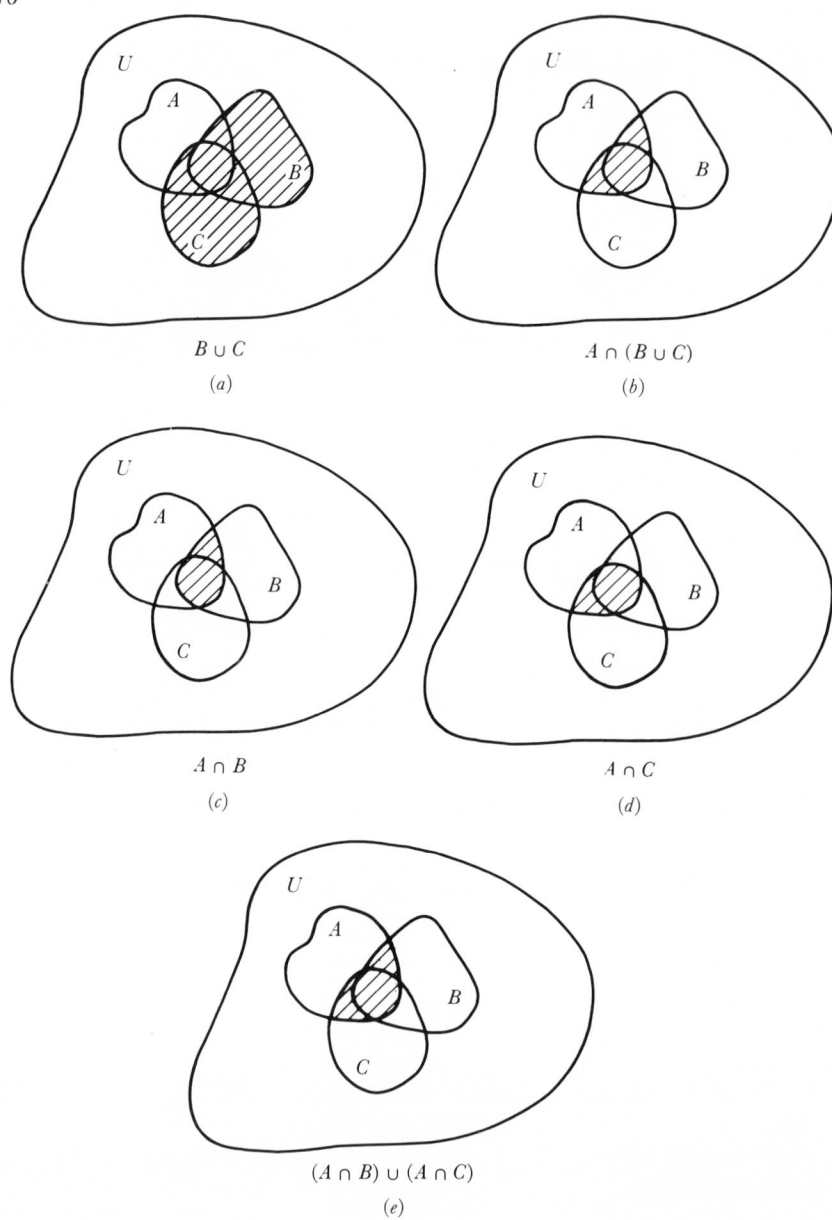

$B \cup C$

(a)

$A \cap (B \cup C)$

(b)

$A \cap B$

(c)

$A \cap C$

(d)

$(A \cap B) \cup (A \cap C)$

(e)

4   Let U be a universal set from which sets A, B, and C have been formed, and let $N(A)$ represent the number of elements in a finite set A.

Assume that $N(A) = 380$, $N(B) = 280$, $N(C) = 370$, $N(A \cap B) = 150$, $N(A \cap C) = 180$, $N(B \cap C) = 90$, and $N(A \cap (B \cap C)) = 10$. Use a Venn diagram to determine each of the following values.

a) $N(A \cup B)$ \hspace{2cm} b) $N(A \cup C)$

c) $N(B \cup C)$ \hspace{2cm} d) $N(A \cup (B \cap C))$

SOLUTION. The Venn diagram of Figure 11 illustrates that

a) $N(A \cup B) = 510$ \hspace{1.5cm} b) $N(A \cup C) = 570$

c) $N(B \cup C) = 560$ \hspace{1.5cm} d) $N(A \cup (B \cap C)) = 460$

Figure 11

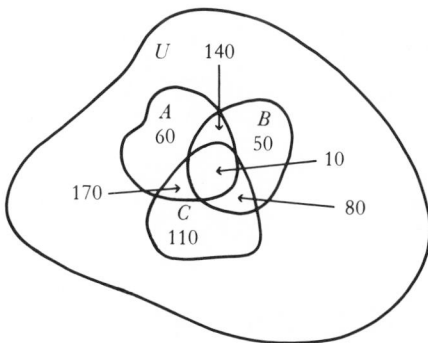

PROBLEM SET 1

1 Indicate which of the following statements are true and which are false.

a) $2 \in \{2\}$ \hspace{2cm} b) $\{\emptyset\}$ is empty.

c) $\{2,3\} \in \{2,3,7,8\}$ \hspace{1cm} d) $5 = \{5\}$

e) $\{2,3,4\}$ and $\{3,2,4\}$ are unequal sets.

f) $3 \in \{3,4\}$ \hspace{2.5cm} g) $\{3\} \in \{3,4\}$

h) $\{3\} \subseteq \{3,4\}$ \hspace{2cm} i) $\{3\} \subset \{3,4\}$

j) $\{1,3\}$ and $\{1,5,15\}$ are disjoint.

k) $\{\{x,y\}\} = \{y,x\}$ \hspace{2.5cm} l) $\{x,y\} = \{y,x\}$

2 Use set builder notation, $\{x|x$ has property $P\}$, to describe each of the following sets. Also describe the set by enumeration, if possible. Indicate which of the sets are finite and which are infinite.

a) A is the set of all even counting numbers.

b) A is the set of all counting numbers greater than 7 and less than 29.

c) A is the set of all counting numbers divisible by 3, that is, all counting numbers which have a zero remainder when divided by 3.

3 A is the set of numbers greater than 2 but less than 8. Describe A by enumeration if the universal set from which A is formed is

a) $\{10,11,12\}$ \hspace{2cm} b) $\{1,4,7,10,13,16\}$

c) The set of all counting numbers

d) $\{1,2,3,4,5,6,7,8\}$ \hspace{1.5cm} e) $\{7,3,10,2,5\}$

4 List all the subsets of each of the following sets. Indicate which of the subsets are proper subsets.

a) $\{3\}$ b) $\{\emptyset, \{0\}\}$

c) $\{1,2,3\}$ d) $\{a,b,c,d\}$

5 a) Why is it true that any set is a subset of itself?

    b) Use examples to illustrate that if A is a proper subset of B, then A is a subset of B, but if A is a subset of B, then A is not necessarily a proper subset of B.

    c) *Theorem* (*transitive law*). If $A \subseteq B$ and $B \subseteq C$, then $A \subseteq C$. Give two examples of this theorem.

6 Tabulate the number of distinct subsets of a set having:

a) 0 elements   b) 1 element (see Problem 4a)

c) 2 elements (see Problem 4b)   d) 3 elements (see Problem 4c)

e) 4 elements (see Problem 4d)

Can you generalize your result? (That is, if a set has n elements, how many subsets can be formed?)

7 Indicate which of the set relations (proper subset, equal, disjoint, overlap) holds between each pair of the following sets.

a) $\{12,13\}$; $\{2,3,4\}$

b) Set of all distinct letters in the word "mathematics";
    Set of all letters in the alphabet

c) The set of all counting numbers greater than 3;
    The set of all counting numbers less than 8

d) The set of all counting numbers greater than 3;
    The set of all counting numbers greater than 8

e) The set of all even counting numbers less than 11; $\{2,4,6,8,10\}$

8 Use $A = \{1,4,7\}$, $B = \{1,2,5,7\}$, and $C = \{5,6,7,8\}$ to form each of the following sets.

a) $A \cup C$ b) $B \cap C$

c) $A \cap C$ d) $A \cup (B \cap C)$

e) $A \cap (B \cup C)$

9 a) Use Venn diagrams to illustrate the validity of each of the following properties of the set operations.

      i *Commutativity of set union:*

$$A \cup B = B \cup A$$

      ii *Commutativity of set intersection:*

$$A \cap B = B \cap A$$

iii *Associativity of set union:*

$$(A \cup B) \cup C = A \cup (B \cup C)$$

iv *Associativity of set intersection:*

$$(A \cap B) \cap C = A \cap (B \cap C)$$

v *Intersection distributes over union:*

$$A \cap (B \cup C) = (A \cap B) \cup (A \cap C)$$

vi *Union distributes over intersection:*

$$A \cup (B \cap C) = (A \cup B) \cap (A \cup C)$$

b) Give two examples to illustrate each of the six properties of part (a).

10 Let A, B, and C be any sets. Use Venn diagrams to determine equalities between the sets of column I and the sets of column II.

Column I	Column II
i $A \cup (B \cup C)$	1 $A \cap (C \cap B)$
ii $(C \cap B) \cap A$	2 $(A \cap B) \cap C$
iii $A \cap (B \cup C)$	3 $(A \cup B) \cap (A \cup C)$
iv $A \cap (B \cap C)$	4 $(A \cup B) \cup C$
v $A \cup (B \cap C)$	5 $(A \cap B) \cup (A \cap C)$

11 Let U be a universal set from which sets A, B, and C have been formed and let $N(A)$ represent the number of elements in a finite set A. Assume that $N(U) = 700$, $N(A) = 345$, $N(B) = 75$, $N(C) = 45$, $N(A \cap B \cap C) = 10$, $N(A \cap C) = 20$, $N(A \cap B) = 30$, and $N(B \cap C) = 15$. Use Venn diagrams to determine each of the following values.

a) $N(A \cup B)$ b) $N(A \cup C)$
c) $N(B \cup C)$ d) $N(B \cap (A \cap C))$
e) $N(B \cup (A \cap C))$

12 a) A is a set and x is a number. Fill in the table.
Compare the role of $\emptyset$ in the algebra of sets with the role of 0 in the algebra of numbers.

$A \cup \emptyset =$	$x + 0 =$
$A \cap \emptyset =$	$x \cdot 0 =$

b) A is a set formed from a universal set U and x is a number. Fill in the table. Does $x + 1$ simplify? Compare the role of U in the algebra of sets to the role of 1 in the algebra of numbers.

$A \cup U =$	$x + 1 =$
$A \cap U =$	$x \cdot 1 =$

2 Real Numbers

The language of sets will be used to describe some of the number sets of algebra. By repeatedly adding 1 to itself, we can generate the set of *positive integers* $I_p = \{1,2,3,4, \ldots\}$. The set of *negative integers*, $I_n = \{-1,-2,-3, \ldots\}$, consists of the negatives of the positive integers. The set $I_p \cup I_n \cup \{0\} = \{\ldots,-3,-2,-1,0,1,2,3,4, \ldots\}$ is called the set of *integers* and is denoted by I.

A *rational number* is any number that *can be* expressed in the form x/y, where x and y are integers with $y \neq 0$. For example, 3, $2\frac{1}{2}$, and 53 percent are considered to be rational numbers, since they can be written as $\frac{3}{1}$, $\frac{5}{2}$, and $\frac{53}{100}$, respectively. Q is generally used to denote the set of all rational numbers; hence,

$$Q = \left\{ q \mid q = \frac{x}{y}, \ x \in I, y \in I, y \neq 0 \right\}$$

Since x is considered to be the same as $x/1$ and $x \div 1$, we identify an integer as a rational number, so that $I \subseteq Q$. More precisely, since $I \neq Q (\frac{1}{2} \in Q$, but $\frac{1}{2} \notin I)$, I is a proper subset of Q; that is, $I \subset Q$ (Figure 1).

Figure 1

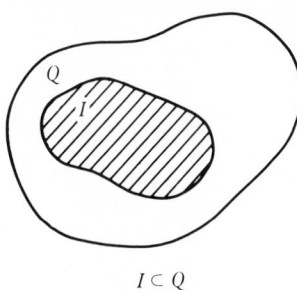

$$I \subset Q$$

Let us consider the specific rational number $\frac{3}{7}$. The number $\frac{3}{7}$ can be interpreted as $3 \div 7$, as shown in Figure 2.

Figure 2

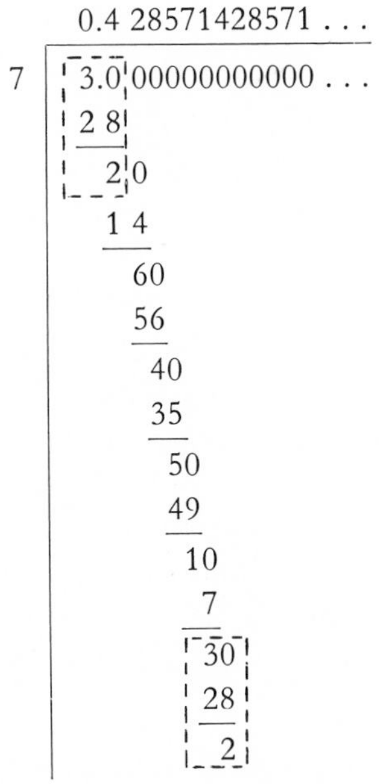

```
              0.4 28571428571 . . .
        ┌─ ─ ─
   7  │ ┌ 3.0┐00000000000 . . .
        │ 2 8│
        │ ──┘
        │  2│0
        └─ ─┘
          1 4
          ──
           60
           56
           ──
            40
            35
            ──
             50
             49
             ──
              10
               7
              ──
             ┌ 30 ┐
             │ 28 │
             │ ── │
             └  2 ┘
```

Notice the pattern. In each step within the division, the remainder must be either 0, 1, 2, 3, 4, 5, or 6. (Why?) Therefore, if enough zeros are added after the decimal of the dividend (this does not change the value of the dividend) and the division by 7 is performed more than seven times, one of the remainders must reoccur; but as soon as a remainder appears again (in this example it is 3), the digits in the quotient repeat. In this example,

$$\frac{3}{7} = 0.428571428571\overline{428571}$$

where the bar identifies the block of digits which repeats infinitely often.

This concept can be generalized; for if x/y is a rational number, where $x \in I$ and $y \in I$, $y \neq 0$, the division

$$y\overline{)x.0000\ldots}$$

can be performed until a remainder repeats [There are only y or $-y$ remainders possible, depending on whether y is a positive or negative integer. (Why?)] When the remainder repeats, the digits in the quotient repeat. Hence, it follows that *every rational number can be represented by an eventually repeating decimal.* The converse of this statement also holds; that is, *every eventually repeating decimal represents a rational number.*

This means that any decimal number which "eventually" has a repeating block of digits in its decimal part can be represented by a ratio of two integers.

EXAMPLES

1    $2 = \frac{2}{1} = 2.\overline{0}$

2    $\frac{2}{3} = 0.666\overline{6}$

3    $\frac{1310}{99} = 13.23\overline{23}$

Rational numbers, such as 2 and $\frac{14}{2}$, in which the repeating block is the digit 0, are sometimes called *terminating decimals.*

In summary, a rational number is a number which can be considered from two different viewpoints: either as a ratio of two integers or as a repeating decimal. A more formal treatment of repeating decimals is given in Chapter 4, Section 8, when geometric series are considered.

If a rational number is represented in either of the two forms, it can be converted to the other form, as we will see in the first two examples below.

EXAMPLES

1   Show that each of the following numbers is a rational number by examining the decimal representation of the number.

a) $\frac{8}{2}$ b) 17 percent   c) $\frac{10}{3}$

d) $\frac{1310}{3}$ e) 7.142845845

SOLUTION

a) $\frac{8}{2} = 4.0$ is a terminating decimal (the repeating block is the digit 0).

b) 17 percent $= 0.17$ is a terminating decimal.

c) $\frac{10}{3} = 3.33\overline{3}$ has a repeating block (the digit 3).

d) $\frac{1310}{3} = 436.6\overline{6}$ has a repeating block (the digit 6).

e) The number $7.142845\overline{845}$ is a rational number since $\overline{845}$ is a repeating block.

2 Express each of the following rational numbers as the ratio of two integers.

a) 2.03
b) $0.33\overline{3}$
c) $7.25134\overline{134}$
d) $0.99\overline{9}$

SOLUTION

a) $2.03 = 2 + \frac{3}{100} = \frac{203}{100}$

b) Let $x = 0.33\overline{3}$; then

$$
\begin{array}{rl}
10x = & 3.33\overline{3} \\
- \quad x = & -.33\overline{3} \\
\hline
9x = & 3
\end{array}
$$

so that

$$x = \tfrac{3}{9} \qquad \text{or} \qquad x = \tfrac{1}{3}$$

c) Let $x = 7.25134\overline{134}$; then

$$
\begin{array}{rl}
100000x = & 725134.134\overline{134} \\
- \quad 100x = - & 725.134\overline{134} \\
\hline
99900x = & 724409
\end{array}
$$

Here

$$x = \tfrac{724409}{99900}$$

d) If $x = 0.99\overline{9}$, then

$$
\begin{array}{rl}
10x = & 9.99\overline{9} \\
- \quad x = & -0.99\overline{9} \\
\hline
9x = & 9
\end{array}
$$

Here

$$x = 1$$

3 Show that there exists no rational number whose square is equal to 2.

PROOF. We will show that the assumption "a rational r exists such that $r^2 = 2$" leads to a contradiction.

Let $r = (x/y)$ (x and y are positive integers) be in its lowest term. If we assume that $r^2 = 2$, then

$$2 = \frac{x^2}{y^2} \qquad \text{or} \qquad 2y^2 = x^2$$

The number $2y^2$ is even; therefore x^2 is even and x must be even.

Since x is even, x can be written in the form $x = 2k$, where k is a positive integer. Hence,

$$2y^2 = (2k)^2 \qquad \text{or} \qquad y^2 = 2k^2$$

Since y^2 is even, y must be even. But both x and y cannot be even numbers, since x/y was given in lowest terms. Therefore the assumption that r is rational is false, and r is not a rational number.

We denote the number r by $\sqrt{2}$ (Figure 3). By the Pythagorean theorem $r^2 = 1^2 + 1^2 = 2$ so that the length of the hypotenuse of the isosceles right triangle with two legs of length 1 is $\sqrt{2}$.

Figure 3

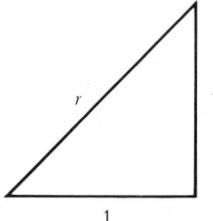

We have seen that the set of rational numbers is the set of numbers represented by repeating decimals, and repeating decimals represent rational numbers. But there are decimals which do not repeat, for example, the decimal 1.01001000100001 . . . , where there is one more "0" after each "1" than there is before the "1." Another example of a non-repeating decimal is $\pi = 3.14159265358 \ldots .$ $\sqrt{2}$ is not rational, and it can be shown that $\sqrt{2}$ has a nonrepeating decimal representation, $\sqrt{2} = 1.4142135 \ldots . \; 1 + \sqrt{2}, \; 3 - \sqrt{2}, \; 5\sqrt{2}, \; 3 + \sqrt{2}, \; \sqrt{3}, \; \sqrt[3]{2},$ and $\sqrt{5}$ also have nonrepeating decimal forms. Such numbers are called *irrational numbers*.

Consider the two irrational numbers $2\sqrt{5}$ and $1 + \sqrt{5}$. The sum $(2\sqrt{5}) + (1 + \sqrt{5}) = 1 + 3\sqrt{5}$ and the product $2\sqrt{5}(1 + \sqrt{5}) = 2\sqrt{5} + 10$ are also irrational; however, if we consider the irrational numbers $3 + \sqrt{2}$ and $3 - \sqrt{2}$, we find that the sum $(3 + \sqrt{2}) + (3 - \sqrt{2}) = 6$ and the product $(3 + \sqrt{2})(3 - \sqrt{2}) = 7$ are rational numbers. Hence, the sum and the product of two irrational numbers can be rational or irrational numbers.

If we denote the set of irrational numbers by L, then $Q \cup L$ determine⁻ a set R called the set of *real numbers* (Figure 4). Hence, real numbers are those numbers which can be written as decimal numbers. Real numbers include repeating decimals (rational numbers) and nonrepeating decimals (irrational numbers).

Figure 4

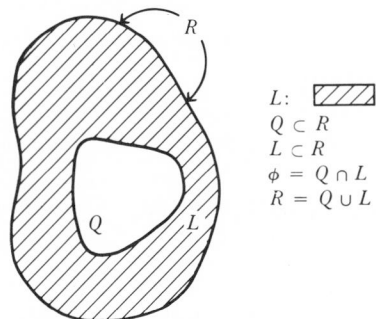

$$L: \quad \text{▨}$$
$$Q \subset R$$
$$L \subset R$$
$$\phi = Q \cap L$$
$$R = Q \cup L$$

The Venn diagram in Figure 5 summarizes the set relations among the subsets of R which have been surveyed above.

Figure 5

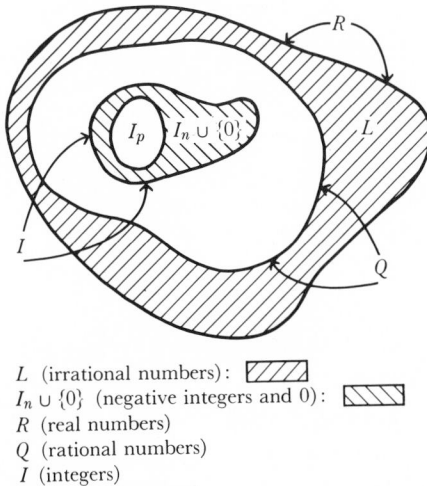

L (irrational numbers): ▨
$I_n \cup \{0\}$ (negative integers and 0): ⧄
R (real numbers)
Q (rational numbers)
I (integers)
I_p (positive integers)

2.1 One-to-One Correspondence

The set of real numbers can be represented geometrically as the set of all points on a straight line. This geometric representation is possible because the set of real numbers can be put in "one-to-one correspondence" with points on a line, a correspondence in which each real number is associated with *exactly* one point on the line, and, conversely, a correspondence which associates each point on the line with exactly one real number.

Since the concept of a one-to-one correspondence between two sets will be used later in other situations, it is worthwhile to give some special attention to the topic here before we apply it to real numbers.

Suppose a dinner party is being arranged. For each guest there is provided a place setting, and, conversely, for each place setting there is a guest. We say that the place settings are in one-to-one correspondence with the guests. Similarly, at a party attended only by married couples, we could establish a one-to-one correspondence between the females and the males in attendance. For each female there is a male (her husband, for example), and for each male there is a female. In general, two sets A and B can be put in *one-to-one correspondence* if it is possible to associate each member of set A with exactly one member of set B, and, conversely, if it is possible to associate each member of set B with exactly one member of set A.

The concept of a one-to-one correspondence is not difficult to understand when the sets are finite sets. Quite simply, two finite sets can be placed in a one-to-one correspondence whenever both sets have the same number of members. For example, it is *not* possible to establish a one-to-one correspondence between set $A = \{1,3,4\}$ and set $B = \{1,2\}$; for, although it is true that for each member of set B we can associate exactly one member of set A, it is not possible to associate each member of set A with exactly one member of set B.

$$
\begin{array}{cc}
B & A \\
1 \longleftrightarrow 1 \\
2 \longleftrightarrow 3 \\
\longleftarrow ? \longrightarrow 4
\end{array}
$$

EXAMPLE

Show that $A = \{1,2,3\}$ and $B = \{a,b,c\}$ can be put in one-to-one correspondence in more than one way.

SOLUTION

$$
\begin{array}{ccccc}
1 \longleftrightarrow a & & 1 \longleftrightarrow b & & 1 \longleftrightarrow c \\
2 \longleftrightarrow b & \text{or} & 2 \longleftrightarrow c & \text{or} & 2 \longleftrightarrow a \\
3 \longleftrightarrow c & & 3 \longleftrightarrow a & & 3 \longleftrightarrow b
\end{array}
$$

The concept of one-to-one correspondence is not so easy to understand, however, if the sets have infinitely many members. Let us consider two examples of this type.

EXAMPLES

1 The set of positive integers $\{1,2,3,4, \ldots\}$ can be put in one-to-one correspondence with the even numbers $\{2,4,6,8, \ldots\}$ using the following scheme.

$$1 \longleftrightarrow 2$$

$$2 \longleftrightarrow 4$$

$$3 \longleftrightarrow 6$$

$$\cdots \cdots \cdots$$

$$n \longleftrightarrow 2n$$

2 Consider triangle ABC with line segment DE (Figure 6). Show that the points of segment DE can be put in one-to-one correspondence with the points of segment AC.

Figure 6

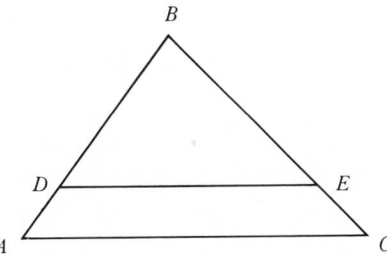

SOLUTION. Consider all line segments from point B to line segment AC (Figure 7). Each such line segment associates a point on DE with exactly one point on AC; and, conversely, each point of AC is associated with exactly one point on DE. Hence, as point sets, segments DE and AC are in one-to-one correspondence.

Figure 7

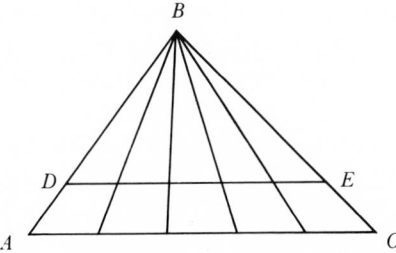

2.2 Real Line

Let us now examine a one-to-one correspondence between the real numbers and points on a line. The resulting "numbered line" is called a *real line* or *real axis*.

An arbitrary point on the line is selected to represent 0 and, another arbitrary point to the right of 0 is selected to represent 1. The point 0 is called the *origin* and the *line segment* determined by the point 0 and the point 1 is called the *scale unit* (Figure 8a). By repeating the scale unit, moving from left to right, starting at 0, we can associate the set of positive integers $I_p = \{1,2,3,4,\ldots\}$, with (equispaced) points on the line. Moving from right to left, starting at 0, we can associate the set of negative integers $I_n = \{-1,-2,-3,-4,\ldots\}$, with (equispaced) points on the line (Figure 8b). The remaining real numbers can be "located" or "plotted" on the real line by using decimal representations or by using the geometry of the number line.

Figure 8

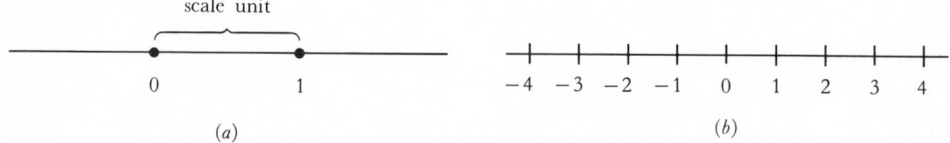

(a)   (b)

EXAMPLES

1 Locate 2.3 and 2.38 on the real line.

SOLUTION.   We can locate 2.3 by subdividing the portion of the number line between 2 and 3 into 10 equal parts; then, starting at 2, we move 3 units to the right to 2.3 (Figure 9). 2.38 can be located by subdividing the segment between 2.3 and 2.4 into 10 equal parts; then, starting at 2.3, we move eight units to the right (Figure 10).

Figure 9

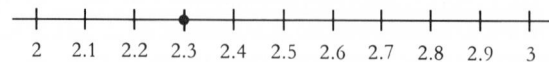

Figure 10

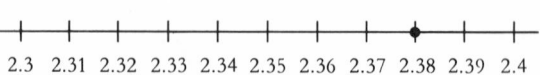

2 Locate $\frac{17}{8}$ on the real line by using the decimal representation of $\frac{17}{8}$.

SOLUTION

$$\frac{17}{8} = 2.125 \qquad \text{(Figure 11)}$$

Figure 11

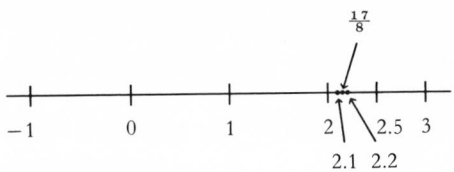

3 Locate $\sqrt{2}$ on the number line.

SOLUTION. We have seen that $\sqrt{2}$ is an irrational number so that $\sqrt{2}$ has a decimal representation which is a nonterminating decimal ($\sqrt{2} = 1.41421\ldots$). Hence, if we were to attempt to locate $\sqrt{2}$ by using the decimal representation we would become involved in an unending process in which we would "approach" but never actually locate the point. (Why?) We can, however, locate $\sqrt{2}$ by using the geometry of the number line as illustrated in Figure 12.

Figure 12

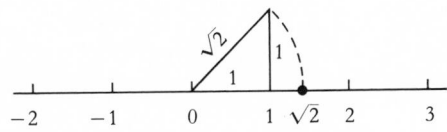

4 What number corresponds to the point midway between 2.7 and 2.8?

SOLUTION. The point 2.75 is midway between the points 2.7 and 2.8 on the real line (Figure 13).

Figure 13

Notice that when a real number is plotted on the directed line, the number is not the point nor is the point the number; the point *represents* the number. It is customary, however, to use the words *real number* and *point* interchangeably. Thus, we speak of the point $\frac{3}{4}$ rather than the point corresponding to the real number $\frac{3}{4}$.

PROBLEM SET 2

1 Establish, if possible a one-to-one correspondence between the two sets in each of the following parts.

a) $\{1,2,3,4,6\}$; $\{a,c,d,e,f\}$

b) Positive integers; negative integers

c) $\{\ \}$; $\{0\}$ d) $\{7,8,9\}$; $\{8,9,91\}$

e) $\{1,2,4\}$; $\{a,b,c,4\}$ f) Positive integers; integers

2 Locate each of the following real numbers on the real line.

a) $-2\frac{1}{7}$ b) π

c) $\sqrt{5}$ d) 1.93 percent

e) $\frac{17}{5}$ f) $-\frac{1}{2}$

g) $-\sqrt{2}$ h) $\frac{7}{3}$

i) 6.99   j) 6.999

3 Show that each of the following numbers are rational numbers, first by examining the decimal representation, and second by representing the numbers as ratios of integers.

a) -5 b) 0

c) 0.2   d) $5\frac{7}{15}$

e) $3.464\overline{646}$ f) $\frac{2}{9}$

g) $\frac{4}{13}$ h) 33 percent

i) $0.499\overline{9}$ j) $7.3621\overline{621}$

4 Use decimal representations to construct a rational number between each of the following pairs of real numbers.

a) 8.3 and 8.4   b) 3 and π

c) $\sqrt{2}$ and $\sqrt{3}$

5 Using I_p, I_n, I, Q, L, and R as defined in the Venn diagram of Figure 5 of Section 2, describe each of the following number sets.

a) $I_p \cap I_n$ b) $I_p \cup I_n$

c) $L \cap Q$ d) $I \cap L$

e) $I \cup Q$

6 Show that there exists no rational number whose square is 3. (*Hint:* See the proof of Example 3 in Section 2.)

3 Order

The purpose here is to use an intuitive understanding of the real line to motivate and develop some of the properties of the inequality relation.

3.1 Positive and Negative Numbers

All real numbers which are represented by points on the real line that lie to the "right" of the zero point are *positive numbers*, whereas all real numbers which are "left" of the zero point are *negative numbers*. Zero, then, is neither positive nor negative. The diagram in Figure 1 illustrates the following principle:

TRICHOTOMY. If a is a real number, then one and only one of the following conditions must hold:

> either a is positive
>
> or $-a$ is positive
>
> or a is zero.

Figure 1

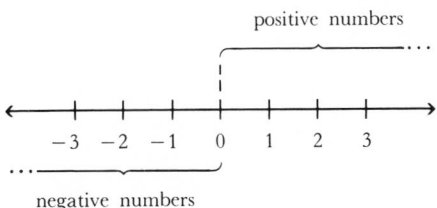

positive numbers

negative numbers

In set language, if R_p is the set of all positive numbers and R_n is the set of all negative numbers, then

$$R = R_n \cup \{0\} \cup R_p \quad \text{where} \quad R_n \cap \{0\} \cap R_p = \emptyset \text{ (Why?)}$$

The next axiom establishes the basic assumptions which are made to characterize the set of positive numbers R_p.

3.2 Positive Number Axiom

The set of positive numbers is *closed under addition;* that is, the sum of any two positive numbers is always a positive number. The set of positive numbers is *closed under multiplication;* that is, the product of two positive numbers is always a positive number. ☐

Using the notion of positive numbers, it is possible to give a precise "algebraic" characterization of the order of real numbers which is suggested by the "geometry" of the real line.

Geometrically, a real number a is less than a real number b if the point associated with a is to the "left" of the point associated with b on the real line (Figure 2).

Figure 2

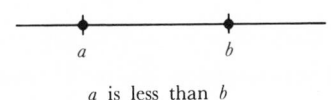

a is less than b

The next definition formalizes this ordering of the real numbers.

3.3 Definition

Assume that a and b are real numbers. We say that a *is less than* b, written $a < b$, or, equivalently, b *is greater than* a, written $b > a$, if $b - a$ is a positive number. ☐

Thus $2 < 3$ or $3 > 2$ because $3 - 2 = 1$ is a positive number; $-3 < -2$ because $-2 - (-3) = 1$; $-2 < 3$ (Figure 3).

Figure 3

If $b > 0$, then $b - 0 = b$ is positive; and, if $a < 0$, then $0 - a = -a$ is positive or a is negative (Figure 4).

Figure 4

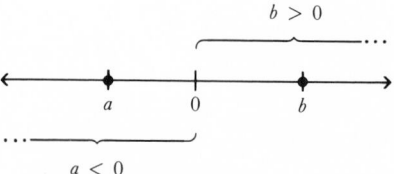

Notice that $-x$ *is not necessarily a negative number.* In fact, $-x < 0$ only when $0 - (-x) = x$ is positive. Is $-(-2)$ negative? What about $-(-x)$?

3.4   Properties of Order Relations

The positive number axiom and the definition of order can be used to prove some important properties of the order relation.

THEOREM 1   TRANSITIVE PROPERTY OF ORDER

If a, b, and c are real numbers such that $a < b$ and $b < c$, then $a < c$.

GEOMETRIC INTERPRETATION.   If a is left of b and b is left of c, then a is left of c (Figure 5). For example, if $x < y$ and $y < 7$, then $x < 7$.

Figure 5

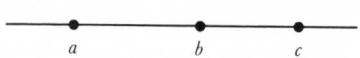

PROOF OF THEOREM.   By Definition 3.3, $a < b$ implies that $b - a = p$ is positive, and $b < c$ implies that $c - b = q$ is positive, so that

$$(b - a) + (c - b) = p + q$$

which is positive because the positive numbers are closed under addition. After simplifying, we get

$$c - a = p + q$$

so that $c - a$ is positive, from which we can conclude, by Definition 3.3, that $a < c$.

THEOREM 2

If a and b are real numbers with $a < b$, then $a + c < b + c$ for any real number c.

GEOMETRIC INTERPRETATION.   If a is to the left of b and if any number c is added to both a and b, then the result $a + c$ is to the left of $b + c$. In other words, $a + c$ and $b + c$ can be obtained by "shifting" or "translating" a and b c units to the right if c is positive (Figure 6) or

Figure 6

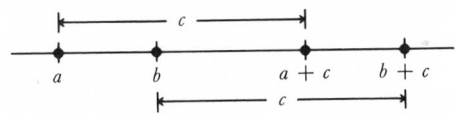

to the left if c is negative. For example, let us examine the situation in which 5 is added to both sides of the inequality $-3 < 2$. $-3 < 2$ so that -3 is left of 2 (Figure 7). Geometrically, after adding

Figure 7

5 to each side, -3 and 2 are "translated" 5 units to the right, so that the two results 2 and 7 have the same relative positions as -3 and 2 (Figure 8).

Figure 8

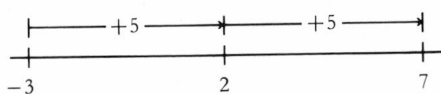

PROOF OF THEOREM. $a < b$ implies that $b - a = p$ is positive. (Why?) But

$$b - a = b - a + 0$$
$$= b - a + c - c$$
$$= (b + c) - (a + c)$$

so that

$$(b + c) - (a + c) = p$$

is positive. Hence, by Definition 3.3,

$$a + c < b + c$$

THEOREM 3

If a, b, and c are real numbers such that $c > 0$ and $a < b$, then $ac < bc$.

GEOMETRIC INTERPRETATION.   If a is to the left of b and each number is multiplied by a *positive* number c, then ac is to the left of bc. For example, if $2 < 4$ and $x > 0$, then $2x < 4x$ (Figure 9).

Figure 9

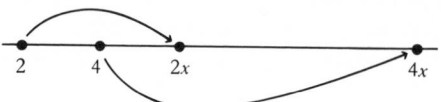

PROOF OF THEOREM.   Since $a < b$, $b - a = p$, a positive number. But $c > 0$ and $p > 0$ implies that $pc > 0$, since the positive numbers are closed under multiplication. Hence, $(b - a)c = pc$ is positive, so that $bc - ac$ is positive; that is,

$$ac < bc$$

THEOREM 4

If a, b, and c are real numbers such that $c < 0$ (c is negative) and $a < b$, then $ac > bc$.

GEOMETRIC INTERPRETATION.   If a is to the left of b and each number is multiplied by a *negative* number c, the order is reversed; that is, ac is right of bc. For example, let us see what happens to the inequality $-3 < 2$ when we multiply each side by -3. -3 is left of 2; however, $(-3)(-3) = 9$ is right of $(2)(-3) = -6$ (Figure 10).

Figure 10

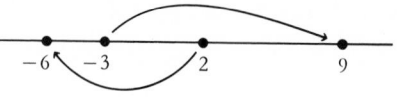

PROOF OF THEOREM.   By Definition 3.3, $a < b$ implies that $b - a = p$, a positive number. But c is negative, so that by the trichotomy axiom $-c$ is positive. Hence,

$$p(-c) \qquad \text{is a positive number}$$

since the positive numbers are closed under multiplication. Consequently,

$$p(-c) = (b - a)(-c) = ac - bc$$

is positive, so that, by Definition 3.3,

$$bc < ac$$

In other words, Theorems 2, 3, and 4 tell us that an inequality maintains the same sense if the same number is added or subtracted (see Problem 10) on both sides or if the same *positive* number is multiplied or divided (see Problem 10) on both sides, whereas if the same *negative* number is multiplied or divided (see Problem 10) on both sides, the sense of the inequality is reversed.

EXAMPLES

1   $-4 < 2$ because $2 - (-4) = 6$ is positive. Hence, $-4 + 3 < 2 + 3$; $(-4)(5) < (2)(5); [(-4)/7] < \frac{2}{7}; (-4)(-1) > (2)(-1)$.

2   Prove that if a and b are real numbers such that $a < b$, then $-a > -b$.

PROOF.   Let $c = -1$. Then, by Theorem 4, $(-1)a > (-1)b$ or, equivalently, $-a > -b$.

3   Find an example to disprove the following assertion. (Such an example is called a *counterexample*).

If $a < b$ then $a^2 < b^2$

SOLUTION.   Let $a = -3$ and $b = 2$. Then $b - a = 2 - (-3) = 5 > 0$ so that $a < b$. However, $b^2 - a^2 = 4 - 9 = -5$ implies

$b^2 < a^2$ or $a^2 \nless b^2$ ($\nless$ is read "is not less than")

4   Prove that if $a < b$ and $a > 0$, then $a^2 < b^2$. (Compare this statement to the statement of Example 3.)

PROOF. $a < b$ implies that $b - a > 0$. But $0 < a$ and $a < b$ implies, by the transitive property, that $b > 0$. Since the positive numbers are closed under addition, $b + a > 0$, so that

$$b^2 - a^2 = (b - a)(b + a) > 0$$

because the positive numbers are closed under multiplication. Hence,

$$a^2 < b^2$$

5   If $a \neq 0$, then $a^2 > 0$.

PROOF.   By the trichotomy axiom, $a > 0$ or $a < 0$. If $a > 0$, then, by Theorem 3, $a^2 > 0 \cdot a$; that is, $a^2 > 0$. If $a < 0$, then, by Theorem 4, $a^2 > 0 \cdot a$; that is, $a^2 > 0$.

3.5   Notation for Order Relations

There is some standard shorthand notation used in connection with the order relation.

1   *Betweenness.* $a < b < c$ means that $a < b$ *and simultaneously* $b < c$ (Figure 11). For example, $-1 < 4 < 5$ is correct, since $-1 < 4$ and, simultaneously, $4 < 5$. But $2 < a < 1$ is not correct, since $2 < a < 1$ suggests that $2 < a$ and, *simultaneously*, $a < 1$, from which we conclude, by the transitive property, that $2 < 1$, which is false. In other words, if $a < b < c$ is used, b must be *between* a and c on the real line and $a < c$.

Figure 11

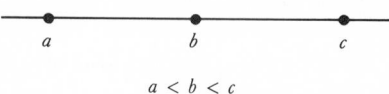

$$a < b < c$$

2    $a \not< b$ means that a is not less than b. Because of trichotomy, this implies that $a = b$ or $a > b$. For example, if $3 \not< x$, then $3 = x$ or $3 > x$ (Figure 12).

Figure 12

3    $a \leq b$ means that either $a = b$ or $a < b$. For example, $x \leq 2$ suggests that $x < 2$ or $x = 2$ (Figure 13).

Figure 13

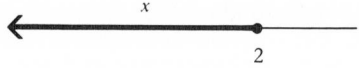

In view of statements 1, 2, and 3, the meanings of $a \not> b$, $a \geq b$, $a \leq b$, and $a \geq b$ should be obvious. Notice that different notations may be used to represent the same relation. For example, $a \leq b$ means the same as $a \not> b$ and $a \geq b$ means the same as $a \not< b$.

Now we can combine concepts from three areas — set theory, order relations, and the geometric interpretation of order relations — to introduce some convenient notation.

4   *Bounded intervals.*   We will assume here that a and b are real numbers such that $a < b$. The *open interval from a to b*, denoted by (a,b), is

defined as

$$(a,b) = \{x | a < x < b\}$$

Figure 14

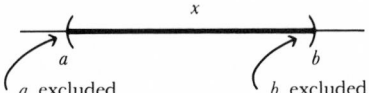

Notice that $a \notin (a,b)$ and $b \notin (a,b)$.

The *closed interval from a to b*, denoted by $[a,b]$ is defined as

$$[a,b] = \{x | a \leq x \leq b\}$$

Figure 15

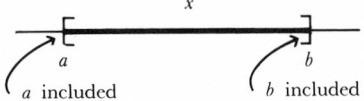

The closed interval includes the end points, whereas the open interval does not include the end points. For example, $[0,1]$ is the set of all real numbers between 0 and 1 including 0 and 1, whereas $(0,1)$ is the set of all real numbers between 0 and 1 excluding 0 and 1 (Figures 16a and b).

Figure 16

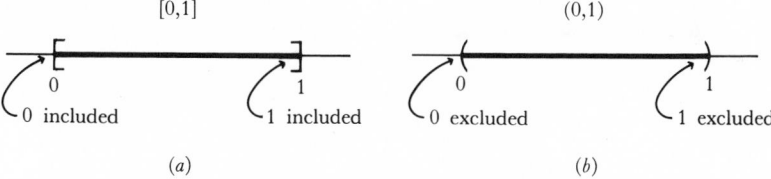

(a)   (b)

An interval from a to b including one end point but excluding the other end point is said to be *half-open* (or *half-closed*). This can happen in one of two ways.

i $$[a,b) = \{x | a \leq x < b\}$$

Figure 17a

ii $$(a,b] = \{x | a < x \leq b\}$$

Figure 17b

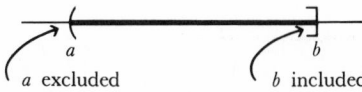

5   *Unbounded intervals.* We use the symbols ∞ and $-\infty$ (∞ and $-\infty$ are *not* real numbers) to describe unbounded intervals as follows. If a is a real number, then

i $[a,\infty) = \{x|x \geq a\}$

Figure 18a

ii $(-\infty,a] = \{x|x \leq a\}$

Figure 18b

iii $(a,\infty) = \{x|x > a\}$

Figure 18c

iv $(-\infty,a) = \{x|x < a\}$

Figure 18d

For example,

$$(-\infty,3) \cap (0,\infty) = (0,3)$$

Figure 19

Finally, we use interval notation $(-\infty,\infty)$ to denote the set of all real numbers R.

EXAMPLES

1   If $2 \leq x \leq 4$, the set of values of x determines the interval in Figure 20 and this set can be denoted by $[2,4]$.

Figure 20

2 $[3,3] = \{3\}$. (Why?)

3 $(2,4) \subset [2,4]$, since $2 \in [2,4]$ but $2 \notin (2,4)$.

Figure 21

4 $(-\infty,2) \cap (-3,\infty) = (-3,2)$

Figure 22

5 $[2,5) \cup (-3,0]$

Figure 23

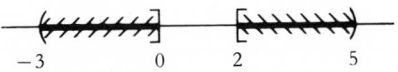

6 $(-\infty,3) \cap [3,4) = \emptyset$

Figure 24

7 $[2,3] \cap (2,3) = (2,3)$

Figure 25

8 $\{x|x > 1 \text{ or } x < -2\} = \{x|x > 1\} \cup \{x|x < -2\}$
$$= (1,\infty) \cup (-\infty,-2)$$

Figure 26

The *complement* A^c of a set A of real numbers is the set of all real numbers that are not contained in A. Thus, if A is a set of real numbers, $A^c = \{x|x \notin A\}$. For example, if A is the interval set $[2,\infty)$, then the complement of the set A is $(-\infty,2)$ (Figure 27). If Q is the set of rational numbers, then the complement of Q, Q^c, relative to the set of numbers R, is the set of irrational numbers.

Figure 27

$A^c = (-\infty, 2)$ $A = [2, \infty)$

2

EXAMPLE

Find the complement of each of the following sets relative to the set of real numbers R.

a) R b) $(3, \infty)$ c) $(8, 9)$

SOLUTION

a) $R^c = \emptyset$

b) $(3, \infty)^c = (-\infty, 3]$

Figure 28

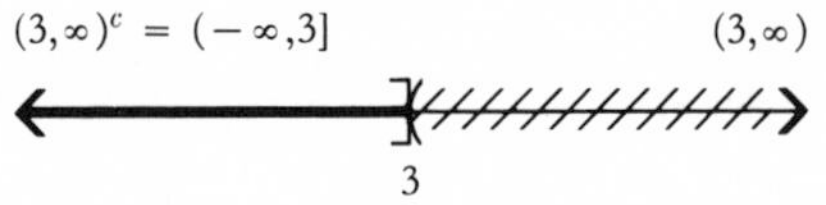

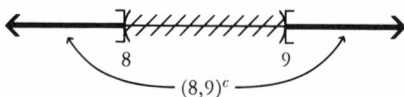

$(3, \infty)^c = (-\infty, 3]$ $(3, \infty)$

3

c) $(8, 9)^c = (-\infty, 8] \cup [9, \infty)$

Figure 29

8   9

$(8, 9)^c$

3.6   Linear Inequalities in One Unknown

Linear inequalities in one unknown can be solved in much the same manner as linear equations. We replace an inequality by an equivalent inequality which has a solution which is obvious. As with equations, two *inequalities* are *equivalent* if their solution sets are the same. The properties of inequalities enable us to convert a given inequality to an equivalent one. A few examples will help to clarify the method for solving linear inequalities in one unknown.

EXAMPLES

Solve each of the following inequalities and represent the solution in set notation. Finally, show the solution set on the real line.

1) $3x - 2 < 7$

SOLUTION

$$\{x | 3x - 2 < 7\} = \{x | 3x - 2 + 2 < 7 + 2\} \quad \text{(Theorem 2)}$$
$$= \{x | 3x < 9\}$$
$$= \{x | (\tfrac{1}{3})(3x) < (\tfrac{1}{3})(9)\} \quad \text{(Theorem 3)}$$
$$= \{x | x < 3\}$$
$$= (-\infty, 3) \quad \text{(Figure 30)}$$

Figure 30

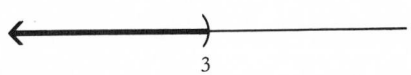

3

2) $x + 2 < 7x - 1$

SOLUTION

$$\{x | x + 2 < 7x - 1\} = \{x | x - 7x + 2 < 7x - 1 - 7x\} \quad \text{(Theorem 2)}$$
$$= \{x | -6x + 2 < -1\}$$
$$= \{x | -6x + 2 - 2 < -1 - 2\} \quad \text{(Theorem 2)}$$
$$= \{x | -6x < -3\}$$
$$= \{x | (-\tfrac{1}{6})(-6x) > (-\tfrac{1}{6})(-3)\} \quad \text{(Theorem 4)}$$
$$= \{x | x > \tfrac{1}{2}\}$$
$$= (\tfrac{1}{2}, \infty) \quad \text{(Figure 31)}$$

Figure 31

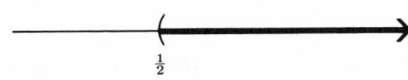

$\tfrac{1}{2}$

3) $3x + 5 \leq 12$

SOLUTION

$$\{x | 3x + 5 \leq 12\} = \{x | 3x + 5 - 5 \leq 12 - 5\} \quad \text{(Theorem 2)}$$
$$= \{x | 3x \leq 7\}$$
$$= \{x | (\tfrac{1}{3})(3x) \leq (\tfrac{1}{3})(7)\} \quad \text{(Theorem 3)}$$
$$= \{x | x \leq \tfrac{7}{3}\}$$
$$= (-\infty, \tfrac{7}{3}] \quad \text{(Figure 32)}$$

Figure 32

$\tfrac{7}{3}$

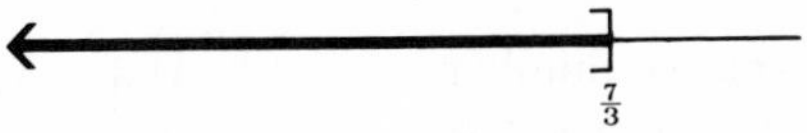

4) $3 - x > -4$

SOLUTION

$$\{x|3 - x > -4\} = \{x|3 - 3 - x > -4 - 3\} \quad \text{(Theorem 2)}$$
$$= \{x|-x > -7\}$$
$$= \{x|(-1)(-x) < (-1)(-7)\} \quad \text{(Theorem 4)}$$
$$= \{x|x < 7\}$$
$$= (-\infty,7) \quad \text{(Figure 33)}$$

Figure 33

7

PROBLEM SET 3

1 a)   Using the fact that the notation $a > 0$ can be used to indicate that a number (a in this case) is positive, restate the trichotomy principle and the positive number axiom using this notation.

b)   Give three examples of each of these axioms.

2   If we were to replace the positive number set with the negative number set, would the axiom of Section 3.2 hold? Give numerical examples to support your assertion.

3 a)   Under what condition is $-x < 0$?

b)   Under what condition is $-x > 0$?

c)   Give two numerical examples to support your assertion in (a) and (b) and represent the examples on the number line.

4 a)   *Theorem 1.*   If a, b, and c are real numbers such that a is less than b and b is less than c, then a is less than c. For example, if $-2 < 3$ and $3 < 5$ then $-2 < 3$. Restate Theorems 2, 3, and 4 in words and give two numerical examples of each theorem. Illustrate the examples on the real line.

b)   *Principle of duality.*   Consider Theorems 1 and 2, in Section 3.4. If we replace $<$ with $>$ and $>$ with $<$, then the theorems still hold. Rewrite the theorems with these substitutions, and then give two examples of each theorem and illustrate them geometrically.

5   In each of the following parts, state the appropriate axiom, definition, or theorem which proves the statement if it is valid. If the statement is not valid, then give a counterexample to disprove it. R_p is used to denote the set of positive numbers.

a) $-a$ is a negative number.   b)   If $a \in R_p$, then $3a \in R_p$.

c)   If $a \in R$, then $a + b \in R_p$.   d) $0 \in R_p$

e)   If $a < 4$ and $b > 4$, then $a < b$.   f) $3 + a < 8 + a$

g)   If $a < b$, then $-7a > -7b$.   h) $-\frac{3}{4} < -\frac{1}{2}$

i)   If $a < 0$, then $a^3 < 0$.   j)   If $a > 1$ and $b > a$, then $b > 0$.

k) If $a < b$, then $[a/-10] > [b/-10]$.

l) If $a^2 < 4$, then $a < 2$.

6 In each of the following parts, restate the assertion *in words*, and then use Theorem 3 or 4 to prove the statement. Give two examples of each statement.

a) If $a < 0$ and $b > 0$, then $ab < 0$.

b) If $a < 0$ and $b < 0$, then $ab > 0$.

7 Sketch each of the following sets on a real line.

a) $[-1,2)$ b) $(-4,5] \cap [-8,3)$

c) $[-1,0] \cup [-\frac{1}{2},0]$ d) $(-2,1) \cup (3,8)$

e) $(0,\infty) \cap (2,\infty)$ f) $[3,10] \cup (7,9)$

g) $(0,5) \cup (2,7)$ h) $(-\infty,-1) \cap (-\infty,-4)$

8 Use interval notation to represent each of the following sets.

a)

1   4   7   10

b)

5   8

c)

3   5   8

d)

2   3   7

e)

-1   1

9 a) Prove that if $a < b$, then $a < [(b + a)/2] < b$. [*Hint:* $a + a < b + a < b + b$. (Why?)]

b) Prove that if $0 < a < 1$, then $a^2 < a$, $a^3 < a^2$, etc. (*Hint:* use Theorem 3 repeatedly).

10 a) Theorem 2, together with the fact that $a - c = a + (-c)$, implies that if the same number is subtracted from both sides of an equality, the order of the inequality remains the same; that is, if $a < b$, then $a - c < b - c$ for any real number c. Prove this implication and give two examples.

b) Using the fact that $a \div c = a(1/c)$ for $c \neq 0$, restate Theorems 3 and 4 for division. Prove the statement and give two examples.

11 Find the solution set of each of the following inequalities and represent the solution in set form and in interval form. Also show the solution set on the real line.

a) $7x > \frac{3}{2}x + 1$ b) $4x + 3 \geq 12$

c) $x + 6 \leq 4 - 3x$ d) $5 \leq 3x < 17$

e) $3 \leq 5x \leq 2x + 11$ f) $3x - 2 > 7$

g) $x + 1 \leq 3x + 2 < 5 + x$ h) $5 - x < -x + 3$

i) $2x < 0$ j) $3 + x > -1 + x$

12   a)   A car was driven 10 miles, and, during the entire trip, the speed was between 70 and 75 miles per hour. Use set interval notation to find all possible times required for such a trip.

     b)   If one of the dimensions of a rectangular room is 13 feet and its area is less than 432 square feet, what can be concluded about the other dimension of the room?

13   a)   If a and b are real numbers such that $a > 0$ and $b > 0$, show that $[(a + b)/2] \geq \sqrt{ab}$.

     b)   Generalize part (a) to the case of four positive real numbers, that is,

$$\frac{a + b + c + d}{4} \geq \sqrt[4]{abcd}$$

     (*Hint:* Use (a) with a similar inequality for c and d and apply (a) to these two inequalities.)

14   Prove that if $a < b$ and $c < d$, then $a + c < b + d$.

15   Give two examples of each of the following identities.

     a) $(A^c)^c = A$ b) $(A \cup B)^c = A^c \cap B^c$

     c) $(A \cap B)^c = A^c \cup B^c$

16   Find the complement of each of the following sets relative to the set of real numbers R.

     a) $A = \{x \mid x < 3\}$ b) $B = \{x \mid 3 < x < 4\}$

     c) $C = \{x \mid x^2 \neq 9\}$ d) $D = \{x \mid 5x > 3x\}$

4   Absolute Value

If a and b are real numbers such that $a \leq b$, then the distance between a and b is considered to be the nonnegative number $b - a$ (Figure 1).

Figure 1

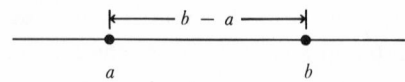

For example, the distance between -1 and 4 is given by $4 - (-1) = 5$ (Figure 2). The distance between -5 and -2 is equal to $(-2) - (-5) = 3$ (Figure 3).

Figure 2

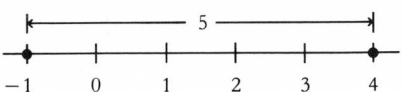

Figure 3

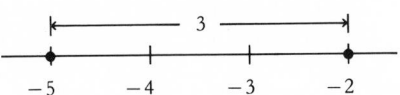

Suppose that we are interested in finding the distance between 0 and any real number x. For convenience, we will use the notation $|x|$, which is read the *absolute value of* x, to represent the distance between x and 0. Then, $|3| = 3$, $|0| = 0$, and $|-5| = 5$.

In fact, if $x < 0$, we have

$$|x| = 0 - x = -x$$

Figure 4a

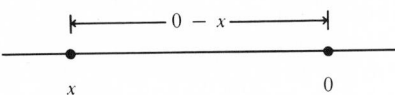

If $x > 0$,

$$|x| = x - 0 = x$$

Figure 4b

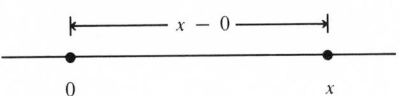

Finally, if $x = 0$,

$$|x| = 0 - 0 = 0$$

4.1 Definition

If x is a real number, the *absolute value of* x, denoted by $|x|$, is defined as follows.

$$|x| = \begin{cases} x & \text{if } x \geq 0 \\ -x & \text{if } x < 0. \end{cases} \quad \square$$

It follows from Definition 4.1 that $|3| = 3$ because $3 > 0$; $|0| = 0$; $|-5| = -(-5) = 5$ because $-5 < 0$.

4.2 Properties of Absolute Value Equality

We can use Definition 4.1 to prove some theorems about equations containing absolute value.

THEOREM 1

Given any two real numbers x and y, $|x - y|$ represents the distance between x and y.

PROOF.   The trichotomy axiom indicates that there are three possible situations:

$$x < y, \qquad x = y, \qquad \text{or} \qquad x > y$$

CASE I.   If $x < y$ (Figure 5), then

$$y - x > 0 \qquad \text{or} \qquad x - y < 0$$

so that, by Definition 4.1,

$$|(x - y)| = -(x - y) = y - x$$

the distance between x and y.

Figure 5

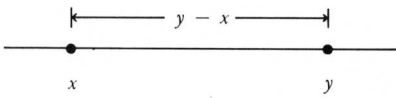

CASE II.   If $x > y$ (Figure 6), then $x - y > 0$ so that, by Definition 4.1,

$$|(x - y)| = x - y$$

the distance between x and y.

Figure 6

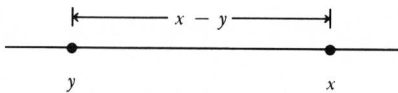

CASE III.   Finally, if $x = y$, $|x - y| = |0| = 0$, which is clearly the distance between x and y.

THEOREM 2

$|x| \geq 0$ for any real number x.

PROOF.   Using Definition 4.1, if $x \geq 0$,

$$|x| = x \geq 0$$

and if $x < 0$,

$$|x| = -x > 0 \qquad \text{(Why?)}$$

THEOREM 3

$|-x| = |x|$ for any real number x.

GEOMETRIC INTERPRETATION. $|-x| = |x|$ means that the distance between 0 and x is the same as the distance between 0 and $-x$. (See Figure 7 for the case in which $x > 0$.) For example, $|-7| = |7| = 7$.

Figure 7

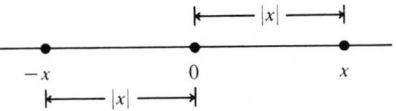

PROOF OF THEOREM.   If $x \geq 0$, then $-x \leq 0$, so that, by Definition 4.1,

$$|x| = x \qquad \text{and} \qquad |-x| = -(-x) = x$$

On the other hand, if $x < 0$, then $-x > 0$ so that, by Definition 4.1,

$$|x| = -x \qquad \text{and} \qquad |-x| = -x$$

In any case,

$$|x| = |-x|$$

THEOREM 4

$|x|^2 = x^2$ for any real number x.

PROOF.   (See Problem 6a.)

EXAMPLES

1   Prove that $|x - y| = |y - x|$ for any real numbers x and y.

PROOF.   By Theorem 3 above,

$$|x - y| = |-(x - y)| = |y - x|$$

2   Solve $|x - 3| = 4$.

SOLUTION.   Since $|4| = |-4| = 4$, $x - 3 = 4$ or $x - 3 = -4$ (Figure 8), so that $x = 7$ or $x = -1$; that is, the solution set is $\{-1,7\}$.

Figure 8

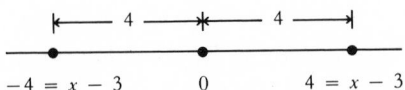

3 Solve $|3x - 4| = 5$.

SOLUTION.   Since $|-5| = |5| = 5$, $3x - 4 = 5$ or $3x - 4 = -5$
(Figure 9), so that $x = 3$ or $x = -\frac{1}{3}$, that is, the solution set is
$\{-\frac{1}{3}, 3\}$.

Figure 9

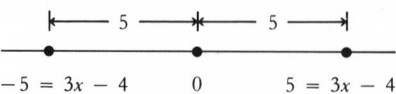

$$-5 = 3x - 4 \qquad 0 \qquad 5 = 3x - 4$$

4 Simplify $x/|x|$ if x is a nonzero real number.

SOLUTION.   If $x > 0$, $|x| = x$, so that $x/|x| = x/x = 1$. If $x < 0$,
$|x| = -x$, so that $x/|x| = x/-x = -1$. Consequently,

$$\frac{x}{|x|} = \begin{cases} 1 & \text{if } x > 0 \\ -1 & \text{if } x < 0 \end{cases}$$

5 Solve $|x + 2| = |x - 7|$.

SOLUTION 1.   By Theorem 4, $|x + 2|^2 = |x - 7|^2$ yields $x^2 + 4x +
4 = x^2 - 14x + 49$, so that $18x = 45$; that is, $x = \frac{5}{2}$.

SOLUTION 2.   We can also solve the equation by considering the various
cases suggested by Definition 4.1.
i) $|x + 2| = x + 2$ if $x + 2 \geq 0$, that is, if $x \geq -2$; and $|x + 2| =
-x - 2$ if $x + 2 < 0$, that is, if $x < -2$ (Figure 10a).

Figure 10a

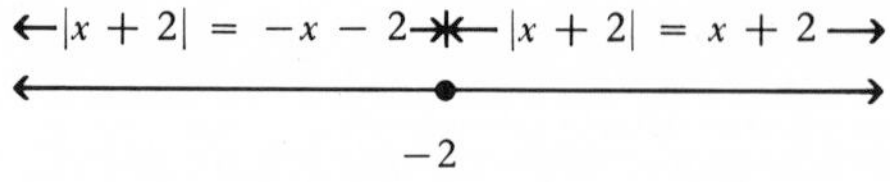

$$\leftarrow|x + 2| = -x - 2 \text{---}\ast\text{---}|x + 2| = x + 2 \rightarrow$$
$$-2$$

ii) $|x - 7| = x - 7$ if $x - 7 \geq 0$, that is, if $x \geq 7$; and $|x - 7| =
-x + 7$ if $x - 7 < 0$, that is, if $x < 7$ (Figure 10b).

Figure 10b

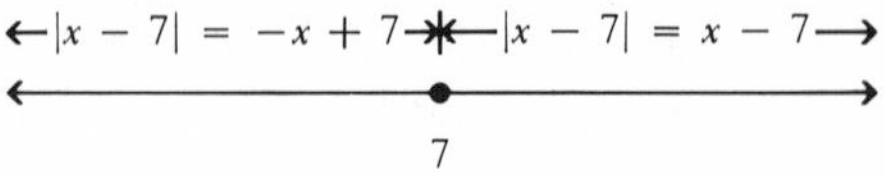

$$\leftarrow|x - 7| = -x + 7 \text{---}\ast\text{---}|x - 7| = x - 7 \rightarrow$$
$$7$$

Combining the above cases, we have the following possibilities
(Figure 11).

Figure 11

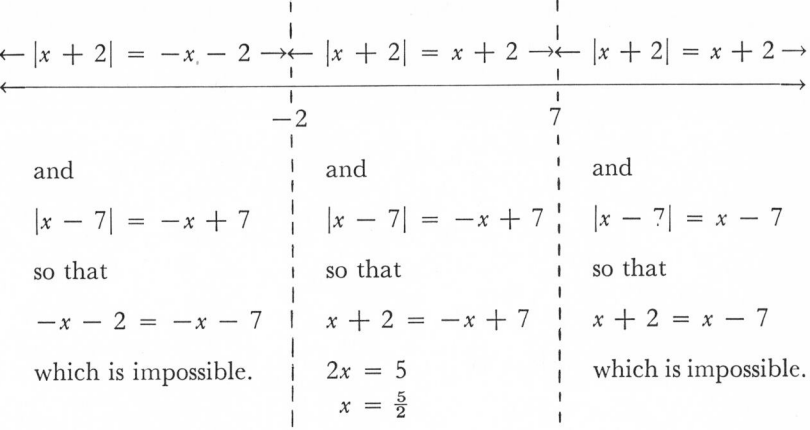

$$\leftarrow |x + 2| = -x - 2 \rightarrow\leftarrow |x + 2| = x + 2 \rightarrow\leftarrow |x + 2| = x + 2 \rightarrow$$

and	and	and
$|x - 7| = -x + 7$	$|x - 7| = -x + 7$	$|x - 7| = x - 7$
so that	so that	so that
$-x - 2 = -x - 7$	$x + 2 = -x + 7$	$x + 2 = x - 7$
which is impossible.	$2x = 5$	which is impossible.
	$x = \frac{5}{2}$	

Hence, the solution set is $\{\frac{5}{2}\}$.

4.3 Properties of Absolute Value Inequalities

We know that $|x|$ represents the distance between 0 and x as shown in Figure 12 where x is illustrated as a positive number. Now we can use this geometric interpretation, together with the results above, to get a clear understanding of absolute value inequalities of the forms $|x| < a$ or $|x| > a$ where a is a positive number.

Figure 12

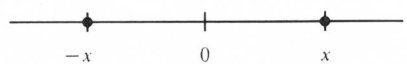

THEOREM 1

If $|x| < a$, then $-a < x < a$ where $a > 0$; that is,

$$\{x \mid |x| < a\} = \{x \mid -a < x < a\} = (-a, a)$$

GEOMETRIC INTERPRETATION. Quite simply, $|x| < a$ means that the distance between 0 and x is less than a units; or, equivalently, x is within a units of 0 (Figure 13). Using interval notation, $x \in (-a, a)$.

Figure 13

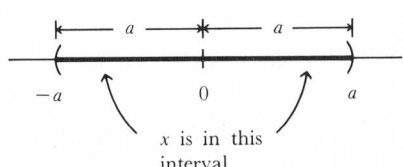

x is in this
interval

Using inequalities, this means that

$$-a < x < a$$

PROOF OF THEOREM.   If $|x| < a$, then $-a < -|x|$. (Why?) By Definition 4.1,

$$|x| = x \qquad \text{or} \qquad |x| = -x$$

Hence,

$$-a < -|x| \leq x \leq |x| < a \qquad \text{(see Problem 8a)}$$

so that, by the transitive property of inequalities,

$$-a < x < a$$

EXAMPLES

1   Solve $|x| < 3$.

SOLUTION.   By Theorem 1,

$$\{x \mid |x| < 3\} = \{x \mid -3 < x < 3\} = (-3,3)$$

Figure 14

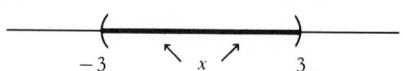

2   Solve $|3x - 2| < 8$.

SOLUTION.   By Theorem 1,

$$\begin{aligned}
\{x \mid |3x - 2| < 8\} &= \{x \mid -8 < 3x - 2 < 8\} \\
&= \{x \mid -6 < 3x < 10\} \\
&= \{x \mid -2 < x < \tfrac{10}{3}\} \\
&= (-2, \tfrac{10}{3})
\end{aligned}$$

Figure 15

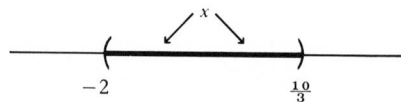

THEOREM 2

If $|x| > a$, then $x < -a$ or $x > a$ where $a > 0$; that is,

$$\begin{aligned}
\{x \mid |x| > a\} &= \{x \mid x < -a\} \cup \{x \mid x > a\} \\
&= (-\infty, -a) \cup (a, \infty)
\end{aligned}$$

GEOMETRIC INTERPRETATION. $|x| > a$ means that the distance between 0 and x is more than a units, or, equivalently, x is more than a units from 0 (Figure 16).

Figure 16

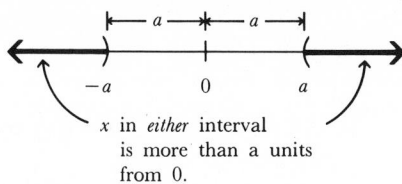

a
a
−a
0
a
x in *either* interval
is more than a units
from 0.

PROOF OF THEOREM. By Definition 4.1, either $|x| = x$ or $|x| = -x$. Hence,

$$|x| = x > a \qquad \text{or} \qquad |x| = -x > a$$

that is,

$$x > a \qquad \text{or} \qquad -x > a$$

But $-x > a$ implies $x < -a$ (Why?), so that

$$x > a \qquad \text{or} \qquad x < -a$$

that is,

$$\begin{aligned}\{x \,|\, |x| > a\} &= \{x|x > a\} \cup \{x|x < -a\} \\ &= (a,\infty) \cup (-\infty,-a)\end{aligned}$$

EXAMPLES

1 Solve $|x| > 7$.

SOLUTION. By Theorem 2,

$$\{x \,|\, |x| > 7\} = \{x|x < -7\} \cup \{x|x > 7\} = (-\infty,-7) \cup (7,\infty)$$

Figure 17

−7
7
x

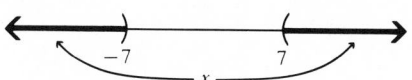

2 Solve $|2x - 3| \geq 5$.

SOLUTION. $|2x - 3| \geq 5$ suggests that

$$(2x - 3) \leq -5 \qquad \text{or} \qquad (2x - 3) \geq 5$$

Figure 18

5
5
−5
0
5
(2x − 3)

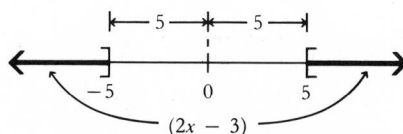

so that

$$2x \leq -2 \quad \text{or} \quad 2x \geq 8$$

that is

$$x \leq -1 \quad \text{or} \quad x \geq 4$$

Figure 19

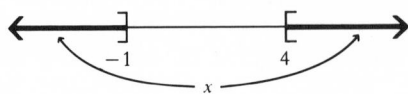

Hence,

$$\{x||2x - 3| \geq 5\} = \{x|x \leq -1\} \cup \{x|x \geq 4\} = (-\infty,-1] \cup [4,\infty)$$

3 Solve $|2x + 7| \geq 11$.

SOLUTION. $|2x + 7| \geq 11$ suggests that

$$(2x + 7) \leq -11 \quad \text{or} \quad (2x + 7) \geq 11$$

Figure 20

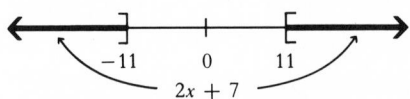

so that

$$2x \leq -18 \quad \text{or} \quad 2x \geq 4$$

that is

$$x \leq -9 \quad \text{or} \quad x \geq 2$$

Hence,

$$\{x||2x + 7| \geq 11\} = \{x|x \leq -9\} \cup \{x|x \geq 2\} = (-\infty,-9] \cup [2,\infty$$

Figure 21

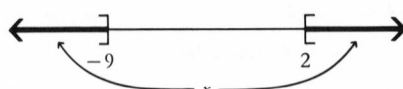

THEOREM 3 TRIANGLE INEQUALITY

If a and b are real numbers, then $|a + b| \leq |a| + |b|$.

PROOF. We have that $-|a| \leq a \leq |a|$ and $-|b| \leq b \leq |b|$ (see Problem 8a). Adding inequalities (see Problem 14 of Problem Set 3), we get

$$-(|a| + |b|) \leq a + b \leq (|a| + |b|)$$

Now, if $a + b \geq 0$,

$$|a + b| = a + b \leq |a| + |b|$$

whereas if $a + b < 0$,

$$|a + b| = -(a + b)$$

so that we have, after multiplying each side of $-(|a| + |b|) \leq a + b$ by -1,

$$|a + b| = -(a + b) \leq |a| + |b|$$

In either case,

$$|a + b| \leq |a| + |b|$$

EXAMPLES

1 Show that if $|x| < 3$ and $|y| < 1$, then $|x + y| < 4$.

SOLUTION. By Theorem 3,

$$|x + y| \leq |x| + |y| < 3 + 1$$

so that

$$|x + y| < 4$$

2 If $x, y,$ and z are real numbers, then $|x - y| < |x - z| + |y - z|$.

PROOF. Let $a = x - z$ and $b = z - y$ in Theorem 3 to get

$$|(x - z) + (z - y)| \leq |x - z| + |z - y|$$

that is,

$$|x - y| \leq |x - z| + |z - y|$$

from which it follows that

$$|x - y| \leq |x - z| + |y - z|$$

(See Example 1, Section 4.2.)

3   Use the triangle inequality to find a real number c such that $|x^3 + 3x^2 - 2x + 5| \leq c$ for all values of x such that $|x| \leq 2$.

SOLUTION.   By repeated use of the triangle inequality, we have

$$\begin{aligned}
|x^3 + 3x^2 - 2x + 5| &\leq |x^3 + 3x^2 - 2x| + |5| \\
&\leq |x^3 + 3x^2| + |-2x| + |5| \\
&\leq |x^3| + |3x^2| + |-2x| + |5| \\
&= |x^3| + 3x^2 + 2|x| + 5 \\
&\leq 8 + 3(4) + 2(2) + 5 \\
&= 29 \qquad \text{so that } c = 29.
\end{aligned}$$

4   Express $\{x | -2 < x < 4\}$ as an absolute value inequality.

SOLUTION.   Interval $(-2,4)$ is of length 6 and has midpoint 1 (Figure 22). Now we saw in Section 4.2 that $|x - 1|$ represents the distance between x and 1; hence

$$|x - 1| < 3$$

Figure 22

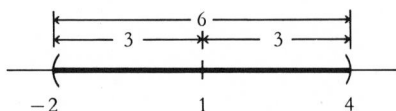

that is,

$$\{x | -2 < x < 4\} = \{x | |x - 1| < 3\}$$

PROBLEM SET 4

1   If $x = 3$ and $y = -4$, compute each of the following numbers.
   a) $|x| + |y|$ b) $|x + y|$
   c) $|x - y|$ d) $|x| - |y|$
   e) $|xy|$ f) $|x||y|$
   g) $|y|^2$ h) $|x/y|$
   i) $|3x| + |-4y|$ j) $3|x| - 4|y|$

2 a) Give two examples of each of the four theorems of Section 4.2.
   b) Give two examples of each of the three theorems of Section 4.3.

3 What restrictions, if any, must be put on x in order for each of the following statements to be true?

a) $|5x| = 5x$
b) $|x - 2| = 2 - x$
c) $|x + 2| = |x| + |2|$
d) $|1/x| = |x|$
e) $|3x| > 0$

4 Solve each of the following equations.

a) $|x| = 4$
b) $|3x + 2| = 5$
c) $|x - 7| = |3x + 1|$
d) $|2x - 9| = |5x - 3|$
e) $|x| = -3$
f) $|x| = |-3|$
g) $|x - 5| = |-3x + 7|$
h) $3|x| = 15$
i) $|3x| = 15$
j) $|-3x| = 15$

5 a) Compute $|x/|x||$ if x is a nonzero real number.
b) For what values of x, if any, is $|x^3| = x^3$?
c) Under what conditions does $|x + y| = |x| + |y|$?
d) Under what conditions does $|x| = |y|$?

6 Prove each of the following assertions.

a) $|x|^2 = x^2$
b) $|x/y| = |x|/|y|$

(*Hint:* Consider three cases.)

7 Solve each of the following inequalities. Represent your answer in interval notation. Illustrate the solution on the real line.

a) $|x| > 1$
b) $|x| < 2$
c) $|3 - 2x| < 5$
d) $|x - 1| < 3$
e) $|x + 2| \geq 5$
f) $|3 + 2x| < 1$
g) $|3x - 1| > 0.1$
h) $|4 - 7x| \leq 0.0001$
i) $|x + 5| < |x + 1|$
j) $|4x - 2| \leq 1$
k) $|5 - 1/x| < 1$

8 Give two examples and prove each of the following assertions.

a) $-|x| \leq x \leq |x|$
b) $|x| + |y| = ||x| + |y||$
c) $|x - y| \leq |x| + |y|$
d) $||x| - |y|| \leq |x - y|$
e) If $|x - a| < \frac{1}{10}$ and $|a - y| < \frac{1}{10}$, show that $|x - y| < \frac{1}{5}$.

(*Hint:* Use the triangle inequality for parts c, d, and e.)

9 For what values of x, if any, is each of the following statements true?

a) $|x - 2| \leq |x| + 2$
b) $|x - 5| \leq |x - 3|$
c) $|x| > |x - 1|$
d) $|x| < -3$
e) $|x| > -3$

10 Write each of the following inequalities as an absolute value inequality.

a) $-3 < x < 3$
b) $1.99 < x < 2.0$
c) $-3.1 < x < -3$

11   Solve for x:

a) $|x - 3| + |x - 5| \leq 8$ b) $|x - 1| - 2|x - 3| \geq 4$

12   a)   Use Theorem 1, Section 4.3, to prove that if $|x - c| < a$ then
             $-a + c < x < a + c$ where $a > 0$.

b)   Use Theorem 2, Section 4.3, to prove that if $|x - c| > a$ then
       $x < c - a$ or $x > a + c$ where $a > 0$.

5   Cartesian Coordinate System and Distance Formula

We have seen that the real line provides us with a geometric representation of the real numbers as points on a line. This geometric representation was used in investigating the order of the real numbers and the notion of distance between points on a line. In this section, we will investigate a method of representing "ordered pairs" of real numbers as points in a plane. Then this geometric representation will be used to determine a method of finding the distance between two points in a plane.

5.1   Ordered Pairs

The elements in the set $\{a,b\}$ do not have to be listed in any particular order. This set could be written either as $\{a,b\}$ or as $\{b,a\}$; in other words $\{a,b\} = \{b,a\}$.

By contrast, (a,b) is an *ordered pair* consisting of *first the element a* and *second the element b*. [This notation is the same as that which is used to denote open intervals. The text will be sufficiently clear to indicate what (a,b) represents.]

Two ordered pairs are considered to be *equal* only when the two ordered pairs have equal first members *and* equal second members. For example, $(1,2) \neq (2,1)$, even though each pair contains the same entries. Likewise, $(4,3) \neq (4,4)$ and $(7,8) \neq (-7,8)$, whereas $(9,x) = (y,8)$ only if $x = 8$ and $y = 9$.

If $A = \{1,2\}$ and $B = \{a,b\}$, the set of all possible ordered pairs formed by selecting the first member of the ordered pair from A and the second member of the ordered pair from B is denoted by $A \times B$ and is given by

$$A \times B = \{(1,a),(1,b),(2,a),(2,b)\}$$

A simple method of grouping the elements in order to form the ordered pairs of two sets is to arrange the elements in a rectangular pattern as shown in the table below.

Set B

$\times$	a	b
Set A 1	$(1,a)$	$(1,b)$
2	$(2,a)$	$(2,b)$

$A \times B$

By contrast,

$$B \times A = \{(a,1),(b,1),(a,2),(b,2)\}$$

In general, if A and B are any two sets, $A \times B$, which reads "A cross B", denotes the set of all ordered pairs of the form (x,y) with x an element of set A and y an element of set B. Symbolically,

$$A \times B = \{(x,y)|x \in A \text{ and } y \in B\}$$

The set $A \times B$ is called the *Cartesian product* of sets A and B.

EXAMPLE

Let $A = \{2,3\}$ and $B = \{2,7,5\}$.

a)   Determine $A \times A$ and $B \times B$.

b)   Form $(A \times B) \cup (B \times A)$ and $(A \times B) \cap (B \times A)$.

c)   Give the set relation between $A \times B$ and $B \times A$.

SOLUTION

a) $A \times A = \{(2,3),(3,2),(2,2),(3,3)\}$

   and

   $B \times B = \{(2,2),(2,7),(2,5),(7,2),(7,7),(7,5),(5,2),(5,7),(5,5)\}$

b) $A \times B = \{(2,2),(2,7),(2,5),(3,2),(3,7),(3,5)\}$

   whereas,

   $B \times A = \{(2,2),(7,2),(5,2),(2,3),(7,3),(5,3)\}$

Hence,

$$(A \times B) \cup (B \times A)$$
$$= \{(2,2),(2,7),(7,2),(2,5),(5,2),(3,2),(2,3),(3,7),(7,3),(5,3),(3,5)\}$$

and

$$(A \times B) \cap (B \times A) = \{(2,2)\}$$

c) We have, from part (b), that $(2,2) \in [(A \times B) \cap (B \times A)]$. Also, $(2,7) \in A \times B$, but $(2,7) \notin B \times A$; and, $(5,2) \in B \times A$, but $(5,2) \notin A \times B$, so that $A \times B$ and $B \times A$ are overlapping sets.

This example shows that $A \times B$ and $B \times A$ are not always equal.

5.2 Cartesian Coordinate System

$R \times R$, the set of all ordered pairs of real numbers, can be represented as the set of points in a plane by using a two-dimensional indexing system called the *Cartesian coordinate system*, which is constructed as follows.

First, two perpendicular lines L_1 and L_2 are constructed. (Figure 1). The point of intersection of the two lines is called the *origin*. Next, L_1

Figure 1

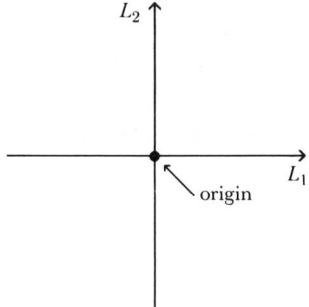

and L_2 are scaled as real lines by using the origin as the 0 point for each of the two lines, the portion of L_2 above the origin is the positive direction and the portion below the origin is the negative direction of the number line; the portion of L_1 to the right of the origin is the positive direction and the portion to the left is the negative direction (Figure 2). The resulting two real lines are called the *coordinate axes*. The coordinate axes, L_1 and L_2, are often referred to as the *horizontal axis* and the *vertical axis*, respectively.

Figure 2

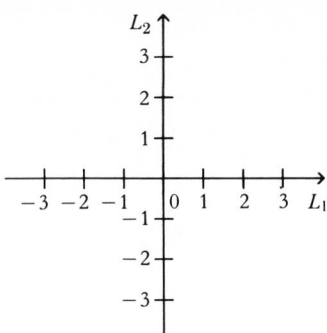

Given an ordered pair of real numbers (x,y) (the first member of the pair, x, is called the *abscissa;* the second member of the pair, y, is called the *ordinate;* x and y are called the *coordinates*), we can use the coordinate system to represent (x,y) as a point on the plane as follows.

The abscissa x is located on the L_1 axis. Then a line is drawn perpendicular to this axis at point x; the ordinate y is located on the L_2 axis at point y. The intersection of the two lines which have just been constructed is the point in the plane used to represent the ordered pair (x,y) (Figure 3). Thus for each ordered pair in $R \times R$ we can associate a point in the plane. Conversely, for each point in the plane, we can associate an ordered pair in $R \times R$. Hence, there is a one-to-one correspondence between $R \times R$ and the points in the plane.

Figure 3

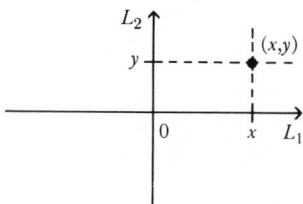

The horizontal axis is usually called the *x axis* and the vertical axis is usually called the *y axis.*

EXAMPLES

1 Plot points $(1,-2)$, $(3,4)$, $(0,3)$, $(-2,-3)$, $(\pi,0)$.

SOLUTION. These points are plotted in Figure 4.

2 If $A = \{1,2,3\}$ and $B = \{-1,-2\}$, locate the members of $A \times B$ in the plane.

Figure 4

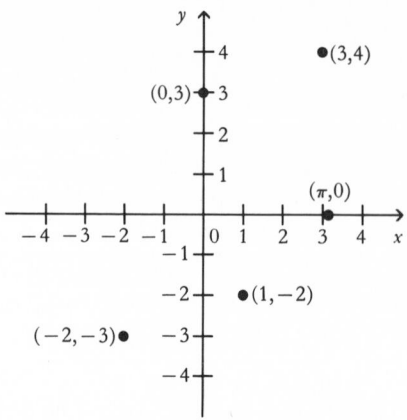

SOLUTION.

$$A \times B = \{(1,-1),(1,-2),(2,-1),(2,-2),(3,-1),(3,-2)\}$$

Figure 5

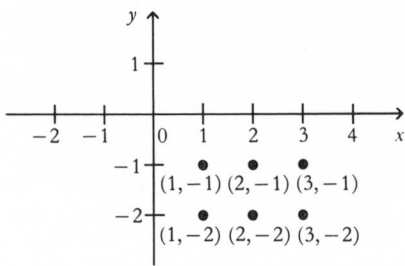

3 Locate all points with abscissas greater than 1 and ordinates less than or equal to −2; that is, indicate the region on the plane containing all points corresponding to $\{(x,y)|x > 1 \text{ and } y \leq -2\}$.

Figure 6

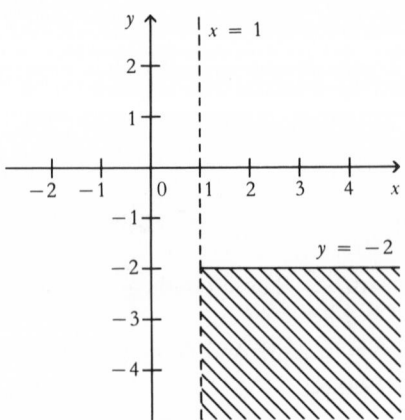

SOLUTION.   The region is the shaded region in Figure 6. Note that the unbroken line is part of the region, whereas the broken line is not part of the region.

The coordinate axes divides the plane into four disjoint regions called *quadrants,* which are described in Figure 7. Notice that the coordinate axes have no point in common with the four quadrants.

Figure 7

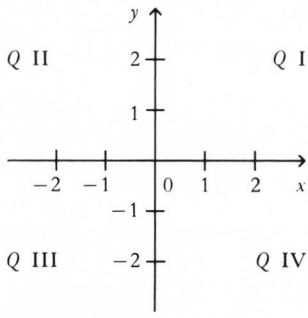

$$Q\ I = \{(x,y)|x > 0, y > 0\};$$
$$Q\ II = \{(x,y)|x < 0, y > 0\};$$
$$Q\ III = \{(x,y)|x < 0, y < 0\};$$
$$Q\ IV = \{(x,y)|x > 0, y < 0\}.$$

EXAMPLE

Indicate which quadrant, if any, contains each of the following points.

a) $(\frac{1}{2}, -\frac{1}{2})$ b) $(\pi, 1/\pi)$

c) $(-2, -6)$ d) $(-3, 4)$

e) $(-\sqrt{2}, 0)$ f) $(0, -5)$

SOLUTION.   After plotting the points (Figure 8), we see that

a) $(\frac{1}{2}, -\frac{1}{2})$ lies in quadrant IV.

b) $(\pi, 1/\pi)$ lies in quadrant I.

c) $(-2, -6)$ lies in quadrant III.

d) $(-3, 4)$ lies in quadrant II.

e) $(-\sqrt{2}, 0)$ is not in any quadrant.

f) $(0, -5)$ is not in any quadrant.

Figure 8

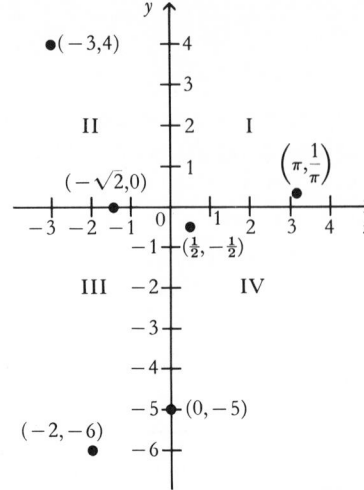

5.3 Distance Between Points

Suppose a Cartesian coordinate system is established using the same scale for the x axis and the y axis. We could then find the distance between any two points, say, P_1 and P_2, by connecting the two points with a line segment and then "measuring" or marking off the number of scale units along this segment. The total number of such units would be the length of the segment or the distance between the two points (Figure 9). This process is purely geometric and the accuracy of the result is dependent upon physical measurement. The coordinates of P_1 and P_2 have played no part in this measurement.

Figure 9

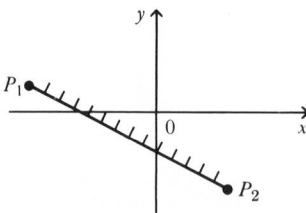

The question arises: Is it possible to use the coordinates of the two given points to get an *exact* value for the distance between them? This question will be answered in the affirmative by deriving the *distance formula*.

5.4 Distance Formula

Given any two points P_1 and P_2 with coordinates (x_1, y_1) and (x_2, y_2), respectively, a formula for the distance d between P_1 and P_2 in terms of coordinates $x_1, y_1, x_2,$ and y_2 can be derived by considering three cases:

i   If the two points lie on the same vertical line, that is, $x_1 = x_2$, then $|y_1 - y_2| = d$ (Figure 10).

Figure 10

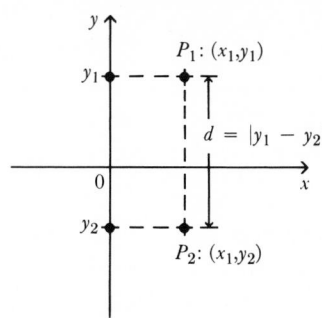

ii If the two points lie on the same horizontal line, that is, $y_1 = y_2$, then $|x_1 - x_2| = d$ (Figure 11).

Figure 11

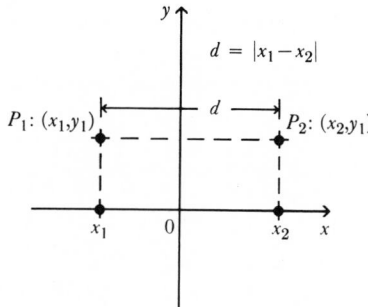

iii If the two points lie on a line which is neither horizontal or vertical, a right triangle, that is, a triangle with a 90° angle, is determined (Figure 12).

Figure 12

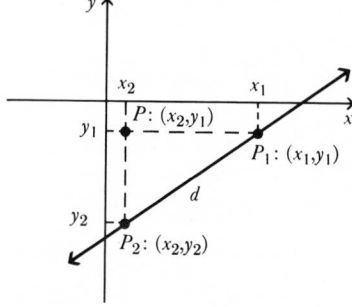

Now we use the Pythagorean theorem:

$$(\text{length of segment } PP_1)^2 + (\text{length of segment } PP_2)^2 = d^2$$

that is,

$$|x_1 - x_2|^2 + |y_1 - y_2|^2 = d^2$$

so that

$$(x_1 - x_2)^2 + (y_1 - y_2)^2 = d^2 \quad \text{(Why?)}.$$

Hence, the *distance formula*

$$d = \sqrt{(x_1 - x_2)^2 + (y_1 - y_2)^2}$$

Notice that this formula is also applicable in the special cases where P_1 and P_2 are on the same vertical line or same horizontal line. (Why?) Since $(a - b)^2 = (b - a)^2$, the "order" of subtracting the abscissas or the ordinates is irrelevant.

EXAMPLES

1 Find the distance between $(-1, -2)$ and $(3, -4)$.

SOLUTION.   The distance d is given by

$$d = \sqrt{[3 - (-1)]^2 + [-4 - (-2)]^2} = \sqrt{4^2 + 2^2} = 2\sqrt{5}$$

Figure 13

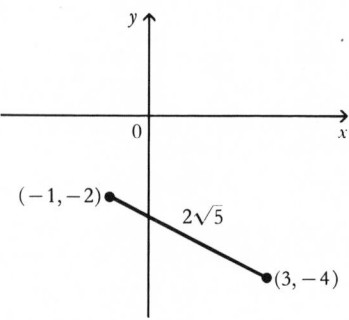

2 Derive a formula for the distance between the origin and any point (x, y) on the plane.

SOLUTION.   The distance d between $(0, 0)$ and (x, y) is given by

$$d = \sqrt{(x - 0)^2 + (y - 0)^2}$$

Figure 14

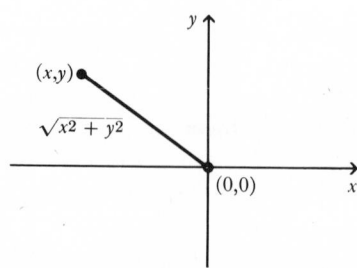

so that the formula is

$$d = \sqrt{x^2 + y^2}$$

3 Derive a formula for the distance between the x axis and any point (a,b).

SOLUTION. The distance is given by $\sqrt{0^2 + b^2} = |b|$.

Figure 15

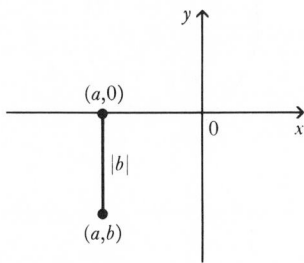

4 Find the distance between $(2,-3)$ and $(-2,1)$.

SOLUTION

$$\begin{aligned}
d &= \sqrt{[2 - (-2)]^2 + (-3 - 1)^2} \\
&= \sqrt{(2 + 2)^2 + (-4)^2} \\
&= \sqrt{4^2 + (-4)^2} \\
&= \sqrt{32} \\
&= 4\sqrt{2}
\end{aligned}$$

Figure 16

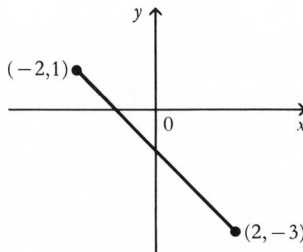

5 The *unit circle* is the circle with center at the origin and radius 1. Use the distance formula to drive the equation of the unit circle.

SOLUTION. Suppose that (x,y) is any point on the unit circle. For illustrative purposes (x,y) will be sketched as a point in the first quadrant (Figure 17). Then, by the distance formula,

$$1 = \sqrt{(x - 0)^2 + (y - 0)^2}$$

so that $1 = x^2 + y^2$. In other words, $\{(x,y)|x^2 + y^2 = 1\}$ is the set of all points on the unit circle, so that $x^2 + y^2 = 1$ is the equation of the unit circle.

Figure 17

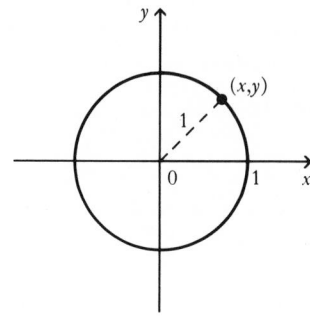

PROBLEM SET 5

1 $S = \{2,4,6\}$ and $T = \{a,b\}$. Form sets $S \times T$, $S \times S$, $T \times T$, and $T \times S$.

a)   How are each of these related to the others?
b)   Take each of the four sets of ordered pairs and form the union with each of the others.
c)   Do the same for the intersection.

2 Let $S = \{1,2,3,4\}$ and $T = \{1,2,3\}$

a)   Form $S \times T$.
b)   Plot the points of $S \times T$.
c)   Form the set $A = \{(x,y)|(x,y) \in S \times T,\ x = y\}$.
d)   Form $B = \{(x,y)|(x,y) \in S \times T,\ x < y\}$.
e)   Form $C = \{(x,y)|(x,y) \in S \times T,\ x > y\}$.
f)   Complete the sentence: $A \cup B \cup C = $?.
g)   Match each of the sets in column **I** with an equal set in column **II**.

Column I	*Column II*
i $\{(x,y)|(x,y) \in S \times T,\ x \leq y\}$	1 $A \cup B$
ii $\{(x,y)|(x,y) \in S \times T,\ x \geq y\}$	2 $A \cup C$
iii $\{(x,y)|(x,y) \in S \times T,\ x \neq y\}$	3 $B \cup C$
iv $\{(x,y)|(x,y) \in S \times T,\ x \nless y\}$	

3   a) $A \times B = B \times A$. Does $A = B$? Give an example to illustrate this
        situation.
    b) $A = B$. Does $A \times B = B \times A$? Explain.

4   Plot each of the following points and indicate what quadrant, if any,
    contains the point.

    a) (3,3)   b) (−2,4)   c) $(\pi, \sqrt{2})$
    d) (0,7)   e) (−1,−5)   f) (−3,0)

5   Given $A = \{-2,0,1\}$ and $B = \{-1,3,4\}$, form $A \times B$. Plot the mem-
    bers of $A \times B$.

6   Give the coordinates of four points which are exactly 1 unit from the
    origin (see Example 5 of Section 5.3).

7   a) Give the coordinates of any five points on the x axis.
    b) What is common to the coordinates of all points on the x axis?

8   Do Problem 7 for the vertical axis.

9   a) Using point (−4,−4) as center, sketch a circle which is tangent to
        both coordinate axes. What is the radius of the circle?
    b) Is it possible to sketch such a circle using (2,3) as center? Explain.

10 a) Draw the line segment between points (1,3) and (−2,5). Do all the
        points lie in either quadrant I or II?
    b) Find the intersection of the line segment and the vertical axis.

11 Find the distance between each of the following pair of points.

    a) $(-\frac{1}{2},1)$; (2,3)   b) (−3,−4); (−5,−7)
    c) (5,0); (−7,3)   d) $(t,8)$; $(t,7)$

12 Given points $P_1:(-3,-2)$; $P_2:(1,2)$; and $P_3:(3,4)$, do the following:

    a) Plot the points.
    b) Find the lengths of segments P_1P_2, P_2P_3, and P_1P_3.
    c) Three points are said to be *collinear* if they all lie on the same
        straight line. Are P_1, P_2, and P_3 collinear? Explain.

13 Given points $P_1:(a,b)$; $P_2:(c,d)$; and $P_3:[(a + c)/2, (b + d)/2]$, do the
    following:

    a) Find the lengths of segments P_1P_3 and P_2P_3 in terms of a, b, c,
        and d.
    b) How do these two lengths compare?
    c) What can you conclude about the geometric position of P_3 with
        respect to P_1 and P_2?
    d) Give a specific example to illustrate this situation.

REVIEW PROBLEM SET

1   Use the following sets for each of the parts.

I_p, the set of positive integers
I, the set of integers
F, the set of quotient numbers (rational numbers which are not integers)
Q, the set of rational numbers
L, the set of irrational numbers
R, the set of real numbers
$\emptyset$, the empty set

Each description below corresponds to at least one of the above sets. Identify these sets.

a)   A set that contains 49 but not -49.
b)   A set that contains both $\frac{2}{3}$ and π.
c)   A set that contains $-\frac{3}{4}$ but not π.
d) $I_p \cup I$
e) $F \cap Q$
f) $L \cup R$
g)   A subset of the quotient numbers which contains $\frac{3}{2}$ but not 3.
h)   A subset of the real numbers which does not contain 1, but which is not the empty set.
i)   A subset of the irrational numbers which does not contain π.
j)   A set which is disjoint from the positive integers and which is not a subset of the integers.

2   Let A be a set that contains five elements and let B be a set that contains three elements. Which of the following are true?

a) $A \cap B$ contains exactly five elements.
b) $A \cup B$ contains at least five elements.
c) $A \cup B$ contains exactly four elements.
d) $A \cap B$ is a subset of A.
e) B is a subset of A.
f) $A \cup B$ can contain no more than eight elements.
g)   If $A \cap B = \emptyset$, then $A \cup B = \emptyset$.
h)   If $x \in A$ and $x \in B$, then $A \cap B$ is not an empty set.
i)   If $A \cap B$ contains three elements, then B is a subset of A.
j)   If $A \cup B$ contains six elements, then $A \cap B$ contains two elements.

3   What set could you select as a universal set U from which each given pair of sets has been formed?

a)   {All single women} ; {All married women}
b)   {All even integers} ; {All odd integers}
c)   {All Southern states} ; {All Western states}

4 Use $A = \{x,y,z\}$ and $B = \{c,y,x\}$ to say whether the following are true or false.

a) $x \in \{x\} \cup B$

b) $c \in A \cup B$

c) $A = B$

d) $y \in A \cap B$

e) $A \cap B = \{y,z\}$

f) $\{x\} = A \cap B$

5 Notice that $\frac{1}{9} = 0.11\overline{1}$ repeats in one digit blocks, and $\frac{1}{3} = 0.333\overline{3}$ repeats in one digit blocks. Compare the decimal representations of $\frac{1}{9} \cdot \frac{1}{3}$ and $\frac{1}{9} + \frac{1}{3}$ to the decimal representations of $\frac{1}{9}$ and $\frac{1}{3}$.

6 Let $U = \{x,y,u,v\}$. If $A = \{x,y\}$, $A \cap B = \{x\}$, and $A \cup B = U$, find the set B.

7 Given $A = \{a,b,c\}$ and $B = \{x,y\}$:

a) List all the ordered pairs of $A \times B$.

b) List all the ordered pairs of $B \times A$.

8 Let $A = \{1,2,3,4,5,6,7,8\}$ and $B = \{1,2,3,4,5,6,7,8,9\}$.

a) How many elements of $A \times B$ are of the form (x,x)?

b) How many elements (x,y) of $A \times B$ satisfy the condition that x is less than y?

9 A positive integer m is said to be a multiple of a positive integer n if there exists a positive integer k such that $m = kn$. For example, 18 is a multiple of 6 since $18 = 3 \cdot 6$. Describe $A \cap B$ in each of the following cases where x is assumed to be a positive integer.

a) $A = \{x|x$ is a multiple of $3\}$ and $B = \{x|x$ is a multiple of $5\}$

b) $A = \{x|x$ is a multiple of $3\}$ and $B = \{x|x$ is a multiple of $6\}$

c) $A = \{x|x$ is a multiple of $9\}$ and $B = \{x|x$ is a multiple of $12\}$

10 Let $A = \{2,3,4,5,6\}$ and $B = \{6,7,8,9,10\}$. Verify that each of the following is true by computing the values.

a) $N(A \cup B) = N(A) + N(B) - N(A \cap B)$

b) $N(A \times B) = N(A) \cdot N(B)$

c) $N(A \times A) = N(A) \cdot N(A)$

11 Indicate which of the following are true and which are false. If the assertion is false give a counterexample to support your answer. Assume that a and b are real numbers such that $a < b$.

a) $a < 3b$

b) $2a > -(-2)b$

c) $a + c < b + c, \quad c \in R$

d) $a + 3 < b + 4$

e) $a - 4 < b - 4$

f) $a - 2 < b - 3$

g) $1/a < 1/b$

h) $|a| < b$

12 Solve the following inequalities, show your solution on the real line, and write the solution using interval notation.

a) $5x - 9 > 2x + 3$
b) $2x/3 + \frac{1}{5} > \frac{7}{15} + 4x/5$
c) $x/2 + \frac{5}{6} < 2x/3 + \frac{1}{12}$
d) $5x - 2 > 6x + 5$
e) $5x - 11 < 8x - 5$

13 Let x, y, and z be real numbers. Which of the following is true? Give a counterexample to disprove any false statement.

a)   If $-\frac{1}{2} < x < \frac{1}{2}$, then $-1 < x < 1$.
b)   If $0 < x < \frac{1}{2}$, then $-\frac{1}{3} < x < \frac{1}{3}$.
c)   If $x > y$, then $x - z > y - z$.
d)   If $x > y$ and $z > 0$, then $x/z > y/z$.
e)   If $x > y$, $x > 0$ and $y > 0$, then $x^2 > y^2$ and $1/x < 1/y$.
f)   If $x^3 > y^3$, $x > 0$ and $y > 0$, then $x < y$.

14 Find any value of m that satisfies the following inequality.

$$|x^4 + 3x^3 - 5x^2 + x - 2| < m \quad \text{if} \quad |x - 1| < 2$$

15 Solve each of the following; indicate your solution set by using interval notation and represent the solution on the real line.

a) $|x - 5| \geq \frac{3}{2}$
b) $|3x + 1| > 8$
c) $|x - 3| = 0$
d) $|x - 2| < 3$
e) $|x - 2| = |2 - x|$
f) $|2x - 5| < 9$
g) $|x - 2| \geq -5$
h) $|2/x - 3| < 1$

16 Find the distance between the points

a) $(2,1)$ and $(4,-5)$
b) $(-3,2)$ and $(6,-1)$
c) $(-6,-3)$ and $(2,1)$
d) $(0,-7)$ and $(4,3)$
e) $(-2,6)$ and $(-2,-1)$

17 Show that the points $(-5,7)$, $(2,6)$, and $(1,-1)$ lie on a circle whose center is $(-2,3)$.

CHAPTER 2

Relations and Functions

2 RELATIONS AND FUNCTIONS

1 Relations

The statements "Joe is married to Rose," "Barbara is a sister of Jim," "New York is larger than Michigan," and "5 is less than 8" involve what is commonly understood to be a relationship. Expressions of the type "is married to," "is a sister of," "is larger than," and "is less than" are classified as relations. Hence, a *relation* suggests a correspondence or an association between the elements of two sets. For example, Table 1 suggests a relation between the numbers in the x column with the numbers in the y column. Here, the correspondence between the numbers in the x column and the numbers in the y column is given by the formula $y = 2x$, where x is a positive integer.

Table 1

x	$\rightarrow$	y
1	$\rightarrow$	2
2	$\rightarrow$	4
3	$\rightarrow$	6
4	$\rightarrow$	8
5	$\rightarrow$	10
. . . .		
x	$\rightarrow$	$2x$

Similarly, Table 2 suggests a correspondence between the numbers in two sets. Here, the correspondence between the numbers is given by the formula $y = 2x + 1$, where x is a positive integer.

Table 2

$$
\begin{array}{ccc}
x & \rightarrow & y \\
\hline
1 & \rightarrow & 3 \\
2 & \rightarrow & 5 \\
3 & \rightarrow & 7 \\
4 & \rightarrow & 9 \\
\cdots & \cdots & \cdots \\
x & \rightarrow & 2x + 1
\end{array}
$$

In each of the above examples, there are three main ingredients: a first set, a second set, and a correspondence between the members of the two sets. These two examples suggest a relation between two sets. In order to describe a relation so that the corresponding members of the two sets are clearly identified, the ordered pair notation is used.

1.1   Definition

A *relation* is a set of ordered pairs (see Section 5.1, Chapter 1). The *domain* of a relation is the set of all first members of the ordered pairs and the *range* of a relation is the set of all second members of the ordered pairs. □

Hence, $\{(x,y)|y = 2x, x \in I_p\}$ is the relation suggested by Table 1. $\{(x,y)|y = 2x + 1, x \in I_p\}$ is the relation suggested by Table 2.

Since we will consider only those relations which are formed from real numbers, we can use the Cartesian coordinate system to represent relations as points in a plane. This representation of a relation is called the *graph* of the relation; the graph provides us with a "geometric picture" of the relation.

EXAMPLES

1   Assume that $U = \{1,2,3\}$ for each of the following relations. Enumerate the members of the relation, indicate the domain and range, and graph the relation.

a) $R_1 = \{(x,y)|y = x$ where $x \in U, y \in U\}$
b) $R_2 = \{(x,y)|y > x$ where $x \in U, y \in U\}$

SOLUTION

a) $R_1 = \{(1,1),(2,2),(3,3)\}$, so that the domain and range are the same set $\{1,2,3\}$. The graph is composed of three points (Figure 1).

Figure 1

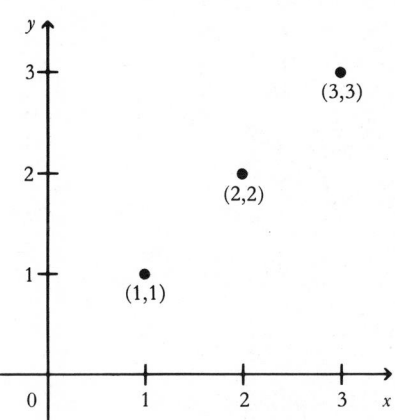

b) $R_2 = \{(x,y)|y > x\} = \{(1,2),(1,3),(2,3)\}$, so that the domain of R_2 is $\{1,2\}$ and the range of R_2 is $\{2,3\}$. The graph has three points (Figure 2).

Figure 2

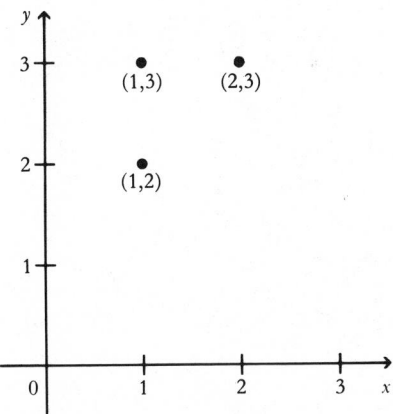

2   Graph the relation $\{(x,y)|y = 3x, x \in R\}$.

SOLUTION.   It is impossible here to list all members of this relation. The best that we can do is to plot some of the points to discover the "pattern" of the graph (Figure 3). Tables are often used to list members of a relation; $(0,0)$, $(1,3)$, $(3,9)$, $(-\frac{1}{3},-1)$, and $(-1,-3)$ are recorded in the table next to Figure 3.

Figure 3

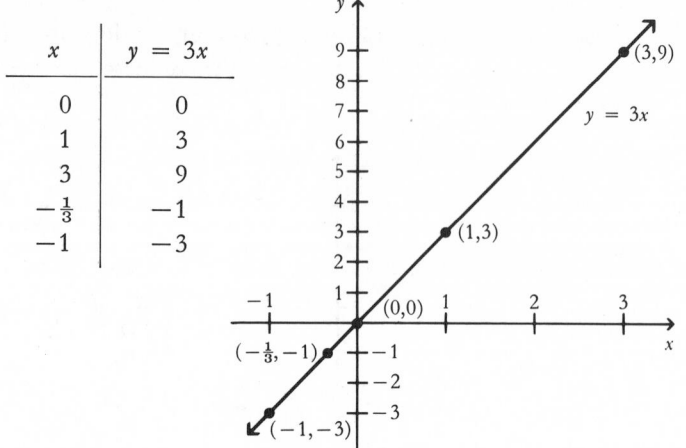

3   Use a table to graph $\{(x,y)|x^2 + y^2 = 4,\ x \in \{-2,-1,0,1,2\}\}$. Indicate the domain and range.

SOLUTION

Figure 4

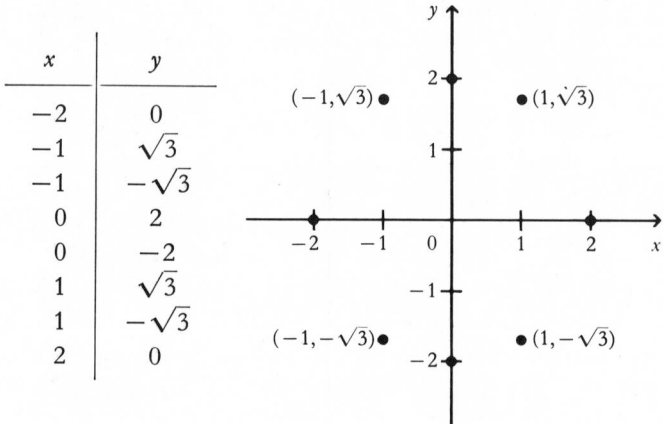

The domain is $\{-2,-1,0,1,2\}$ and the range is $\{0,\sqrt{3},-\sqrt{3},2,-2\}$.

   Quite often set notation is not used to describe a relation. When this is the case, the set of ordered pairs is implied. For example, $x < y$ is an abbreviated way of writing the relation $\{(x,y)|x < y, x \in R\}$.

   $y = 1/x$ implies the relation $\{(x,y)|y = 1/x\}$. Assuming that x and y represent real numbers, the domain of $y = 1/x$ does *not* include 0 (Figure 5), since division by zero is not defined. Here, the nature of the equation $y = 1/x$ implies that 0 must be excluded from the domain.

Figure 5

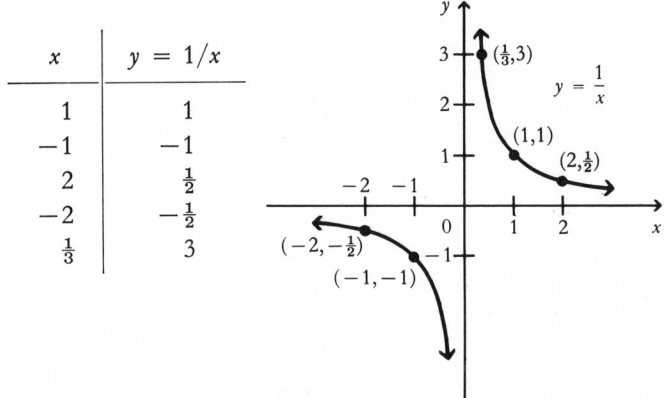

In general, the domain and/or range of a relation is not always given. If this is the case, we determine the domain by inspection as we did with $y = 1/x$. Also, if the universal set is not given, we will assume the universal set for the relation to be $R \times R$, where R is the set of real numbers.

Note that if (x,y) is a member of a relation, we can consider the real numbers x and y from two viewpoints. On the one hand, x is a member of the domain and y is the corresponding member of the range of the relation. On the other hand, x represents the abscissa and y represents the ordinate of a point in a plane. On the graph, then, the members of the domain are the abscissas, and the members of the range are the

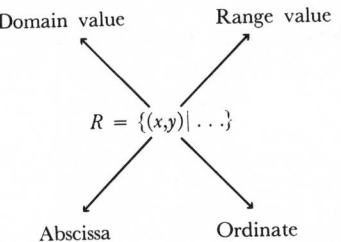

ordinates. Any restriction on the domain is a restriction on "the horizontal position of the graph," and any restriction on the range is a restriction on "the vertical position of the graph."

EXAMPLES

1 Graph $y = x^2$.

SOLUTION. $y = x^2$ implies the relation $\{(x,y)|y = x^2\}$ with universal set $R \times R$. Since any real number can be squared and since the square of a real number is always nonnegative, the domain is R, and the range is set $[0,\infty)$. This means that the graph "lies" in the region above and on the x axis (Figure 6).

Figure 6

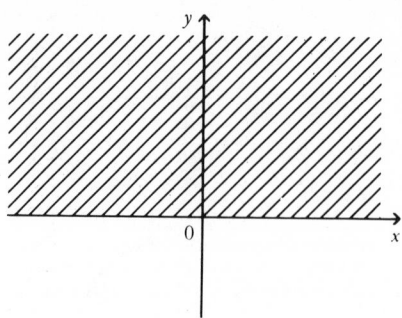

Finally, we can use a table to determine the graph (Figure 7).

Figure 7

x	$y = x^2$
0	0
1	1
−1	1
2	4
−2	4

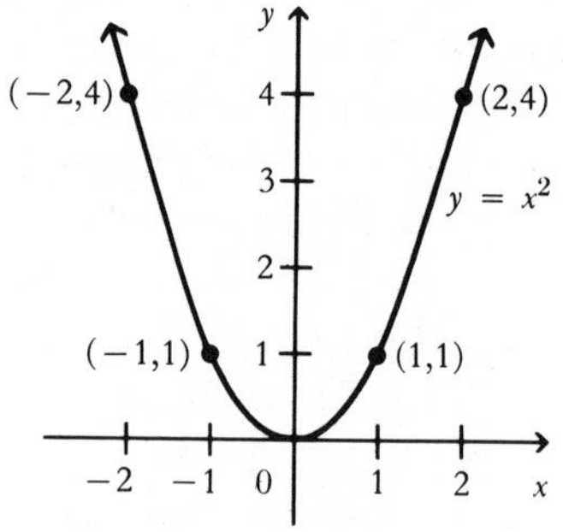

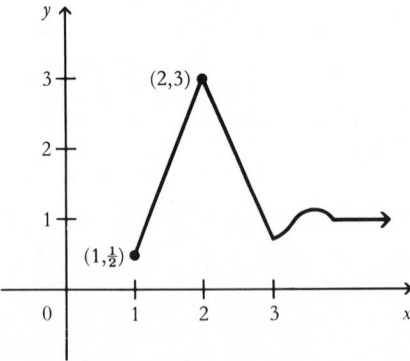

2   Assume that the graph of a relation is given in Figure 8. Use the graph to identify the domain and the range of the relation.

Figure 8

SOLUTION.   It can be seen from the graph in Figure 8 that any of the abscissas x satisfies $x \geq 1$ and any of the ordinates y satisfies $\frac{1}{2} \leq y \leq 3$; consequently, the domain is set $[1,\infty)$ and the range is set $[\frac{1}{2},3]$.

4   Sketch the graph of each of the following relations on the same coordinate system.

a) $R_1 = \{(x,y)|y = 4x\}$
b) $R_2 = \{(x,y)|y < 4x\}$
c) $R_3 = \{(x,y)|y > 4x\}$

SOLUTION

a)   We will list a few points and plot them to determine the graph of $y = 4x$ (Figure 9).
b)   The graph of $y < 4x$ is the shaded area R_2 (Figure 9).
c)   The graph of $y > 4x$ is the shaded area R_3 (Figure 9).

Figure 9

x	$y = 4x$
-1	-4
0	0
1	4
2	8
3	12

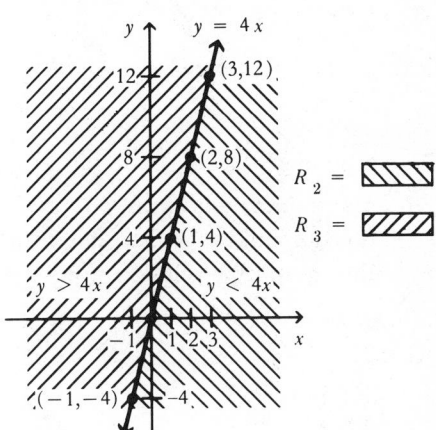

PROBLEM SET 1

1   Which of the following sets are relations?
a) $\{(1,2),(2,3),(3,4)\}$ b) $\{1,5,9\}$
c) $\{\{1,2\},\{2,3\}\}$ d) $\{(a,b),(c,d),(b,b),(b,a)\}$

2   Let $U \times U$ be the universal set where $U = \{0,1,2,3\}$ for each of the following relations. Tabulate each of the relations. State the domain and the range for each and graph the relation.
a) $R_1 = \{(x,y)|y = x\}$ b) $R_2 = \{(x,y)|y > x\}$
c) $R_3 = \{(x,y)|y < x\}$ d) $R_4 = \{(x,y)|x + y = 1\}$
e) $R_5 = \{(x,y)|x^2 + y^2 = 1\}$

3   Shade in the region in the plane which contains the graph of a relation with domain D and range R_0.
a) $D = [-1,1]$ and $R_0 = [3,5]$
b) $D = [0,\infty)$ and $R_0 = \{5\}$
c) $D = (-\infty,0]$ and $R_0 = [0,\infty)$
d) $D = \{2,3\}$ and $R_0 = [-2,3]$
e) $D = [-1,0)$ and $R_0 = (1,4)$

4 Suppose that a relation has the graph in Figure 10. What is the domain? What is the range?

Figure 10

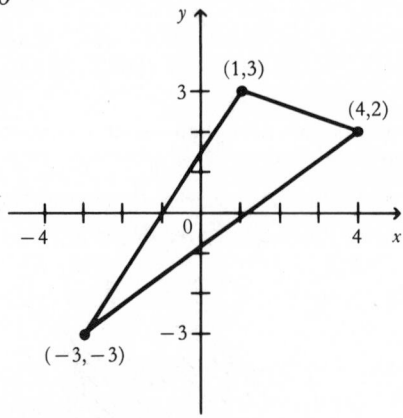

5 Use set notation to describe each of the implied relations. State the domain and range. List five members of the relation in table form, and then graph the relation.

a) $y = 2x + 1$
c) $y^2 = x$
e) $y < 2x + 1$
g) $x = 7$
i) $y = |x + 1|$

b) $y = -2$
d) $2x + 2y = 3$
f) $x^2 = y^2$
h) $x^2 + y^2 = 1$
j) $|x| + |y| = 1$

6 Give two examples to show that it is possible for two different ordered pairs of a relation to have the same first member.

7 Let $U = \{1,2\}$. Indicate the different relations which are subsets of $U \times U$.

2 Functions

We have already encountered the usage of functions in everyday living. For example, the amount of sales tax charged for a purchase of $5.00 is a function of the sales tax rate; the number of books to be ordered for a course is a function of the number of students in the course; the number of members in the house of representatives for a particular state is a function of the population of the state.

Suppose that there is a 5 percent sales tax on all purchases. A purchase of $1.00 would yield 5¢ tax; $2.50 would yield 13¢ tax; in general, a purchase of x dollars would have a sales tax of $0.05x$ rounded off to the nearest cent. The sales tax is a function of cost.

Intuitively, a function suggests some kind of a correspondence. In each of the examples above, there is an established correspondence between numbers — the amount of sales tax corresponds with the cost, the number of books with the number of students, the number of representatives with the number of people.

A *function* is a correspondence that assigns to each member in a certain set, called the *domain* of the function, *exactly one member* in a second set, called the *range* of the function. Now, we will see how the concept of a function can be formalized by using the notion of a relation.

Suppose, for example, that at the beginning of the term, as each student registers for classes, the tuition charge is recorded with the student account number as illustrated by the following partial table.

Student account number	Tuition charge
895	315.00
475	323.50
182	260.90
743	315.00
234	370.00

Here, the set of account numbers is the domain; the set of tuition charges is the range; the correspondence between the domain members and range members is suggested by the following table.

Domain	"Corresponds to"	Range
895	"Corresponds to"	315.00
475	"Corresponds to"	323.50
182	"Corresponds to"	260.90
743	"Corresponds to"	315.00
234	"Corresponds to"	370.00

Ordered pair notation is well suited to representing functions; for if x is a member of the domain of a function and y is the member of the range corresponding to x, we can represent the correspondence between x and y as the ordered pair (x,y). In fact, we can say that the function is the set of all such ordered pairs. (In the example above, then, we can represent the function as the set of ordered pairs {. . . ,(895,315.00),(475,323.50), (182,260.90),(743,315.00),(234,370.00), . . .}.) In this sense, we define a function as follows, recalling that a relation is a set of ordered pairs.

2.1 Definition

A *function* is a relation in which no two different pairs have the same first member. The set of all first members (of the ordered pairs) is called the *domain* of the function. The set of all second members (of the ordered pairs) is called the *range* of the function. For each ordered pair (x,y) of the function we say that x in the domain has y as the corresponding member of the range. ☐

We have seen above that a 5 percent sales tax on any purchase can be considered as a function. We can describe this function using ordered pair notation as $\{(x,0.05x)|x$ is the amount of the purchase and $0.05x$ is the tax rounded to the nearest cent} ; a purchase of x dollars corresponds to a $0.05x$ sales tax. We could also display this correspondence by a table as follows.

Purchase in dollars (domain)	Sales tax in dollars (range)
0.25	0.01
0.50	0.03
1.00	0.05
. . . .	. . . .
x	$0.05x$

From Definition 2.1, we conclude that all functions are relations; however, not all relations are functions. For example, $\{(1,1),(2,2),(3,7),(3,5)\}$ is a relation, with domain $\{1,2,3\}$ and range $\{1,2,7,5,\}$, but it is not a function because $(3,7)$ and $(3,5)$ have the same first members (see Definition 2.1). By contrast, $\{(1,2),(3,4),(4,4)\}$ is a relation which is a function with domain $\{1,3,4\}$ and range $\{2,4\}$. Note that in the latter example, there are two pairs which have the same second member; this does *not* violate the definition of a function.

Hence, if at least two different ordered pairs of a relation have the same first member, the relation is not a function. In other words, if a domain member appears with more than one range member, the relation is not a function. Geometrically, this means that if the graph of a relation has more than one point with the same abscissa, the relation is not a function.

Consider the graphs of the relations in Figure 1a and b. The relation $\{(x,y)|y = \sqrt{25 - x^2}\}$ in Figure 1a represents a function since the graph does not have two different points with the same x coordinates, whereas the relation $\{(x,y)|x = \sqrt{25 - y^2}\}$ in Figure 1b is not a function, since there are two different points with the same x coordinates; for example, $(3,4)$ and $(3,-4)$ are two such points.

Figure 1

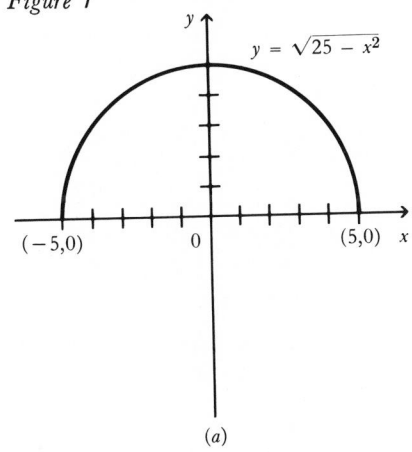

(a)

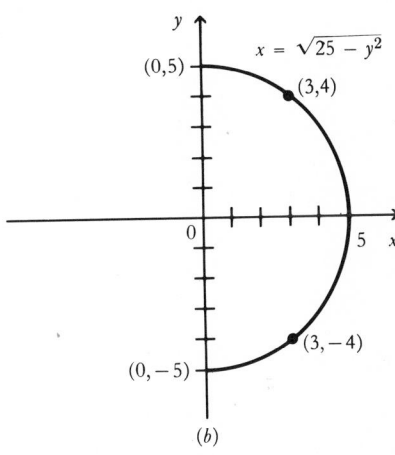

(b)

EXAMPLES

1   In each of the following parts, indicate whether the relation is a function. What is the domain and range? Graph the relation.

a) $\{(1,2),(2,3),(3,4),(4,4),(5,6)\}$ b) $\{(x,y)|y > x\}$
c) $y = 3$ d) $x = 1$
e) $y = 3x$ f) $y = 3x,\ x \in \{-1,0,2,3\}$

SOLUTION

a) $\{(1,2),(2,3),(3,4),(4,4),(5,6)\}$ is a function with domain $\{1,2,3,4,5\}$ and range $\{2,3,4,6\}$; the graph is given in Figure 2.

Figure 2

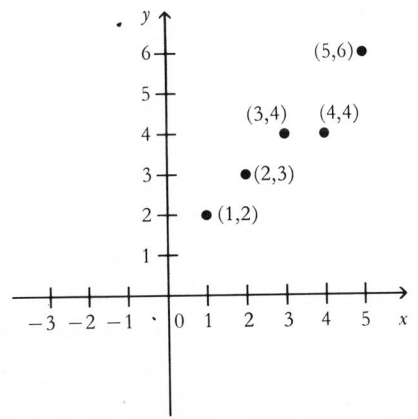

b) $\{(x,y)|y > x\}$ is not a function because, for example, $(1,2)$ and
$(1,\frac{5}{2})$ are two different ordered pairs with the same first members.
The domain is the set of all real numbers and the range is also
the set of all real numbers. The shaded region of Figure 3 is the
graph of $\{(x,y)|y > x\}$. Notice that the graph does *not* include the
points on the dotted line.

Figure 3

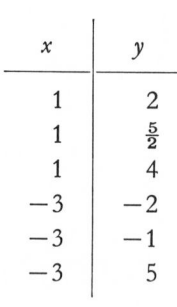

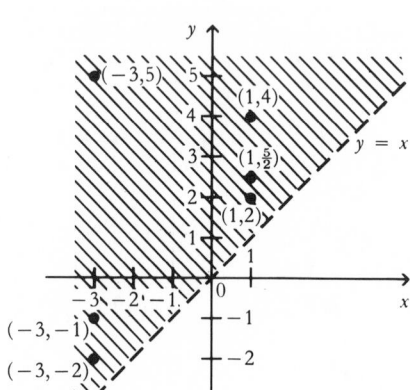

c) $y = 3$ is an abbreviated way of writing the relation $\{(x,y)|y = 3\}$.
The domain is the set of all real numbers because there is no restriction on x, whereas the range is $\{3\}$. The relation is a function
because no two different ordered pairs have the same first members. The graph is the line parallel to the x axis in Figure 4.

Figure 4

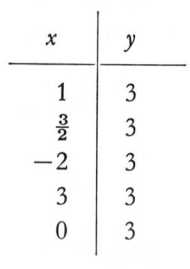

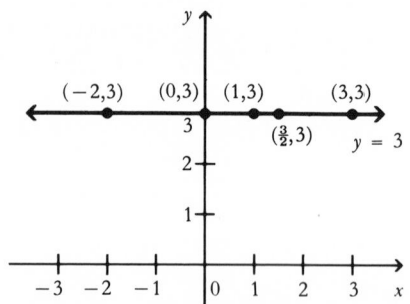

d) $x = 1$ is the relation $\{(x,y)|x = 1\}$. This relation is not a function
because $(1,3)$ and $(1,4)$ are members of the set. The domain of the
relation is $\{1\}$ and the range is the set of all real numbers. The
graph is the line parallel to the y axis in Figure 5. We can see geo-

metrically that $x = 1$ is not a function because there are at least two (actually an infinite number of) points with the same abscissa.

Figure 5

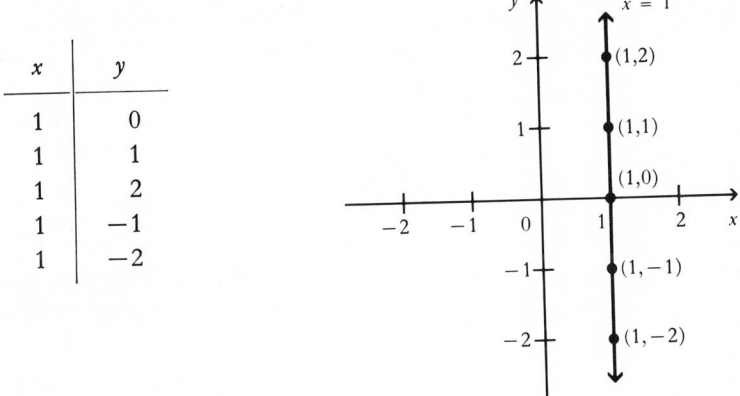

x	y
1	0
1	1
1	2
1	-1
1	-2

e) $y = 3x$ is the relation $\{(x,y)\,|\,y = 3x\}$. It is a function; the domain and range is the set of all real numbers. The graph is given in Figure 6. It can be seen geometrically that this relation is a function since no two points have the same abscissa.

Figure 6

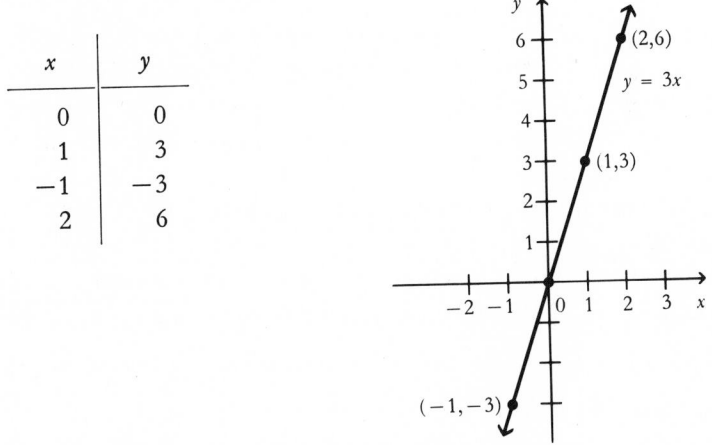

x	y
0	0
1	3
-1	-3
2	6

f) $y = 3x$ with $x \in \{-1,0,2,3\}$ is the relation $\{(-1,-3),(0,0),(2,6),$ $(3,9)\}$. It is a function with domain $\{-1,0,2,3\}$ and range $\{-3,0,6,9\}$ and the graph is composed of the four points in Figure 7. Notice that the equation which is used in this function is the same as the equation used in part (e) above; however, the functions are different. (They have different domains.)

Figure 7

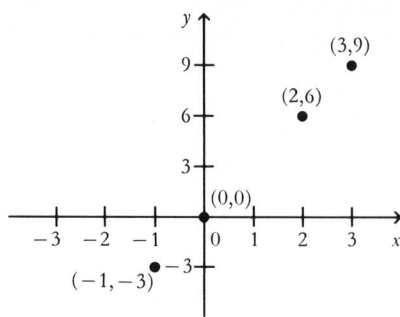

2   Examine the graphs of each of the following relations given in Figure
8*a* and *b* to decide whether or not the relation is a function.

Figure 8

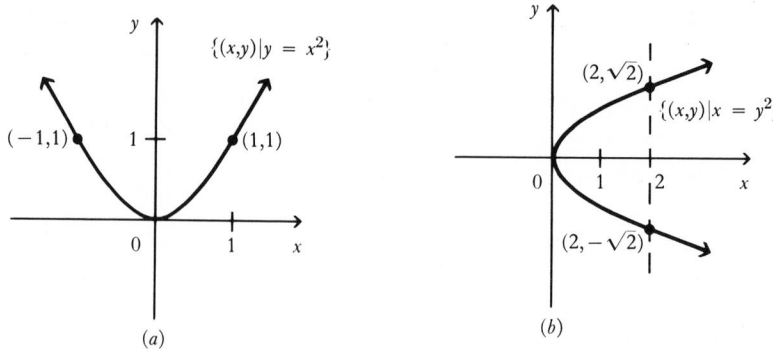

(*a*)   (*b*)

SOLUTION.   Since the graph in Figure 8*a* does not have two different
points with equal abscissas, no two different ordered pairs of the rela-
tion have equal first members, so that the relation $\{(x,y)|y = x^2\}$ is a
function.

It can be seen from the graph in Figure 8*b* that there are two dif-
ferent points with abscissa 2, so that the relation $\{(x,y)|x = y^2\}$ is not a
function.

2.2   Function Notation

Let $y = 2x - 1$ be a function with domain $\{0,1,2\}$. The range is
$\{-1,1,3\}$. This function could also be described as $\{(0,-1),(1,1),(2,3)\}$.
This latter representation gives a more complete picture of the function
than the first representation in the sense that the ordered pairs indicate
precisely which member of the domain is associated with each member
of the range. A function can also be described as a "mapping" of members of the domain to corresponding members of the range. In this
example, 0 is "mapped" to -1, 1 is "mapped" to 1, and 2 is "mapped"
to 3.

In general, if (a,b) is a member of a function f, then f associates a in the domain with b in the range and we say that f *maps a to b* or a *is mapped to b by f* or, equivalently, b *is the image of a under f*. This is written $f:a \mapsto b$ or $a \overset{f}{\mapsto} b$. If f is understood, we will sometimes use the notation $a \mapsto b$. The notation $f:A \mapsto B$ is also used to denote the fact that the function f "maps" the domain set A into set B where B is a set containing the range of function f.

EXAMPLES

Interpret each of the following functions as mappings.

1 $f = \{(1,2),(3,4),(4,4)\}$

SOLUTION. $1 \overset{f}{\mapsto} 2; 3 \overset{f}{\mapsto} 4; 4 \overset{f}{\mapsto} 4$.

2 $y = 3x$, where x represents members of the domain.

SOLUTION.   Here, 6 is the image of 2, 0 is the image of 0, and $-\frac{3}{2}$ is the image of $-\frac{1}{2}$. In mapping notation, we write $2 \overset{f}{\mapsto} 6, 0 \overset{f}{\mapsto} 0$, and $-\frac{1}{2} \overset{f}{\mapsto} -\frac{3}{2}$. In general, if x is any real number, then $f:x \mapsto 3x$.

3 $y = 3$ where y represents members of the range.

SOLUTION.   Each real number is mapped to 3; that is, $f:R \mapsto \{3\}$.

4 $f = \{(x,y)|y = 1/|x|\}$.

SOLUTION. $1 \overset{f}{\mapsto} 1, -1 \overset{f}{\mapsto} 1, \pi \overset{f}{\mapsto} 1/\pi, -\pi \overset{f}{\mapsto} 1/\pi$, and so on. This function maps each nonzero number to a positive real number.

Now, if a function is to be described by use of an equation, we must have additional information to determine the mapping. For example, $3r + 5t = 3$ might have either r or t representing the members of the domain. If t represents members of the domain, then, after solving for r in terms of t, $t \mapsto (3 - 5t)/3$ would be the mapping, and we say that r is a function of t; whereas if r represents members of the domain, after solving for t in terms of r, we get $r \mapsto (3 - 3r)/5$, so that t is a function of r.

If x represents members of the domain of $y = x^2$, then y is considered to be a function of x and we indicate this by writing $f(x) = x^2$, which reads "f of x equals x squared." Hence, $f(x) = x^2$ is another way of writing the function $\{(x,y)|y = x^2\}$.

In other words, $y = f(x)$ means that (x,y) is a member of the function. For example, if $4x - 2y = 1$ and $y = f(x)$, then after solving for y in terms of x, we could write the function either as $\{(x,y)|y = 2x - \frac{1}{2}\}$ or as $f(x) = 2x - \frac{1}{2}$.

It is important to realize that letters other than x, y, or f can be used to denote functions. For example, $h(r) = r^2 - 1$ is the function given by $\{(r,h(r))|h(r) = r^2 - 1\}$; $3r + 5t = 3$ with $t = g(r)$ is the function given by $\{(r,t)|t = (3 - 3r)/5\}$; and $c(d) = \pi d$ is the function given by $\{(d,c(d))|c(d) = \pi d\}$.

EXAMPLES

1   Let $f(x) = x + 1$. Then $f(2) = 3$ means that $(2,3)$ is a member of the function, or, equivalently, $2 \mapsto 3$.

2   $f(x) = 1/x$ represents the function given by $\{(x,y)|y = 1/x\}$ with the implied domain and range the same, that is, the set of nonzero numbers.

When functional notation is used, sometimes it is helpful to think of the variable which represents the members of the domain as a "missing blank." For example, $g(t) = t^2$ can be thought of as $g(\ ) = (\ )^2$; hence, if any expression (representing a real number) is used to represent a member of the domain, it is easy to see where this same expression is to be substituted in the equation describing the function.

Using $g(t) = t^2$ again, $g(x + h)$ can be determined by first writing the function as

$$g(\ ) = (\ )^2$$

so that, by substitution,

$$g(x + h) = (x + h)^2 = x^2 + 2xh + h^2$$

Similarly,

$$g(3 - 5x) = (3 - 5x)^2$$

EXAMPLES

1   Assume that $g(t) = t^2 + 1$. Determine each of the following expressions.

a) $g(2)$ b) $g(x + 1)$
c) $g(x) + 1$ d) $g(x^2 - y^2)$
e) $g(x^2) - g(y^2)$

SOLUTION. $g(t) = t^2 + 1$ can be written as $g(\ ) = (\ )^2 + 1$.

a) $g(2) = (2)^2 + 1 = 4 + 1 = 5$
b) $g(x + 1) = (x + 1)^2 + 1 = x^2 + 2x + 1 + 1 = x^2 + 2x + 2$
c) $g(x) + 1 = (x)^2 + 1 + 1 = x^2 + 1 + 1 = x^2 + 2$
d) $g(x^2 - y^2) = (x^2 - y^2)^2 + 1 = x^4 - 2x^2y^2 + y^4 + 1$
e) $g(x^2) - g(y^2) = [(x^2)^2 + 1] - [(y^2)^2 + 1] = x^4 - y^4$

2   Given that $f(x) = x^2 - 1$, what is the domain and the range of f? Find each of the following expressions.

a) $f(3) + f(5)$ b) $f(x + 1)$
c) $f(2a + 4)$ d) $2f(a - 2)$

SOLUTION. The domain of the function f is the set of real numbers and the range of f is the set $[-1, \infty)$.

a) $f(3) = 3^2 - 1 = 8$ and $f(5) = 5^2 - 1 = 24$

so that

$f(3) + f(5) = 8 + 24 = 32$

b) $f(x + 1) = (x + 1)^2 - 1 = x^2 + 2x$
c) $f(2a + 4) = (2a + 4)^2 - 1 = 4a^2 + 16a + 15$
d) $2f(a - 2) = 2[(a - 2)^2 - 1] = 2[a^2 - 4a + 3]$
$= 2a^2 - 8a + 6$

3   Display the corresponding domain and range elements using the mapping interpretation of a function, the ordered pair interpretation of a function, and functional notation for $\{(x, y) | y = 7x + 2,$ $x \in \{1, 2, 3, 4\}\}$.

SOLUTION

Mapping $f : x \to 7x + 2$	Ordered pairs (x, y)	Functional notation $y = f(x)$
$1 \to 9$	$(1, 9)$	$f(1) = 9$
$2 \to 16$	$(2, 16)$	$f(2) = 16$
$3 \to 23$	$(3, 23)$	$f(3) = 23$
$4 \to 30$	$(4, 30)$	$f(4) = 30$

4   The *difference quotient* of a function $y = f(x)$ is defined as

$$\frac{f(x + h) - f(x)}{h} \qquad h \neq 0$$

Compute the difference quotient for each of the following functions.

a) $f(x) = 2x + 1$ b) $f(x) = x^2$
c) $f(x) = 1/x$

SOLUTION

a) $f(x + h) = 2(x + h) + 1$, so that

$$\frac{f(x + h) - f(x)}{h} = \frac{[2(x + h) + 1] - (2x + 1)}{h}$$

$$= \frac{2x + 2h + 1 - 2x - 1}{h}$$

$$= 2 \qquad h \neq 0$$

b) $f(x + h) = (x + h)^2 = x^2 + 2xh + h^2$ implies that

$$\frac{f(x + h) - f(x)}{h} = \frac{x^2 + 2xh + h^2 - x^2}{h}$$

$$= 2x + h \qquad h \neq 0$$

c) $f(x + h) = 1/(x + h)$, so that

$$\frac{f(x + h) - f(x)}{h} = \frac{1/(x + h) - 1/x}{h}$$

$$= \frac{x - x - h}{hx(x + h)}$$

$$= \frac{-1}{x(x + h)} \qquad h \neq 0$$

5   Use functional notation to express the area of a square as a function of the length of its diagonal.

SOLUTION.   By the Pythagorean theorem, $x^2 + x^2 = z^2$, where z is the length of the diagonal and x is the length of a side (Figure 9). Hence, $2x^2 = z^2$. The area of the square is x^2 or $z^2/2$, from which it follows that the area can be expressed as a function of z by $A(z) = z^2/2$.

Figure 9

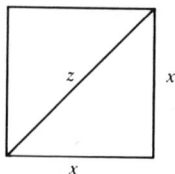

2.3   Algebra of Functions

Now that we have a clear understanding of what a function is, we can develop an *algebra of functions;* that is, we can examine ways of combining two functions under the operations of addition, subtraction, multiplication, and division to form new functions.

Let f and g be two functions and suppose that D_f and D_g denote the domains of f and g, respectively; then we define the functions $f + g$, $f - g, f \cdot g$ and f/g as follows.

$$f + g = \{(x,y)|y = f(x) + g(x) \text{ and } x \in D_f \cap D_g\}$$
$$f - g = \{(x,y)|y = f(x) - g(x) \text{ and } x \in D_f \cap D_g\}$$
$$f \cdot g = \{(x,y)|y = f(x) \cdot g(x) \text{ and } x \in D_f \cap D_g\}$$
$$\frac{f}{g} = \left\{(x,y)|y = \frac{f(x)}{g(x)}, \ g(x) \neq 0 \text{ and } x \in D_f \cap D_g\right\}$$

where $g(x) \neq 0$ means that f/g has meaning only if we exclude any $x \in D_g$ which yields $g(x) = 0$.

EXAMPLES

1   Use $f = \{(1,2),(2,2),(3,5),(4,6)\}$ and $g = \{(2,2),(-1,3),(3,7)\}$ to form each of the following functions:

a) $f + g$ b) $f - g$
c) $f \cdot g$ d) f/g

SOLUTION.   Since $D_f \cap D_g = \{1,2,3,4\} \cap \{2,-1,3\} = \{2,3\}$ and since $g(2) \neq 0$ and $g(3) \neq 0$, $\{2,3\}$ is the domain of each of the four functions.

a)   Since $(f + g)(2) = f(2) + g(2) = 2 + 2 = 4$ and
     $(f + g)(3) = f(3) + g(3) = 5 + 7 = 12$, $f + g = \{(2,4),(3,12)\}$.
b)   Since $(f - g)(2) = f(2) - g(2) = 2 - 2 = 0$ and
     $(f - g)(3) = f(3) - g(3) = 5 - 7 = -2$, $f - g = \{(2,0),(3,-2)\}$.
c)   Since $(f \cdot g)(2) = f(2) \cdot g(2) = 2 \cdot 2 = 4$ and
     $(f \cdot g)(3) = f(3) \cdot g(3) = 5 \cdot 7 = 35$, $f \cdot g = \{(2,4),(3,35)\}$.
d)   Since $(f/g)(2) = [f(2)/g(2)] = \frac{2}{2} = 1$ and
     $(f/g)(3) = [f(3)/g(3)] = \frac{5}{7}$, $f/g = \{(2,1),(3,\frac{5}{7})\}$.

The following table illustrates how the four functions above are formed.

Domain	f	g	$f + g$	$f - g$	$f \cdot g$	f/g
2	2	2	4	0	4	1
3	5	7	12	-2	35	$\frac{5}{7}$

2   Use $f(x) = x^2$ and $g(x) = x - 1$ to form each of the following functions.

a) $f + g$ b) $f - g$
c) $f \cdot g$ d) f/g

SOLUTION.   The domain of both f and g is the set of all real numbers, so that the domain of $f + g$, $f - g$, and $f \cdot g$ is also the set of all real numbers. The domain of f/g, however, is the set of real numbers except 1, since $g(1) = 0$.

a) $(f + g)(x) = f(x) + g(x) = x^2 + x - 1$
b) $(f - g)(x) = f(x) - g(x) = x^2 - x + 1$
c) $(f \cdot g)(x) = f(x)g(x) = x^2(x - 1) = x^3 - x^2$
d) $(f/g)(x) = [f(x)/g(x)] = x^2/(x - 1)$

For example, $(f + g)(2) = 5$, $(f - g)(2) = 3$, $(f \cdot g)(2) = 4$, and $(f/g)(2) = 4$.

Suppose we are given a function f which is formed as the sum of two other functions, g and h; that is, $f = g + h$. How can the graphs of $y = g(x)$ and $y = h(x)$ be used to get the graph of $y = f(x)$? Let us consider two examples of such a situation.

EXAMPLES

1   Use the graphs of $g(x) = 3x^2$ and $h(x) = 1$ to graph $f(x) = 3x^2 + 1$.

SOLUTION

x	$g(x)$ $3x^2$	$h(x)$ 1	$f(x)$ $3x^2 + 1$
0	0	1	1
1	3	1	4
−1	3	1	4
2	12	1	13
−2	12	1	13

Figure 10

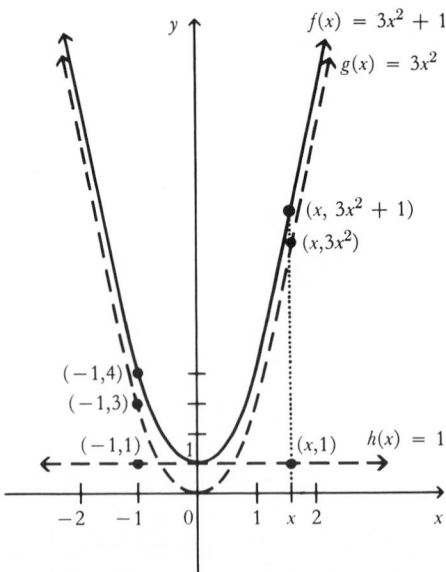

2   $f(x) = x^2 + 2x$. Here $g(x) = x^2$ and $h(x) = 2x$. If we place the graphs of $g(x) = x^2$ and $h(x) = 2x$ on the same coordinate system, then we can obtain the graph of $f(x) = x^2 + 2x$ by adding x^2 and $2x$ graphically (Figure 11).

x	$g(x)$ x^2	$h(x)$ $2x$	$f(x)$ $x^2 + 2x$
1	1	2	3
0	0	0	0
-1	1	-2	-1
2	4	4	8
-2	4	-4	0

Figure 11

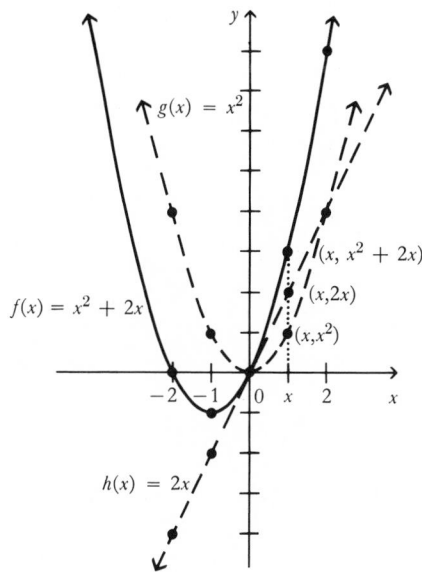

PROBLEM SET 2

1 a) Let $R_1 = \{(1,2),(3,2\}$ be a relation. Is R_1 a function? Explain.
   b) Give an example of a relation which is not a function. Explain.
   c) Give an example of two different functions which have the same domain and the same range.

2 In each of the following parts, identify which of the relations is a function and which is not a function. If it is not a function, then state the reason. In any case, identify the domain and range and graph the relation.
   a) $\{(-8,0),(-7,1),(-6,2),(-5,3),(-4,0),(-3,1),(-2,2)\}$
   b) $\{(1,1),(2,1),(3,1)\}$
   c) $\{(x,y)|y = 5x + 1\}$
   d) $|y| = |x|$, where $x \in \{1,2,3,4\}$
   e) $|y| = |x|$
   f) $y = \sqrt{x}$. (Note that $\sqrt{}$ represents the principle root; that is, it is only positive or zero.)
   g) $\{(x,y)|-3x^2 = y\}$

h) $f(x) = x^3$

i) $y = 1/x^2$

j) $f(x) = 1/\sqrt{x} - 1$

k) $\{(x,y)\,|\,y \leq x + 3\}$

3 a)   Let $f(x) = |x + 1|$. Find $f(2)$, $f(-3)$, and $f(a + b)$.

b)   If $f(x) = x^2$, find the image of 3. What numbers have 1 as an image?

c)   Let $f(4x) = x^2$. If $f(a) = 1$, find a.

4   Form the difference quotient $[f(x + h) - f(x)]/h$, $h \neq 0$, and then simplify the resulting expression for each of the following functions.

a) $f(x) = 2$

b) $f(x) = 3x + 5$

c) $f(x) = x^2/2 + 1$

d) $f(x) = 3x^2 - x + 2$

e) $f(x) = 1/x^2$

5   Describe each of the functions of Problem 4 using both the mapping interpretation and the ordered pair interpretation of functions.

6 a)   Let $f(x) = x(x + 1)(x + 2)(x + 3)$. Show that

$$\frac{f(a + 1)}{a + 1} = \frac{f(a + 2)}{a + 5}$$

b)   If $f(x) = (x - 3)/(5x + 7)$, find $f(a/5)$ and $f(4/x)$.

c)   If $f(x) = (3x - 1)/(1 + 2x)$, find $f(a^2)$, $[f(a)]^2$, $f(1/a)$ and $1/f(a)$.

7 a)   Write an equation that expresses the radius r of a circle as a function of its circumference c.

b)   Find an expression for the length l of the diagonal of a rectangular prism as a function of the width s if the length is twice the width and the height is three times the width.

c)   Equal squares are cut from the four corners of a rectangular piece of cardboard 10 inches by 14 inches. An open box is then formed by folding up the flaps. Express the volume V of the box as a function of x where x is the length of the side of the squares removed.

8   Let $f = \{(1,1),(2,4),(3,9),(-1,1),(-2,4),(-3,6)\}$, and $g = \{(1,4),(2,1),(4,5),(-2,0)\}$. Form each of the following functions and indicate the domain and range of each.

a) $f + g$

b) $f - g$

c) $f \cdot g$

d) f/g

9   Let $f = \{(x,y)\,|\,y = x - 2\}$ and $g = \{(x,y)\,|\,y = x^2 + 7\}$. Form each of the following functions.

a) $f + g$

b) $f - g$

c) $f \cdot g$

d) f/g

10   Use $f(x) = x + 2$, $g(x) = 2x - 1$, and $h(x) = x - 1$ to answer each of the following parts.

a)   Verify that $f + g = g + f$ (commutativity).

b)   Verify that $(f + g) + h = f + (g + h)$ (associativity).

c) Verify that $f \cdot (g + h) = f \cdot g + f \cdot h$ (distributivity).
d) Verify that $f + (-f) = 0$ (additive inverse).
e) Is $f(1/x) = 1/f(x)$?
f) Does $g(x) \cdot [1/g(x)] = 1$ for all x?
g) Is $h(x - 1) = h(x) - h(1)$?
h) Is $f(x + 2) = f(x) + f(2)$?
i) Is $g(2x) = 2 \cdot g(x)$?

11 Suppose that each of the ordinates of the points on a graph were increased by 3. How would the "new" graph compare with the original graph? Give an example of this situation.

12 Use the graphs of the functions f and g to sketch the graph of $h = f + g$ for each of the following pairs of functions.

a) $f(x) = x^2$ and $g(x) = 1$
b) $f(x) = x^3$ and $g(x) = 2x^2$
c) $f(x) = x$ and $g(x) = -5$

3 Symmetry

The recognition of *symmetry* often simplifies the graphing of relations. Suppose that we have graphed a relation; assume that the part of the graph which lies to the right of the y axis is drawn with wet ink. Now, "fold" the plane along the y axis. If the "inked" part of the graph coincides with the part of the graph which lies to the left of the y axis, we say that the relation is *symmetric with respect to the y axis*. For example, the graph in Figure 1 is symmetric with respect to the y axis.

Figure 1

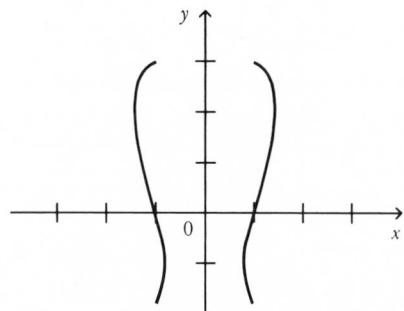

What does symmetry with respect to the y axis mean in terms of the points which are on the graph? Very simply, a graph is symmetric with respect to the y axis if, whenever (x,y) is on the graph, $(-x,y)$ is also on the graph (Figure 2).

Figure 2

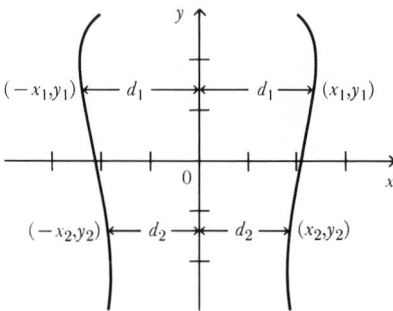

If an equation represents a relation, then we can test for symmetry with respect to the y axis merely by substituting $-x$ for x. If the new equation, when simplified, is the same as the given equation, this means that either x or $-x$ results in the same y, that is, the graph is symmetric with respect to the y axis.

EXAMPLES

1 Suppose the graph of a relation is symmetric with respect to the y axis, and $(1,2),(3,4),(7,0),(2,-3)$, and $(4,-2)$ are members of the relation. What other points are on the graph of the relation?

SOLUTION.   The graph of the relation also contains $(-1,2)$, $(-3,4)$, $(-7,0)$, $(-2,-3)$, and $(-4,-2)$ (Figure 3).

Figure 3

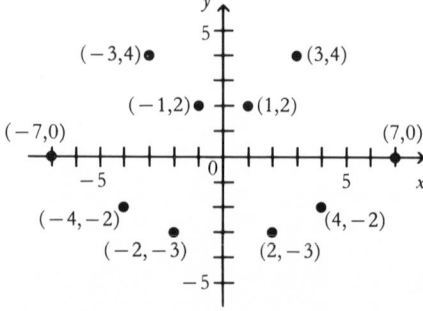

2 Test $y = x^2$ for symmetry with respect to the y axis, and then use the result to simplify the graphing.

SOLUTION. Replace x with $-x$ to get $(-x)^2 = x^2 = y$, so that the graph is symmetric with respect to the y axis. It is only necessary to graph the relation for nonnegative abscissas. The remainder of the graph is determined by "reflection" across the y axis (Figures 4a and b).

x	y
1	1
2	4
3	9

Figure 4

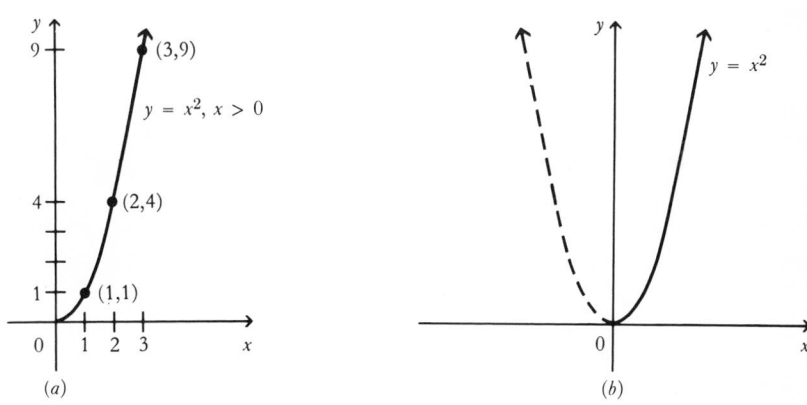

(a)   (b)

Figure 5 illustrates a graph which is *symmetric with respect to the x axis*. In general, a graph is *symmetric with respect to the x axis* if, whenever the point (x,y) is on the graph, then the point $(x,-y)$ is also on the graph (Figure 5).

Figure 5

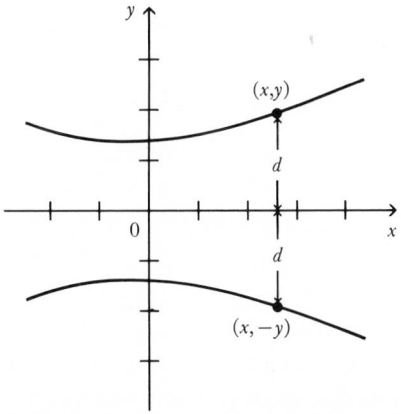

If an equation represents a relation, then we can test the graph for symmetry with respect to the x axis by substituting $-y$ for y. If the new equation, when simplified, is the same as the original equation, this means that either y or $-y$ will result in the same value for x; that is, the graph will be symmetric with respect to the x axis.

EXAMPLES

1   Test relation $x^2 + y^2 = 4$ for symmetry with respect to the x axis and y axis, and then use the result to graph the relation.

SOLUTION.   First, we can plot only those points which are in quadrant I (Figure 6). After replacing x with $-x$, we get $(-x)^2 + y^2 = 4$ or,

Figure 6

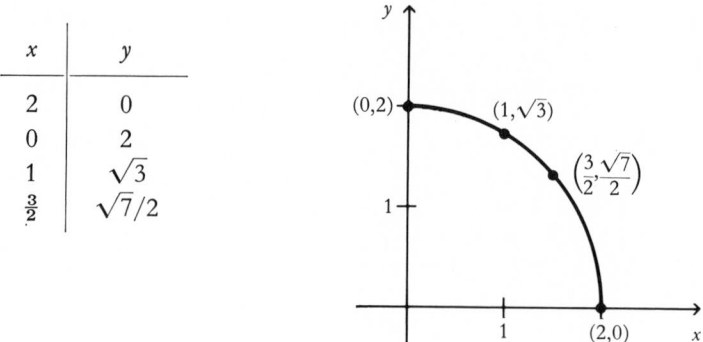

x	y
2	0
0	2
1	$\sqrt{3}$
$\frac{3}{2}$	$\sqrt{7}/2$

equivalently, $x^2 + y^2 = 4$. Thus the graph of the relation is symmetric with respect to the y axis (Figure 7).

Figure 7

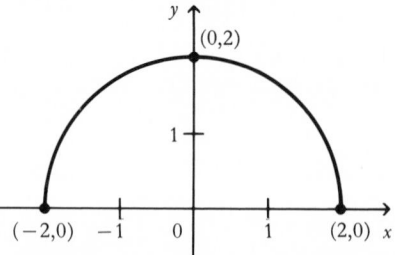

Finally, after replacing y with $-y$, we get $x^2 + (-y)^2 = 4$ or, equivalently, $x^2 + y^2 = 4$, so that the graph of the relation is symmetric with respect to the x axis. Hence, we can get the graph of the relation $x^2 + y^2 = 4$ (Figure 8) by first plotting points in the first quadrant, and then reflecting this graph across the y axis followed by reflecting the latter graph across the x axis.

Figure 8

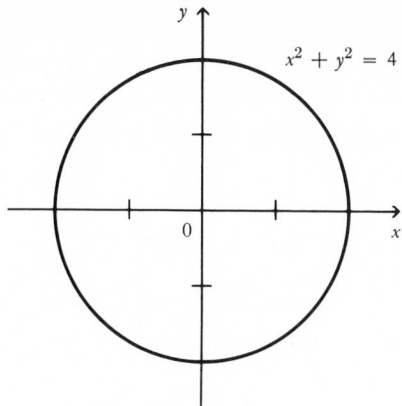

$$x^2 + y^2 = 4$$

2 Test $y^2 = x^2 - x$ for symmetry with respect to the x axis and the y axis.

SOLUTION. Upon replacing y with $-y$ in the equation, we get $(-y)^2 = x^2 - x$, which is the same as $y^2 = x^2 - x$, so that there is symmetry with respect to the x axis.

$y^2 = x^2 - x$ is not symmetric with respect to the y axis, since, for example, when $x = 1$, $y = 0$ and when $x = -1$, $y = \sqrt{2}$ or $y = -\sqrt{2}$. In order for $y^2 = x^2 - x$ to be symmetric with respect to the y axis, $x = 1$ and $x = -1$ should yield the same corresponding y values. (Why?)

Finally, a graph is *symmetric with respect to the origin* if, whenever the point (x,y) is on the graph, then the point $(-x,-y)$ is also on the graph (Figure 9).

Figure 9

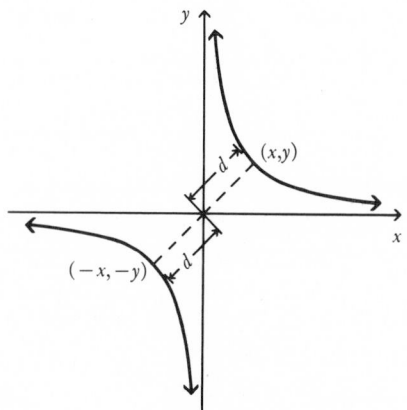

(x,y)

$(-x,-y)$

If an equation represents a relation, then we can "test" for symmetry with respect to the origin merely by substituting $-x$ for x and $-y$ for y simultaneously. If the new equation, when simplified, is the same as the original, this means that $(-x,-y)$ is on the graph whenever (x,y) is on the graph; that is, the graph will be symmetric with respect to the origin.

EXAMPLES

1   If a relation R_1 is symmetric with respect to the origin and contains points $(2,3)$, $(-2,-5)$, $(2,0)$, and $(4,-4)$, then it must also contain $(-2,-3)$, $(2,5)$, $(-2,0)$, and $(-4,4)$ (Figure 10). Notice that if each pair of corresponding points is connected by a line, the line passes through the origin.

Figure 10

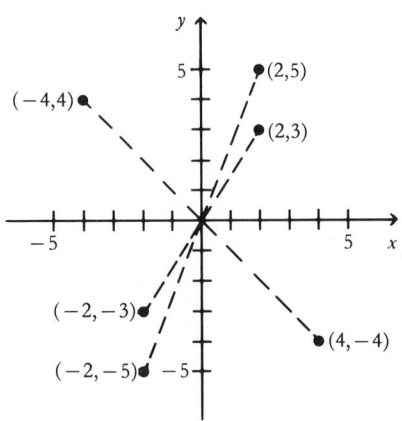

2   Test $y^2 = x^4 + 3$ for symmetry with respect to the origin.

        SOLUTION.   We replace x by $-x$, and y by $-y$ simultaneously to get $(-y)^2 = (-x)^4 + 3$, which is the same as $y^2 = x^4 + 2$, so that the graph is symmetric with respect to the origin.

PROBLEM SET 3

1   Test each of the following relations for symmetry with respect to the x axis, the y axis, and the origin. Use your results to simplify the graphing of the relations.

a) $y^2 = x^2$ b) $y = x^2 + 1$
c) $y^2 = x - 1$ d) $x^2/4 + y^2/9 = 1$
e) $y^2 = x + 2$ f) $y = 3x^2 - 7$

2   Discuss the symmetry of each of the following functions and sketch the graphs.

a) $f(x) = \sqrt{1 - x^2}$ b) $f(x) = x^4$
c) $f(x) = x^3$ d) $g(x) = x + 3$

3 The graph of a function other than $f(x) = 0$ cannot be symmetric with respect to the x axis. Why is this true? Give an example to support your argument.

4 How are $f(x)$ and $f(-x)$ related if the graph of the equation $y = f(x)$ is symmetric with respect to the y axis? If the graph of the equation $y = f(x)$ is symmetric with respect to the origin?

5 If a graph is symmetric with respect to the x axis and with respect to the y axis, then it must be symmetric with respect to the origin. Justify this statement by an example.

6 Assume that f and g are functions that are symmetric with respect to the y axis. Indicate which of the functions formed from f and g is symmetric with respect to the y axis.

a) $f + g$ b) $f - g$
c) $f \cdot g$ d) f/g

7 Answer Problem 6 if f and g are symmetric with respect to the origin.

4 Types of Functions

Besides determining the domain, range, and graph of functions, there will be occasions when we will investigate other properties of functions.

4.1 Increasing and Decreasing Functions

The concepts of increasing and decreasing functions can be motivated by the graphs of $f(x) = x^3$, $f(x) = -3x + 1$, and $f(x) = 7$ (Figure 1). If x increases, how do the corresponding values of $f(x)$ change? In the first case, where $f(x) = x^3$, we see from the graph that as x increases (varies from left to right) the corresponding y values given by $y = x^3$ increase (rise); for $f(x) = -3x + 1$, as x increases (varies from left to right) the corresponding y values given by $y = -3x + 1$ decrease; finally, as x increases, $f(x) = 7$ neither increases nor decreases. Thus, "$f(x) = x^3$ is an increasing function on R," "$f(x) = -3x + 1$ is a decreasing function on R," and "$f(x) = 7$ is neither increasing nor decreasing."

Figure 1

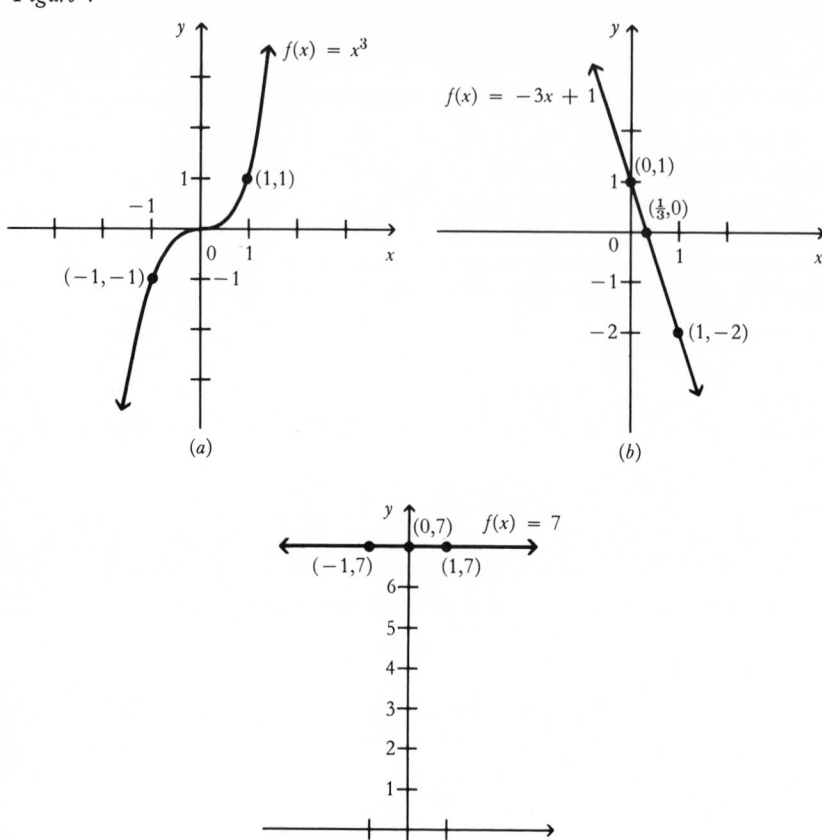

(a)

(b)

(c)

More formally, a function f is said to be a *(strictly) increasing function* in an interval I, if, whenever a and b are two numbers in I such that $a < b$, we have $f(a) < f(b)$ (Figure 2). A function f is said to be a *(strictly) decreasing function* in an interval I, if, whenever a and b are two numbers in I such that $a < b$, we have $f(a) > f(b)$ (Figure 3).

Figure 2

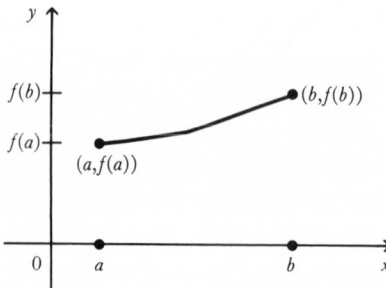

Figure 3

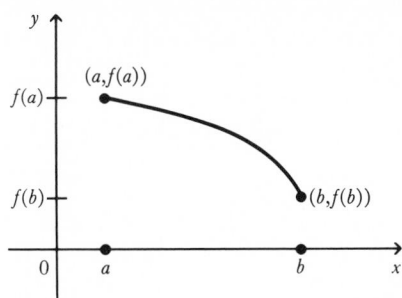

If f is an increasing or decreasing function in R, the entire real line, we will refer to the function f merely as an increasing or decreasing function without mentioning the interval. Hence, for the three examples above, $f(x) = x^3$ is an increasing function, since for any two real numbers x_1 and x_2 such that $x_1 < x_2$, we have $x_1^3 < x_2^3$; $f(x) = -3x + 1$ is a decreasing function, since for any two real numbers x_1 and x_2 such that $x_1 < x_2$, we have $-3x_1 + 1 > -3x_2 + 1$; and $f(x) = 7$ is neither increasing nor decreasing, since $x_1 < x_2$ yields $f(x_1) = f(x_2)$.

EXAMPLE

Let $f(x) = x^2$ with domain the set $[-2,2]$. $f(x)$ is increasing in $[0,2]$; for example, $\frac{1}{2} < 1$ implies $f(\frac{1}{2}) < f(1)$, whereas $f(x)$ is decreasing in $[-2,0]$; for example, $f(-2) > f(-1)$ (Figure 4).

Figure 4

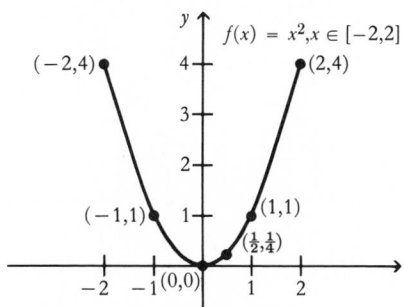

4.2 Even and Odd Functions

Even and odd functions can be described by using the idea of symmetry (see Section 3). If the graph of f is symmetric with respect to the y axis, then it is an even function. If it is symmetric with respect to the origin, then it is an odd function.

In general, a function f is said to be an *even function* if $f(x) = f(-x)$ for all x in the domain of f; a function f is said to be an *odd function* if $f(-x) = -f(x)$ for all x in the domain of f. It is important to realize that not all functions fall into these two categories.

EXAMPLE

Determine whether the following functions are even, odd, or neither.

a) $f(x) = x^2$ b) $f(x) = x^3$

c) $f(x) = x^2 + 8x + 1$

SOLUTIONS

a) For $f(x) = x^2$, $f(x) = x^2 = (-x)^2 = f(-x)$; hence, f is an even function. Note that the graph is symmetric with respect to the y axis (Figure 5).

Figure 5

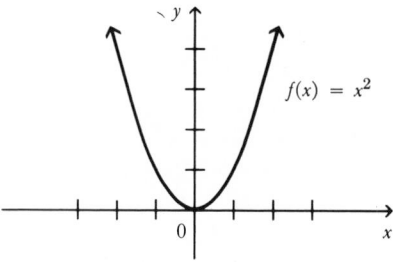

b) For $f(x) = x^3$, $f(-x) = (-x)^3 = -x^3 = -f(x)$, so that f is an odd function and the graph is symmetric with respect to the origin (Figure 6).

Figure 6

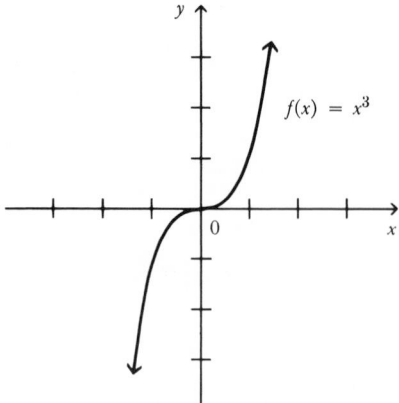

c) If $f(x) = x^2 + 8x + 1$, $f(-x) = x^2 - 8x + 1$. Since it is not true that $f(x) = f(-x)$ for all x (let $x = 1$), f is not even. Also, $f(-x) \neq -f(x)$ for all x (let $x = 1$); hence, f is not odd.

4.3   Special Functions

The properties of functions can now be used to investigate the following special functions.

Identity Function. The *identity function* is $f(x) = x$. $f = \{(x,y)|y = x\}$ is the ordered pair representation of the identity function. The domain is R, the set of all real numbers, and the range is also R. Since $f(-x) = -x = -f(x)$, the function is symmetric with respect to the origin; or, in other words, f is an *odd* function. Also, $x < y$ implies that $f(x) < f(y)$ (Why?), so that it is an increasing function. The graph of the function is given in Figure 7.

Figure 7

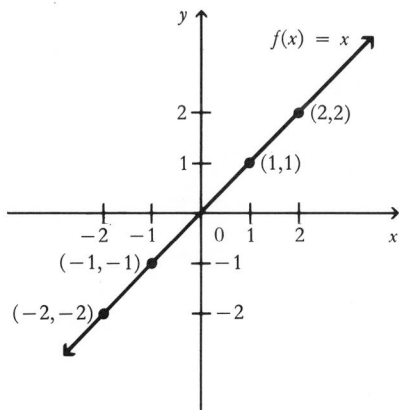

Absolute Value Function. The *absolute value function* is $f(x) = |x|$, or, equivalently, in ordered pair notation, $f = \{(x,y)|y = |x|\}$. The domain is R and the range is the set of all nonnegative real numbers. Since $|x| = |-x|$, it follows that $f(x) = f(-x)$; that is, f is an even function and its graph is symmetric with respect to the y axis. Also, f is increasing on interval $[0,\infty)$ and it is decreasing on interval $(-\infty,0]$ (Figure 8).

Figure 8

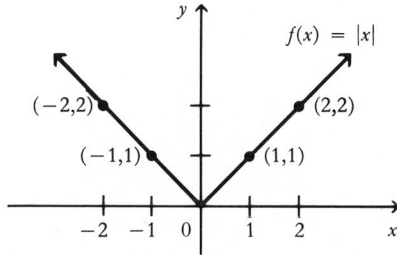

Greatest Integer Function. The *greatest integer of a real number x*, written $[\![x]\!]$, is the integer n which satisfies $n \le x < n + 1$. In other words, $[\![x]\!]$ is the "nearest" integer less than or equal to x. Thus $[\![5\frac{1}{4}]\!] = 5$; $[\![-2\frac{1}{2}]\!] = -3$; $[\![-\frac{1}{2}]\!] = -1$; and $[\![\sqrt{2}]\!] = 1$. The function $f(x) = [\![x]\!]$ is the *greatest integer function*. In ordered pair notation the greatest integer function is $\{(x,y)\,|\,y = [\![x]\!]\}$. The domain is R and the range is I, the set of integers.

Since $f(-3\frac{1}{2}) = -4$ and $f(3\frac{1}{2}) = 3$, the greatest integer function is neither even nor odd. The graph is shown in Figure 9.

Figure 9

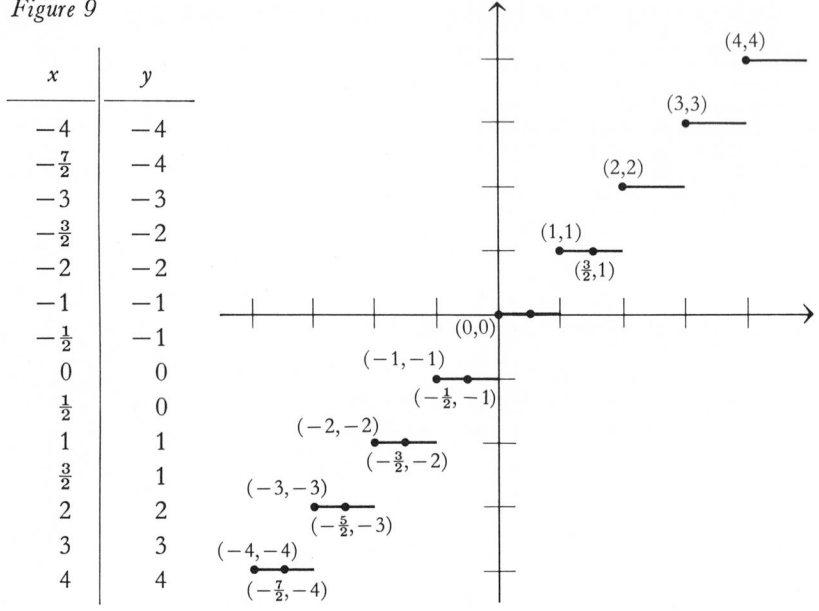

x	y
-4	-4
$-\frac{7}{2}$	-4
-3	-3
$-\frac{3}{2}$	-2
-2	-2
-1	-1
$-\frac{1}{2}$	-1
0	0
$\frac{1}{2}$	0
1	1
$\frac{3}{2}$	1
2	2
3	3
4	4

Notice that the graph of $f(x) = [\![x]\!]$ has "jumps" or "gaps" at each of the integers; it is an example of a *discontinuous* function. By contrast, $f(x) = x$ and $f(x) = |x|$ are *continuous* functions; their graphs are un-broken and can be drawn without lifting the pencil off the paper.

The term "continuous function" is used to describe such functions be-cause intuitively one can move "continuously," that is, without breaks or jumps, from one point on the graph to another. However, this statement is very imprecise and, in fact, is not correct in all cases. For the functions considered in this text however, it will be sufficient. (It is beyond our scope to examine continuous functions using the formal definition ac-cepted today.)

EXAMPLE

$f(x) = 1/x$ is not continuous at $x = 0$, and the graph of $f(x) = 1/x$ displays a "jump" at $x = 0$ (Figure 10).

Figure 10

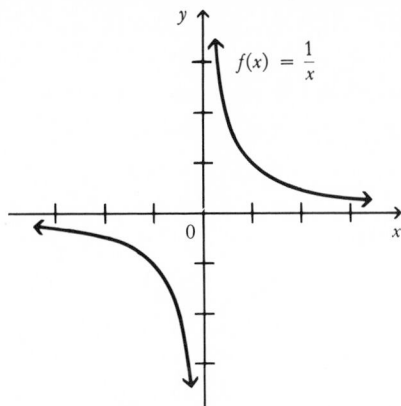

Sequences. A *sequence* is a function whose domain is the set of positive integers. For example, $f(n) = 2/n$, where n is a positive integer, is a sequence. The graph of f consists of discrete points (Figure 11). Notice that in graphing f, the points which are displayed in Figure 11 are not to be connected.

Figure 11

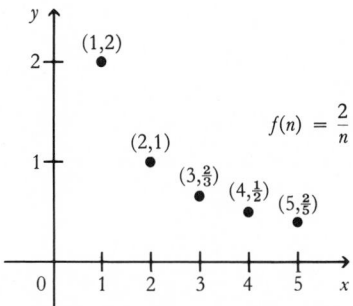

Quite often, subscript notation is used to describe sequences. For example, $f(n) = 2/n$ can be written in the form $S_n = 2/n$, so that

$$S_1 = f(1) = 2$$
$$S_2 = f(2) = 1$$
$$S_3 = f(3) = \tfrac{2}{3}$$
$$S_4 = f(4) = \tfrac{1}{2}$$
$$S_5 = f(5) = \tfrac{2}{5}$$

EXAMPLES

1 If $f(x) = [\![3x]\!]$, then $f(-\tfrac{3}{2}) = [\![-\tfrac{9}{2}]\!] = -5$, $f(\tfrac{7}{2}) = [\![\tfrac{21}{2}]\!] = 10$, and $f(0) = [\![0]\!] = 0$.

2   If $f(x) = [\![2x]\!] - 2x$, $f(\frac{1}{3}) = [\![2(\frac{1}{3})]\!] - 2(\frac{1}{3}) = -\frac{2}{3}$; $f(-\frac{1}{5}) = [\![2(-\frac{1}{5})]\!] + 2(\frac{1}{5}) = -\frac{3}{5}$; $f(\frac{9}{2}) = [\![2(\frac{9}{2})]\!] - 2(\frac{9}{2}) = 9 - 9 = 0$.

3   For each of the following sequences, write the first five terms, describe the range, and plot five points of the graph.

a) $S_n = (-1)^n$ b) $S_n = 3 - 1/n$

SOLUTION

a) We have $S_n = (-1)^n$, $S_1 = -1$, $S_2 = 1$, $S_3 = -1$, $S_4 = 1$, and $S_5 = -1$. The range is the set $\{-1,1\}$. Figure 12 contains five points of the graph.

Figure 12

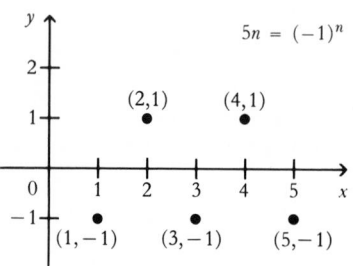

b) We have $S_n = 3 - 1/n$, $S_1 = 2$, $S_2 = \frac{5}{2}$, $S_3 = \frac{8}{3}$, $S_4 = \frac{11}{4}$, and $S_5 = \frac{14}{5}$. The range is a subset of the rational numbers. Figure 13 contains five points of the graph.

Figure 13

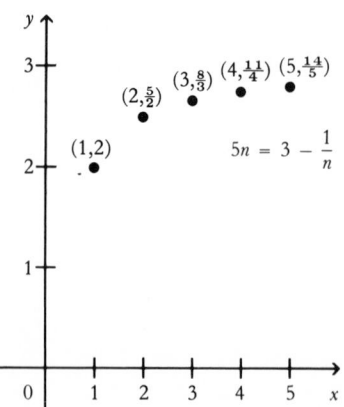

PROBLEM SET 4

1   Let $f(x) = \sqrt{x}$. Sketch the graph for $x \in [1,9]$. Is $f(x)$ increasing or decreasing in the interval $[1,9]$?

2 Let $f(x) = x^2 + 4x + 1$.

    a) Sketch the graph of f.

    b) Indicate whether f is increasing or decreasing.

3 Let $f(x) = x^3 - 2x + 1/x$.

    a) Show that $f(a) + f(-a) = 0$.

    b) Is f an even or odd function?

4 Let $f(x) = x^4 - 3x^2 + 10$.

    a) Find the value of $f(2a) - 2f(a)$.

    b) Show that f is an even function.

5 Suppose that f is an even function and g is an even function. Which of the following functions are even functions?

    a) $f + g$ b) $f - g$

    c) $f \cdot g$ d) f/g

6 In each of the following spaces answer true if the equation holds for all real numbers. If the equation is false, give a counterexample.

$f(x)$	$[f(x)]^3 = f(x^3)$	$f(2x) = 2f(x)$	$f(x + y) = f(x) + f(y)$	$f(xy) = f(x) \cdot f(y)$
x				
$|x|$				
$[[x]]$				

7 Answer these questions for each of the following functions. What is the domain? What is the range? Is f even or odd? Does the graph of f have symmetry? Where is f increasing? Decreasing? Graph f.

    a) $f(x) = 5x + 2$ b) $f(x) = x^{1/3}$

    c) $f(x) = |x - 1|$ d) $f(x) = 1/(x^2 - 1)$

    e) $f(x) = [[5x]]$ f) $f(x) = -2x + 2$

    g) $f = \{(x,y)|x^2 = y^3, y \leq 0\}$ h) $f = \{(x,y)|y = x^2 + 3\}$

8 We are given that $f_1(x) = 2x + 1$, and $f_2(x) = x^2 + 1$. Answer each of the questions yes or no for both f_1 and f_2 and demonstrate your answer algebraically.

    a) Is $f(x + 3) = f(x) + 3$?   b) Is $f(x + a) = f(x) + a$?

    c) Is $f(x) + a = f(x) + f(a)$?   d) Is $f(x + a) = f(x) + f(a)$?

    e) Is $f(ax) = af(x)$?

9 For each of the following sequences, write the first five terms, describe the range, and plot five points of the graph.

    a) $S_n = 1/(n + 1)$ b) $S_n = 2/(n^2 + 1)$

    c) $S_n = 1 + (-1)^n$ d) $S_n = 1/[n(n + 1)]$

5 Composite Functions

We know from solid geometry that the volume V of a sphere of radius r is given by the formula $V = \frac{4}{3}\pi r^3$. V can be interpreted as a function of r, and we can use function notation to write

$$V = V(r) = \tfrac{4}{3}\pi r^3$$

Now, suppose that air is being pumped into a spherical balloon so that at the end of t seconds, the radius r satisfies $r = t^2 + 1$. Assuming that r is a function of t, we can write

$$r = r(t) = t^2 + 1$$

We see here that given a specific value of t, we can determine the volume V of the balloon by *first* finding $r(t)$, followed by determining $V(r)$.

$$t \mapsto r(t) \mapsto V(r) = V[r(t)]$$

For example,

$$1 \overset{r}{\mapsto} 2 \overset{V}{\mapsto} \frac{32\pi}{3}$$

$$2 \overset{r}{\mapsto} 5 \overset{V}{\mapsto} \frac{500\pi}{3}$$

$$3 \overset{r}{\mapsto} 10 \overset{V}{\mapsto} \frac{4000\pi}{3}$$

In general,

$$t \overset{r}{\mapsto} t^2 + 1 \overset{V}{\mapsto} \tfrac{4}{3}\pi(t^2 + 1)^3$$

The volume, then, is determined by applying two functions in succession, "r followed by V," and we say the function that maps $t \mapsto \frac{4}{3}\pi(t^2 + 1)^3$ is "composed of the function r followed by the function V," written $V \circ r$. Hence, $(V \circ r)(t) = \frac{4}{3}\pi(t^2 + 1)^3$.

Let us consider another example. Assume that $f(x) = 2x + 7$ and $g(x) = x^2 + 2$. We can find the image of 3 by applying the functions in succession — first f, then g — that is, by finding $g \circ f$ of 3.

$$3 \overset{f}{\mapsto} f(3) \overset{g}{\mapsto} g[f(3)]$$

Thus,

$$g[f(3)] = g(13) = 13^2 + 2 = 171$$

In general, the image of x under the "successive function," f followed by g, written $g \circ f$, is formed as follows

$$x \overset{f}{\longmapsto} f(x) \overset{g}{\longmapsto} g[f(x)]$$
$$\underset{g \circ f}{\rule{0pt}{0pt}}$$

and is given by

$$(g \circ f)(x) = g[f(x)] = g(2x + 7) = (2x + 7)^2 + 2$$
$$= 4x^2 + 28x + 51$$

The function $g \circ f$ which has been constructed here is called the composition of f by g.

5.1 Definition

The *composite function of f by g*, denoted by $g \circ f$, is the function defined as $(g \circ f)(x) = g[f(x)]$. The *domain of $g \circ f$* is the subset of the domain of f containing those values for which $g \circ f$ is defined. □

Schematically, $g \circ f$ is shown in Figure 1.

Figure 1

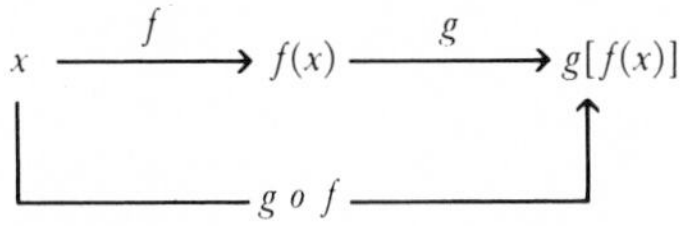

$$x \xrightarrow{\quad f \quad} f(x) \xrightarrow{\quad g \quad} g[f(x)]$$
$$\underset{g \circ f}{\rule{0pt}{0pt}}$$

EXAMPLES

1   Let $f(x) = x^2$ and $g(x) = 2x - 3$.

a)   Compare $(g \circ f)(2)$ with $(f \circ g)(2)$.

b)   Compare $(g \circ f)(2)$ with $(g \cdot f)(2)$ where $g \cdot f$ denotes the product.

SOLUTION

a) $(g \circ f)(2) = g[f(2)]$
$$= g(4)$$
$$= 5$$

whereas

$$(f \circ g)(2) = f[g(2)]$$
$$= f(1)$$
$$= 1$$

so that

$$(g \circ f)(2) \neq (f \circ g)(2)$$

b) We have seen above that $(g \circ f)(2) = 5$. On the other hand,

$$(g \cdot f)(2) = g(2) \cdot f(2)$$
$$= 1 \cdot 4$$
$$= 4$$

Hence,

$$(g \circ f)(2) \neq (g \cdot f)(2)$$

Example 1a illustrates the fact that the composition of functions is *not* commutative; that is, $(g \circ f)(x)$ and $(f \circ g)(x)$ are not always equal. Example 1b emphasizes the fact that the composed function $g \circ f$ is different from the product $g \cdot f$.

2   Use $f(x) = 2x^2$ and $g(x) = 4x + 1$ to determine an expression to represent each of the following composed functions. Also, indicate the domain of each composed function.

a) $(g \circ g)(x)$ b) $(f \circ g)(x)$ c) $(g \circ f)(x)$

SOLUTION

a) $x \xrightarrow{g} g(x) \xrightarrow{g} g[g(x)]$
$\underline{\qquad g \circ g \qquad}$

$$(g \circ g)(x) = g[g(x)]$$
$$= g(4x + 1)$$
$$= 4(4x + 1) + 1$$
$$= 16x + 5$$

Since the domain of g (considered as the "first" function) is R and since g (considered as the "second" function) is defined for all real numbers, the domain of $g \circ g$ is also R.

b) $x \xrightarrow{g} g(x) \xrightarrow{f} f[g(x)]$
$\underline{\qquad f \circ g \qquad}$

$$(f \circ g)(x) = f[g(x)]$$
$$= f(4x + 1)$$
$$= 2(4x + 1)^2$$
$$= 32x^2 + 16x + 2$$

The domain of g is R, and since $(f \circ g)(x) = 32x^2 + 16x + 2$ is defined for all real numbers, the domain of $f \circ g$ is also R.

c) $x \xrightarrow{f} f(x) \xrightarrow{g} g[f(x)]$
$\underline{\qquad g \circ f \qquad}$

$$(g \circ f)(x) = g[f(x)]$$
$$= g(2x^2)$$
$$= 4(2x^2) + 1$$
$$= 8x^2 + 1$$

The domain of f is R. Since $(g \circ f)(x) = 8x^2 + 1$ is defined for all reals, the domain of $g \circ f$ is also R.

3   Let $f(x) = x - 1$ and $g(x) = \sqrt{x}$. Determine the expression and domain for the following composed functions.

a) $(f \circ g)(x)$ b) $(g \circ f)(x)$

SOLUTION

a) $x \overset{g}{\longmapsto} g(x) \overset{f}{\longmapsto} f[g(x)]$
$\underset{f \circ g}{\underline{}}$

$(f \circ g)(x) = f[g(x)]$
$\qquad\qquad = f(\sqrt{x})$
$\qquad\qquad = \sqrt{x} - 1$

The domain of g is the set $[0, \infty)$ and since $(f \circ g)(x) = \sqrt{x} - 1$ is defined for all numbers in $[0, \infty)$, the domain of $f \circ g$ is also $[0, \infty)$.

b) $x \overset{f}{\longmapsto} f(x) \overset{g}{\longmapsto} g[f(x)]$
$\underset{g \circ f}{\underline{}}$

$(g \circ f)(x) = g[f(x)]$
$\qquad\qquad = g(x - 1)$
$\qquad\qquad = \sqrt{x - 1}$

The domain of f is R; however, $(g \circ f)(x) = \sqrt{x - 1}$ is defined only when $x - 1$ represents a nonnegative number, so that the domain of $g \circ f$ is $\{x | x - 1 \geq 0\} = [1, \infty)$, which is a (proper) subset of the domain of f (Reexamine Definition 5.1).

4   The function where $I(f) = 144f$ enables us to convert from f square feet to I square inches; and the function where $f(y) = 9y$ enables us to convert from y square yards to f square feet. Use the composition of functions to determine a function which will convert y square yards to I square inches.

SOLUTION

$y \overset{f}{\longmapsto} 9y \overset{I}{\longmapsto} 144(9y)$ so that
$\underset{I \circ f}{\underline{}}$

$(I \circ f)(y) = I[f(y)] = I(9y) = (144)(9y) = 1296y$ is the composed function which converts square yards into square inches.

PROBLEM SET 5

1   Let $A = \{2,3,4,5,6\}$ and let the functions $f : A \to A$ and $g : A \to A$ be defined by $f(2) = 3$, $f(3) = 4$, $f(5) = 2$, $f(4) = 6$, $f(6) = 5$, $g(2) = 5$, $g(3) = 6$, $g(5) = 3$, $g(4) = 5$, and $g(6) = 2$. Find each of the following values.

a) $(f \circ g)(2)$ b) $(f \circ g)(3)$
c) $(f \circ g)(5)$ d) $(f \circ g)(4)$
e) $(f \circ g)(6)$ f) $(g \circ f)(2)$

g) $(g \circ f)(3)$ h) $(g \circ f)(5)$
i) $(g \circ f)(4)$ j) $(g \circ f)(6)$

2 If $f(x) = 2x^2 + 6$, and $g(x) = 7x + 2$, find each of the following expressions.

a) $(g \circ f)(4)$ b) $(f \circ f)(3)$
c) $(g \circ g)(2)$ d) $(f \circ g)(5)$
e) $(g \circ f)(5)$ f) $(f \circ f)(x)$ and the domain of $f \circ f$
g) $(g \circ f)(x)$ and the domain of $g \circ f$
h) $(f \circ g)(x)$ and the domain of $f \circ g$

3 a) Let $f(x) = 3x - 7$ and $g(x) = 2x + k$. Determine k so that $(f \circ g)(x) = (g \circ f)(x)$.
   b) Suppose that $f(x) = (2x^3 + 7)^3$. Find a function g such that $(f \circ g)(x) = (g \circ f)(x)$.

4 a) Let $f(x) = x^2 + 2x$ and $g(x) = 3x + 4$. Find the domains of $f \circ g$ and $g \circ f$.
   b) If $f(x) = x^2$ and $g(x) = 1/x$, find the domains and ranges of $g \circ f$ and $f \circ g$.

5 Assume that f is an even function and g is an odd function. Indicate whether each of the following functions is even or odd.

a) $f \circ f$ b) $f \circ g$
c) $g \circ g$ d) $g \circ f$

6 Suppose that a 10 percent surtax is levied on an income tax of 15 percent of the gross income.

a) Express the income tax T as a function of gross income G.
b) Express the surtax tax S as a function of the income tax T.
c) Use (a) and (b) to construct a composed function which determines the surtax as a function of gross income.

7 Suppose that a right cylindrical vessel has a circular base of radius 4 inches.

a) Express the volume V of the vessel as a function of the height h.
b) Express the height h as a function of time if, after t seconds, the height is $2t + 4$.
c) Use (a) and (b) to construct a composed function which expresses the volume of the vessel as a function of time.

8 Suppose that the functions f, g, and h map real numbers into real numbers.

a) Give an example to display that $(f + g) \circ h = f \circ h + g \circ h$ is true.
b) Give a counterexample to prove that $f \circ (g + h) = f \circ g + f \circ h$ is false.

6 Inverse Functions

If $f(x) = x + 5$ and $g(x) = x - 5$, then

$$
\begin{aligned}
(g \circ f)(x) &= g[f(x)] \\
&= g(x + 5) \\
&= (x + 5) - 5 \\
&= x
\end{aligned}
$$

and

$$
\begin{aligned}
(f \circ g)(x) &= f[g(x)] \\
&= f(x - 5) \\
&= (x - 5) + 5 \\
&= x
\end{aligned}
$$

Schematically,

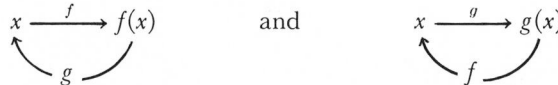

Both of the compositions of f and g result in the identity function, that is, $(f \circ g)(x) = (g \circ f)(x) = x$.

Let us consider another example. Suppose that $f = \{(1,2),(3,4),(-1,0)\}$ and $g = \{(2,1),(4,3),(0,-1)\}$. Then

$$
\begin{aligned}
(g \circ f)(1) &= g[f(1)] = g(2) = 1 \\
(g \circ f)(3) &= g[f(3)] = g(4) = 3
\end{aligned}
$$

and

$$
(g \circ f)(-1) = g[f(-1)] = g(0) = -1
$$

Similarly,

$$
\begin{aligned}
(f \circ g)(2) &= 2 \\
(f \circ g)(4) &= 4
\end{aligned}
$$

and

$$
(f \circ g)(0) = 0
$$

Here we have $(g \circ f)(x) = x$ for $x \in \{1,3,-1\}$, the domain of f, and $(f \circ g)(x) = x$ for $x \in \{2,4,0\}$, the domain of g.

The functions f and g, which have been defined in each of the two examples above, are called "invertible functions." We can formalize this concept as follows.

6.1 Definition

Let f and g be two functions such that $(g \circ f)(x) = x$ for every element x in the domain of f and $(f \circ g)(x) = x$ for every element x in the domain of g, then f and g are said to be *invertible*, and each is said to be the *inverse* of the other. We use the notation:

$$g = f^{-1} \quad \text{and} \quad f = g^{-1} \quad \square$$

Hence, in the first example above, we can write $f^{-1}(x) = x - 5$ for $f(x) = x + 5$ or we could write $g^{-1}(x) = x + 5$ for $g(x) = x - 5$; in the second example, $f^{-1} = g = \{(2,1),(4,3),(0,-1)\}$ or $g^{-1} = f = \{(1,2),(3,4),(-1,0)\}$.

EXAMPLES

1   Suppose that $f(x) = 5x$ and $g(x) = x/5$. Show that $f = g^{-1}$.

SOLUTION

$$(f \circ g)(x) = f[g(x)] = f\left(\frac{x}{5}\right) = 5\left(\frac{x}{5}\right) = x$$

and

$$(g \circ f)(x) = g[f(x)] = g(5x) = \tfrac{1}{5}(5x) = x$$

Since $(f \circ g)(x) = (g \circ f)(x) = x$, it follows that $f = g^{-1}$.

2   Suppose that $f(x) = 3x + 7$ and $g(x) = (x - 7)/3$. Show that f and g are invertible.

SOLUTION

$$(f \circ g)(x) = f[g(x)] = f\left(\frac{x - 7}{3}\right) = 3\left(\frac{x - 7}{3}\right) + 7 = x$$

and

$$(g \circ f)(x) = g[f(x)] = g(3x + 7) = \frac{3x + 7 - 7}{3} = x$$

Hence, f and g are invertible.

3   Suppose that $f(x) = \sqrt{x}$ and $g(x) = x^2$ for x in the set of positive real numbers. Show that f and g are invertible.

SOLUTION

$$(f \circ g)(x) = f[g(x)] = f(x^2) = \sqrt{x^2} = x$$

since x is positive, and

$$(g \circ f)(x) = g[f(x)] = g(\sqrt{x}) = (\sqrt{x})^2 = x$$

Hence, f and g are invertible.

6.2   One-to-one Functions

Let us examine the functions $f_1 = \{(1,2),(3,4),(-1,0)\}$ and $f_2 = \{(1,2),(4,2)\}$. Since f_1 and f_2 are functions, it follows from the definition of a function that for each member of the domain, there is one and only one corresponding member of the range.

$$
\begin{array}{ll}
f_1 : 1 \rightarrow 2 & \quad f_2 : 1 \rightarrow 2 \\
 3 \rightarrow 4 & \quad 4 \rightarrow 2 \\
 -1 \rightarrow 0 &
\end{array}
$$

Now it is also true that for each member of the range of f_1 there is one and only one corresponding member of the domain of f_1, whereas for f_2, 2 in the range corresponds to more than one member of the domain. We say that f_1 is a "one-to-one function," whereas f_2 is not one-to-one.

In general, a *function f is one-to-one* if each member of the range of the function is the image of one and only one member of the domain.

Although it is possible to investigate one-to-one functions in a more formal way, we will use the graph of a function to determine whether or not the function is one-to-one. If $y = f(x)$, we know from the definition of a function that for each x there is one and only one y; hence, each of all possible vertical lines (representing all possible values of x) intersects the curve no more than once. Now, f is one-to-one if it is also true that for each y there is one and only one x; this property holds for a function if each of all possible horizontal lines (representing all possible values of y) intersects the curve of $y = f(x)$ no more than once.

EXAMPLES

Use the graph of the given function to decide whether or not the function is one-to-one.

1   $f = \{(x,y) \,|\, y = x^2\}$

SOLUTION.   Clearly, any horizontal line above the x axis intersects the curve twice. Hence, the function is not one-to-one. For example, 1 in the range is the image of both -1 and 1 in the domain (Figure 1).

Figure 1

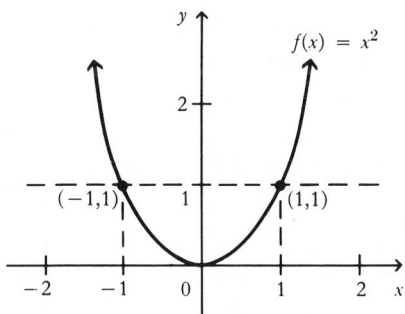

2    $f(x) = 3x - 5$

SOLUTION.   From Figure 2, it can be seen that no horizontal line intersects the graph more than once; hence, for each range number there is
one and only one corresponding domain number, so that f is one-to-one.

Figure 2

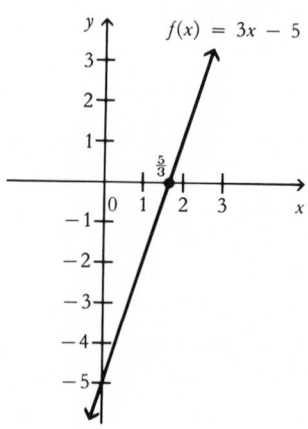

3    $f = \{(x,y)|y = \sqrt{4 - x^2}\}$

SOLUTION.   Figure 3 shows that f is not one-to-one. For example,
$\sqrt{15}/4$ is the image of both $-\frac{7}{4}$ and $\frac{7}{4}$.

Figure 3

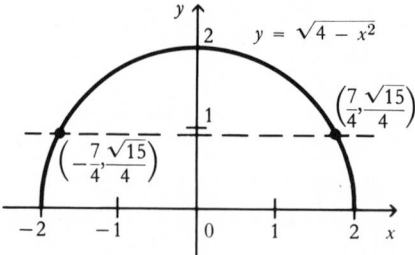

The next theorem, given without proof, tells us that invertible functions
and functions which are one-to-one are the same.

THEOREM 1

If a function is one-to-one, then the function has an inverse; and,
conversely, if a function has an inverse, then the function is one-to-one.

This means that we can use the graph to determine whether or not a
function is one-to-one (Examples 1, 2, 3 above) and in doing so we also
discover whether or not the function has an inverse.

Also, if a one-to-one function is defined by $y = f(x)$, then the equation which defines the inverse can be constructed by interchanging the roles of x and y by expressing x in terms of y to obtain $x = f^{-1}(y)$. In ordered pair notation this means that whenever $(x,y) \in f$, then $(y,x) \in f^{-1}$. In other words, f^{-1} can be constructed from f by reversing the members in each ordered pair of f. This process will be demonstrated with a few examples.

EXAMPLES

Examine the graph of each of the given functions in 1, 2, 3, 4, and 5 to determine whether or not the function has an inverse f^{-1}. If f^{-1} exists, find it and graph f^{-1} on the same coordinate system as one containing the graph of the given function f.

1   $f(x) = 2x - 3$

SOLUTION.   Figure 4 shows $f(x) = 2x - 3$ to be a one-to-one function; hence, by Theorem 1, f^{-1} exists. If we let $y = 2x - 3$, then $x = (y + 3)/2$ results from solving for x in terms of y; therefore, $f^{-1}(y) = (y + 3)/2$, or, after changing notation, $f^{-1}(x) = (x + 3)/2$. This can be verified as follows.

$$(f \circ f^{-1})(x) = f[f^{-1}(x)] = f\left(\frac{x + 3}{2}\right) = 2\left(\frac{x + 3}{2}\right) - 3 = x$$

and

$$(f^{-1} \circ f)(x) = f^{-1}[f(x)] = f^{-1}(2x - 3) = \frac{2x - 3 + 3}{2} = x$$

After graphing $f(x) = 2x - 3$ and $f^{-1}(x) = (x + 3)/2$ on the same coordinate system, we can observe that the graph of the inverse function f^{-1} can be obtained by reflection of the graph of f across the line $y = x$, since $(x,y) \in f$ implies that $(y,x) \in f^{-1}$ (Figure 4).

Figure 4

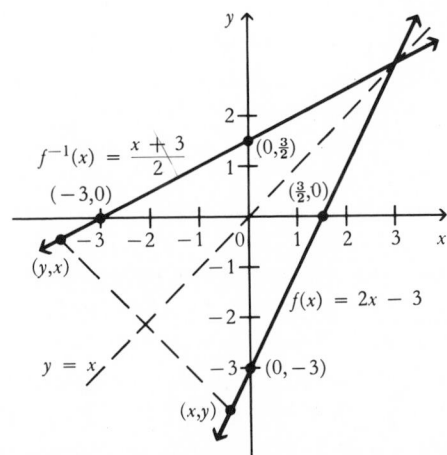

2 $f(x) = x^3$

SOLUTION.   The graph of $f(x) = x^3$ (Figure 5) shows that the function
is one-to-one, so that we know that f^{-1} exists. Next, we can find f^{-1} by
first letting $y = x^3$ and solving for x in terms of y to get $x = \sqrt[3]{y}$.
Hence, $f^{-1}(y) = \sqrt[3]{y}$, or, after changing notation, $f^{-1}(x) = \sqrt[3]{x}$ which
can be verified as follows.

$$(f \circ f^{-1})(x) = f[f^{-1}(x)] = f(\sqrt[3]{x}) = (\sqrt[3]{x})^3 = x$$

and

$$(f^{-1} \circ f)(x) = f^{-1}[f(x)] = f^{-1}(x^3) = \sqrt[3]{x^3} = x$$

When both $f(x) = x^3$ and $f^{-1}(x) = \sqrt[3]{x}$ are graphed on the same coordinate system, we discover again that the graph of f^{-1} can be obtained by reflecting the graph of f across the line $y = x$ (Figure 5).

Figure 5

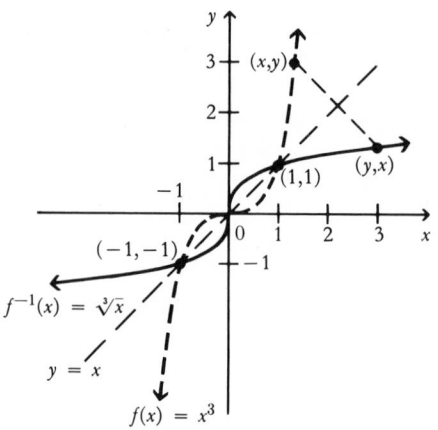

3 $f(x) = x^2$

SOLUTION.   The graph of $f(x) = x^2$ (see Figure 7, page 71) shows
that f is not one-to-one (for example, $(2,4)$ and $(-2,4)$ are members of
the function); hence, by Theorem 1, f^{-1} does not exist.

4 $f(x) = x^2$ $x \in [0, \infty)$

SOLUTION.   The graph of $f(x) = x^2$, $x \in [0, \infty)$ (Figure 6) shows that f
is one-to-one; hence, by Theorem 1, f^{-1} exists.
   If we let $y = x^2$, we can solve for x in terms of y to obtain $x = \sqrt{y}$
so that $f^{-1}(y) = \sqrt{y}$, or, after changing notation, $f^{-1}(x) = \sqrt{x}$.
The graph of f^{-1} is a reflection of the graph of f across $y = x$
(Figure 6).

Figure 6

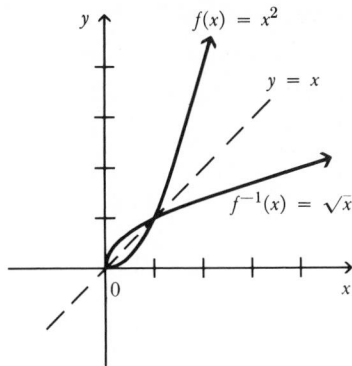

Notice that in Examples 3 and 4, the function expression is the same; however, by restricting the domain to $[0,\infty)$, we have an invertible function, whereas for domain R, the function $f(x) = x^2$ is not invertible.

5   $f(x) = \dfrac{1}{x}$

SOLUTION.   The graph of $f(x) = 1/x$ (Figure 7) shows that f^{-1} exists. (Why?) Solving for x in terms of y for $y = 1/x$, we obtain $x = 1/y$. This implies that $f^{-1}(y) = 1/y$ or, after changing notation, $f^{-1}(x) = 1/x$. Notice that this function is its own inverse. Again the graph of f^{-1} can be obtained by a reflection of the graph of f across $y = x$ (Figure 7). (The graphs of f and f^{-1} coincide.)

Figure 7

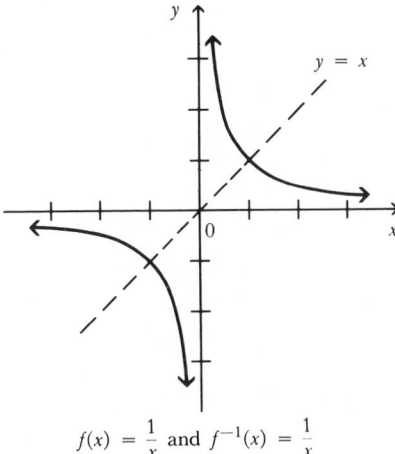

$f(x) = \dfrac{1}{x}$ and $f^{-1}(x) = \dfrac{1}{x}$

6   Prove that every increasing function has an inverse.

PROOF.   Assume that f is an increasing function. If x_1 and x_2 are different members of the domain of f and $x_1 < x_2$, then, since f is increasing, $f(x_1) < f(x_2)$ (Figure 8). This means that no two different ordered pairs of the function f have the same second members. In other words, each member of the range is the image of one and only one member of the domain; that is, f is one-to-one from which we can conclude by Theorem 1 that f^{-1} exists.

Figure 8

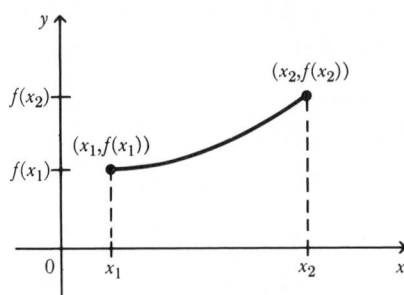

PROBLEM SET 6

1 Verify that $g = f^{-1}$ for each of the following pairs of functions.

a) $f(x) = 3x + 2$ and $g(x) = x/3 - \frac{2}{3}$.

b) $f(x) = x^4$ where x is a positive real number and $g(x) = \sqrt[4]{x}$.

2 Graph each pair of functions in Problem 1 on the same coordinate system to see that the graph of f^{-1} is a reflection of the graph of f across the line $y = x$.

3 Let $A = \{-1,1\}$. State whether or not each of the following functions has an inverse. If so, find it.

a) $f(x) = x^2$, $x \in A$

b) $f(x) = x^5$, $x \in A$

c) $f(x) = 2$, $x \in A$

d) $f(x) = 1/(2x + 1)$, $x \in A$

4 Let $f:R \to R$ be defined by $f(x) = x^3 + 1$. Find:

a) $f^{-1}(5)$

b) $f^{-1}(0)$

c) $f^{-1}(10)$

d) $f^{-1}(-5)$

5 Does every decreasing function have an inverse? Support your assertion by giving an example.

6 Show that $f(x) = 2x + 1$ is one-to-one. Find f^{-1}.

7 Show that $f(x) = -5x + 2$ is decreasing. Find f^{-1}.

8 Given an example of an increasing function f. Find f^{-1}.

9 Show that $f(x) = |x + 1|$ is not one-to-one. Does f^{-1} exist? Explain.

10 a) Use the graph of $f(x) = -3x^2 + 1$ to show that f^{-1} does not exist.

b) Show that $f(x) = -3x^2 + 1$, $x \in (-\infty,0]$, has an inverse function f^{-1}. Find f^{-1}.

c) Explain the difference between the two functions in parts (a) and (b).

11 Examine the graphs of each of the following functions to determine whether or not f^{-1} exists. If f^{-1} exists, find it and graph f^{-1} on the same coordinate system as f.

a) $f(x) = 3$ b) $f(x) = 7x + 5$
c) $f(x) = 3/x$ d) $f = \{(x,y)|y = 1/|x|\}$
e) $f(x) = 1 - 3x$ f) $f(x) = x^3 + 5$
g) $f = \{(x,y)|y = x^2 + 2,\ x \geq 2\}$
h) $f(x) = [\![2x]\!]$

REVIEW PROBLEM SET

1 Indicate which of the following relations is a function. Indicate the domain and the range of each.

a) $f(x) = 7x - 2$ b) $f(x) = 25 - x^2$
c) $f = \{(1,2),(2,3),(1,5),(6,7)\}$ d) $\{(x,y)|\ |y| > |x|\}$

2 Figure 9 contains graphs of relations. Which graphs represent functions? Which of the functions have inverses?

Figure 9

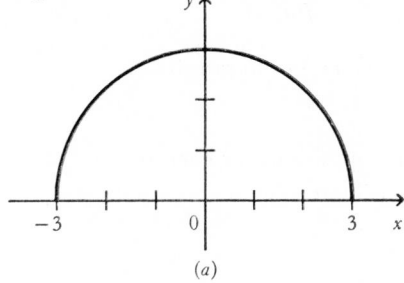

(a)

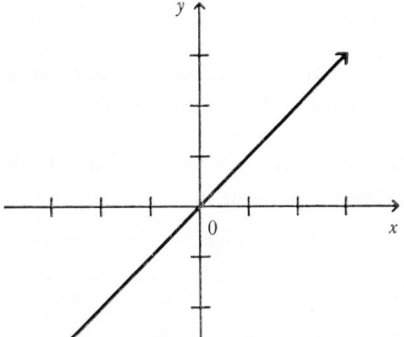

(b)

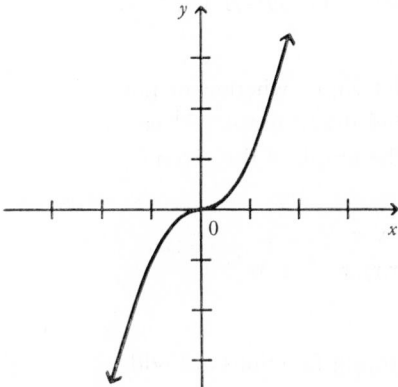

(c)

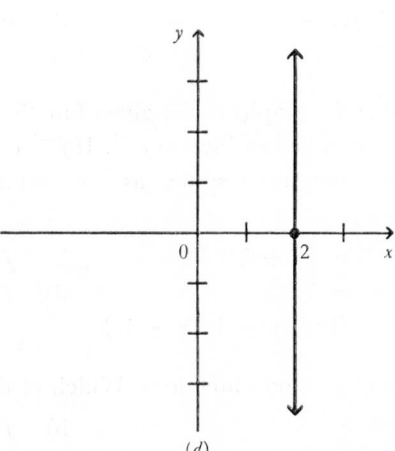

(d)

3   Note that the diagram below illustrates a function as a mapping from
    x into y. What is the domain of f? What is the range of f? Find $f(3)$,
    $f(1)$, and $f(5)$.

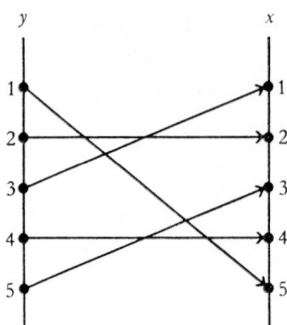

4   Let $f(x) = 3x^2 + 2$. Find each of the following expressions.

   a) $f(-1)$ b) $f(0)$
   c) $f(1)$ d) $f(\frac{2}{3})$
   e) $f(a)$ f) $f(b)$
   g) $f(a + b)$ h) $[f(a + b) - f(a)]/b$

5   Use the graphs of the functions $f(x) = x^3$ and $g(x) = -x$ to graph
    $f + g$. What is the domain of $f + g$?

6   Sketch the graphs of $f \cdot g$ (product) and $f \circ g$ (composition) for each of
    the following pairs of functions on the same coordinate system.

   a) $f(x) = x + 2$ and $g(x) = x - 1$
   b) $f(x) = 1 - x$ and $g(x) = x$
   c) $f(x) = \sqrt{4 - x^2}$, $-2 \le x \le 2$, and $g(x) = 4$
   d) $f(x) = 3x - 2$ and $g(x) = 2x + 3$

7   Let $f(x) = |x|$ and $g(x) = 2x - 3$. Find

   a) x if $f(x + 3) = 7$ b) x if $f(x - 2) < 1$
   c) x if $g(x - 5) > 2$ d) $[(g \circ f)(x) - (g \circ f)(2)]/(|x| - 2)$
   e) g^{-1}

8   Examine the graphs of the given functions to determine whether or not
    the function has an inverse f^{-1}. If f^{-1} exists, find it and graph f^{-1} on
    the same coordinate system as one containing the graph of the given
    function f.

   a) $f(x) = \frac{1}{2}x + 2$ b) $f(x) = \sqrt{x}$
   c) $f(x) = 3|x|$ d) $f = \{(x,y)|y = -3x^4\}$
   e) $f = \{(x,y)|y = 1/(x - 1)\}$

9   Let f and g be odd functions. Which of the following functions are odd?

   a) $f + g$ b) $f - g$
   c) $f \cdot g$ d) f/g

10 Let $f(x) = 7 - x^2$ and $g(x) = 1 + 5x$. Find an expression for each of the following functions. Also, indicate the domain.

a) $(f \circ f)(x)$
b) $(g \circ f)(x)$
c) $(g \circ g)(x)$
d) $(f \circ g)(x)$
e) $f[1/g(x)]$
f) $g[1/f(x)]$

11 A rectangle of sides x and y units is inscribed in a circle of radius 3 units. Express y as a function of x. Express the area of the rectangle A as a function of x.

12 Find some function (if possible) such that each of the following statements is true.

a) $f(x + y) = f(x) + f(y)$
b) $f(2x) = 2f(x)$
c) $|f(x)| = f(|x|)$
d) $f(\llbracket x \rrbracket) = \llbracket f(x) \rrbracket$

13 Let $f(x) = 7x - 13$ and $g(x) = 3x + 7$.

a) Find f^{-1} and g^{-1}.
b) Show that $(f \circ g)^{-1} = g^{-1} \circ f^{-1}$.
c) Show that $f[f^{-1}(x)] = x$.
d) Show that $g^{-1}[g(x)] = x$.

14 Indicate whether each of the following relations is symmetric with respect to the y axis, x axis, or origin. Graph the relation. Indicate which of the relations are functions. Indicate the domain and range. Are the functions increasing or decreasing? Are the functions even or odd? Are the functions continuous?

a) $\{(x,y)|y = |2x + 11|\}$
b) $\{(x,y)|y = 4\}$
c) $\{(x,y)|x = -4\}$
d) $\{(x,y)|y = x - 1\}$
e) $\{(x,y)|y = -\frac{1}{3}x + 2\}$
f) $\{(x,y)|y = |x|^2\}$
g) $\{(x,y)|y = |3x| + 3x\}$
h) $\{(x,y)|y = -x^2/2\}$
i) $\{(x,y)|y \leq 2x - 3\}$
j) $\{(x,y)|x = y^2\}$

15 Test each of the following relations for symmetry with respect to the x axis, the y axis, and the origin. Use your results to simplify graphing the relations.

a) $y = -2x^3$
b) $y^3 = 4x$
c) $y = x^4 + 1$
d) $y^2 = x^6$
e) $y = |x + 3|$
f) $y^2 = |x + 1|^2$

CHAPTER 3

Polynomial Functions

3 POLYNOMIAL FUNCTIONS

1 Introduction

In Chapter 2, some of the general properties of functions were considered. In this chapter, we will investigate particular types of functions, called polynomial functions, by investigating the various properties of functions which were presented in Chapter 2. These properties are listed here for convenience:

1 The domain and the range
2 The graph
3 Increasing or decreasing or neither
4 Even or odd or neither
5 Inverse if it exists

Any function expressible in the form

$$f(x) = a_n x^n + a_{n-1} x^{n-1} + a_{n-2} x^{n-2} + \cdots + a_1 x + a_0$$

where n is a positive integer and $a_n, a_{n-1}, \ldots, a_1$ and a_0 are real numbers with $a_n \neq 0$, is called a *polynomial function of degree n in x*. The constant numbers $a_n, a_{n-1}, \ldots, a_1$, and a_0 are called the *coefficients* of the polynomial function. If $n = 0$, then $f(x) = a$, where $a \neq 0$, is called a *zero degree* polynomial function. $f(x) = 0$ is called the *zero polynomial* and no degree is assigned to it.

EXAMPLES

1   $f(x) = 3x - 7x^3$ is a polynomial function of degree 3 because it can be expressed as $f(x) = (-7)x^3 + 0x^2 + 3x + 0$. Here, $a_3 = -7$, $a_2 = 0$, $a_1 = 3$, and $a_0 = 0$.

2   $f(x) = 3$ is a polynomial function of degree 0.

3   If $y = f(x)$ is a polynomial function of degree 4, then $f(x)$ is of the form $f(x) = a_4x^4 + a_3x^3 + a_2x^2 + a_1x + a_0$ with $a_4 \neq 0$.

4   $f(x) = 2x + 1/x^2 = 2x + x^{-2}$ is not a polynomial function in x because of the negative 2 exponent.

2   Linear Functions

Suppose we have two thermometers which are used simultaneously to measure temperature — one graduated according to the Fahrenheit scale, the other graduated according to the Centigrade scale. If x represents the Centigrade reading and y represents the Fahrenheit reading, a functional relationship between x and y can be found as follows.

The freezing point (of water) is $0°$ Centigrade or $32°$ Fahrenheit, whereas the boiling point (of water) is $100°$ Centigrade or $212°$ Fahrenheit. Consequently, each Fahrenheit degree is equivalent to $\frac{180}{100} = \frac{9}{5}$ of one Centigrade degree. Now, if x is the Centigrade reading,

Figure 1

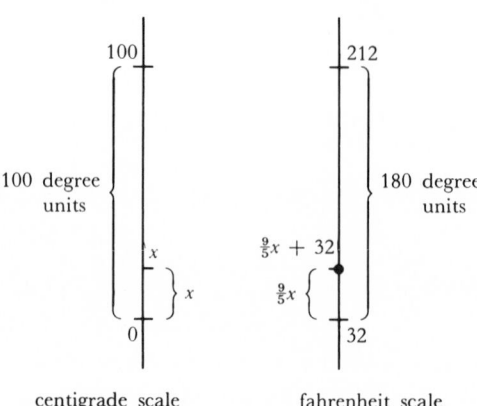

centigrade scale   fahrenheit scale

x represents the "directed" number (x may be negative) of Centigrade degrees, so that $\frac{9}{5}x$ represents the corresponding directed number of Fahrenheit degrees. Since the "starting point" of the Fahrenheit scale is 32, as compared with 0 on the Centigrade scale, it follows that a Fahrenheit reading of y corresponding to a Centigrade reading of x is given by $y = \frac{9}{5}x + 32$ (Figure 1).

If x is assumed to represent members of the domain, then $y = \frac{9}{5}x + 32$ determines the function $f(x) = \frac{9}{5}x + 32$ (Figure 2).

Figure 2

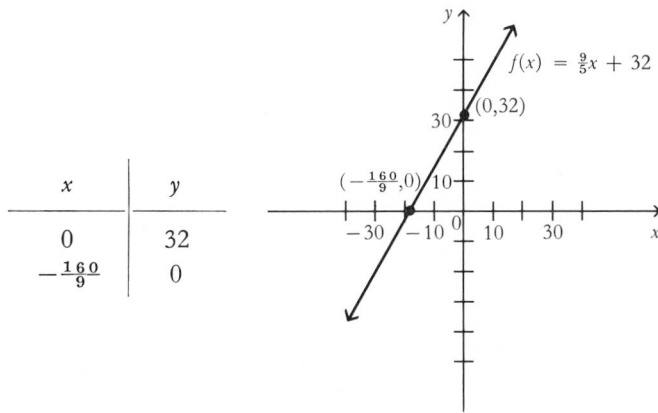

This is an example of a linear function. In general, polynomial functions of the form $f(x) = mx + b$ are called *linear functions*, where m and b are constant real numbers.

The graph of a linear function $f(x) = mx + b$ is a straight line; hence, it is enough to plot two points to determine the graph.

If $m = 0$, then $f(x) = b$. In this case, f is called a *constant function*. Its graph is the set of all points with an ordinate of b; if $b \neq 0$, it is a line parallel to the x axis through the point $(0,b)$. If, for example $b = 3$, then $f(x) = 3$ has the set representation $f = \{(x,y)|y = 3\}$ and its graph is shown in Figure 3.

Figure 3

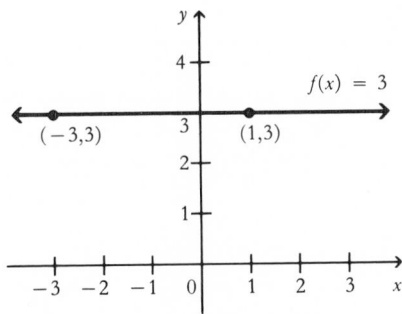

EXAMPLES

1   Explain why the linear function $f(x) = 2x + 5$ has an inverse f^{-1}. Determine f^{-1}.

SOLUTION. f^{-1} exists since f is increasing (Figure 4). f^{-1} can be constructed by using the method of Chapter 2, Section 6.

First, let $y = f(x)$, so that $y = 2x + 5$. After solving for x in terms of y, we get $x = (y - 5)/2$, so that $f^{-1}(y) = (y - 5)/2$, or, after changing notation, it follows that $f^{-1}(x) = (x - 5)/2$ (Figure 4).

Figure 4

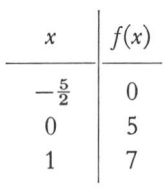

x	$f(x)$
$-\frac{5}{2}$	0
0	5
1	7

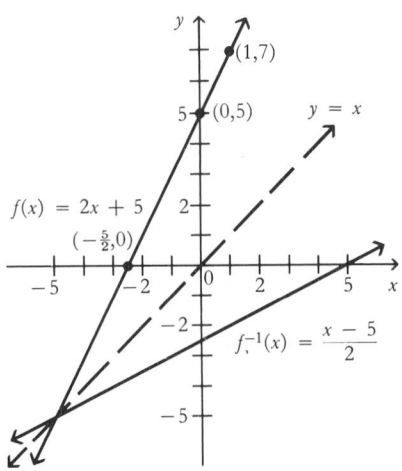

2   Suppose that $y = f(x)$ is a linear function whose graph contains $(3, -4)$ and $(-2, 5)$. Find f in equation form.

SOLUTION.   Since $(3, -4)$ and $(-2, 5)$ both lie on the same line, they must both satisfy the functional relationship $f(x) = mx + b$ simultaneously; hence, we have to solve

$$-4 = 3m + b \quad \text{and} \quad 5 = -2m + b$$

simultaneously, so that $m = -\frac{9}{5}$ and $b = \frac{7}{5}$; hence, $f(x) = -\frac{9}{5}x + \frac{7}{5}$ (Figure 5).

3   Show that a linear function of the form $f(x) = mx$ is an odd function.

SOLUTION.   Since $f(x) = mx$, $f(-x) = m(-x) = -mx$, so that $f(-x) = -f(x)$; hence, the function is odd and the graph is symmetric with respect to the origin.

Figure 5

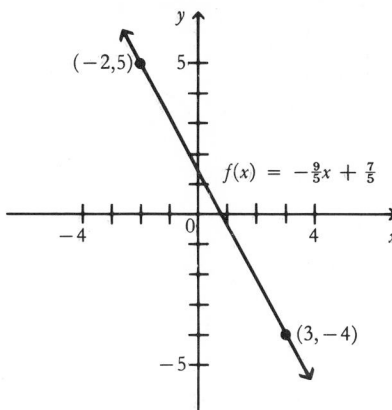

2.1 Definition

Suppose that (x_1, y_1) and (x_2, y_2) are any two points of a line such that $x_1 \neq x_2$ (Figure 6). The number s that is defined by the equation

$$s = \frac{y_2 - y_1}{x_2 - x_1} \qquad x_1 \neq x_2$$

is called the *slope* of the line. ☐

Figure 6

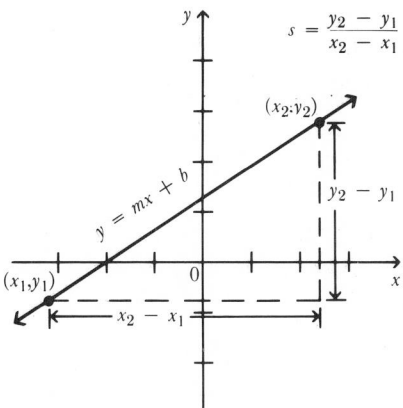

Since

$$\frac{y_1 - y_2}{x_1 - x_2} = \frac{-(y_1 - y_2)}{-(x_1 - x_2)} = \frac{y_2 - y_1}{x_2 - x_1}$$

the order in which the two points are taken when the coordinates are subtracted does not change the value. For example, the slope of the line containing the points $(-2, 5)$ and $(3, -4)$ (Figure 7) is

$$\frac{-4 - 5}{3 - (-2)} = -\frac{9}{5}$$

or, equivalently,

$$\frac{5 - (-4)}{-2 - 3} = -\frac{9}{5}$$

Figure 7

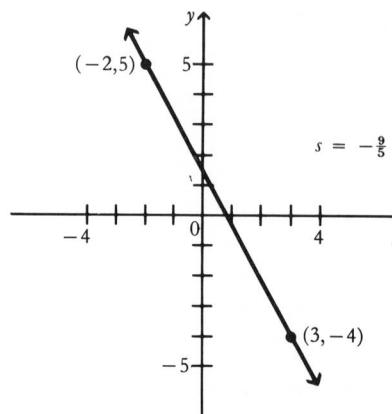

Notice that the value of the slope depends on the two points $(-2,5)$ and $(3,-4)$. Will the value of the slope of this line be the same if two other points on the line are used to compute the slope? This question is answered by the following theorem.

THEOREM 1

The slope of the line determined by the function $f(x) = mx + b$ is m. In other words, no matter which points are selected to compute the slope, the result will be the same value, m, the coefficient of x.

PROOF.   Consider any x_1 and x_2 such that $x_1 \neq x_2$. Then $(x_1, f(x_1))$ and $(x_2, f(x_2))$ are two points of the line, so that the slope s can be computed as follows.

$$s = \frac{f(x_2) - f(x_1)}{x_2 - x_1} = \frac{(mx_2 + b) - (mx_1 + b)}{x_2 - x_1}$$

$$= \frac{mx_2 - mx_1}{x_2 - x_1}$$

$$= \frac{m(x_2 - x_1)}{x_2 - x_1} = m$$

Notice that if the slope is zero, then the linear function assumes the form $f(x) = b$; that is, the function is constant and its graph is parallel to the x axis or coincides with the x axis (see Figure 3).

If $x_1 = x_2$ for all points on a line, then the slope

$$m = \frac{y_2 - v_1}{x_2 - x_1}$$

is not defined. This situation occurs when the line contains two points with the same abscissas; such a line is parallel to the y axis or coincides with the y axis and is not a function (see Problem 15a). For example, $x = 4$ is a line parallel to the y axis (Figure 8); the slope of this line is not defined.

Figure 8

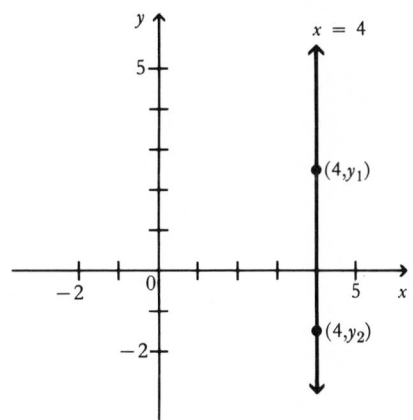

Assume that the slope of a line m is either positive or negative and let (x_1, y_1) and (x_2, y_2) be two points of the line with $x_1 < x_2$. Then, by Definition 2.1, together with Theorem 1,

$$m = \frac{y_2 - y_1}{x_2 - x_1}$$

so that

(1) $$m(x_2 - x_1) = y_2 - y_1 \quad \text{with} \quad x_2 - x_1 > 0$$

If $m > 0$, then $y_2 - y_1 > 0$, so that $y_1 < y_2$. Hence, the function is increasing and its graph rises from left to right (Figure 9). If $m < 0$

Figure 9

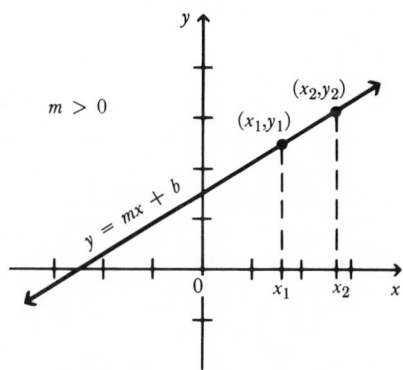

when $x_1 < x_2$, then $y_2 - y_1 < 0$ in (1) (Why?), so that $y_2 < y_1$; hence, the function is decreasing and the graph falls from left to right (Figure 10). Hence, if $m \neq 0$, $f(x) = mx + b$ is either increasing or decreasing, and, consequently $f(x)$ has an inverse.

Figure 10

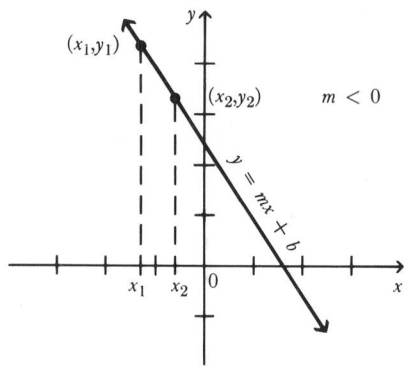

EXAMPLE

Determine the slope of each of the following lines. Is the function increasing or decreasing? Find the inverse if it exists.

a) $y + 3x = 7$ b) $5x - y + 13 = 0$

SOLUTION

a) $y + 3x = 7$ can be written as $y = -3x + 7$; hence, the slope is -3; and the function is decreasing. Furthermore its inverse is given by $f^{-1}(x) = (x - 7)/-3$ (Figure 11).

Figure 11

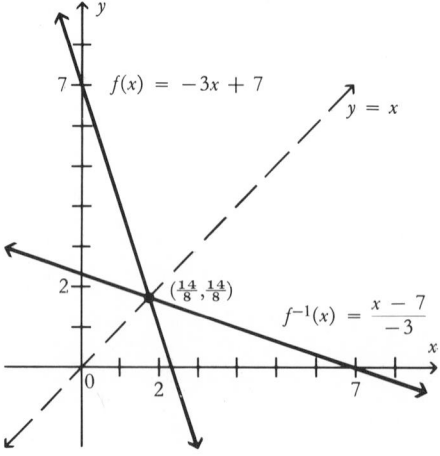

b) $5x - y + 13 = 0$ is equivalent to $y = 5x + 13$; hence the slope is 5. The function is increasing and the inverse is $f^{-1}(x) = (x - 13)/5$ (Figure 12).

Figure 12

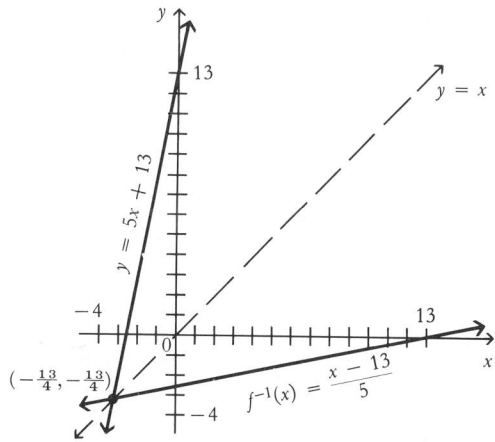

2.2 Forms of Equations of Lines

f is a linear function if there are numbers m and b such that $f(x) = mx + b$. Since $(0,b)$ is the point on the graph of $f(x) = mx + b$ which also is on the y axis, we say that $(0,b)$ is the y *intercept* of the line (Figure 13). The form $f(x) = mx + b$ is called the *slope-intercept* form of the line.

Figure 13

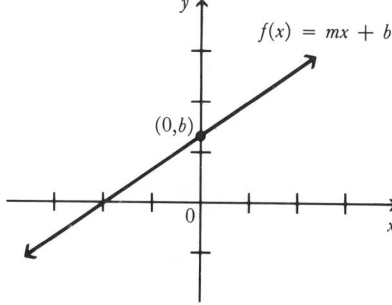

Suppose that the slope of a line is m and that (x_1, y_1) is a point on the line. If $(x,y) \neq (x_1, y_1)$ is used to represent any point on the line, then $m = (y - y_1)/(x - x_1)$, so that $y - y_1 = m(x - x_1)$. This form of the equation of the line is called the *point-slope form* (Figure 14). Notice that the point (x_1, y_1) also satisfies the equation.

Figure 14

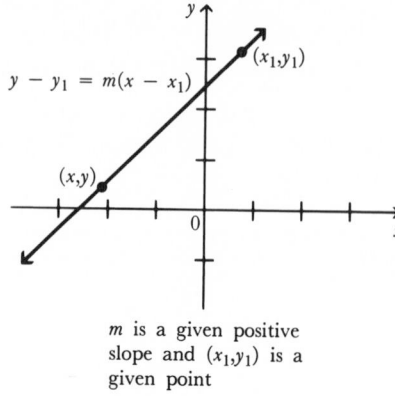

m is a given positive slope and (x_1,y_1) is a given point

EXAMPLES

1 Find the equation of a line whose slope is 5 and containing the point (2,3).

SOLUTION. Using the point-slope form, that is,

$$y - y_1 = m(x - x_1) \quad \text{with} \quad m = 5 \quad \text{and} \quad (x_1,y_1) = (2,3)$$

we have $y - 3 = 5(x - 2)$, or, equivalently, $y = 5x - 7$, which is the slope-intercept form of the line (Figure 15).

Figure 15

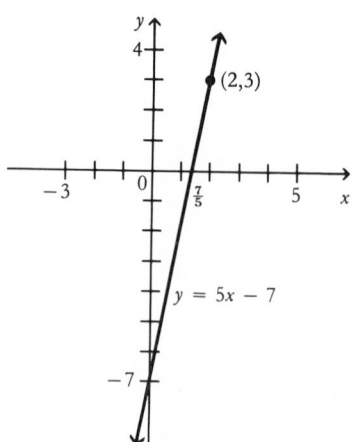

$y = 5x - 7$

2 Find the equation of the linear function f whose slope is -2 such that $f(3) = 1$.

SOLUTION. $f(x) = mx + b$, so that $f(3) = -2(3) + b = 1$; hence, $b = 7$ and $f(x) = -2x + 7$ (Figure 16).

Figure 16

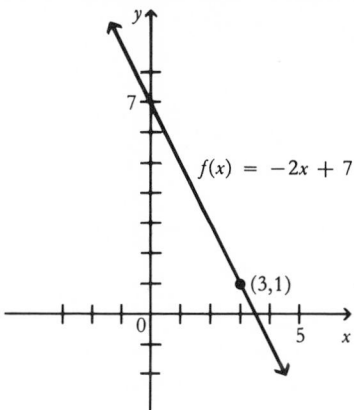

$f(x) = -2x + 7$

(3,1)

2.3   Geometry of Lines

Suppose that $f_1(x) = m_1x + b_1$, and $f_2(x) = m_2x + b_2$. If the graphs of the two lines intersect, there must be a value of x which satisfies the equations simultaneously, that is, $m_1x + b_1 = m_2x + b_2$ or, equivalently, $(m_1 - m_2)x = b_2 - b_1$. If $m_1 \neq m_2$, then $x = (b_2 - b_1)/(m_1 - m_2)$ satisfies this equation, and the lines intersect (Figure 17). If $m_1 = m_2$

Figure 17

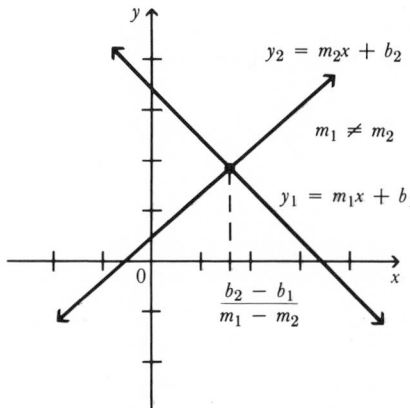

$y_2 = m_2x + b_2$

$m_1 \neq m_2$

$y_1 = m_1x + b_1$

$$\frac{b_2 - b_1}{m_1 - m_2}$$

and $b_1 \neq b_2$, $x = (b_2 - b_1)/(m_1 - m_2)$ is undefined and the two lines are parallel (Figure 18).

In summary, we have:

1    $m_1 \neq m_2$ implies that the lines intersect.

2    $m_1 = m_2$ and $b_1 \neq b_2$ implies that the lines are parallel.

3    $m_1 = m_2$ and $b_1 = b_2$ implies that the lines coincide.

Figure 18

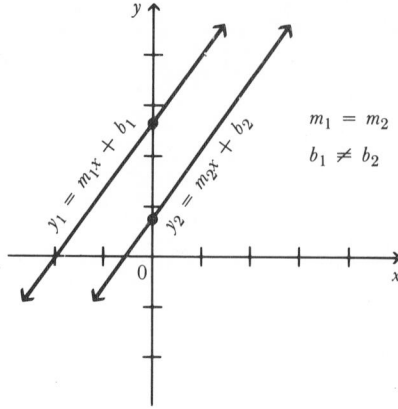

Finally, we state without proof that the two lines are perpendicular whenever $m_1 m_2 = -1$ (see Problem 17) (Figure 19).

Figure 19

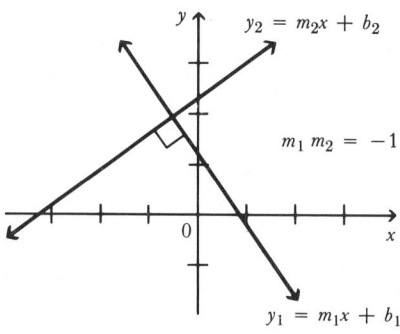

EXAMPLES

1   Find the equation of a line containing the point $(3, -2)$ and

   a)   parallel to the x axis   b)   parallel to the y axis

SOLUTION

   a)   The slope of the line containing the point $(3, -2)$ and parallel to the x axis is 0. Hence, the equation of that line is $y = -2$ (Figure 20).

   b)   The slope of the line containing the point $(3, -2)$ and parallel to the y axis is undefined. Hence, the equation of that line is $x = 3$ (Figure 20).

2   Find a value for a so that the line represented by $3x + ay = 5$ is parallel to $y = -2x + 1$.

SOLUTION. $y = -3x/a + 5/a$, so that $-3/a = -2$; that is, $a = \frac{3}{2}$.

Figure 20

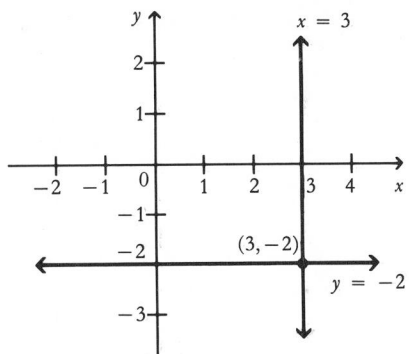

3 a) Find the equation of the line containing (3,2) and perpendicular
        to the line containing the points $(-4,-2)$ and $(-2,2)$.
    b) Also find the equation of the line containing (3,2) and parallel
        to the line containing the points $(-4,-2)$ and $(-2,2)$.

SOLUTION

a) The slope of the line containing points $(-4,-2)$ and $(-2,2)$
    is $[2 - (-2)]/[-2 - (-4)] = \frac{4}{2} = 2$, so that the slope of
    the perpendicular line is $-\frac{1}{2}$. Hence, the equation of the line
    perpendicular to the given line and containing the point (3,2)
    is $y - 2 = -\frac{1}{2}(x - 3)$, or, equivalently, $y = -\frac{1}{2}x + \frac{7}{2}$
    (Figure 21).

Figure 21

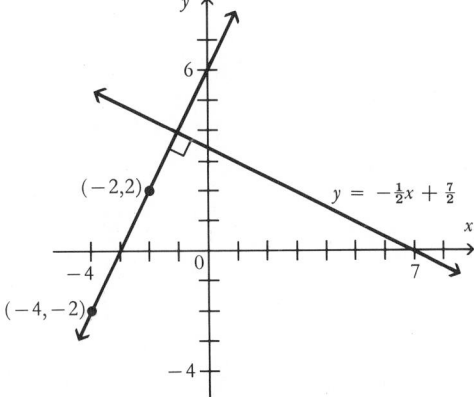

b) Since the line is parallel to the given line its slope must be
    equal to 2. Hence, the equation of the line is $y - 2 = 2(x - 3)$
    or, equivalently, $y = 2x - 4$ (Figure 22).

Figure 22

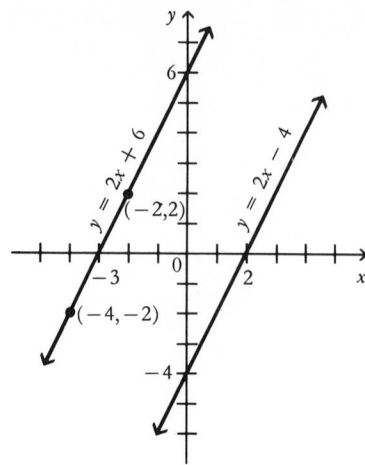

4   Find the point of intersection of the lines $x - 2y = 4$ and $3x + 2y = 4$.

SOLUTION.   The graphs of the equations are shown in Figure 23. The point (x,y) that satisfies the equations $x - 2y = 4$ and $3x + 2y = 4$ simultaneously can be determined by solving $3(2y + 4) + 2y = 4$ to get $y = -1$. Substituting $y = -1$ into $x - 2y = 4$, we have $x = 2$; therefore, the point of intersection of the lines is $(2,-1)$.

Figure 23

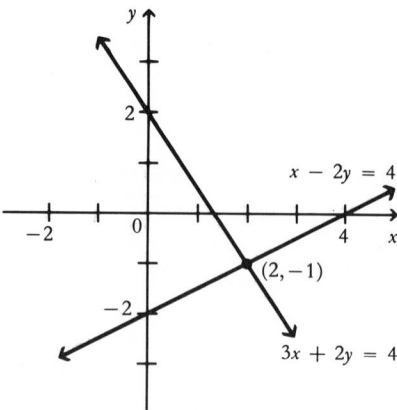

5   Let Q be the amount of heat required to change 1 gram of solid ice at $0°$ Centigrade to water at t degrees Centigrade. Assume that Q is a linear function of t, the temperature of water, and also assume that $0 \leq t \leq 100$. If $Q = 70$ at $t = 15°$ and $Q = 140$ at $t = 85°$, what is the amount of heat required to transform the ice into $5°$ Centigrade water?

SOLUTION. Since the function is linear:

$$Q = f(t) = mt + b$$

so that $70 = 15m + b$ and $140 = 85m + b$

Hence, $m = 1$ and $b = 55$; therefore, $Q = t + 55$, so that when $t = 5$, $Q = 60$.

PROBLEM SET 1

1 Which of the following functions are polynomial functions? Indicate the degree of each polynomial function and put it in the polynomial form.

a) $\{(x,y)|y = 7x - 5x^2 + \pi\}$ b) $f(x) = x^{-2} + x$
c) $f(x) = 5^{-1}$ d) $f(x) = 1/x^3 + 2x^2 + x - 2$
e) $f(x) = 2x - 3^{1/2}x^2 + 5x^3 - 7$

2 Let f be a linear function that contains the point $(0,0)$. Find $f(2)$ if

a) $f(3) = 6$ b) $f(7) = -4$
c) $f(1) = 0$ d) $f(-2) = 13$

3 Find the linear function which satisfies each of the following conditions, and then graph the line. Indicate the form of the equation of the line used.

a) The slope is 3 and the line contains the point $(1,1)$.
b) The line contains the point $(-2,5)$ and the point $(2,-3)$.
c) The slope is 0 and the line contains the point $(-3,-2)$.
d) The line is parallel to the line $3x + 2y + 2 = 0$ and it contains the point $(-3,-1)$.
e) The line is perpendicular to $3x + 2y + 2 = 0$ and it contains the point $(-3,-5)$.

4 Find the slope and the y intercept of each of the following lines. Sketch the graphs.

a) $2y = 3x - 12$ b) $y = 3 - x$
c) $3x + 5y - 6 = 0$ d) $2x - y + 5 = 0$

5 a) Show that the equation of a line with y intercept $b \neq 0$ and with x intercept $a \neq 0$ can be written in the form $x/a + y/b = 1$. (This equation is called the *intercept form* of the equation of a line.)
b) Use the equation of part (a) to write the equation of the line that contains the points $(4,0)$ and $(0,-6)$.

6 a) Show that if a, b, and c are constant real numbers such that a and b are not both zero, then the graph of the equation $ax + by + c = 0$ is a line. (This equation is called the *general form* of the equation of a line.)

b) Find the slope and the y intercept of the line whose equation is
$2x - 3y + 5 = 0$.

c) Show that $ax + by + c = 0$, where $a \neq 0$ and $b \neq 0$, determines
a line that intersects the x and y axes at the points $(-c/a,0)$ and
$(0,-c/b)$, respectively.

7 Prove that the triangles with the following vertices are right triangles.

a) $(-4,-2)$, $(2,-8)$, and $(4,6)$ b) $(2,3)$, $(5,3)$, and $(5,7)$

8 Use the slope to decide whether or not $(2,5)$, $(4,3)$, and $(3,4)$ are
collinear.

9 In each of the following parts, determine a linear function f which
satisfies the given conditions.

a) $f(1) = -1$ and $f(3) = 4$ b) $f(5x + 2) = 5f(x) + 2$

c) $f(7x) = 7f(x)$

10 Discuss the following linear functions. Indicate the domain and range.
Is the function increasing or decreasing? Is it continuous? Is it even or
odd? Find the inverse if it exists. What is the slope?

a) $\{(x,3)|x \in R\}$ b) $f(x) = 5 - 3x$

c) $y + 1 = 2(x - 1)$ d) $y/2 - 3x/5 = 1$

e) $3x - y + 5 = 0$

11 Find the point of intersection of the following pairs of lines if it exists.
Sketch the lines and label the point of intersection.

a) $3x - y + 5 = 0$ and $y = 2x - 3$

b) $5x + 6y = 4$ and $3x + 4y - 3 = 0$

c) $x = 4$ and $3x + 4y + 7 = 0$

d) $x = 3$ and $y = 5$

e) $y - 2x + 3 = 0$ and $5y - 6x - 10 = 0$

12 Given $f(x) = -7x + 13$, find a linear function: (i) whose graph is
parallel to the graph of f, (ii) whose graph is perpendicular to the graph
of f, and which contains the point

a) $(2,3)$ b) $(-2,5)$

13 Show that if f is a linear function and $f(0) = 0$, then $f(x + y) = f(x) + f(y)$ for all real numbers x and y.

14 Given the lines $L_1 = \{(x,y)|y = m_1x + b_1\}$ and $L_2 = \{(x,y)|y = m_2x + b_2\}$, discuss (geometrically) all the possibilities for $L_1 \cap L_2$. How
do the slopes "predict" each of the possible geometric situations?

15 a) Let k be a constant. Discuss the relation $\{(x,y)|x = k\}$. What is the
domain? The range? Is the relation a function? Graph it.

b) Graph on the same coordinate system all the linear functions

$$y = mx \quad \text{where} \quad m \in \{-10, -5, -2, -1, 0, 1, 2, 5, 10\}$$

What happens to the position of a line as the slope increases from -10 to 10?

16 Let the temperature k feet above the surface of the earth be $t°$ Centigrade and assume that the function that relates t and k is linear. If the temperature on the surface of the earth is $80°$ Centigrade and the temperature at 2,500 feet is $56°$ Centigrade, what is the temperature at 5,000 feet?

17 Prove that if the product of the slopes of two lines is -1, then the two lines are perpendicular; and, conversely prove that if the two lines are perpendicular, then the product of the slopes is -1. (*Hint:* Use the distance formula.)

18 Prove that the difference quotient for $f(x) = mx + b$ is m, the slope of the line.

3 Systems of Linear Equations

The graphs of linear functions can be used to motivate the study of solving systems of linear equations. A set of linear equations is called a *system of linear equations. The solution of a linear system* containing two variables is the set of all ordered pairs of numbers which satisfy all the equations in the system simultaneously. Geometrically, the solution of a system containing two linear equations with two variables is the set of ordered pairs of numbers corresponding to the points of intersection of the graphs of the two linear equations (provided that such points exist).

For example, let us consider the solution of the linear system

$$\begin{cases} 3x + 4y = 12 \\ 3x - 8y = 0 \end{cases}$$

The graphs of the two corresponding linear functions $y = -\frac{3}{4}x + 3$ and $y = \frac{3}{8}x$ are shown in Figure 1. The solution of the system is the ordered pair $(\frac{8}{3}, 1)$, where $x = \frac{8}{3}$ and $y = 1$, and the point of intersection of the two linear equations is the same ordered pair $(\frac{8}{3}, 1)$.

Figure 1

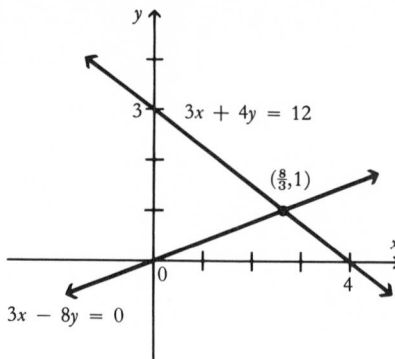

It may happen that the graphs of the linear equations are parallel lines. In such a case the intersection is the null set, and the system is called *inconsistent*. For example, the linear system

$$\begin{cases} x + 2y = 4 \\ 3x + 6y = -3 \end{cases} \quad \text{is inconsistent}$$

Note that if the two lines are expressed in the slope-intercept form, the system becomes

$$\begin{cases} y = -\frac{1}{2}x + 2 \\ y = -\frac{1}{2}x - \frac{1}{2} \end{cases}$$

Both of the slopes are equal but the intercepts are different, so that we have two parallel lines (Figure 2) and the solution set is empty.

Figure 2

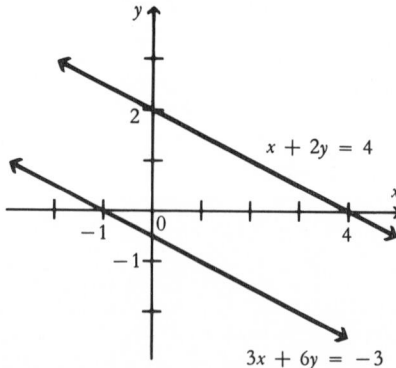

If the graphs of the linear equations coincide, then the intersection is every point of the line. In this case, the system is said to be *dependent*.

For example, the system

$$\begin{cases} 3x - y = -1 \\ 6x - 2y = -2 \end{cases}$$

can be written in the slope-intercept form as

$$\begin{cases} y = 3x + 1 \\ y = 3x + 1 \end{cases}$$

Here, the lines have the same slope with the same intercepts; consequently, each equation represents the same line (Figure 3), and the solution set is $\{(x,y)\,|\,y = 3x + 1\}$.

Figure 3

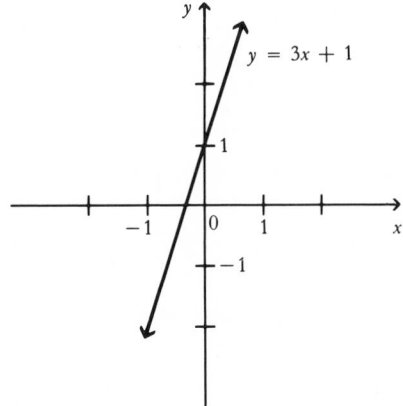

In general, a linear system

$$\begin{cases} a_1x_1 + b_1x_2 = c_1 \\ a_2x_1 + b_2x_2 = c_2 \end{cases}$$

can fall in one of three possible categories:

1 If the two lines $a_1x_1 + b_1x_2 = c_1$ and $a_2x_1 + b_2x_2 = c_2$ intersect in a unique (one) point, the solution is an ordered pair of numbers.

2 If the two lines $a_1x_1 + b_1x_2 = c_1$ and $a_2x_1 + b_2x_2 = c_2$ are parallel, the solution set is the null set. In this case, the system is said to be *inconsistent*.

3 If the two lines $a_1x_1 + b_1x_2 = c_1$ and $a_2x_1 + b_2x_2 = c_2$ are coincident, the solution set is the set of all points on the line. The system in this case is said to be *dependent*.

3.1   Elimination Method

Now we will investigate an algebraic procedure for solving a system of two linear equations. We will see that this method can be extended to systems containing more than two linear equations and more than two variables.

Let us consider a specific example of the method by solving the following system.

$$\begin{cases} x - y = 1 \\ 3x + 2y = 8 \end{cases}$$

First, multiply the first equation by -3 and add it to the second equation, so that the system becomes

$$\begin{cases} x - y = 1 \\ 0 + 5y = 5 \end{cases}$$

Next, multiply the second equation by $\frac{1}{5}$ to get

$$\begin{cases} x - y = 1 \\ y = 1 \end{cases}$$

Substituting $y = 1$ into the first equation yields $x = 2$. Thus, the solution set is $\{(2,1)\}$, since $x = 2$ and $y = 1$ satisfy each equation in the system simultaneously (Figure 4).

Figure 4

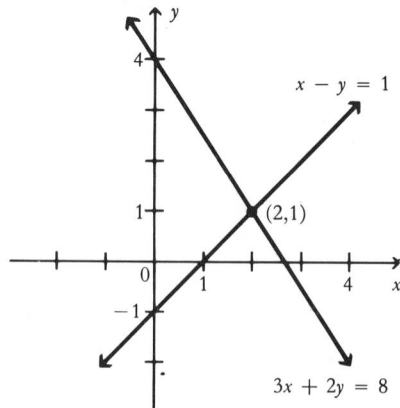

This procedure for solving a system of linear equations is called the *elimination method* or, equivalently, the *process of elimination*.

The process of elimination may also be applied to systems containing more than two unknowns. We illustrate this application by solving the following system (A).

$$\text{(A)} \quad \begin{cases} 2x_1 + x_2 - 2x_3 = 10 \\ 3x_1 + 2x_2 + 2x_3 = 1 \\ 5x_1 + 4x_2 + 3x_3 = 4 \end{cases}$$

First, replace the second equation by the sum of -3 times the first equation and 2 times the second equations to obtain the system (B):

$$\text{(B)} \quad \begin{cases} 2x_1 + x_2 - 2x_3 = 10 \\ x_2 + 10x_3 = -28 \\ 5x_1 + 4x_2 + 3x_3 = 4 \end{cases}$$

The system (B) is *equivalent* to the system (A), since every solution of the system (B) is also a solution of the system (A). Next, replace the third equation of (B) by the sum of -5 times the first equation and 2 times the third to obtain the equivalent system (C):

$$\text{(C)} \quad \begin{cases} 2x_1 + x_2 - 2x_3 = 10 \\ x_2 + 10x_3 = -28 \\ 3x_2 + 16x_3 = -42 \end{cases}$$

Now replace the third equation of (C) by the sum of -3 times the second equation and the third equation to get the equivalent system (D):

$$\text{(D)} \quad \begin{cases} 2x_1 + x_2 - 2x_3 = 10 \\ x_2 + 10x_3 = -28 \\ - 14x_3 = 42 \end{cases}$$

Next multiply the third equation by $-\frac{1}{14}$ and add -1 times the second equation to the first equation to obtain the equivalent system (E):

$$\text{(E)} \quad \begin{cases} 2x_1 - 12x_3 = 38 \\ x_2 + 10x_3 = -28 \\ x_3 = -3 \end{cases}$$

Finally, multiply the first equation by $\frac{1}{2}$ to obtain the equivalent system (F):

$$\text{(F)} \quad \begin{cases} x_1 - 6x_3 = 19 \\ x_2 + 10x_3 = -28 \\ x_3 = -3 \end{cases}$$

From the third equation, $x_3 = -3$, so that after substituting into the second equation we get $x_2 = 2$; then, after substituting into the first equation, we obtain $x_1 = 1$. Thus the solution is $\{(1,2,-3)\}$, since $x_1 = 1$, $x_2 = 2$, and $x_3 = -3$ satisfy each equation in the system simultaneously.

In order to see that the six systems given above are equivalent, observe that each system is obtained from the preceding one by performing one or more of the following equation operations:

1   Interchange the positions of two equations in the system.

2   Replace an equation in the system by a nonzero multiple of itself.

3   Replace an equation in the system by the sum of a nonzero multiple of that equation and a multiple of another equation of the system.

3.2   Matrices and Row-Reduction

Notice that in the elimination process there is little reason to continue writing the variables. All we need to do is to maintain a record of the coefficients that belong to each variable in each equation. The standard device used for doing this is a *matrix*.

A *matrix* is a rectangular array of numbers. The *size* of a matrix is described by specifying the number of rows and columns. The numbers occurring in a matrix are called the *entries* of the matrix. For example, the matrix

$$A = \begin{bmatrix} 1 & 2 \\ 3 & -1 \end{bmatrix}$$

has two rows and two columns and we say that A is a 2×2 matrix and 1, 2, 3, and -1 are the entries of A. The matrix

$$B = \begin{bmatrix} 1 & 3 & 5 \\ -2 & 5 & 6 \end{bmatrix}$$

has two rows and three columns, so that B is a 2×3 matrix. B has entries 1, 3, 5, -2, 5, and 6. The matrix

$$C = \begin{bmatrix} 3 \\ 1 \\ 2 \end{bmatrix}$$

is a 3×1 matrix with entries 3, 1, and 2. Notice that when the size of a matrix is specified, the number of rows is given first and then the number of columns.

The entry of a matrix is identified by using subscripts to indicate its row and its column position. For example, the entry of the second row and the second column of a matrix D is denoted by d_{22}; the entry of the first row and the fourth column of a matrix D is d_{14}. In general, the entry of the ith row and the jth column of matrix D is denoted by d_{ij}.

For example, if

$$A = \begin{bmatrix} 3 & 2 & -1 \\ 4 & 1 & 5 \end{bmatrix}$$

$a_{11} = 3$, $a_{12} = 2$, $a_{13} = -1$, $a_{21} = 4$, $a_{22} = 1$, and $a_{32} = 5$.

Now, let us see how matrix notation, together with the elimination method, can be used to solve linear systems.

Suppose we are to solve the linear system

(A) $\begin{cases} 3x - y = 1 \\ x + 2y = 0 \end{cases}$

The matrix form of (A) is written as

$$A = \begin{bmatrix} 3 & -1 & \vdots & 1 \\ 1 & 2 & \vdots & 0 \end{bmatrix}$$

A is called an *augmented matrix*. The augmented matrix can be used to "maintain a record" of the coefficients of the linear equations when the elimination method is applied to solve (A). ($\downarrow$ will be used to indicate that the systems are equivalent.)

System	*Matrix form of system*
(A) $\begin{cases} 3x - y = 1 \\ x + 2y = 0 \end{cases}$	$A = \begin{bmatrix} 3 & -1 & \vdots & 1 \\ 1 & 2 & \vdots & 0 \end{bmatrix}$
$\downarrow$ First, multiply the second equation by -3.	First, multiply the second row by -3.
(B) $\begin{cases} 3x - y = 1 \\ -3x - 6y = 0 \end{cases}$	$B = \begin{bmatrix} 3 & -1 & \vdots & 1 \\ -3 & -6 & \vdots & 0 \end{bmatrix}$
$\downarrow$ Next, replace equation two with the sum of equations one and two.	Next, replace row two with the sum of rows one and two.
(C) $\begin{cases} 3x - y = 1 \\ \quad\ -7y = 1 \end{cases}$	$C = \begin{bmatrix} 3 & -1 & \vdots & 1 \\ 0 & -7 & \vdots & 1 \end{bmatrix}$
$\downarrow$ Multiply equation two by $-\frac{1}{7}$.	$\downarrow$ Multiply row two by $-\frac{1}{7}$.
(D) $\begin{cases} 3x - y = 1 \\ \quad\ y = -\frac{1}{7} \end{cases}$	$D = \begin{bmatrix} 3 & -1 & \vdots & 1 \\ 0 & 1 & \vdots & -\frac{1}{7} \end{bmatrix}$

| Replace equation one with the sum of equations one and two. | Replace row one with the sum of rows one and two. |

(E) $\begin{cases} 3x & = \frac{6}{7} \\ & y = -\frac{1}{7} \end{cases}$

$$E = \begin{bmatrix} 3 & 0 & | & \frac{6}{7} \\ 0 & 1 & | & -\frac{1}{7} \end{bmatrix}$$

| Multiply equation one by $\frac{1}{3}$. | Multiply row one by $\frac{1}{3}$. |

(F) $\begin{cases} x & = \frac{2}{7} \\ & y = -\frac{1}{7} \end{cases}$

$$F = \begin{bmatrix} 1 & 0 & | & \frac{2}{7} \\ 0 & 1 & | & -\frac{1}{7} \end{bmatrix}$$

Hence, the solution of (A) is $\{(\frac{2}{7}, -\frac{1}{7})\}$.

Realizing that the numbers to the left of the dotted line represent the coefficients of x and y, we have $\{(\frac{2}{7}, -\frac{1}{7})\}$ as the solution set.

Consider the system of linear equations

$$\text{(A)} \quad \begin{cases} x_1 - 2x_2 + 3x_3 = -1 \\ 2x_1 - x_2 + 2x_3 = 2 \\ 3x_1 + x_2 + 2x_3 = 3 \end{cases}$$

The matrix form of system (A) is written as

$$A = \begin{bmatrix} 1 & -2 & 3 & | & -1 \\ 2 & -1 & 2 & | & 2 \\ 3 & 1 & 2 & | & 3 \end{bmatrix}$$

| *System* | *Matrix form of system* |

(A) $\begin{cases} x_1 - 2x_2 + 3x_3 = -1 \\ 2x_1 - x_2 + 2x_3 = 2 \\ 3x_1 + x_2 + 2x_3 = 3 \end{cases}$ $A = \begin{bmatrix} 1 & -2 & 3 & | & -1 \\ 2 & -1 & 2 & | & 2 \\ 3 & 1 & 2 & | & 3 \end{bmatrix}$

| First, replace the second equation by the sum of -2 times the first equation and the second equation. | First, replace the second row by the sum of -2 times the first row and the second row. |

(B) $\begin{cases} x_1 - 2x_2 + 3x_3 = -1 \\ 3x_2 - 4x_3 = 4 \\ 3x_1 + x_2 + 2x_3 = 3 \end{cases}$ $B = \begin{bmatrix} 1 & -2 & 3 & | & -1 \\ 0 & 3 & -4 & | & 4 \\ 3 & 1 & 2 & | & 3 \end{bmatrix}$

Next, replace equation three with the sum of -3 times equation one and the third equation.

Next, replace row three with the sum of -3 times row one and row three.

(C)
$$\begin{cases} x_1 - 2x_2 + 3x_3 = -1 \\ \quad\;\; 3x_2 - 4x_3 = \quad 4 \\ \quad\;\; 7x_2 - 7x_3 = \quad 6 \end{cases}$$

$$C = \begin{bmatrix} 1 & -2 & 3 & | & -1 \\ 0 & 3 & -4 & | & 4 \\ 0 & 7 & -7 & | & 6 \end{bmatrix}$$

Multiply equation two by $\frac{1}{3}$.

Multiply row two by $\frac{1}{3}$.

(D)
$$\begin{cases} x_1 - 2x_2 + 3x_3 = -1 \\ \quad\;\; x_2 - \frac{4}{3}x_3 = \frac{4}{3} \\ \quad\;\; 7x_2 - 7x_3 = \quad 6 \end{cases}$$

$$D = \begin{bmatrix} 1 & -2 & 3 & | & -1 \\ 0 & 1 & -\frac{4}{3} & | & \frac{4}{3} \\ 0 & 7 & -7 & | & 6 \end{bmatrix}$$

Now, replace the third equation with -7 times the second equation plus the third equation.

Now, replace the third row with -7 times the second row plus the third row.

(E)
$$\begin{cases} x_1 - 2x_2 + 3x_3 = -1 \\ \quad\;\; x_2 - \frac{4}{3}x_3 = \frac{4}{3} \\ \quad\;\;\;\;\;\; \frac{7}{3}x_3 = -\frac{10}{3} \end{cases}$$

$$E = \begin{bmatrix} 1 & -2 & 3 & | & -1 \\ 0 & 1 & -\frac{4}{3} & | & \frac{4}{3} \\ 0 & 0 & \frac{7}{3} & | & -\frac{10}{3} \end{bmatrix}$$

Next replace equation one with 2 times equation two plus equation one.

Next replace row one with 2 times row two plus row one.

(F)
$$\begin{cases} x_1 \quad\;\;\; + \frac{1}{3}x_3 = \frac{5}{3} \\ \quad\;\; x_2 - \frac{4}{3}x_3 = \frac{4}{3} \\ \quad\;\;\;\;\;\; \frac{7}{3}x_3 = -\frac{10}{3} \end{cases}$$

$$F = \begin{bmatrix} 1 & 0 & \frac{1}{3} & | & \frac{5}{3} \\ 0 & 1 & -\frac{4}{3} & | & \frac{4}{3} \\ 0 & 0 & \frac{7}{3} & | & -\frac{10}{3} \end{bmatrix}$$

Multiply equation three by $\frac{3}{7}$.

Multiply row three by $\frac{3}{7}$.

(G)
$$\begin{cases} x_1 \quad\;\;\; + \frac{1}{3}x_3 = \frac{5}{3} \\ \quad\;\; x_2 - \frac{4}{3}x_3 = \frac{4}{3} \\ \quad\;\;\;\;\;\; x_3 = -\frac{10}{7} \end{cases}$$

$$G = \begin{bmatrix} 1 & 0 & \frac{1}{3} & | & \frac{5}{3} \\ 0 & 1 & -\frac{4}{3} & | & \frac{4}{3} \\ 0 & 0 & 1 & | & -\frac{10}{7} \end{bmatrix}$$

Now replace equation one with the sum of $-\frac{1}{3}$ times equation three and equation one.

Now replace row one with the sum of $-\frac{1}{3}$ times row three and row one.

(H)
$$\begin{cases} x_1 \quad\quad\quad\;\;\; = \frac{15}{7} \\ \quad\;\; x_2 - \frac{4}{3}x_3 = \frac{4}{3} \\ \quad\;\;\;\;\;\; x_3 = -\frac{10}{7} \end{cases}$$

$$H = \begin{bmatrix} 1 & 0 & 0 & | & \frac{15}{7} \\ 0 & 1 & -\frac{4}{3} & | & \frac{4}{3} \\ 0 & 0 & 1 & | & -\frac{10}{7} \end{bmatrix}$$

<table>
<tr>
<td>

Finally, replace equation two with the sum of $\frac{4}{3}$ times equation three and equation two.

</td>
<td>

Finally, replace row two with the sum of $\frac{4}{3}$ times row three and row two.

</td>
</tr>
</table>

(I) $\quad \begin{cases} x_1 & = & \frac{15}{7} \\ x_2 & = & -\frac{4}{7} \\ x_3 & = & -\frac{10}{7} \end{cases} \qquad\qquad I = \begin{bmatrix} 1 & 0 & 0 & \vdots & \frac{15}{7} \\ 0 & 1 & 0 & \vdots & -\frac{4}{7} \\ 0 & 0 & 1 & \vdots & -\frac{10}{7} \end{bmatrix}$

<table>
<tr>
<td>

Hence, the solution is $\{(\frac{15}{7}, -\frac{4}{7}, -\frac{10}{7})\}$.

</td>
<td>

Hence, the solution set can be read from the augmented column as $\{(\frac{15}{7}, -\frac{4}{7}, -\frac{10}{7})\}$.

</td>
</tr>
</table>

Notice that in solving the system of linear equations (A), the system was replaced by an augmented matrix A whose elements are the coefficients and constants occurring in the equations. Notice also that we can work with the augmented matrix instead of the actual equations by performing the following operations on the augmented matrix (compare with equation operations (1) through (3) on page 144):

1′ Interchange two rows of the matrix $(R_i \leftrightarrow R_j)$.

2′ Multiply the elements in a row of the matrix by a nonzero number $(R_i \rightarrow kR_i, k \neq 0)$.

3′ Replace a row with the sum of a nonzero multiple of itself and a multiple of another row $(R_i \rightarrow kR_j + cR_i, c \neq 0)$.

The operations (1′), (2′), and (3′) are called the *elementary row operations*. The resulting matrix I in the above example is called a row-reduced echelon matrix. In general, a matrix is a *row-reduced echelon* matrix if all of the following conditions hold:

i The first nonzero entry in each row is 1; all other entries in that column are zeros.

ii Each row that consists entirely of zeros is below each row which contains a nonzero entry.

iii The first nonzero entry in each row is to the right of the first nonzero entry in the preceding row.

EXAMPLES

Solve the linear system (A) by performing the elementary row operations if the system has a unique solution for each of the following situations.

1 (A) $\begin{cases} 4x + y = 2 \\ x + 4y = 1 \end{cases}$

SOLUTION.   The matrix form of the system is

$$\left[\begin{array}{cc|c} 4 & 1 & 2 \\ 1 & 4 & 1 \end{array}\right]$$

First, multiply row one by $\frac{1}{4}$ $(R_1 \to \frac{1}{4}R_1)$ to get

$$\left[\begin{array}{cc|c} 1 & \frac{1}{4} & \frac{1}{2} \\ 1 & 4 & 1 \end{array}\right]$$

Next, replace row two with the sum of row two and -1 times row one $(R_2 \to R_2 + (-1)R_1)$ to get

$$\left[\begin{array}{cc|c} 1 & \frac{1}{4} & \frac{1}{2} \\ 0 & \frac{15}{4} & \frac{1}{2} \end{array}\right]$$

Multiply row two by $\frac{4}{15}$ $(R_2 \to \frac{4}{15}R_2)$ to get

$$\left[\begin{array}{cc|c} 1 & \frac{1}{4} & \frac{1}{2} \\ 0 & 1 & \frac{2}{15} \end{array}\right]$$

Finally, replace row one with the sum of row one and $-\frac{1}{4}$ times row two $(R_1 \to R_1 + (-\frac{1}{4})R_2)$ to get

$$\left[\begin{array}{cc|c} 1 & 0 & \frac{7}{15} \\ 0 & 1 & \frac{2}{15} \end{array}\right]$$

Hence, the solution set is $\{(\frac{7}{15}, \frac{2}{15})\}$.

2 (A) $\begin{cases} x_1 + 2x_2 - 3x_3 = 6 \\ 2x_1 - x_2 + 4x_3 = 2 \\ 4x_1 + 3x_2 - 2x_3 = 14 \end{cases}$

SOLUTION.   The matrix form of the system is

$$\left[\begin{array}{ccc|c} 1 & 2 & -3 & 6 \\ 2 & -1 & 4 & 2 \\ 4 & 3 & -2 & 14 \end{array}\right]$$

First, replace the second row by the sum of -2 times the first row and the second row $(R_2 \to -2R_1 + R_2)$ to obtain the equivalent matrix

$$\left[\begin{array}{ccc|c} 1 & 2 & -3 & 6 \\ 0 & -5 & 10 & -10 \\ 4 & 3 & -2 & 14 \end{array}\right]$$

Next, replace the third row by the sum of -4 times the first row and the third row $(R_3 \rightarrow -4R_1 + R_3)$ to obtain

$$\begin{bmatrix} 1 & 2 & 3 & \vdots & 6 \\ 0 & -5 & 10 & \vdots & -10 \\ 0 & -5 & 10 & \vdots & -10 \end{bmatrix}$$

Since the second row R_2 and the third row R_3 are identical, the corresponding linear system will have two identical equations

$$-5x_2 + 10x_3 = -10$$

In this case, we say that the system is a dependent system, and the system does not have a unique solution.

$$3 \quad (A) \quad \begin{cases} 3x_1 - x_2 + x_3 = 1 \\ 7x_1 + x_2 - x_3 = 6 \\ 2x_1 + x_2 - x_3 = 2 \end{cases}$$

SOLUTION.   The augmented matrix that corresponds to the linear system is given by

$$\begin{bmatrix} 3 & -1 & 1 & \vdots & 1 \\ 7 & 1 & -1 & \vdots & 6 \\ 2 & 1 & -1 & \vdots & 2 \end{bmatrix}$$

which can be reduced by the following row operations.

$$\begin{bmatrix} 3 & -1 & 1 & \vdots & 1 \\ 7 & 1 & -1 & \vdots & 6 \\ 2 & 1 & -1 & \vdots & 2 \end{bmatrix} \xrightarrow[R_3 \rightarrow R_1 + R_3]{} \begin{bmatrix} 3 & -1 & 1 & \vdots & 1 \\ 7 & 1 & -1 & \vdots & 6 \\ 5 & 0 & 0 & \vdots & 3 \end{bmatrix}$$

$$\xrightarrow[R_2 \rightarrow R_1 + R_2]{} \begin{bmatrix} 3 & -1 & 1 & \vdots & 1 \\ 10 & 0 & 0 & \vdots & 7 \\ 5 & 0 & 0 & \vdots & 3 \end{bmatrix}$$

$$\xrightarrow[R_2 \rightarrow R_2 + (-2)R_3]{} \begin{bmatrix} 3 & -1 & 1 & \vdots & 1 \\ 0 & 0 & 0 & \vdots & 1 \\ 5 & 0 & 0 & \vdots & 3 \end{bmatrix}$$

But R_2 implies that $0 \cdot x_1 + 0 \cdot x_2 + 0 \cdot x_3 = 1$, that is, $0 = 1$, which, of course, is not possible. Hence the system has no solution, and we say that the system is inconsistent.

In summary, the procedure for solving a linear system is to form the augmented matrix and proceed to reduce it to echelon form:

1   If a resulting augmented echelon matrix has no row with its first
    nonzero entry in the last column, then the system has one (unique)
    or more solutions (dependent).

2   If a resulting augmented echelon matrix has a row with its first
    nonzero entry appearing in the last column, then the system has no
    solution, and the system is said to be inconsistent.

PROBLEM SET 2

1   Solve each of the following systems of linear equations using the elimi-
    nation method and show the corresponding matrix form of the
    system. Also, sketch each system on the same coordinate system.

a) $3x + y = 14$
    $2x - y = 1$

b) $4x + 3y = 15$
    $3x + 5y = 14$

c) $-2x + 3y = 8$
    $2x - y = 5$

d) $x - 2y = 5$
    $3x - 6y = 4$

e) $x/2 + y/6 = \frac{2}{3}$
    $3x + y = 4$

f) $x - 2y - 4 = 0$
    $x + y + 3 = 0$

2   Solve the following systems of linear equations by using the elimination
    method. In each step of the process, show the corresponding matrix
    form of the system.

a) $x + y + z = 6$
    $3x - y + 2z = 7$
    $2x + 3y - z = 5$

b) $2x + 3y + z = 6$
    $x - 2y + 3z = -3$
    $3x + y - z = 8$

c) $x + y + 2z = 4$
    $x + y - 2z = 0$
    $x - y = 0$

d) $x + y + z = 4$
    $x - y + 2z = 8$
    $2x + y - z = 3$

e) $2x + y - z = 7$
    $y - x = 1$
    $z - y = 1$

f) $3x + 2y + 2z = 6$
    $x - 5y + 6z = 2$
    $6x - 8z = 12$

3   Suppose that

$$A = \begin{bmatrix} -4 & 0 & 1 \\ 2 & 3 & -1 \\ 5 & 2 & 8 \end{bmatrix}$$

a) What is the size of matrix A?
b) Use subscript notation to identify each of the entries of matrix A.

4   Indicate which of the following augmented matrices are in row-reduced
    echelon form. Assuming that the matrix represents a linear system, what
    can be concluded about the solution of the system?

a) $\begin{bmatrix} 1 & 0 & 1 & | & 3 \\ 0 & 1 & 0 & | & 4 \\ 0 & 0 & 0 & | & 0 \end{bmatrix}$
b) $\begin{bmatrix} 1 & 1 & 0 & | & 0 \\ 0 & 1 & 0 & | & 0 \\ 0 & 0 & 1 & | & 2 \end{bmatrix}$

c) $\begin{bmatrix} 1 & 0 & 0 & | & 3 \\ 0 & 0 & 1 & | & 0 \\ 0 & 0 & 0 & | & 5 \end{bmatrix}$
d) $\begin{bmatrix} 1 & 1 & | & 2 \\ 0 & 0 & | & 3 \end{bmatrix}$

e) $\begin{bmatrix} 1 & 0 & | & 1 \\ 0 & 1 & | & 1 \end{bmatrix}$
f) $\begin{bmatrix} 1 & 0 & 0 & 0 & | & 3 \\ 0 & 1 & 0 & 0 & | & -2 \\ 1 & 0 & 0 & 1 & | & 1 \\ 0 & 0 & 1 & 0 & | & 5 \end{bmatrix}$

g) $\begin{bmatrix} 0 & 1 & | & -3 \\ 1 & 0 & | & 4 \end{bmatrix}$

5 For each of the following systems find the augmented matrix, reduce it to a row-reduced echelon matrix, and determine the solution if it is unique. If the solution is not unique, indicate whether the system is dependent or inconsistent.

a) $\begin{aligned} x - 2y + z &= -1 \\ 3x + y - 2z &= 4 \\ y - z &= 1 \end{aligned}$
b) $\begin{aligned} x + y - 2z &= 3 \\ 3x - y + z &= 5 \\ 3x + 3y - 6z &= 9 \end{aligned}$

c) $\begin{aligned} 2x + y + z &= 1 \\ 4x + 2y + 3z &= 1 \\ -2x - y + z &= 2 \end{aligned}$
d) $\begin{aligned} x + y + z &= 0 \\ 2x - y - 4z &= 15 \\ x - 2y - z &= 7 \end{aligned}$

e) $\begin{aligned} 2x - 3y + z &= 4 \\ x - 4y - z &= 3 \\ x - 9y - 4z &= 5 \end{aligned}$
f) $\begin{aligned} 2x + 3y - z &= -2 \\ x - y + 2z &= 4 \end{aligned}$

4 Determinants

The study of linear functions has led us into an investigation of solving systems of linear equations. Before returning to the main topic of this chapter — the study of polynomial functions — we will study a function called the determinant, which can be used to solve linear systems that have unique solutions. The determinant is a function which associates with each square matrix a real number.

The determinant is quite difficult for the beginning student to understand if it is presented in the precise, formal way that is usually reserved for an advanced presentation of linear algebra. Since it is so difficult to digest the general definition, we will restrict our attention to the manipulative properties of the determinant and its application to solving linear systems.

The *determinant* is a function which has the *set of square matrices as its domain* and the *set of real numbers as its range*. If A is a square matrix, the determinant of A is denoted by det A or $|A|$.

The determinant of the 2×2 matrix

$$\begin{bmatrix} a_{11} & a_{12} \\ a_{21} & a_{22} \end{bmatrix}$$

is defined to be the number $a_{11}a_{22} - a_{21}a_{12}$, and we write

$$\det \begin{bmatrix} a_{11} & a_{12} \\ a_{21} & a_{22} \end{bmatrix} = a_{11}a_{22} - a_{21}a_{12}$$

Thus,

$$\det \begin{bmatrix} 5 & 3 \\ -3 & -6 \end{bmatrix} = 5(-6) - (-3)(3) = -30 + 9 = -21$$

The determinant of the 3×3 matrix

$$\begin{bmatrix} a_{11} & a_{12} & a_{13} \\ a_{21} & a_{22} & a_{23} \\ a_{31} & a_{32} & a_{33} \end{bmatrix}$$

is defined as follows:

$$\det \begin{bmatrix} a_{11} & a_{12} & a_{13} \\ a_{21} & a_{22} & a_{23} \\ a_{31} & a_{32} & a_{33} \end{bmatrix}$$

$$= a_{11} \det \begin{bmatrix} a_{22} & a_{23} \\ a_{32} & a_{33} \end{bmatrix} - a_{12} \det \begin{bmatrix} a_{21} & a_{23} \\ a_{31} & a_{33} \end{bmatrix} + a_{13} \det \begin{bmatrix} a_{21} & a_{22} \\ a_{31} & a_{32} \end{bmatrix}$$

$$= a_{11}(a_{22}a_{33} - a_{32}a_{23}) - a_{12}(a_{21}a_{33} - a_{31}a_{23}) + a_{13}(a_{21}a_{32} - a_{31}a_{22})$$

For example,

$$\det \begin{bmatrix} 3 & 2 & 7 \\ -1 & 5 & 3 \\ 2 & -3 & -6 \end{bmatrix}$$

$$= 3 \det \begin{bmatrix} 5 & 3 \\ -3 & -6 \end{bmatrix} - 2 \det \begin{bmatrix} -1 & 3 \\ 2 & -6 \end{bmatrix} + 7 \det \begin{bmatrix} -1 & 5 \\ 2 & -3 \end{bmatrix}$$

$$= 3(-30 + 9) - 2(6 - 6) + 7(3 - 10)$$

$$= 3(-21) - 2(0) + 7(-7)$$

$$= -63 - 49 = -112$$

(Although this function can be generalized to any square matrix, we will restrict ourselves here to 2 × 2 and 3 × 3 matrices only.)

4.1   Properties of Determinants

The determinant possesses properties that can be used to simplify the task of its evaluation. Although we will be restricting the investigation of these properties to 2 × 2 and 3 × 3 matrices, it is important to realize that the properties hold for evaluating the determinant of *any* square matrix.

THEOREM 1

A common factor which appears in all entries in some one row of a determinant can be factored out of the determinant.

For example,

$$\begin{vmatrix} 6 & 9 \\ 1 & 4 \end{vmatrix} = 3 \begin{vmatrix} 2 & 3 \\ 1 & 4 \end{vmatrix}$$

and

$$\begin{vmatrix} 15 & 45 & 60 \\ 1 & 2 & -1 \\ 2 & 4 & 8 \end{vmatrix} = 15 \begin{vmatrix} 1 & 3 & 4 \\ 1 & 2 & -1 \\ 2 & 4 & 8 \end{vmatrix}$$

$$= (15)(2) \begin{vmatrix} 1 & 3 & 4 \\ 1 & 2 & -1 \\ 1 & 2 & 4 \end{vmatrix}$$

PROOF.   (For $n = 2$.)

$$\begin{vmatrix} a_{11} & a_{12} \\ a_{21} & a_{22} \end{vmatrix} = a_{11}a_{22} - a_{21}a_{12}$$

Hence,

$$\begin{vmatrix} ka_{11} & ka_{12} \\ a_{21} & a_{22} \end{vmatrix} = ka_{11}a_{22} - ka_{21}a_{12}$$

$$= k(a_{11}a_{22} - a_{21}a_{12})$$

$$= k \begin{vmatrix} a_{11} & a_{12} \\ a_{21} & a_{22} \end{vmatrix}$$

THEOREM 2

If two (not necessarily adjacent) rows of a square matrix are interchanged, the values of the determinants of the two matrices differ only in the algebraic sign.

For example,

$$\begin{vmatrix} 2 & 3 \\ 4 & 1 \end{vmatrix} = -10$$

whereas

$$\begin{vmatrix} 4 & 1 \\ 2 & 3 \end{vmatrix} = 10$$

and

$$\begin{vmatrix} 1 & -1 & 0 \\ 3 & 0 & 4 \\ 2 & 1 & 5 \end{vmatrix} = 3 \qquad \text{(Why?)}$$

whereas

$$\begin{vmatrix} 2 & 1 & 5 \\ 3 & 0 & 4 \\ 1 & -1 & 0 \end{vmatrix} = -3 \qquad \text{(Why?)}$$

PROOF.   (For $n = 2$.)

$$\begin{vmatrix} a_{11} & a_{12} \\ a_{21} & a_{22} \end{vmatrix} = a_{11}a_{22} - a_{21}a_{12}$$

$$= -(a_{21}a_{12} - a_{11}a_{22})$$

$$= -\begin{vmatrix} a_{21} & a_{22} \\ a_{11} & a_{12} \end{vmatrix}$$

THEOREM 3

If any nonzero multiple of one row is added to any other row of a square matrix, the value of the determinant is unaltered.

For example, consider

$$\begin{vmatrix} 1 & 0 & 2 \\ 4 & 6 & 1 \\ -1 & 0 & -1 \end{vmatrix}$$

If we multiply the third row by 2 and add the result to the first row, we get

$$\begin{vmatrix} -1 & 0 & 0 \\ 4 & 6 & 1 \\ -1 & 0 & -1 \end{vmatrix}$$

and we are assured by the theorem that the latter determinant has the same value as the original. Note that this operation effects only the first row, whereas the other two rows remain the same. But we need not stop here; indeed, we can add the third row to the second row in the latter determinant to obtain

$$\begin{vmatrix} -1 & 0 & 0 \\ 3 & 6 & 0 \\ -1 & 0 & -1 \end{vmatrix}$$

Again, this does not change the value of the determinant. Determinants such as the last one, which contain many zero entries, are relatively easy to evaluate; hence, the above theorem simplifies the task of calculating determinants.

For the proof of this theorem see Problem 4a.

EXAMPLES

Use the three theorems above to evaluate each of the following determinants.

1
$$\begin{vmatrix} 1 & 0 & 2 \\ 4 & 6 & 1 \\ -1 & 0 & -1 \end{vmatrix}$$

SOLUTION

$$\begin{vmatrix} 1 & 0 & 2 \\ 4 & 6 & 1 \\ -1 & 0 & -1 \end{vmatrix} = \begin{vmatrix} -1 & 0 & 0 \\ 4 & 6 & 1 \\ -1 & 0 & -1 \end{vmatrix}$$
(Theorem 3)
$(R_1 \rightarrow R_1 + 2R_3)$

$$= \begin{vmatrix} -1 & 0 & 0 \\ 3 & 6 & 0 \\ -1 & 0 & -1 \end{vmatrix}$$
(Theorem 3)
$(R_2 \rightarrow R_2 + R_3)$

$$= \begin{vmatrix} -1 & 0 & 0 \\ 3 & 6 & 0 \\ 0 & 0 & -1 \end{vmatrix}$$
(Theorem 3)
$(R_3 \rightarrow R_3 + (-1)R_1)$

$$= 3 \begin{vmatrix} -1 & 0 & 0 \\ 1 & 2 & 0 \\ 0 & 0 & -1 \end{vmatrix}$$
(Theorem 1)

$$= (3)(-1) \begin{vmatrix} 1 & 0 & 0 \\ 1 & 2 & 0 \\ 0 & 0 & -1 \end{vmatrix}$$
(Theorem 1)

$$= (3)(-1)(-1) \begin{vmatrix} 1 & 0 & 0 \\ 1 & 2 & 0 \\ 0 & 0 & 1 \end{vmatrix}$$
(Theorem 1)

$$= 3 \begin{vmatrix} 1 & 0 & 0 \\ 0 & 2 & 0 \\ 0 & 0 & 1 \end{vmatrix}$$
(Theorem 3)
$(R_2 \rightarrow R_2 + (-1)R_1)$

$$= (3)(2) \begin{vmatrix} 1 & 0 & 0 \\ 0 & 1 & 0 \\ 0 & 0 & 1 \end{vmatrix}$$
(Theorem 1)

$$= 6 \cdot 1$$
(Why?)

2
$$\begin{vmatrix} 3 & 1 & -1 \\ 0 & 2 & 4 \\ -1 & 4 & 2 \end{vmatrix}$$

SOLUTION

$$\begin{vmatrix} 3 & 1 & -1 \\ 0 & 2 & 4 \\ -1 & 4 & 2 \end{vmatrix} = 2 \begin{vmatrix} 3 & 1 & -1 \\ 0 & 1 & 2 \\ -1 & 4 & 2 \end{vmatrix} \qquad \text{(Theorem 1)}$$

$$= 2 \begin{vmatrix} 0 & 13 & 5 \\ 0 & 1 & 2 \\ -1 & 4 & 2 \end{vmatrix} \qquad \begin{array}{l} \text{(Theorem 3)} \\ (R_1 \rightarrow R_1 + 3R_3) \end{array}$$

$$= 2 \begin{vmatrix} 0 & 13 & 5 \\ 0 & 1 & 2 \\ -1 & 3 & 0 \end{vmatrix} \qquad \begin{array}{l} \text{(Theorem 3)} \\ (R_3 \rightarrow R_3 + (-1)R_2) \end{array}$$

$$= (2)(-1) \begin{vmatrix} 0 & 13 & 5 \\ 0 & 1 & 2 \\ 1 & -3 & 0 \end{vmatrix} \qquad \text{(Theorem 1)}$$

$$= (2)(-1)(-1) \begin{vmatrix} 1 & -3 & 0 \\ 0 & 1 & 2 \\ 0 & 13 & 5 \end{vmatrix} \qquad \text{(Theorem 2)}$$

$$= 2 \begin{vmatrix} 1 & -3 & 0 \\ 0 & 1 & 2 \\ 0 & 0 & -21 \end{vmatrix} \qquad \begin{array}{l} \text{(Theorem 3)} \\ (R_3 \rightarrow R_3 + (-13)R_2) \end{array}$$

$$= (2)(-21) \begin{vmatrix} 1 & -3 & 0 \\ 0 & 1 & 2 \\ 0 & 0 & 1 \end{vmatrix} \qquad \text{(Theorem 1)}$$

$$= (-42) \left(1 \begin{vmatrix} 1 & 2 \\ 0 & 1 \end{vmatrix} + 3 \begin{vmatrix} 0 & 2 \\ 0 & 1 \end{vmatrix} + 0 \begin{vmatrix} 0 & 1 \\ 0 & 0 \end{vmatrix} \right)$$

$$= -42$$

4.2 Cramer's Rule

We have seen what the determinant function is, and we have investigated methods for computing determinants. *Cramer's rule* provides us with a technique for using determinants to solve systems of linear equations. Although Cramer's rule is not the most practical way to solve linear systems, we will investigate the rule as an example of an application of determinants.

Before stating Cramer's rule, let us establish some useful notation. Suppose we are given a linear system (S) containing the same number of equations as unknowns.

$$(S) \quad \begin{cases} a_{11}x_1 + a_{12}x_2 + \cdots + a_{1n}x_n = c_1 \\ a_{21}x_1 + a_{22}x_2 + \cdots + a_{2n}x_n = c_2 \\ \cdots \cdots \cdots \cdots \cdots \cdots \cdots \cdots \cdots \cdots \\ a_{n1}x_1 + a_{n2}x_2 + \cdots + a_{nn}x_n = c_n \end{cases}$$

The determinant of the matrix of coefficients occurring in the system is called the *determinant of the coefficient matrix* and will be denoted by D. Hence,

$$D = \begin{vmatrix} a_{11} & a_{12} & \cdots & a_{1n} \\ a_{21} & a_{22} & \cdots & a_{2n} \\ \cdots\cdots\cdots\cdots\cdots \\ a_{n1} & a_{n2} & \cdots & a_{nn} \end{vmatrix}$$

D_j will be used to denote the determinant of the matrix obtained by replacing the jth column in D by the column of constant terms in the system, so that

$$\downarrow j\text{th column}$$

$$D_j = \begin{vmatrix} a_{11} & a_{12} & \cdots & c_1 & \cdots & a_{1n} \\ a_{21} & a_{22} & \cdots & c_2 & \cdots & a_{2n} \\ \cdots\cdots\cdots\cdots\cdots\cdots\cdots\cdots \\ a_{n1} & a_{n2} & \cdots & c_n & \cdots & a_{nn} \end{vmatrix}$$

For example, for

$$\begin{cases} 2x + 3y = 1 \\ x - y = 2 \end{cases}$$

$$D = \begin{vmatrix} 2 & 3 \\ 1 & -1 \end{vmatrix} = -5$$

$$D_1 = \begin{vmatrix} 1 & 3 \\ 2 & -1 \end{vmatrix} = -7$$

and

$$D_2 = \begin{vmatrix} 2 & 1 \\ 1 & 2 \end{vmatrix} = 3$$

and for

$$\begin{cases} 3x - y + 3z = 1 \\ x + y = 4 \\ -5x + 7y - 2z = -2 \end{cases}$$

$$D = \begin{vmatrix} 3 & -1 & 3 \\ 1 & 1 & 0 \\ -5 & 7 & -2 \end{vmatrix} = 28$$

$$D_1 = \begin{vmatrix} 1 & -1 & 3 \\ 4 & 1 & 0 \\ -2 & 7 & -2 \end{vmatrix} = 80$$

$$D_2 = \begin{vmatrix} 3 & 1 & 3 \\ 1 & 4 & 0 \\ -5 & -2 & -2 \end{vmatrix} = 32$$

and

$$D_3 = \begin{vmatrix} 3 & -1 & 1 \\ 1 & 1 & 4 \\ -5 & 7 & -2 \end{vmatrix} = -60$$

THEOREM 1 (CRAMER'S RULE)

Let (S) be the system of n linear equations in n unknowns described in Section 4.2. Let D be the determinant of the coefficient matrix of (S). If $D \neq 0$, then the system (S) has exactly one solution, namely:

$$x_j = \frac{D_j}{D}, \quad j = 1, 2, \ldots, n$$

where D_j is the determinant defined in Section 4.2.

The proof of Cramer's rule is beyond the scope of this text. However, we will consider its application for cases in which $n = 2$ or 3.

For $n = 2$, Cramer's rule indicates that the solution of

$$\begin{cases} a_{11}x_1 + a_{12}x_2 = c_1 \\ a_{21}x_1 + a_{22}x_2 = c_2 \end{cases}$$

is given by

$$x_1 = \frac{\begin{vmatrix} c_1 & a_{12} \\ c_2 & a_{22} \end{vmatrix}}{\begin{vmatrix} a_{11} & a_{12} \\ a_{21} & a_{22} \end{vmatrix}} \quad \text{and} \quad x_2 = \frac{\begin{vmatrix} a_{11} & c_1 \\ a_{21} & c_2 \end{vmatrix}}{\begin{vmatrix} a_{11} & a_{12} \\ a_{21} & a_{22} \end{vmatrix}}$$

if

$$\begin{vmatrix} a_{11} & a_{12} \\ a_{21} & a_{22} \end{vmatrix} \neq 0$$

For $n = 3$, Cramer's rule can be applied to

$$\begin{cases} a_{11}x_1 + a_{12}x_2 + a_{13}x_3 = c_1 \\ a_{21}x_1 + a_{22}x_2 + a_{23}x_3 = c_2 \\ a_{31}x_1 + a_{32}x_2 + a_{33}x_3 = c_3 \end{cases}$$

as follows.

First, we determine

$$D = \begin{vmatrix} a_{11} & a_{12} & a_{13} \\ a_{21} & a_{22} & a_{23} \\ a_{31} & a_{32} & a_{33} \end{vmatrix} \qquad D_1 = \begin{vmatrix} c_1 & a_{12} & a_{13} \\ c_2 & a_{22} & a_{23} \\ c_3 & a_{32} & a_{33} \end{vmatrix}$$

$$D_2 = \begin{vmatrix} a_{11} & c_1 & a_{13} \\ a_{21} & c_2 & a_{23} \\ a_{31} & c_3 & a_{33} \end{vmatrix} \quad \text{and} \quad D_3 = \begin{vmatrix} a_{11} & a_{12} & c_1 \\ a_{21} & a_{22} & c_2 \\ a_{31} & a_{32} & c_3 \end{vmatrix}$$

If $D \neq 0$, then $x_1 = D_1/D$, $x_2 = D_2/D$, and $x_3 = D_3/D$.

Notice that Cramer's rule has nothing to say about the existence of solutions in the case in which $D = 0$. Actually, if $D = 0$, either (1) the system has no solution (inconsistent) or (2) the system has an infinite number of different solutions (dependent).

EXAMPLES

Use Cramer's rule to solve each of the following linear systems if possible.

1 $\begin{cases} 3x + 4y = 12 \\ 3x - 8y = 0 \end{cases}$

SOLUTION. Here,

$$D = \begin{vmatrix} 3 & 4 \\ 3 & -8 \end{vmatrix} = -24 - 12 = -36$$

$$D_1 = \begin{vmatrix} 12 & 4 \\ 0 & -8 \end{vmatrix} = -96 \quad \text{and} \quad D_2 = \begin{vmatrix} 3 & 12 \\ 3 & 0 \end{vmatrix} = -36$$

Since $D \neq 0$, this system has one solution $\{(\frac{8}{3}, 1)\}$, since $x = D_1/D = [-96/-36] = \frac{8}{3}$ and $y = D_2/D = [-36/-36] = 1$ satisfy both equations simultaneously.

2 $\begin{cases} x + 2y = 4 \\ 3x + 6y = -3 \end{cases}$

SOLUTION. Here,

$$D = \begin{vmatrix} 1 & 2 \\ 3 & 6 \end{vmatrix} = 0$$

Since $D = 0$, Cramer's rule is not applicable. This situation is consistent with the geometry of the two lines (they are parallel).

3 $\begin{cases} x_1 + x_2 + x_3 = 2 \\ 2x_1 - x_2 + x_3 = 0 \\ x_1 + 2x_2 - x_3 = 4 \end{cases}$

SOLUTION. Here,

$$D = \begin{vmatrix} 1 & 1 & 1 \\ 2 & -1 & 1 \\ 1 & 2 & -1 \end{vmatrix} = 7 \quad D_1 = \begin{vmatrix} 2 & 1 & 1 \\ 0 & -1 & 1 \\ 4 & 2 & -1 \end{vmatrix} = 6$$

$$D_2 = \begin{vmatrix} 1 & 2 & 1 \\ 2 & 0 & 1 \\ 1 & 4 & -1 \end{vmatrix} = 10 \quad \text{and} \quad D_3 = \begin{vmatrix} 1 & 1 & 2 \\ 2 & -1 & 0 \\ 1 & 2 & 4 \end{vmatrix} = -2$$

Since $D \neq 0$, this system has exactly one solution $\{(\frac{6}{7}, \frac{10}{7}, -\frac{2}{7})\}$. That is, $x_1 = D_1/D = \frac{6}{7}$, $x_2 = D_2/D = \frac{10}{7}$, and $x_3 = D_3/D = -\frac{2}{7}$ satisfy the system.

PROBLEM SET 3

1 Evaluate each of the following determinants.

a) $\begin{vmatrix} -1 & 3 \\ -7 & 4 \end{vmatrix}$

b) $\begin{vmatrix} 2 & 3 \\ 9 & 4 \end{vmatrix}$

c) $\begin{vmatrix} 2 & -1 & 3 \\ 9 & -7 & 4 \\ 11 & -6 & 2 \end{vmatrix}$

d) $\begin{vmatrix} 3 & -1 & 2 \\ 0 & 1 & -5 \\ 6 & 7 & 4 \end{vmatrix}$

e) $\begin{vmatrix} 2 & 2 & 2 \\ 3 & 3 & 3 \\ 4 & 4 & 4 \end{vmatrix}$

f) $\begin{vmatrix} \frac{1}{2} & 4 & 7 \\ 1 & -1 & 2 \\ 3 & 2 & 5 \end{vmatrix}$

2 Solve the following determinants for x.

a) $\begin{vmatrix} x & -x \\ 5 & 3 \end{vmatrix} = 2$

b) $\begin{vmatrix} x & 4 & 5 \\ 0 & 1 & x \\ 5 & 2 & 1 \end{vmatrix} = 7$

c) $\begin{vmatrix} x & 0 & 0 \\ 3 & 1 & 2 \\ 0 & 4 & 1 \end{vmatrix} = 5$

d) $\begin{vmatrix} x & 0 & 1 \\ 2x & 1 & 2 \\ 3x & 2 & 3 \end{vmatrix} = 0$

3 Show why each of the following is true, not by evaluating each side but by citing the appropriate theorems of Section 4.1 that have been used.

a) $\begin{vmatrix} 4 & 5 \\ 3 & -2 \end{vmatrix} = -\begin{vmatrix} 3 & -2 \\ 4 & 5 \end{vmatrix}$

b) $\begin{vmatrix} 3 & 0 & 1 \\ 1 & 1 & 2 \\ 3 & 0 & 1 \end{vmatrix} = \begin{vmatrix} 0 & 0 & 0 \\ 1 & 1 & 2 \\ 3 & 0 & 1 \end{vmatrix}$

c) $\begin{vmatrix} 3 & -6 & 2 \\ 5 & -3 & 0 \\ 0 & 9 & 18 \end{vmatrix} = 9\begin{vmatrix} 3 & -6 & 2 \\ 5 & -3 & 0 \\ 0 & 1 & 2 \end{vmatrix}$

d) $\begin{vmatrix} 2 & 4 & 12 \\ -1 & 0 & 3 \\ 1 & 0 & 6 \end{vmatrix} = 18\begin{vmatrix} 1 & 2 & 6 \\ -1 & 0 & 3 \\ 0 & 0 & 1 \end{vmatrix}$

e) $\begin{vmatrix} 1 & 1 & 1 \\ 3 & 3 & 3 \\ 2 & 2 & 2 \end{vmatrix} = 6\begin{vmatrix} 0 & 0 & 0 \\ 0 & 0 & 0 \\ 1 & 1 & 1 \end{vmatrix}$

4 a) Prove Theorem 3 of Section 4.1 for $n = 2$. (*Hint:* Compare

$$\begin{vmatrix} a_{11} & a_{12} \\ a_{21} & a_{22} \end{vmatrix} \quad \text{with} \quad \begin{vmatrix} a_{11} + ca_{21} & a_{12} + ca_{22} \\ a_{21} & a_{22} \end{vmatrix}.)$$

b) Prove, for $n = 2$, that if two rows of a matrix are the same, then the determinant is zero.

c) Prove, for $n = 2$, that if all the entries in one row of a matrix are zeros, then the determinant is zero.

5 Use the theorems given in Section 4.1 to evaluate each of the following determinants.

a) $\begin{vmatrix} -1 & 0 & 2 \\ 0 & 0 & 0 \\ -1 & 5 & 1 \end{vmatrix}$ b) $\begin{vmatrix} 3 & 1 & 1 \\ -1 & 0 & 3 \\ 2 & 1 & 1 \end{vmatrix}$

c) $\begin{vmatrix} 2 & 1 & 3 \\ 1 & 2 & 1 \\ 4 & 0 & 0 \end{vmatrix}$ d) $\begin{vmatrix} 20 & 12 & 8 \\ 5 & 3 & 2 \\ 5 & 7 & 2 \end{vmatrix}$

e) $\begin{vmatrix} 1 & 0 & 2 \\ 1 & -3 & 0 \\ 0 & 3 & 1 \end{vmatrix}$

6 a) *Principle of duality.* Consider Theorems 1, 2, and 3 in Section 4.1. If we replace the word row with the word column, then the theorems are still valid. Rewrite the three theorems with this substitution.

b) Use the theorems of part (a) to evaluate the determinants in Problem 5.

7 Given the triangle of Figure 1, show that the area of the triangle is given by

$$\frac{1}{2} \begin{vmatrix} x_1 & y_1 & 1 \\ 0 & 0 & 1 \\ x_2 & 0 & 1 \end{vmatrix}$$

Figure 1

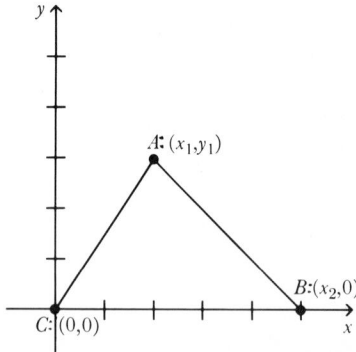

8 Use Cramer's rule to solve each of the following systems if possible.

a) $2x - y = 0$
    $x + y = 1$

b) $-3x + y = 3$
    $-2x - y = -5$

c) $x + y = 0$
    $x - y = 0$

d) $3x + y = 1$
    $9x + 3y = -4$

e) $\begin{aligned} 2x_1 - x_2 + x_3 &= 3 \\ -x_1 + 2x_2 - x_3 &= 1 \\ 3x_1 + x_2 + 2x_3 &= -1 \end{aligned}$

f) $\begin{aligned} 3x \qquad\quad + 2z &= 6 - 2y \\ x - 5y + 6z &= 2 \\ 6x \qquad\quad - 8z &= 12 \end{aligned}$

g) $\begin{aligned} x + y + 2z &= 4 \\ x + y - 2z &= 0 \\ x - y \qquad &= 0 \end{aligned}$

h) $\begin{aligned} 2x_1 - 3x_2 \qquad\quad &= 4 \\ x_1 + x_2 - 2x_3 &= 1 \\ x_1 - x_2 - x_3 &= 5 \end{aligned}$

i) $\begin{aligned} x + y + z &= 4 \\ x - y + 2z &= 8 \\ 2x + y - z &= 3 \end{aligned}$

j) $\begin{aligned} 2x + 3y + z &= 6 \\ x - 2y + 3z &= -3 \\ 3x + y - z &= 8 \end{aligned}$

9 For each of the following problems, set up a linear system which serves as a model of the situation. Then use determinants to solve the system.

a) A watch, chain, and ring together cost $225. The watch costs $50 more than the chain, and the ring costs $25 more than the watch and the chain together. What is the cost of each?

b) Twice the sum of two numbers is 30, and three times the smaller equals twice the larger. Determine the numbers.

5 Quadratic Functions

Let us return to the study of polynomial functions. A *quadratic function* is a polynomial function of degree 2. Hence, if $y = f(x)$ is a quadratic function, the standard form of f is given by $f(x) = ax^2 + bx + c$, where a, b, and c are real numbers, $a \neq 0$. A quadratic function can also be considered in set form as $\{(x,y) \mid y = ax^2 + bx + c, a \neq 0, a, b, c \in R\}$. In graphing any quadratic function, we will locate the x intercepts of f; that is, we will identify those values of x for which $f(x) = 0$. In order to determine the x intercepts, it is necessary to solve equations of the form $ax^2 + bx + c = 0$.

5.1 Quadratic Equations

An equation which can be expressed in the form $ax^2 + bx + c = 0$, where a, b, and c are real numbers, $a \neq 0$, is called a *quadratic equation in* x. For example, $3x^2 = 7x + 3$ and $7x^2 = 5$ are quadratic equations because the first can be expressed as $3x^2 + (-7)x + (-3) = 0$, and the second as $7x^2 + 0x + (-5) = 0$.

The *solution* or *solution set* of a quadratic equation is the set of all possible roots. For example, $\{-7,-1\}$ is the solution set for $x^2 + 8x + 7 = 0$ so that the graph of $f(x) = x^2 + 8x + 7$ intersects the x axis at points $(-7,0)$ and $(-1,0)$; the equation $x^2 + 4x + 4 = 0$ has only one root, -2, so that $f(x) = x^2 + 4x + 4$ intersects the x axis at the point $(-2,0)$. Since $x^2 + 1 = 0$ has no real roots, $f(x) = x^2 + 1$ does not intersect the x axis. Hence, in order to determine the x intercepts of quadratic functions, it is necessary to solve quadratic equations.

Quadratic equations can be solved by the following three methods.

1 FACTOR METHOD SOLUTION

We know from the algebra of real numbers that certain quadratic expressions can be represented in *factored form*, that is, as the product of two linear expressions containing real numbers. This factorization can be used to solve quadratic equations by applying the following rule:

$$\text{If } ab = 0 \qquad \text{then} \qquad a = 0 \text{ or } b = 0$$

For example, the equation $x^2 - 5x + 4 = 0$ may be solved in the following manner:

$$
\begin{aligned}
\{x|x^2 - 5x + 4 = 0\} &= \{x|(x - 4)(x - 1) = 0\} \\
&= \{x|x - 4 = 0 \text{ or } x - 1 = 0\} \\
&= \{x|x - 4 = 0\} \cup \{x|x - 1 = 0\} \\
&= \{1,4\}
\end{aligned}
$$

EXAMPLE

Solve $2x^2 - 5x + 2 = 0$ by the factor method.

SOLUTION

$$
\begin{aligned}
\{x|2x^2 - 5x + 2 = 0\} &= \{x|(2x - 1)(x - 2) = 0\} \\
&= \{x|2x - 1 = 0 \text{ or } x - 2 = 0\} \\
&= \{x|2x - 1 = 0\} \cup \{x|x - 2 = 0\} \\
&= \{\tfrac{1}{2}\} \cup \{2\} \\
&= \{\tfrac{1}{2},2\}
\end{aligned}
$$

2 COMPLETING THE SQUARE

Suppose that we are to solve a quadratic equation which is not readily factorable. Let us say, for example, that we are to solve $3x^2 - 2x - 2 = 0$. This quadratic equation can be solved by a process known as *completing the square*, which proceeds as follows.

First, "isolate" the x terms of

$$3x^2 - 2x - 2 = 0$$

to get

$$3x^2 - 2x = 2$$

Next, change the resulting equation to an equivalent equation which has 1 as the coefficient of the x^2 term to get

$$x^2 - \tfrac{2}{3}x = \tfrac{2}{3}$$

Finally, make the left-hand side a "perfect square" by adding the appropriate number. In order to form a perfect square on the left side, take one-half the coefficient of x, square it, and then add the result to both sides to get

$$x^2 - \tfrac{2}{3}x + (\tfrac{1}{3})^2 = \tfrac{2}{3} + (\tfrac{1}{3})^2$$
$$x^2 - \tfrac{2}{3}x + \tfrac{1}{9} = \tfrac{7}{9}$$

That is,

$$(x - \tfrac{1}{3})^2 = \tfrac{7}{9}$$

This implies, then, that

$$x - \tfrac{1}{3} = \sqrt{\tfrac{7}{9}} \quad \text{or} \quad x - \tfrac{1}{3} = -\sqrt{\tfrac{7}{9}}$$

Hence,

$$x = \frac{1}{3} + \frac{\sqrt{7}}{3} \quad \text{and} \quad x = \frac{1}{3} - \frac{\sqrt{7}}{3}$$

are the solutions of $3x^2 - 2x - 2 = 0$, and the solution set is $\{(1 + \sqrt{7})/3, (1 - \sqrt{7})/3\}$.

Instead of repeating the process of completing the square for each quadratic equation which is not easily factorable, we can generalize the method of completing the square to arrive at a formula which enables us to solve any quadratic equation.

3 THEOREM (QUADRATIC FORMULA)

If $ax^2 + bx + c = 0$, with a, b, and c real numbers, $a \neq 0$, then

$$x = \frac{-b \pm \sqrt{b^2 - 4ac}}{2a}$$

are the roots of the equation.

PROOF. (Follow the method of completing the square given above to understand this proof.)

$$ax^2 + bx + c = 0 \quad a \neq 0$$
$$ax^2 + bx = -c$$
$$x^2 + \frac{bx}{a} = \frac{-c}{a}$$
$$x^2 + \frac{bx}{a} + \left(\frac{b}{2a}\right)^2 = \frac{-c}{a} + \left(\frac{b}{2a}\right)^2$$
$$\left(x + \frac{b}{2a}\right)^2 = \frac{b^2}{4a^2} + \frac{-c}{a} = \frac{b^2 - 4ac}{4a^2}$$
$$\left|x + \frac{b}{2a}\right| = \sqrt{\frac{b^2 - 4ac}{4a^2}}$$

Hence,

$$x + \frac{b}{2a} = \sqrt{\frac{b^2 - 4ac}{4a^2}} \quad \text{or} \quad x + \frac{b}{2a} = -\sqrt{\frac{b^2 - 4ac}{4a^2}}$$

From this, we get

$$x = \frac{-b}{2a} + \frac{\sqrt{b^2 - 4ac}}{2a} \quad \text{or} \quad x = \frac{-b}{2a} - \frac{\sqrt{b^2 - 4ac}}{2a}$$

$x = (-b \pm \sqrt{b^2 - 4ac})/2a$ is usually used as an abbreviated way of writing these two possible roots.

The number $b^2 - 4ac$ is called the *discriminant*. The discriminant of a quadratic equation indicates the type of roots: If it is zero, there is only one real double root. (Why?) If it is positive, there are two real distinct roots. (Why?) If it is negative, there are no real roots. (Why?)

EXAMPLES

1   Solve $2x^2 - 8x + 3 = 0$ by the quadratic formula.

SOLUTION.   Here, $a = 2$, $b = -8$, and $c = 3$. Since the discriminant is 40, this equation has two distinct real roots. The solution set is

$$\begin{aligned}
\{x \mid 2x^2 - 8x + 3 = 0\} &= \left\{ x \mid x = \frac{-(-8) \pm \sqrt{40}}{4} \right\} \\
&= \left\{ x \mid x = \frac{8 \pm 2\sqrt{10}}{4} \right\} \\
&= \left\{ x \mid x = \frac{4 \pm \sqrt{10}}{2} \right\} \\
&= \left\{ 2 + \frac{\sqrt{10}}{2}, \, 2 - \frac{\sqrt{10}}{2} \right\}
\end{aligned}$$

2   Solve $3x^2 - 8x + 5 = 0$ by the quadratic formula.

SOLUTION. $a = 3$, $b = -8$, $c = 5$. The discriminant is 4, and so the solution consists of two roots. The solution set is

$$\left\{ x \mid x = \frac{8 \pm \sqrt{4}}{6} \right\} = \{1, \tfrac{5}{3}\}$$

5.2   Properties of Quadratic Functions

Let us use the methods of solving quadratic equations to examine the graphs of quadratic functions. Consider the function $f(x) = x^2 + x$. The domain of f is the set of real numbers R. Its range can be determined as follows. The equation $y = x^2 + x$ is equivalent to the equation

$x^2 + x - y = 0$. Using the quadratic formula with $a = 1$, $b = 1$, and $c = -y$,

$$x = \frac{-1 \pm \sqrt{1 + 4y}}{2}$$

This equation will have real solutions if the discriminant is nonnegative, that is, if $1 + 4y \geq 0$, or, equivalently, if $y \geq -\frac{1}{4}$. Thus the range of the function, that is, the set of values that y can assume, is $[-\frac{1}{4}, \infty)$. The x intercepts of f are those values of x which satisfy $f(x) = 0$, that is, $x = 0$ or $x = -1$. Hence, the graph of f crosses the x axis at $x = 0$ and $x = -1$ (Figure 1).

Now, let us rewrite the equation $y = x^2 + x$ in the form $y = x^2 + x + (\frac{1}{2})^2 - (\frac{1}{2})^2$, by completing the square, so that $y = (x + \frac{1}{2})^2 - \frac{1}{4}$. The smallest value of y occurs when $(x + \frac{1}{2})^2 = 0$, (Why?) that is, when $x = -\frac{1}{2}$. Since $f(-\frac{1}{2}) = -\frac{1}{4}$, the point $(-\frac{1}{2}, -\frac{1}{4})$ is the lowest (minimum) point on the graph of f, and the graph can only be in the shaded region of Figure 1.

Figure 1

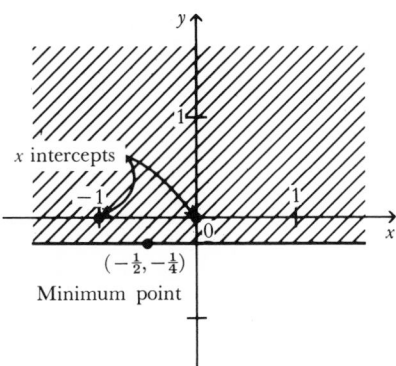

x intercepts

$(-\frac{1}{2}, -\frac{1}{4})$

Minimum point

In general, the domain of a quadratic function is the set of all real numbers. The range can be determined by generalizing the methods used in the above example.

Consider the quadratic function $y = ax^2 + bx + c$. The equation of this function is equivalent to $ax^2 + bx + (c - y) = 0$. By the quadratic formula

$$x = \frac{-b \pm \sqrt{b^2 - 4a(c - y)}}{2a}$$

Since x is a real number, the discriminant cannot be negative. That is, $b^2 - 4a(c - y) \geq 0$, so that $b^2 - 4ac + 4ay \geq 0$, or, equivalently,

$$ay \geq \frac{4ac - b^2}{4}$$

If $a > 0$, then

(1)
$$y \geq \frac{4ac - b^2}{4a} = c - \frac{b^2}{4a}$$

that is, y is always larger than or equal to $c - b^2/4a$.
   If $a < 0$, then

(2)
$$y \leq \frac{4ac - b^2}{4a} = c - \frac{b^2}{4a}$$

that is, y is always less than or equal to $c - b^2/4a$. In either case $c - b^2/4a$ is the "extreme" value of y.
   Now, if we substitute $x = -b/2a$ into the given quadratic function $y = ax^2 + bx + c$, we get $y = a(b^2/4a^2) + b(-b/2a) + c = c - b^2/4a$, which is the same as the right-hand expressions in both (1) and (2). Consequently, if $a > 0$, $f(-b/2a) = c - b^2/4a$ is the *minimum* value of y, the graph of f, a *parabola*, opens upward as in Figure 2a, and its range is $[f(-b/2a), \infty)$; if $a < 0$, $f(-b/2a)$ is the *maximum* value of y, the graph of f, a parabola, opens downward as in Figure 2b, and its range is $(-\infty, f(-b/2a)]$. In either case, the value of the function $f(x) = ax^2 + bx + c$ at $x = -b/2a$ gives the *extreme* value of $y = f(x)$. Thus the *extreme point* of the graph of a quadratic function $y = f(x)$ is $(-b/2a, f(-b/2a))$ (Figure 2).

Figure 2

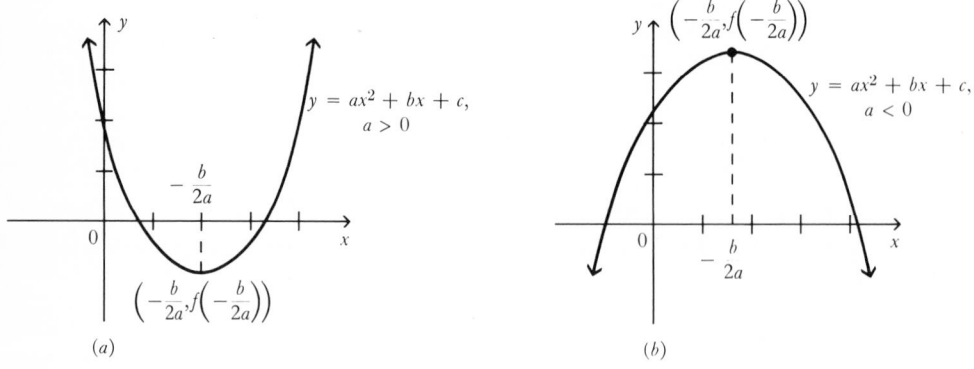

(a)   (b)

   Suppose that we take as abscissas values of x that are p units to the right of $-b/2a$ and p units to the left of $-b/2a$; that is, we take $x = (-b/2a) + p$ and $x = (-b/2a) - p$:

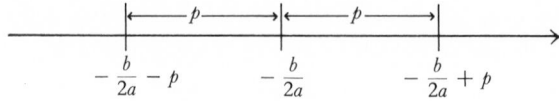

The corresponding ordinate for $x = -b/2a + p$ is given by

$$y = a\left(\frac{-b}{2a} + p\right)^2 + b\left(\frac{-b}{2a} + p\right) + c$$

$$= \frac{-b^2 + 4ac}{4a} + ap^2$$

The corresponding ordinate for $x = -b/2a - p$ is given by

$$y = a\left(\frac{-b}{2a} - p\right)^2 + b\left(\frac{-b}{2a} - p\right) + c$$

$$= \frac{-b^2 + 4ac}{4a} + ap^2$$

In other words, $f((-b/2a) + p) = f((-b/2a) - p)$ (Figure 3) for any $p > 0$, so that the graph of the quadratic function is symmetric with respect to the line $x = -b/2a$.

Figure 3

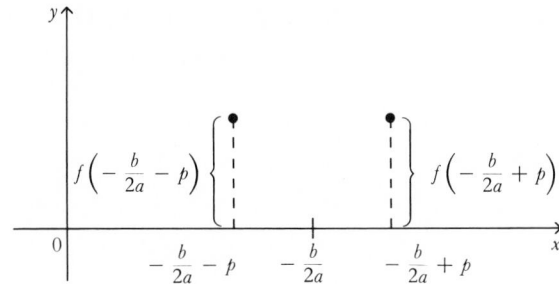

Finally, the y intercept can be determined by setting $x = 0$ so that $(0,c)$ is the y intercept of $f(x) = ax^2 + bx + c$. The x intercepts can be determined by letting $y = 0$ and solving the resulting quadratic equation.

EXAMPLES

1   For each of the following functions, determine the extreme point, the axis of symmetry, the x and y intercepts, and then graph it.

a) $f(x) = x^2 + x$ b) $f(x) = -2x^2 - x + 5$

SOLUTION

a)   We have seen above that $(-\frac{1}{2}, -\frac{1}{4})$ is the extreme point. Since $a > 0$, the graph will open upward, and the point $(-\frac{1}{2}, -\frac{1}{4})$ is a minimum point. The axis of symmetry is given by $x = -b/2a = -\frac{1}{2}$. $(0,0)$ is the y intercept and $0 = x^2 + x = x(x + 1)$ implies that $(-1,0)$ and $(0,0)$ are the x intercepts. Notice that the graph of $f(x) = x^2 + x$ suggests that f does not have an inverse (Figure 4).

Figure 4

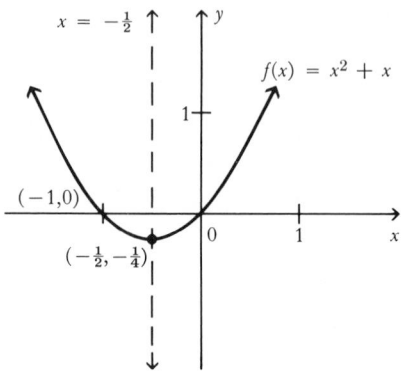

b) $a = -2$ and $b = -1$, so that $x = -b/2a = -\frac{1}{4}$ is the axis of symmetry. Since $a < 0$, $f(-\frac{1}{4}) = \frac{41}{8}$ yields the maximum point $(-\frac{1}{4},\frac{41}{8})$ and the graph will open downward. $(0,5)$ is the y intercept. Solving $0 = -2x^2 - x + 5$ yields $x = (1 \pm \sqrt{41})/-4$, the x intercepts (Figure 5).

Figure 5

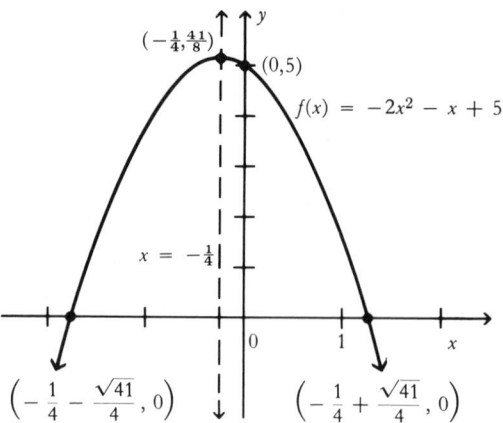

2   The path of a missile is parabolic, and it is represented by $P(t) = -t^2 + t + 1$, where t represents time. Determine the value of t at which the missile reaches its highest point, and the value of t at which the missile strikes the ground. Graph the path.

SOLUTION. $t = (-1/-2) = \frac{1}{2}$ gives the value of t at which the missile reaches its maximum height of $P(\frac{1}{2}) = \frac{5}{4}$. The missile strikes the ground when $P(t) = 0 = -t^2 + t + 1$. $P(t) = 0$ when $t = (-1 \pm \sqrt{5})/-2$. Since t represents time, $t \geq 0$, so that $t = (-1 - \sqrt{5})/-2 = (1 + \sqrt{5})/2$. The graph is given in Figure 6.

Figure 6

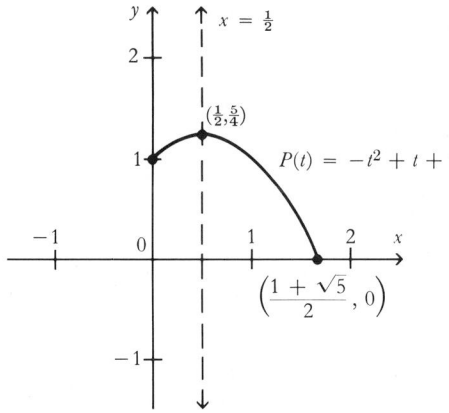

5.3   Quadratic Inequalities

Any quadratic inequality can be expressed either in the form $ax^2 + bx + c > 0$ or in the form $ax^2 + bx + c < 0$. For example, $x^2 < 2x - 2$ can be written as $x^2 - 2x + 2 < 0$, and $3 - x^2 < 2x$ can be written as $-x^2 - 2x + 3 < 0$.

The graphs of quadratic functions can be used to solve quadratic inequalities. For example, consider the graph of the quadratic function

Figure 7

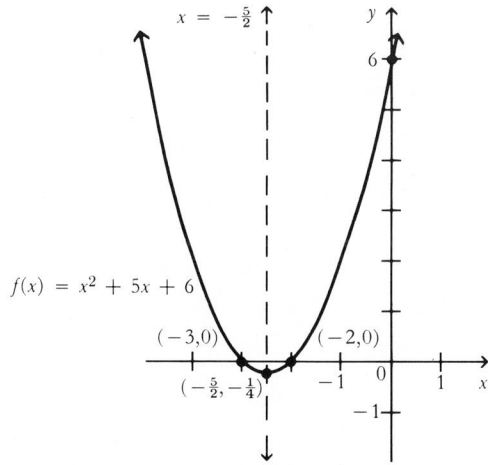

$y = f(x) = x^2 + 5x + 6$ as shown in Figure 7 (page 171). Observe that the graph of f intersects the x axis at the two points $(-3,0)$ and $(-2,0)$. Notice also that if $x < -3$ or if $x > -2$, then $f(x) > 0$; if $-3 < x < -2$, then $f(x) < 0$. Hence,

$$\{x \mid f(x) = x^2 + 5x + 6 > 0\} = \{x \mid x < -3\} \cup \{x \mid x > -2\}$$
$$= (-\infty, -3) \cup (-2, \infty)$$

and

$$\{x \mid f(x) = x^2 + 5x + 6 < 0\} = \{x \mid -3 < x < -2\} = (-3, -2)$$

EXAMPLES

1   Use the graph of $f(x) = 2x^2 + x - 6$ to find the values of x for which $2x^2 + x - 6 < 0$.

SOLUTION.   The inequality is satisfied by all values of x of the graph of f which have ordinates below the x axis, that is, by all x such that $f(x) < 0$. The x intercepts of the graph of $f(x) = 2x^2 + x - 6$ are -2 and $\frac{3}{2}$, and $\{x \mid 2x^2 + x - 6 < 0\} = \{x \mid -2 < x < \frac{3}{2}\} = (-2, \frac{3}{2})$ (Figure 8).

Figure 8

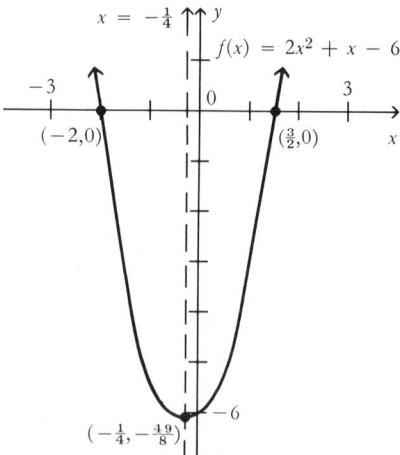

2   Use the graph of $f(x) = x^2 - 2x - 3$ to find the values of x for which $x^2 - 2x - 3 > 0$.

SOLUTION.   The graph of $f(x) = x^2 - 2x - 3$ is given in Figure 9. The inequality is satisfied by all values of x for which the graph of f lies above the x axis, that is, by all x such that $f(x) > 0$. Hence,

$$\{x|x^2 - 2x - 3 > 0\} = \{x|x > 3 \text{ or } x < -1\}$$
$$= \{x|x < -1\} \cup \{x|3 < x\}$$
$$= (-\infty, -1) \cup (3, \infty)$$

Figure 9

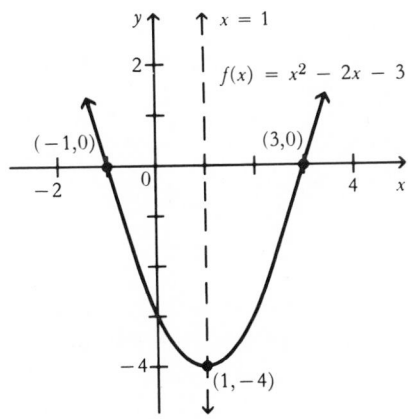

3   Find the values of x for which $x^2 < -1$.

SOLUTION.   Let us examine the graph of the associated function
$f(x) = x^2 + 1$ (Figure 10). Since $x^2 + 1 > 0$ for all real numbers,
$\{x|x^2 + 1 < 0\} = \emptyset$.

Figure 10

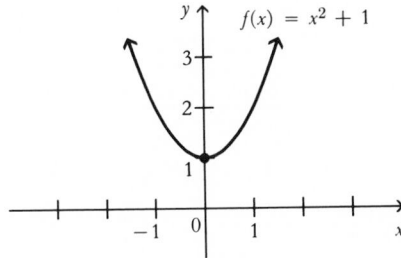

We have seen how to solve quadratic inequalities by using the graphs of
the associated functions. Although this method is easy to follow, another
algebraic method, which we shall refer to as the *cut point method*, can
be used. The cut points of an quadratic inequality are merely the x intercepts of the associated quadratic function.

    For example, the cut points of the inequality $x^2 + 2x - 15 < 0$ are
the x intercepts of the function $f(x) = x^2 + 2x - 15$, $(-5,0)$ and $(3,0)$.

These points divide the number line into three intervals, $(-\infty, -5)$, $(-5,3)$, and $(3,\infty)$ (Figure 11). Notice that the function is either always

Figure 11

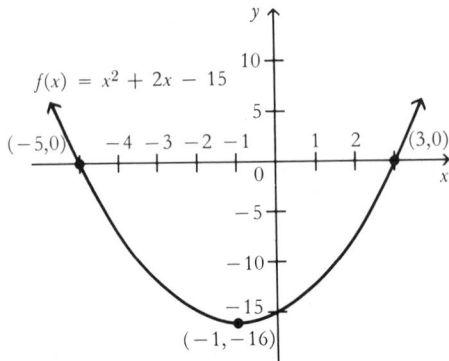

positive or always negative on each of the three intervals; hence, $\{x \mid x^2 + 2x - 15 < 0\} = (-5,3)$ (Figure 12).

Figure 12

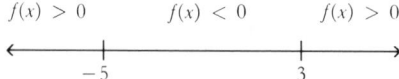

Since the graphs of quadratic functions are parabolas, it follows that there are only three possible cases in determining cut points: either there is no cut point (Figure 13*a*), there is one cut point (Figure 13*b*), or there are two cut points (Figure 13*c*).

In order to determine the intervals on which $f(x)$ preserves its sign, it

Figure 13

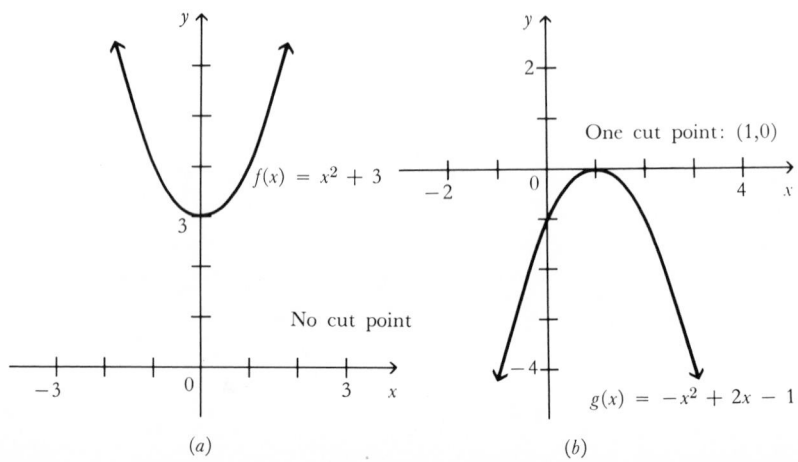

Figure 13 (Cont.)

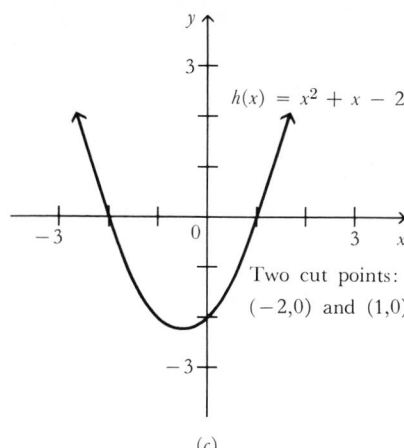

$h(x) = x^2 + x - 2$

Two cut points:
$(-2,0)$ and $(1,0)$

(c)

is enough to know the cut points; hence, in the example of Figure 13*a*, *b*, and *c*, we have the situations given in Figure 14.

Figure 14

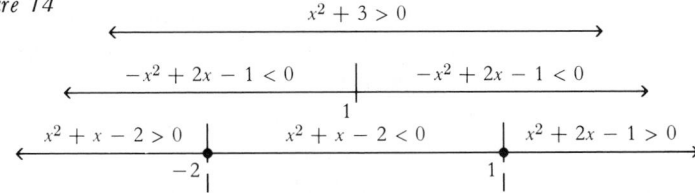

In general, once the cut points are determined, it is enough to test one point in each of the intervals, since the sign of the value of the associated function does not change for any value in each of these intervals.

EXAMPLES

1   Use cut points to solve $x^2 + 5x + 6 < 0$.

SOLUTION.   The cut points of $x^2 + 5x + 6 < 0$ are $(-3,0)$ and $(-2,0)$, since the graph crosses the x axis at the points $(-3,0)$ and $(-2,0)$. Hence, the cut points determine three intervals: $(-\infty,-3)$, $(-3,-2)$, and $(-2,\infty)$ (Figure 15).

Figure 15

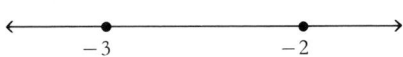

-3 -2

Since $-4 \in (-\infty,-3)$ does not satisfy $x^2 + 5x + 6 < 0$, the interval $(-\infty,-3)$ is not part of the solution set. Similarly, since $0 \in (-2,\infty)$

does not satisfy the given inequality, $(-3,-2)$ is not part of the solution set. However, $-\frac{5}{2} \in (-3,-2)$ does satisfy the inequality, so that the solution of $\{x|x^2 + 5y + 6 < 0\}$ is the interval $(-3,-2)$ (Figure 16).

Figure 16

2   Use cut points to solve $x^2 - 2x - 3 > 0$.

SOLUTION.   Since $\{x|x^2 - 2x - 3 = 0\} = \{x|(x + 1)(x - 3) = 0\} = \{-1,3\}$, the cut points are -1 and 3 (Figure 17).

Figure 17

We now test the three intervals determined by the cut points —
$(-\infty,-1)$, $(-1,3)$, and $(3,\infty)$ — merely by testing one member within each of the three intervals.
    For $x = -2$, $(-2)^2 - 2(-2) - 3 = 5 > 0$. Hence, $(-\infty,-1)$ is part of the solution set. Similarly, for $x = 0$, we get $-3 > 0$, so that the interval $(-1,3)$ is not part of the solution. Finally, for $x = 4$, we have $5 > 0$, so that $(3,\infty)$ is part of the solution set. Hence, $\{x|x^2 - 2x - 3 > 0\} = (-\infty,-1) \cup (3,\infty)$ (Figure 18).

Figure 18

PROBLEM SET 4

1 For each of the following quadratic functions, determine the domain, the range, the extreme point, the x and y intercepts, and the axis of symmetry. Graph the functions.

a) $f(x) = 2x^2 - 3$ b) $f(x) = x^2 + 2x$
c) $f(x) = -x^2 - x - 1$ d) $f(x) = (x + 2)^2$
e) $f(x) = x^2 + 5x + 2$ f) $f(x) = -x^2 - 1$
g) $f(x) = 2x^2 - 3x$ h) $f(x) = -(x + 1)^2$
i) $f(x) = 3x^2 + x + 3$ j) $f(x) = -x^2 + x + 5$

2 Explain why none of the functions in Problem 1 has an inverse.

3 Graph on the same coordinate system $y = ax^2$, where $a \in \{-10, -5, -2, -1, 0, 1, 2, 5, 10\}$. Compare the graphs to the different values of a. What do you notice?

4 Sketch the graph of each of the following functions on the same co-ordinate system.

a) $f(x) = x^2 - 2$ b) $f(x) = x^2 - 1$

c) $f(x) = x^2 + 1$ d) $f(x) = x^2 + 2$

In general, how do graphs of functions of the form $f(x) = x^2 + k$, k a constant, compare?

5 Graph each of the following quadratic functions, and then use the graph to solve the inequality. Write the solution in interval form, and then show the set on the real line.

a) $y = -x^2 + x - 1; \quad -x^2 + x - 1 \le 0$

b) $y = 2x^2 - x - 1; \quad 2x^2 - x - 1 > 0$

c) $y = (x - 1)^2; \quad x^2 - 2x < -1$

d) $y = x^2 + 6x + 8; \quad -x^2 - 6x - 8 \ge 0$

e) $y = -x^2 - 2; \quad x^2 + 2 < 0$

f) $y = 2x^2 - 7x + 6; \quad 2x^2 - 7x + 6 > 0$

g) $y = 3x^2 - 5x + 1; \quad 3x^2 - 5x + 1 < 0$

h) $y = \frac{1}{3}x^2 - \frac{1}{2}x - \frac{3}{2}; \quad \frac{1}{3}x^2 - \frac{1}{2}x - \frac{3}{2} < 0$

6 A projectile is fired from a balloon in such a way that it is h feet above the ground t seconds after the firing. If $h = -16t^2 + 96t + 256$, find

a) h when $t = 0$

b) The maximum height reached by the projectile

c) The graph of the function

7 Use the cut method to solve each of the following inequalities:

a) $2x^2 + 5x - 3 < 0$ b) $3x^2 - 7x + 2 > 0$

c) $x^2 - 4x + 4 \le 0$ d) $2x^2 + 3x - 9 < 0$

e) $x^2 - 7x + 6 \ge 0$ f) $x^2 + 4 > 0$

g) $x^2 + 2x - 3 \le 0$ h) $-x^2 + 16 > 0$

8 A rectangular field is adjacent to a river and is to have fencing on three sides, the side on the river requiring no fencing. Assume also that 50 yards of fencing is used.

a) Construct a quadratic function in which the area of the field A is a function of the width x.

b) Sketch the graph of the function of part (a).

c) What is the maximum point? What is the largest area that can be enclosed?

6 Polynomial Functions of Degree Greater Than 2

We have seen that polynomial functions are functions expressible in the form $f(x) = a_n x^n + a_{n-1} x^{n-1} + \cdots + a_1 x + a_0$, where the coefficients are real numbers, $a_n \neq 0$, and n is a nonnegative integer or $f(x) = 0$.

Let us now investigate the graphs of polynomial functions of degree greater than 2. In graphing a polynomial function, it is helpful to determine the x intercepts, that is, the points where the graph crosses the x axis. For example, the x intercepts for $f(x) = x^3 - x^2$ are $(0,0)$ and $(1,0)$; they are determined by solving the equation $0 = x^3 - x^2$. Clearly, the x intercepts of a function occur at those values of x which, when substituted into the function, give 0 as the corresponding y. These values of x are called the *zeros* of the function. Hence, $x = 0$ and $x = 1$ are the zeros of the polynomial function $f(x) = x^3 - x^2$.

The zeros of the polynomial function $f(x) = 2x^2 + x - 1$ can be determined by solving $0 = 2x^2 + x - 1$ to get $x = -1$ and $x = \frac{1}{2}$; the zeros of $f(x) = 4x^3 - x^2$ are $x = 0$ and $x = \frac{1}{4}$; the function $f(x) = x^2 + 1$ has no real zeros. (Why?)

The graphing of a polynomial function also requires plotting a few points. This means, of course, that specific members of the domain must be substituted into the function so as to determine corresponding range members. For certain situations the computation of the range members is not difficult. For example, if $f(x) = x^3 + 1$, $f(-1) = 0$, $f(0) = 1$, $f(1) = 2$, and $f(2) = 9$ can easily be determined by substitution. In other situations the computation becomes rather tedious. For example, if $f(x) = x^5 - 3x^4 + 7x - 8$, the determination of $f(3)$, $f(-2)$, and $f(7)$ becomes more involved. We will see how a shorthand division process, called *synthetic division*, can be used to simplify computation of the latter type. However, before examining synthetic division, it is necessary to comment briefly on the division of polynomials.

6.1   Division of Polynomials

If $f(x)$ and $g(x)$ are polynomials, then $f(x) + g(x)$, $f(x) - g(x)$, and $f(x) \cdot g(x)$ are also polynomials. However, the quotient $f(x)/g(x)$ is not always a polynomial. For example, $(x + 1)/(x + 3)$, $(x + 7)/(3x^7 + x + 1)$, and $(x^3 + 1)/(x - 3)$ are not polynomials. These latter expressions exist because a polynomial may not always be divisible by another polynomial. For example, $x^3 + 2x^2 - 2x + 3$ is divisible by $x + 3$, so that $x^3 + 2x^2 - 2x + 3 = (x^2 - x + 1)(x + 3)$; whereas the division of $x^2 + 3x + 7$ by $x + 1$ gives a quotient of $x + 2$ and a remainder of 5, so that $x^2 + 3x + 7 = (x + 2)(x + 1) + 5$. In either case, the division of polynomials is based on the following property called the *division algorithm* which is stated as follows:

If $f(x)$ and $D(x)$ are polynomials such that the degree of $f(x)$ is greater than or equal to the degree of $D(x)$ with $D(x) \neq 0$, then there exist unique polynomials $Q(x)$ and $R(x)$ such that $f(x) = D(x) \cdot Q(x) + R(x)$, where the degree of $R(x)$ is less than or equal to the degree of $D(x)$ or $R(x) = 0$. $D(x)$ is called the *divisor*, $f(x)$ the *dividend*, $Q(x)$ the *quotient*, and $R(x)$ the *remainder*.

EXAMPLE

Suppose that $f(x) = 3x^2 + 8x + 26$, and $D(x) = x - 3$. Find $Q(x)$ and $R(x)$ such that $3x^2 + 8x + 26 = Q(x)(x - 3) + R(x)$, where $R(x)$ satisfies the division algorithm.

SOLUTION.   We arrange this division in the following manner:

$$
\begin{array}{r}
3x^2 + 8x\ + 26 \\
x - 3\ \overline{\big)\ 3x^3 - x^2 + 2x - 1} \\
\underline{\pm 3x^3 \mp 9x^2} \\
8x^2 + 2x \\
\underline{\pm 8x^2 \mp 24x} \\
26x - 1 \\
\underline{\pm 26x \mp 78} \\
77
\end{array}
$$

Hence, $Q(x) = 3x^2 + 8x + 26$, and $R(x) = 77$.

6.2 Synthetic Division

Synthetic division is merely a *shorthand method* for performing the division of any polynomial by a polynomial of the form $x - r$. In the example above, the division can be displayed as follows.

Here, the variables are implied rather than explicitly indicated and the $\mp$ or $\pm$ indicates the change of sign necessary in subtracting. This latter form could also be rearranged as

$$
\begin{array}{c|cccc}
 & (1) & (2) & (3) & (4) \\
-3 & 3 & -1 & 2 & -1 \\
 & & \mp 9 & \mp 24 & \mp 78 \\
\hline
 & 3 & 8 & 26 & 77
\end{array}
$$

Note that in this latter representation, the coefficients of the quotient appear in the last row, together with the remainder in the last position. Finally, the last form can be abbreviated as

$$
\begin{array}{r|cccc}
 & (1) & (2) & (3) & (4) \\
\text{Abbreviation} \;\to\; 3 \;\; & 3 & -1 & 2 & -1 \\
\text{for divisor} & & 9 & 24 & 78 \\
\hline
\text{Coefficients} & 3 & 8 & 26 & 77 \\
\text{of quotient}
\end{array}
$$

Abbreviation → 3 for divisor

Coefficients of dividend →

Coefficients of quotient

77 ← Remainder

Notice that if the sign of the number to the left of the bar (-3 in this example) is changed, it is no longer necessary to perform subtraction. All we need do is to add algebraically. Hence, $3x^3 - x^2 + 2x - 1 = (x - 3)(3x^2 + 8x + 26) + 77$. It is this form of the division which is called *synthetic division*.

Let us find another quotient and remainder using synthetic division. Suppose that

$$
\frac{3x^3 - 8x + 1}{x + 2}
$$

is to be determined. First, write $x + 2$ in the form $x - r$ as $x - (-2)$. Then use -2 as the "divisor,"

$$
\begin{array}{r|rrrr}
-2 & 3 & 0 & -8 & 1 \\
 & & -6 & 12 & -8 \\
\hline
 & 3 & -6 & 4 & -7
\end{array}
$$

so that

$$
\frac{3x^3 - 8x + 1}{x + 2} = 3x^2 - 6x + 4 + \frac{-7}{x + 2}
$$

or, equivalently, $3x^3 - 8x + 1 = (3x^2 - 6x + 4)(x + 2) - 7$. Notice that 0 is used as the coefficient of the x^2 term. Also notice the pattern: we bring down the first coefficient, 3, and multiply 3 by -2 to get -6, and then add 0 to -6 to get -6. Next, we multiply -6 by -2 to get 12, and add -8 to 12 to get 4. Finally, we multiply 4 by -2 to get -8, and then add 1 to -8 to get the remainder -7.

EXAMPLE

Use synthetic division to divide $f(x)$ by $x - r$. Then use the result of the division to determine $f(r)$ if $f(x) = x^5 - 6x^2 - 4x^3 - 9$ and $r = -3$.

SOLUTION

$$
\begin{array}{r|rrrrrr}
-3 & 1 & 0 & -4 & -6 & 0 & -9 \\
   &   & -3 & 9 & -15 & 63 & -189 \\
\hline
   & 1 & -3 & 5 & -21 & 63 & -198
\end{array}
$$

Hence,

$$
\begin{aligned}
f(x) &= x^5 - 6x^2 - 4x^3 - 9 \\
     &= (x^4 - 3x^3 + 5x^2 - 21x + 63)(x + 3) + (-198)
\end{aligned}
$$

so that $f(-3) = 0 + (-198) = -198$. Notice that the function value $f(-3)$ is the same as the remainder we get when dividing $f(x)$ by $x - (-3)$.

This example suggests two theorems.

THEOREM 1   REMAINDER THEOREM

Assume that $f(x)$ is a polynomial of degree $n > 0$. If R is the remainder when $f(x)$ is divided by $x - r$, where r is any real number, then $f(r) = R$.

PROOF.   Let $Q(x)$ be the quotient, so that, by the division algorithm, $f(x) = (x - r)Q(x) + R$. This equation holds for all x. In particular, if $x = r$, then

$$f(r) = (r - r)Q(r) + R = 0 + R \quad \text{so that} \quad f(r) = R$$

Now if the remainder $R = f(r)$ is zero, then the divisor $x - r$ and the quotient $Q(x)$ are factors of $f(x)$. Hence, we have a second theorem.

THEOREM 2   COROLLARY* (FACTOR THEOREM)

If $f(r) = 0$, then $x - r$ is a factor of the polynomial $f(x)$ of degree $n > 0$; and, conversely, if $x - r$ is a factor, r is a zero.

PROOF.   Assume $f(x) = (x - r)Q(x) + R$. If $f(r) = 0$, then $R = 0$ and $f(x) = Q(x)(x - r)$. Conversely, if $x - r$ is a factor of $f(x)$, then $f(x) = Q(x)(x - r)$, so that $f(r) = Q(r) \cdot 0 = 0$.

*A corollary of a theorem is a theorem which follows directly from another theorem.

Theorem 1 tells us what was hinted in the example above. The value of a polynomial $f(r)$ is the same as the remainder of the polynomial we get when dividing by $x - r$. But this type of operation can be performed by synthetic division. Hence, the values of a polynomial function needed in graphing can be determined by synthetic division. For example, $f(3)$ for $f(x) = x^5 - 3x^4 + 7x - 8$ can be determined as follows:

$$
\begin{array}{r|rrrrrr}
3 & 1 & -3 & 0 & 0 & 7 & -8 \\
  &   & 3 & 0 & 0 & 0 & 21 \\
\hline
  & 1 & 0 & 0 & 0 & 7 & 13 \\
\end{array}
$$

so that $f(3) = 13$.

EXAMPLES

1   Use synthetic division to find the quotient $Q(x)$ and the remainder R if $f(x) = 3x^5 - 5x^3 + 1$ is divided by $x - 2$. Use your result to determine $f(2)$.

SOLUTION

$$
\begin{array}{r|rrrrrr}
2 & 3 & 0 & -5 & 0 & 0 & 1 \\
  &   & 6 & 12 & 14 & 28 & 56 \\
\hline
  & 3 & 6 & 7 & 14 & 28 & 57 \\
\end{array}
$$

Hence, $Q(x) = 3x^4 + 6x^3 + 7x^2 + 14x + 28$; also, by the remainder theorem, $f(2) = 57$.

2   Find the remainder if $f(x) = x^{1001} + 3$ is divided by $x + 1$.

SOLUTION

$$f(-1) = (-1)^{1001} + 3 = -1 + 3 = 2$$

Hence, by the remainder theorem, the remainder if $f(x) = x^{1001} + 3$ is divided by $x + 1$ is 2.

3   Show that $x + 2$ is a factor of $f(x) = x^4 - 2x^2 + 3x - 2$ and find $Q(x)$.

SOLUTION

$$
\begin{array}{r|rrrrr}
-2 & 1 & 0 & -2 & 3 & -2 \\
   &   & -2 & 4 & -4 & 2 \\
\hline
   & 1 & -2 & 2 & -1 & 0 \\
\end{array}
$$

Hence, $f(-2) = 0$, and $Q(x) = x^3 - 2x^2 + 2x - 1$

so that

$$f(x) = (x + 2)(x^3 - 2x^2 + 2x - 1)$$

4   Find the value of k if $x - 3$ is a factor of $f(x) = 3x^3 - 4x^2 - kx - 33$.

SOLUTION

$$
\begin{array}{c|cccc}
3 & 3 & -4 & -k & -33 \\
  &   & 9 & 15 & 3(-k + 15) \\
\hline
  & 3 & 5 & -k + 15 & -3k + 12
\end{array}
$$

Since $x - 3$ is a factor of $f(x) = 3x^3 - 4x^2 - kx - 33$, it follows from the factor theorem that $-3k + 12 = 0$. Hence, $k = 4$.

6.3   Graphs of Polynomial Functions of Degree Greater Than 2

The general study of polynomial functions of degree greater than 2 is more difficult than the study of polynomial functions of degree less than or equal to 2. It can be shown (in calculus) that polynomial functions are *continuous functions*, and we use this result in graphing polynomial functions. For example, we can graph $f(x) = 1$, $f(x) = x$, $f(x) = x^2$, $f(x) = x^3$, and $f(x) = x^4$ by plotting a few points and assuming continuity between these points to sketch the graph (Figure 1).

Figure 1

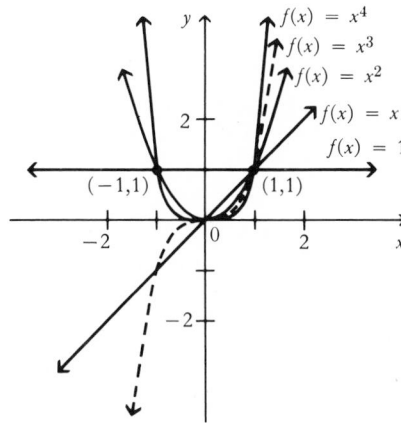

Consider $f(x) = x^3 + \frac{3}{2}x^2 - 6x - 2$. First, we can prepare a table of values of x and $f(x)$. These values can now be determined by using synthetic division. Next, the points can be plotted. From the table we observe that the points $(x, f(x))$ to be plotted are $(-4,-18)$, $(-3,2.5)$, $(-2,8)$, $(-1,4.5)$, $(0,-2)$, $(1,-5.5)$, $(2,0)$, and $(3,20.5)$ (Figure 2).

Figure 2

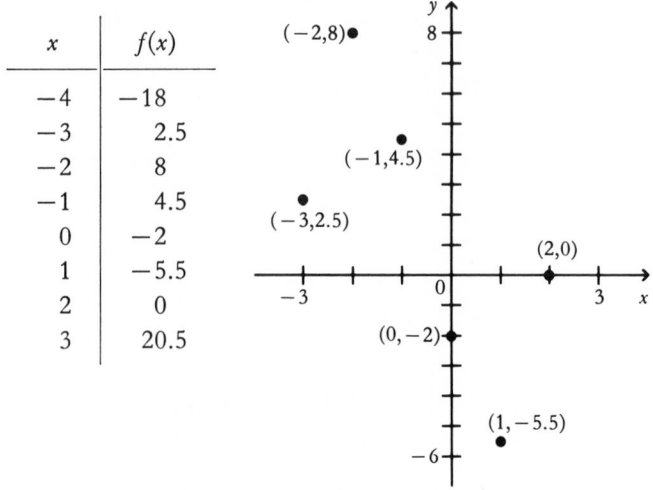

x	$f(x)$
-4	-18
-3	2.5
-2	8
-1	4.5
0	-2
1	-5.5
2	0
3	20.5

Since polynomial functions are continuous, if $a < b$ and $f(a) < 0 < f(b)$, then there is a zero, say c, such that $a < c < b$ and $f(c) = 0$ (Figure 3). The problem, of course, is that there may be more than one such zero between a and b.

Figure 3

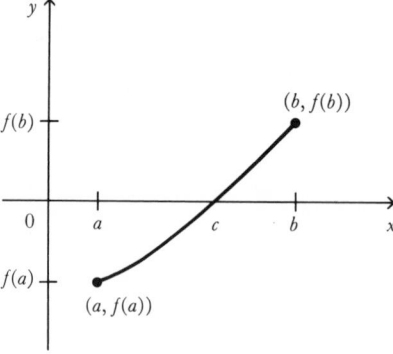

The question is whether the points we have already plotted for $f(x) = x^3 + \frac{3}{2}x^2 - 6x - 2$ are sufficient to give us a fairly accurate sketch of the graph. Are there hidden peaks not shown thus far? We are *not* in a position to answer this question, but if we plot more points in between those already located, we can get a rough sketch of the graph (Figure 4).

Figure 4

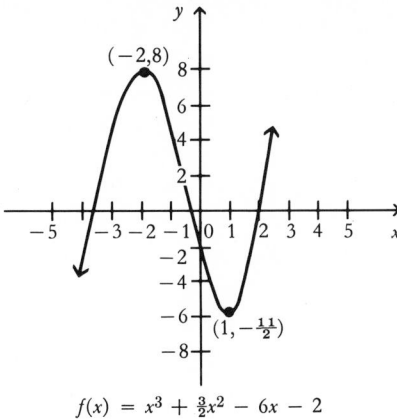

$$f(x) = x^3 + \tfrac{3}{2}x^2 - 6x - 2$$

EXAMPLES

1 Sketch the graph of $f(x) = (x + 1)(x - 2)(x - 3)$. Use the graph to solve the inequality $(x + 1)(x - 2)(x - 3) < 0$.

SOLUTION. The graph of f intercepts the x axis only at $x = -1$, $x = 2$, and $x = 3$. Some additional points on the graph of $f(x)$ are given in the accompanying table. Notice that the portion of the graph (Figure 5) below the x axis suggests the values of x which satisfy the inequality. Thus, the solution set of the inequality is given by
$$\{x \mid (x + 1)(x - 2)(x - 3) < 0\} = (-\infty, -1) \cup (2, 3).$$

Figure 5

x	$f(x)$
$-\tfrac{1}{2}$	$\tfrac{35}{8}$
0	6
1	4
$\tfrac{5}{2}$	$-\tfrac{7}{8}$
$\tfrac{7}{2}$	$\tfrac{27}{8}$

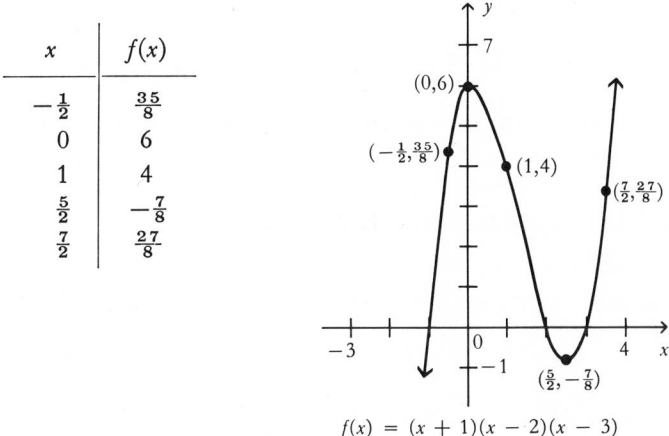

$$f(x) = (x + 1)(x - 2)(x - 3)$$

2 Graph $f(x) = (x - 1)^2(x - 2)(x - 3)^3$. Use the graph to solve the inequality $(x - 1)^2(x - 2)(x - 3)^3 < 0$.

SOLUTION.   The graph of f intercepts the x axis only at $x = 1$, $x = 2$, and $x = 3$, the zeros of $f(x)$. Additional points on the graph of $f(x)$ are given in the accompanying table. Notice that the portion of the graph (Figure 6) below the x axis suggests the values of x which satisfy the inequality, so that $\{x \mid (x - 1)^2(x - 2)(x - 3)^3 < 0\}$ is the set $(2,3)$.

Figure 6

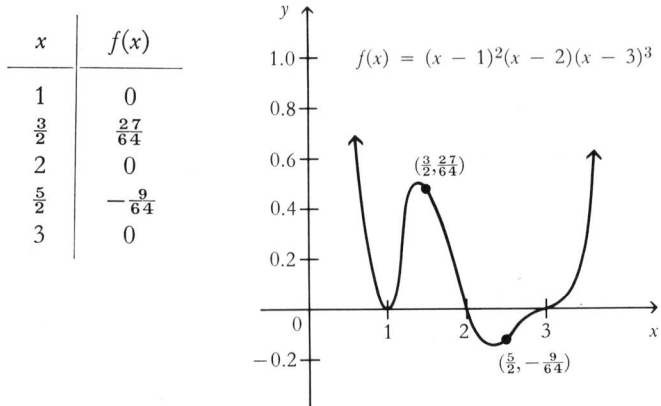

x	$f(x)$
1	0
$\frac{3}{2}$	$\frac{27}{64}$
2	0
$\frac{5}{2}$	$-\frac{9}{64}$
3	0

$f(x) = (x - 1)^2(x - 2)(x - 3)^3$

6.4 Rational Zeros

So far we have seen how the zeros of polynomial equations are used to determine the x intercepts of the graphs of polynomial functions. If the polynomial is of first or second degree it is easy to determine the zeros, but as the degree increases, the problem of determining the zeros becomes much more difficult. The general method to be taken up here enables us to determine zeros which are rational numbers of polynomial functions with integral coefficients. Before stating the result, it is necessary to recall one of the basic properties of the system of integers:

An integer can be written in one and only one way as a product of prime numbers.

THEOREM 1   RATIONAL ROOT THEOREM

If $f(x) = a_n x^n + a_{n-1} x^{n-1} + \cdots + a_1 x + a_0$, and if the coefficients are *integers* and p/q is a rational root in lowest terms, then p is a divisor of a_0 and q is a divisor of a_n.

PROOF.   Since $a_n(p/q)^n + a_{n-1}(p/q)^{n-1} + \cdots + a_1(p/q) + a_0 = 0$, it follows that

$$a_n p^n + a_{n-1} p^{n-1} q + \cdots + a_1 p q^{n-1} + a_0 q^n = 0$$

so that

(1) $$a_n p^n + a_{n-1} p^{n-1} q + \cdots + a_1 p q^{n-1} = -a_0 q^n$$

or, equivalently,

(2) $$a_{n-1}p^{n-1}q + \cdots + a_1 pq^{n-1} + a_0 q^n = -a_n p^n$$

Since both sides of Eq. (1) are integers, p is a divisor of the left side and, therefore, also of the right side. But p and q have no common factors, since p/q is in lowest terms. Hence, every prime factor of p must be a factor of a_0 and the first part of the proof is finished. Similarly, in (2), q is a factor of the left side, and, hence, of the right side. As before, q has no factors in common with p, so that q must be a divisor of a_n.

EXAMPLES

1 Write all the possible rational roots of $f(x) = x^3 + 2x^2 - 4x - 8 = 0$.

SOLUTION. Assume that p/q is a rational root of $f(x) = 0$. By the rational root theorem, p is a divisor of $a_0 = -8$ and q is a divisor of $a_n = 1$, so that p can assume any of the values -1, 1, 2, -2, 4, -4, 8, or -8 and q can assume values 1 or -1; therefore, the possible rational roots p/q are given by 1, -1, 2, -2, 4, -4, 8, or -8. After testing these possible rational roots by synthetic division, we find that $x = 2$ and $x = -2$ are roots; in fact, $x^3 + 2x^2 - 4x - 8 = (x + 2)^2(x - 2)$, so that $x = 2$ and $x = -2$ are the only roots.

2 Use the rational root theorem to prove that $\sqrt{2}$ is an irrational number.

PROOF. $x^2 - 2 = 0$ is a polynomial equation whose root is $\sqrt{2}$. Let p/q be a possible rational root of $x^2 - 2 = 0$, so that $p = 1$, -1, 2, or -2 and $q = 1$ or -1; therefore, by the rational root theorem, 1, -1, 2, or -2 are the only possible rational roots. Since $\sqrt{2}$ is not one of the possible rational roots, $\sqrt{2}$ is not a rational number.

PROBLEM SET 5

1 Find all the zeros of each of the following polynomial functions.
a) $f(x) = 3x + 2$
b) $f(x) = -7x^2 + 5x - 1$
c) $f(x) = x^3 + x^2 + x + 1$. (*Hint:* Try $x = -1$.)
d) $f(x) = x(x - 1)^2(x - 3)(x + 2)(x - \pi)$
e) $f(x) = -(x - 1)^2 + 3$

2 Perform the following division

$$\frac{3x^5 + 5x^4 - 2x^3 + x^2 - 10x + 3}{x - 2}$$

a) Directly
b) By synthetic division

3 Use synthetic division to find $Q(x)$ and $f(r)$, so that
$f(x) = (x - r)Q(x) + f(r)$.

a) $f(x) = 3x^3 - 4x^2 + x + 2$ and $r = 2$
b) $f(x) = 2x^4 - 3x^3 - 3x^2 + x - 4$ and $r = 3$
c) $f(x) = x^4 - 2x^3 - 3x^2 + x + 1$ and $r = \frac{3}{2}$
d) $f(x) = x^3 - 3x + 2$ and $r = 1.7$
e) $f(x) = x^4 - 10x^2 - 12x + 7$ and $r = -2$

4 For what values of a positive integer n do each of the following hold where a is a positive number?

a) $x^n + a^n$ is divisible by $x + a$.
b) $x^n + a^n$ is divisible by $x - a$.
c) $x^n - a^n$ is divisible by $x + a$.
d) $x^n - a^n$ is divisible by $x - a$.

5 Find values of k and m so that each of the following hold.

a) $6x^2 - x - 2$ is divisible by $x - k$.
b) $3x^2 + mx - m^2 - 9$ is divisible by $x - 1$.
c) $x^3 + kx^2 - 3x - 12$ divided by $x - 2$ has remainder 2.
d) $x^3 + kx^2 + mx - 6$ is divisible by $(x - 2)(x - 3)$.
e) $kx^5 + kx^4 + 13x^3 - 11x^2 - 10x - 2k$ is divisible by $x + 1$.

6 a) Show that $x - 1$ is a factor of $f(x) = 14x^{99} - 65x^{56} + 51$.
b) Show that $x + 4$ is a factor of $f(x) = 2x^2 + 3x - 20$.

7 Sketch the graph of each of the following functions by plotting points. Also determine the x and y intercepts.

a) $f(x) = x^4 + x^3$ b) $f(x) = x^3 - 5x + 4$
c) $f(x) = x^4 - 3x^3 + 2x - 6$ d) $f(x) = 2x^3 - 3x^2 - 12x + 20$
e) $f(x) = x^2 - 4x + 5$ f) $f(x) = (x - 2)^4$
g) $f(x) = x(x - 1)(x - 2)(x + 1)$

8 Prove that $f(x) = x^4 - 4x^2$ is an even function. Use this fact, together with the factorization of $x^4 - 4x^2$, to graph the function. Indicate the domain and range.

9 Prove that $f(x) = x^3 - x$ is an odd function. Use this fact, together with the factorization of $x^3 - x$, to graph the function. Indicate the domain and range. Is f increasing or decreasing?

10 Given $g(x) = x^2 + 1$ and $f(x) = 2x + 1$. Form $g \circ f$ and $f \circ g$, and then graph the two functions on the same coordinate system.

11 Use the graphs of the associated functions to solve each of the following inequalities.

a) $(x - 3)^3(x + 7) < 0$ b) $(x - 5)(x + 7)(x - 2) > 0$
c) $(x + 1)(x - 2)(x - 3) < 0$ d) $(x - 2)^2(x + 1)^2 > 0$
e) $(x^2 + 4)(x - 3) < 0$

12 Write down all rational numbers that might be roots of the following polynomials. Test the possibilities to determine which of them are roots.

a) $\{(x, f(x))\,|\,f(x) = x^4 - x^3 + 2x^2 - 4x - 8\}$
b) $\{(x, f(x))\,|\,f(x) = 2x^3 - 6x - 4\}$
c) $\{(x, f(x))\,|\,f(x) = 2x^3 + x^2 - x - 2\}$
d) $\{(x, f(x))\,|\,f(x) = x^4 - 11x^2 - 12x + 4\}$

13 Use the rational root theorem to prove that each of the following numbers is an irrational number.

a) $\sqrt{3}$ 　　　　　　b) $\sqrt{5}$ 　　　　　　c) $\sqrt{2} + \sqrt{3}$

REVIEW PROBLEM SET

1 Find the degree and the coefficients for each of the following polynomial functions.

a) $f(x) = 4x^3 + 2x + 6$
b) $f(x) = 2x^3 + 5x^2 + 7x - 3$
c) $f(x) = 7x^5 - 4x^4 + 3x^3 + 2x^2 - 5x - 7$
d) $f(x) = 2x^7 - 3$

2 Find the equation of each of the lines and sketch the line in each case.

a) Slope $m = 3$; containing the point $(4,5)$
b) Slope $m = 0$; containing the point $(-2,3)$
c) Containing the points $(3,-2)$ and $(5,6)$
d) Containing the points $(0,2)$ and $(3,0)$

3 Identify the slope and the x and y intercepts for each of the following lines and sketch the line in each case.

a) $y = \frac{3}{5}x + \frac{7}{3}$ 　　　　　　b) $x/3 + y/5 = 1$
c) $7x + 5y - 13 = 0$ 　　　　　　d) $y = 5$
e) $x = -3$ 　　　　　　f) $y - 2 = -\frac{5}{3}(x - 1)$

4 Let f be a linear function. Give conditions so that each of the following equations are valid for all real numbers.

a) $3f(x) = f(3x)$ 　　　　　　b) $f(x + 7) = f(x) + f(7)$
c) $f(3x + 4) = 3f(x) + f(4)$ 　　d) $f(3) = 4$ and $f(5) = 6$
e) $f(x) = f(7x + 1)$
f) $f(x) = f[g(x)]$, where $g(x) = 3x + 2$

5 Graph each of the following quadratic functions, and then use the graph to solve the given inequality.

a) $f(x) = 6x^2 - 5x - 4$; $6x^2 - 5x - 4 \leq 0$
b) $f(x) = -3 + 10x - 8x^2$; $-3 + 10x - 8x^2 < 0$
c) $f(x) = (7x - 3)(1 - 2x)$; $(7x - 3)(1 - 2x) > 0$

6 Let f be a linear function. Is $f(3t + 2)$ linear? Prove your assertion.

7   Assume that the slope of a line $f(x) = mx + b$ is negative and that $x_1 < x_2$. Is it true that $f(x_1) > f(x_2)$? Prove your assertion. What if the slope is positive? Zero?

8   Show that if f and g are linear functions, then

a) $f - g$ is a linear function   b) $f \circ g$ is a linear function

9   Assume that $f(x) = c$ is a constant function. Which of the following is always true?

a) $f(x^2) = [f(x)]^2$ b) $f(|x|) = |f(x)|$
c) $f(5x) = 5f(x)$ d) $f(x^2 + y^2) = f(x + y)$

10   Given the constant functions $f(x) = c_1$, $g(x) = c_2$, and $h(x) = c_3$, do the following.

a)   Determine $f \circ (g \circ h)$ and $f \circ (h \circ g)$.
b)   Does it follow from part (a) that $g \circ h = h \circ g$ for any two functions h and g? Explain.

11   Is the line containing $(3,5)$ and $(1,9)$ parallel to the line containing $(5,8)$ and $(11,-4)$? Explain.

12   Express by an equation the condition that the line containing (a,b) and $(-5,0)$ is perpendicular to the line containing (a,b) and $(5,0)$, where a and b are constants.

13   Three vertices of a rectangle are $(9,3)$, $(5,9)$, and $(-7,1)$. Find its fourth vertex.

14   Two opposite vertices of a rectangle are $(6,2)$ and $(-5,4)$. Two sides of the rectangle are parallel to the line $8x - 6y + 5 = 0$. Find the equations of the four sides and the coordinates of the other two vertices.

15   A projectile is fired from a balloon in such a way that it is h feet above the ground t seconds after the firing where $h = 88t - 16t^2$.

a)   Find t when $h = 0$.
b)   Find the maximum height reached by the projectile.

16   Solve each of the following inequalities by graphing the corresponding function.

a) $(x + 2)(x + 3)(x - 6) < 0$ b) $(x - 3)(x - 2)(x + 4) > 0$
c) $(x - 2)(x - 3)(x - 2)(x + 6) > 0$

17   Use synthetic division to determine $Q(x)$ and $f(r)$, so that $f(x) = (x - r)Q(x) + f(r)$.

a) $f(x) = 3x^3 + 5x^2 + 7x - 3$, $r = 2$
b) $f(x) = 5x^4 - 2x^3 + 11x^2 + 5x + 36$, $r = 1$
c) $f(x) = 2x^3 + 4x^2 + 3x - 18$, $r = -1$
d) $f(x) = x^7 - 5$, $r = 2$

18 Let $f(x) = x^5 + x^4 - 3x^3 - 5x^2 + x + 7$. Use synthetic division to find each of the following values.

    a) $f(2)$ b) $f(3)$ c) $f(-1)$ d) $f(-2)$

19 Find a value of k such that

    a) The roots of $3x^2 - 5x + 4k = 0$ are real and equal

    b) The roots of $3x^2 - 2x - k = 0$ are real

20 Let a and b be rational numbers. Show that the roots of $(a + b)x^2 - 2ax + (a - b) = 0$ are rational.

21 Solve the following systems of linear equations by using the elimination method. In each step of the process show the corresponding matrix form of the system.

    a) $\begin{aligned} 4x - y - 2z &= -4 \\ 6x + y + 4z &= 15 \\ 2x + 4y - z &= -2 \end{aligned}$ b) $\begin{aligned} 2x + 3y + 4z &= 9 \\ 5x - 2y + 2z &= 5 \\ 3x - 5y - 2z &= -4 \end{aligned}$

    c) $\begin{aligned} 3x - y + 2z &= 1 \\ 6x - 2y + 4z &= 2 \\ 9x - 3y + 6z &= 3 \end{aligned}$ d) $\begin{aligned} 2x + 4y - 3z &= -1 \\ 3x + 2y - 5z &= 7 \\ 5x - 9y + 2z &= 7 \end{aligned}$

22 Use Cramer's rule, if possible, to solve each of the systems in Problem 21.

23 Find all the rational zeros of each of the following functions.

    a) $\{(x, f(x)) \mid f(x) = x^3 - 4x^2 + x + 6\}$

    b) $\{(x, f(x)) \mid f(x) = 48x^4 - 52x^3 + 13x - 3\}$

    c) $\{(x, f(x)) \mid f(x) = 2x^4 + 5x^3 - 9x^2 - 15x + 9\}$

24 Solve for x in each of the following expressions.

    a) $\begin{vmatrix} x & 0 & 0 \\ 3 & x & 2 \\ 0 & 4 & 1 \end{vmatrix} = 5$ b) $\begin{vmatrix} 1 & x^2 & x \\ 1 & 0 & 2 \\ 4 & 3 & 1 \end{vmatrix} = 28$

    c) $\begin{vmatrix} -2 & 1 & x \\ 1 & x+1 & -2 \\ x-6 & 3 & -1 \end{vmatrix} = 0$

25 a) Show that

$$\begin{vmatrix} x & y & 1 \\ x_1 & y_1 & 1 \\ x_2 & y_2 & 1 \end{vmatrix} = 0$$

        is the equation of the line that contains the points (x_1, y_1) and (x_2, y_2).

    b) Use part (a) above to find the equation of the line that contains the points $(4, 5)$ and $(-2, 7)$.

26   Show that the determinant

$$\begin{vmatrix} 1 & x & x^2 \\ 1 & y & y^2 \\ 1 & z & z^2 \end{vmatrix}$$

can be factored as $(y - z)(z - x)(x - y)$.

CHAPTER 4

Exponential and Logarithmic Functions

4 EXPONENTIAL AND LOGARITHMIC FUNCTIONS

1 Introduction

This chapter begins with a brief review of the properties of exponents. Next, we approach the study of exponential functions by answering the questions: What are the domain and range? What are the graphs? Are the functions even or odd? Are the functions increasing or decreasing? Are the functions continuous? Do the exponential functions have inverses? The answer to the last question will lead to the development of logarithmic functions and the properties of logarithms. Also, mathematical induction will be introduced so that some of the properties of exponents and the binomial theorem can be proven. Finally, summation notation and geometric series will be surveyed.

2 Properties of Exponents

Initially, exponents can be considered to be shorthand notations for indicating repeated multiplication of the same factor. For example, a^4 represents $a \cdot a \cdot a \cdot a$, $7^2 = 7 \cdot 7 = 49$, and $(x + y)^3 = (x + y)(x + y)(x + y)$.

In general, if n is a positive integer and a is a real number, then a^n, the *nth power of a*, represents the product of n factors each equal to a, that is,

$$a^n = \overbrace{a \cdot a \cdot a \cdot a \cdots a}^{n \text{ factors of } a}$$

a is called the *base* and n is called the *exponent* of a^n.

The basic laws of exponents are given in the following theorem.

THEOREM 1

Suppose that m and n are positive integers and assume that a and b are real numbers. Then

i $a^n \cdot a^m = a^{n+m}$

ii $(a^m)^n = a^{mn}$

iii $(ab)^n = a^n b^n$

iv $\dfrac{a^m}{a^n} = \begin{cases} a^{m-n}, & \text{if } m > n \\ \dfrac{1}{a^{n-m}}, & \text{if } n > m \\ 1, & \text{if } n = m \end{cases}$ provided that $a \neq 0$

In Section 7 we will use a more formal definition of a^n, together with mathematical induction, to prove parts of this theorem.

The use of exponents can be extended to include the negative integers together with zero exponents so that the properties of Theorem 1 remain valid.

2.1 Definition

If a is a real number different from 0, then a^0 is defined as $a^0 = 1$ and a^{-n} is defined as $a^{-n} = 1/a^n$, where n is a positive integer. $\square$

EXAMPLES

Write each of the following expressions in a "simplified" form which has only positive integral exponents.

1    $\dfrac{3ab^{-2}}{c^3 d^{-4}}$

SOLUTION

$$\dfrac{3ab^{-2}}{c^3 d^{-4}} = \dfrac{(3a)(1/b^2)}{(c^3)(1/d^4)} = \dfrac{3a}{b^2} \cdot \dfrac{d^4}{c^3} = \dfrac{3ad^4}{b^2 c^3}$$

2    $\dfrac{(x^{k-4n})^k}{x^{k(k-5n)} x^{n(k-6n)}}$

SOLUTION

$$\frac{\left(x^{k-4n}\right)^{k}}{x^{k(k-5n)}x^{n(k-6n)}} = \frac{x^{k^2-4nk}}{\left(x^{k^2-5nk}\right)\left(x^{nk-6n^2}\right)} \qquad \text{(Theorem 1, ii)}$$

$$= \frac{x^{k^2-4nk}}{x^{k^2-4nk-6n^2}} \qquad \text{(Theorem 1, i)}$$

$$= x^{6n^2} \qquad \text{(Theorem 1, iv)}$$

3 $$\frac{\left(2^{4x+2}\right)\left(8^{3}\right)}{\left(2^{4x}\right)\left(2^{10}\right) - \left(2^{4x+7}\right)\left(2^{6}\right)}$$

SOLUTION

$$\frac{\left(2^{4x+2}\right)\left(8^{3}\right)}{\left(2^{4x}\right)\left(2^{10}\right) - \left(2^{4x+7}\right)\left(2^{6}\right)} = \frac{\left(2^{4x+2}\right)\left(2^{3}\right)^{3}}{2^{4x+10} - 2^{4x+13}} \qquad \text{(Theorem 1, i)}$$

$$= \frac{\left(2^{4x+2}\right)\left(2^{9}\right)}{2^{4x+10} - 2^{4x+13}} \qquad \text{(Theorem 1, ii)}$$

$$= \frac{2^{4x+11}}{2^{4x+10} - 2^{4x+13}} \qquad \text{(Theorem 1, i)}$$

$$= \frac{2^{4x+11}}{2^{4x+10}(1 - 2^{3})} \qquad \text{(Why?)}$$

$$= \frac{2}{1 - 8} \qquad \text{(Theorem 1, iv)}$$

$$= -\frac{2}{7}$$

The use of exponents can also be extended to include rational numbers. Rational exponents are defined so that the properties of Theorem 1 continue to hold. We begin by defining rational exponents of the form $1/n$.

2.2   Definition

If a is a real number and n is a positive integer, then $a^{1/n}$, called the *nth principle root* of a, is defined to be the number x which satisfies $x^n = a$. If $a > 0$, $a^{1/n} > 0$; if $a < 0$ and n is odd, $a^{1/n} < 0$; if $a < 0$ and n is even, $a^{1/n}$ is not defined. $a^{1/n}$ can also be expressed in the form $\sqrt[n]{a}$; this latter form is called a *radical* with *index n*. $\square$

For example,

$$4^{1/2} = 2 \qquad \text{since } 2^2 = 4$$
$$(-8)^{1/3} = -2 \qquad \text{since } (-2)^3 = 8$$

and

$$(-9)^{1/2} \qquad \text{is not defined}$$

Note that $\sqrt{4} = 2$, not -2, because of Definition 2.2.

Definition 2.2, together with Theorem 1, can be used to motivate the definition of exponents which are rational numbers, for if p/q is a positive rational number, then the rule $(a^n)^m = a^{nm}$ suggests that

$$a^{p/q} = (a^{1/q})^p = (\sqrt[q]{a})^p$$

or, equivalently,

$$a^{p/q} = (a^p)^{1/q} = (\sqrt[q]{a^p})$$

so that we have the following definition.

2.3   Definition

If p/q is a positive rational number and if a is a real number, then $a^{p/q} = (a^p)^{1/q} = (a^{1/q})^p$ where a and q must satisfy the conditions of Definition 2.3. If p/q is a negative rational number and $a \neq 0$, $a^{p/q} = 1/a^{-p/q}$ and the first part of the definition is applicable to $a^{-p/q}$, since $-p/q$ is a positive rational number. $\square$

For example

$$32^{2/5} = (32^{1/5})^2 = (\sqrt[5]{32})^2 = 2^2 = 4$$

and

$$32^{-2/5} = \frac{1}{32^{2/5}} = \frac{1}{4}$$

Care must be taken in applying Theorem 1 to rational exponents. For example, $(-1)^{1/3} = -1$; however, $(-1)^{1/3} = (-1)^{2/6} = [(-1)^2]^{1/6} = 1^{1/6} = 1$ is not valid because $(-1)^{1/6}$ is not defined.

EXAMPLES

Simplify the expression in 1, 2, 3 and 4.

1   $\sqrt{125}$

SOLUTION

$$\sqrt{125} = 125^{1/2} = (5 \cdot 25)^{1/2} = 5^{1/2} \cdot 25^{1/2} = 5^{1/2} \cdot 5 = 5\sqrt{5}$$

2   $\sqrt{(\frac{4}{25})^3}$

SOLUTION

$$\sqrt{(\tfrac{4}{25})^3} = (\tfrac{4}{25})^{3/2} = \frac{4^{3/2}}{25^{3/2}} = \frac{(4^{1/2})^3}{(25^{1/2})^3} = \frac{2^3}{5^3} = \frac{8}{125}$$

3 $\sqrt[3]{\sqrt{9} + \sqrt{25}}$

SOLUTION

$$\sqrt[3]{\sqrt{9} + \sqrt{25}} = (9^{1/2} + 25^{1/2})^{1/3} = (3 + 5)^{1/3} = 8^{1/3} = 2$$

4 $\left(\dfrac{x^{n^2+1}}{x^{1-n}}\right)^{1/(n+1)}$, n is a positive integer.

SOLUTION

$$\left(\frac{x^{n^2+1}}{x^{1-n}}\right)^{1/(n+1)} = (x^{n^2+n})^{1/(n+1)} = (x^{n(n+1)})^{1/(n+1)} = x^n$$

5 Express each of the numbers without radicals in the denominator. (This process is often referred to as *rationalizing the denominator*.)

a) $1/\sqrt{3}$ b) $1/(2 + \sqrt{3})$ c) $\sqrt{2}/(1 + \sqrt{2} + \sqrt{3})$

SOLUTION

a) $\dfrac{1}{\sqrt{3}} = \dfrac{1}{\sqrt{3}}\dfrac{\sqrt{3}}{\sqrt{3}} = \dfrac{\sqrt{3}}{3}$

b) $\dfrac{1}{2 + \sqrt{3}} = \dfrac{1}{2 + \sqrt{3}}\dfrac{2 - \sqrt{3}}{2 - \sqrt{3}} = 2 - \sqrt{3}$

c) $\dfrac{\sqrt{2}}{1 + \sqrt{2} + \sqrt{3}} = \dfrac{\sqrt{2}}{(1 + \sqrt{2}) + \sqrt{3}}\dfrac{(1 + \sqrt{2}) - \sqrt{3}}{(1 + \sqrt{2}) - \sqrt{3}}$

$$= \frac{\sqrt{2} + 2 - \sqrt{6}}{(1 + \sqrt{2})^2 - 3} = \frac{\sqrt{2} + 2 - \sqrt{6}}{1 + 2\sqrt{2} + 2 - 3}$$

$$= \frac{\sqrt{2} + 2 - \sqrt{6}}{2\sqrt{2}}\frac{\sqrt{2}}{\sqrt{2}} = \frac{2 + 2\sqrt{2} - 2\sqrt{3}}{4}$$

$$= \frac{1 + \sqrt{2} - \sqrt{3}}{2}$$

6 For what value of x does $27^x = 81$ hold?

SOLUTION. Since $27 = 3^3$, $27^x = (3^3)^x = 3^{3x}$. Also $81 = 3^4$, so that $3^{3x} = 3^4$. This latter equation holds if $3x = 4$, that is, if $x = \tfrac{4}{3}$.

7 Solve $2^{2x+2} - 9(2^x) + 2 = 0$.

SOLUTION. $2^{2x+2} - 9(2^x) + 2 = 0$ can be written as $(2^x)^2 2^2 - 9(2^x) + 2 = 0$. If we let $y = 2^x$, we get $4y^2 - 9y + 2 = 0$, that is, $(4y - 1)(y - 2) = 0$, so that $y = \tfrac{1}{4}$ or $y = 2$, so that $2^x = \tfrac{1}{4}$ or $2^x = 2$. Hence, $x = -2$ or $x = 1$.

It can be shown, by methods beyond the scope of this text, that the properties of exponents can be extended to include irrational numbers, so that Theorem 1 is valid for all real number exponents if the further restrictions that $a > 0$ and $b > 0$ are imposed. Furthermore, it can be shown that if $a > 0$, then $a^x > 0$ for any real number x. This latter fact will be needed for investigating the properties of exponential functions.

PROBLEM SET 1

1   Simplify each of the following expressions and justify each step by using Theorem 1 and the definitions of Section 2.

a) $(-5)^2$
b) $(3^{-2})(3^7)$
c) $(3^4)(3^{-5})$
d) $5^6/-5^8$
e) $(\frac{1}{3})^2(\frac{1}{3})^4(3^{-5})$
f) $(\sqrt[4]{x^3})(\sqrt[5]{x^2})$
g) $\sqrt[4]{x^2}\sqrt{x}\sqrt[3]{x}$
h) $(\sqrt{2})(\sqrt[3]{3})(\sqrt[4]{4})$
i) $\sqrt{9} + \sqrt{27}$
j) $[\sqrt[3]{x}(16x^{-5/4}/x^{4/3})]^{1/2}$

2   Prove each of the following statements if a and b are real numbers and m and n are positive integers. Also, indicate what conditions a, b, m, and n must satisfy in order for the expressions to be defined (see Definition 2.2).

a) $(\sqrt[n]{a})^n = a$
b) $\sqrt[n]{ab} = \sqrt[n]{a}\,\sqrt[n]{b}$
c) $\sqrt[n]{(a/b)} = \sqrt[n]{a}/\sqrt[n]{b}$
d) $\sqrt[m]{\sqrt[n]{a}} = \sqrt[mn]{a}$

3   Simplify each of the following expressions.

a) $16^{-2}[(2^{-1})(2)(2^5)]^4[(2^{-2})(2^{-4})]^{-2}$

b) $\dfrac{3^{-1}}{(1 + \frac{2}{3} - \frac{1}{3})^3}$

c) $\dfrac{(x^2)(x^3)(x^{-1})(x^{-2})^3}{x^2}$

d) $\dfrac{(x^{-1})(x^2)(x^6)^{-3}}{x^{-4}}$

e) $\dfrac{32^{4/5}(2^{n+1})^4}{8^3 \cdot (16)^{n-1}}$

f) $\dfrac{9^2(27)^{2-n}}{81^{-n}(27)^3(3^{n-1})}$

g) $\sqrt[n]{\dfrac{9(3^{4n+1} + 9^{2n})}{(3^{2n+2})(4)}}$

h) $\sqrt[n]{\dfrac{4^n \cdot 6}{4^{2n+1} + 2^{4n+1}}}$

4   a) Explain why it is *not* true in general that if x is a real number, then $\sqrt{x^2} = x$. Give examples. How should $\sqrt{x^2}$ be defined?
b) Is $\sqrt{x^2} + \sqrt{y^2} = |x| + |y|$? Give two examples.
c) Is $\sqrt{x^2 + y^2} = |x + y|$? Give two examples.

5   Rationalize the denominator in each of the following expressions.

a) $\dfrac{2}{\sqrt{2}}$

b) $\dfrac{5}{\sqrt{3} - \sqrt{2}}$

c) $\dfrac{5}{\sqrt{x} + 1}$

d) $\dfrac{2\sqrt{3} + \sqrt{5}}{\sqrt{3}}$

e) $\dfrac{1}{\sqrt{27}}$

f) $\dfrac{\sqrt{x+1}+\sqrt{x-1}}{\sqrt{x+1}-\sqrt{x-1}}$

g) $\dfrac{\sqrt{3}+1}{\sqrt{2}+\sqrt{3}+\sqrt{5}}$

6 Evaluate -3^2 and $(-3)^2$. In general, what is the difference between $-a^x$ and $(-a)^x$? Are the two numbers ever the same? If one of the two is defined, is it necessarily true that the other is also defined? Give examples to support your assertions.

7 Simplify each of the following expressions

a) $(x^n + 4)(x^n - 6)$

b) $(x^{n+1} - 3y^{n-1})(3y^{n-2} + x^{n+1})$

c) $(x^{n/2} + 7)^2$

d) $\sqrt{150} - 2\sqrt{24} + \sqrt{216}$

e) $\sqrt{125/x} - (3/x)\sqrt{80x} - 4\sqrt{1/5x}$

f) $\sqrt{\sqrt[3]{x^2}}$

g) $(\tfrac{1}{2}x\sqrt{3} + \sqrt{3})(\tfrac{1}{2}x\sqrt{3} - \sqrt{3})$

h) $(\sqrt{1 - \sqrt{1 - x^2}})(\sqrt{1 + \sqrt{1 - x^2}})$

8 Solve for x.

a) $(3^{4x-3})^{-2} = (27)^{-x-8}$

b) $(5^3)^{2x-6} = (5^{-2})^{4-x}$

c) $2^{3-x}(4^{2x-1}) = 16$

d) $2^{x+4x} = \tfrac{1}{8}$

e) $(5^{2x})(25) = (125)^{x-1}$

f) $2^{2x+2} + 2^{x+2} = 3$

9 Indicate the domain and the range for each of the following functions. Indicate whether the function is even or odd and graph it. Is the function increasing or decreasing?

a) $f(x) = x^{1/2}$

b) $f(x) = \sqrt{1 - x}$

c) $f(x) = \sqrt{x^2 + 1}$

d) $f(x) = \sqrt{-x}$

e) $f(x) = \sqrt[4]{x}$

10 Criticize the following "proof" that $-1 = 1$.

Proof

$\dfrac{-1}{1} = \dfrac{1}{-1}$ (Both equal -1)

$\sqrt{\dfrac{-1}{1}} = \sqrt{\dfrac{1}{-1}}$ (If $a = b$, then $\sqrt{a} = \sqrt{b}$)

$\dfrac{\sqrt{-1}}{\sqrt{1}} = \dfrac{\sqrt{1}}{\sqrt{-1}}$ (Quotient property of radicals)

$\sqrt{-1}\cdot\sqrt{-1} = \sqrt{1}\cdot\sqrt{1}$ (Multiply each side by the common denominator)

$\therefore\ -1 = 1$ ($\sqrt{a}\cdot\sqrt{a} = a$)

3 Exponential Functions and Their Properties

Suppose that a biologist grows a colony of a certain kind of bacteria. As part of his investigation he wishes to discover how the number of bacteria changes with time. He discovers that the time required for the number of bacteria to triple does not depend on the number of bacteria which are initially present. To be specific, assume that on a given day there are x_0 bacteria present and the number triples each day. Then, there are $3x_0$ present after one day; $3(3x_0) = 3^2 x_0$ after two days; $3(3^2 x_0) = 3^3 x_0$ after three days, and so on, so that after n days, there are $3^n x_0$ bacteria present. This phenomena of bacteria growth can be represented by the function $f(t) = 3^t x_0$, where t represents the number of days after the experiment begins and x_0 represents the number of bacteria initially present.

Now, although it is true that the actual experiment supplies data only when t is a positive integer, we can assume that the function $f(t) = 3^t x_0$ is continuous, so that $f(t)$ indicates the number of bacteria present after t days where t is any positive number. For example, after two days, four hours, there would be $3^{2\frac{1}{6}} x_0 = 3^{13/6} x_0$ bacteria present.

It is our purpose here to investigate the properties of functions of the type $f(t) = 3^t x_0$.

3.1 Definition

If b is a positive number, then the function $f(x) = b^x$ is called an *exponential function* with *base* b. The domain of $f(x) = b^x$ is the set of all real numbers. For $b \neq 1$, the range of $f(x) = b^x$ is the set of all positive numbers. ☐

For example, $f(x) = 3^x$ is an exponential function with base 3; $f(t) = (\frac{1}{3})^t$ is an exponential function with base $\frac{1}{3}$; $f(x) = 2^{-x} = (2^{-1})^x = (\frac{1}{2})^x$ is an exponential function with base $\frac{1}{2}$.

EXAMPLES

1 Discuss the properties of $f(x) = 3^x$.

SOLUTION. $f(x) = 3^x$ has base 3. The domain of $f(x) = 3^x$, as with all exponential functions, is the set of real numbers R, and the range is the set of positive real numbers. It can be shown by the more advanced techniques of calculus that all exponential functions are continuous over the entire real line, and this property is used to graph the function (Figure 1). The graph of $f(x) = 3^x$ shows that f is an increasing function so that the function has an inverse. Notice that if $x = \sqrt{2}$, then

Definition 2.3 does not apply, since $\sqrt{2}$ is an irrational number. However, the continuity of the exponential function permits us to assume that the point $(\sqrt{2}, 3^{\sqrt{2}})$ is on the graph of $f(x) = 3^x$.

Figure 1

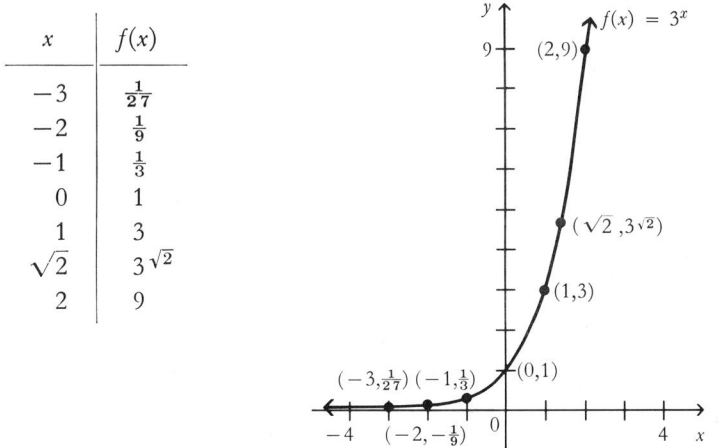

x	$f(x)$
-3	$\frac{1}{27}$
-2	$\frac{1}{9}$
-1	$\frac{1}{3}$
0	1
1	3
$\sqrt{2}$	$3^{\sqrt{2}}$
2	9

2 Discuss the properties of $f(x) = (\tfrac{1}{4})^x$

SOLUTION. $f(x) = (\tfrac{1}{4})^x$ has base $\tfrac{1}{4}$; the domain is the set of real numbers R, and the range is the set of positive real numbers. The graph is given in Figure 2. Here again we use the continuity of exponential functions. $f(x) = (\tfrac{1}{4})^x$ is decreasing, and, consequently, it has an inverse.

Figure 2

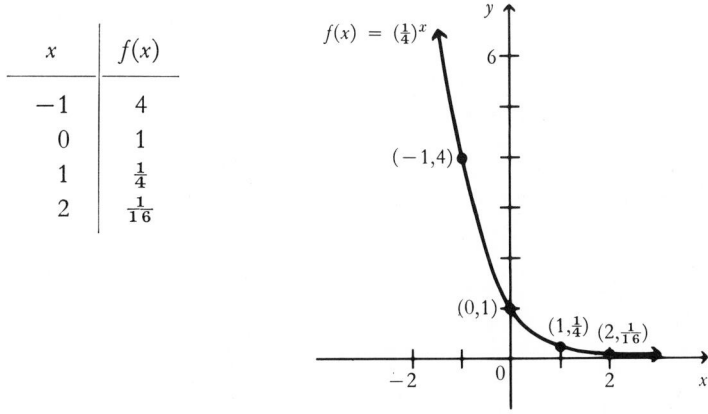

x	$f(x)$
-1	4
0	1
1	$\frac{1}{4}$
2	$\frac{1}{16}$

3 Let $y = f(x)$ be an exponential function with base b. Show that $f(x_1 + x_2) = f(x_1) \cdot f(x_2)$ for any two real numbers x_1 and x_2.

SOLUTION. Since $y = f(x)$ is an exponential function with base b, $f(x) = b^x$. By the rules of exponents, $b^{x_1+x_2} = b^{x_1} \cdot b^{x_2}$, so that $f(x_1 + x_2) = f(x_1) \cdot f(x_2)$.

4   If the graph of an exponential function contains the point (2,25), what is the base?

SOLUTION. Since the function is exponential, it is of the form $f(x) = b^x$. (2,25) on the graph implies that $25 = b^2$, so that $b = 5$ is the base. Note that although -5 satisfies $b^2 = 25$, -5 is not the base because of Definition 3.1.

PROBLEM SET 2

1   Discuss the properties of each of the following functions. Indicate the domain and range. Graph the function. Is the function increasing or decreasing? Does the function have an inverse?

a) $f(x) = 2^x$ b) $f(x) = 1^x$

c) $f(x) = 3^{x+1}$ d) $f(x) = \sqrt{2^x}$

e) $f(x) = (\frac{4}{7})^x$ f) $f(x) = 2^{-x}$

g) $f(x) = (\frac{1}{5})^{-x}$ h) $f(x) = (0.1)^x$

i) $f(x) = (5)(3^x)$ j) $f(x) = -4^x$

2   Use the graph of $f(x) = 3^x$ to approximate each of the following numbers.

a) $3^{1/2}$ b) $3^{2\frac{1}{2}}$ c) 3^π

d) $3^{\sqrt{2}}$ e) $3^{-1.2}$

3   Given exponential function $f(x) = b^x$, indicate whether f is increasing or decreasing for $b = 1$; for $0 < b < 1$; and for $b > 1$. Give examples to support your conclusions.

4   Graph $f(x) = 2^x$ and $f(x) = 2^{-x}$ on the same coordinate system. Are the two graphs symmetric? Explain. Can you generalize this situation?

5   Graph $f(x) = 5^x$ and $f(x) = -5^x$ on the same coordinate system. Compare the functional properties (see Problem 1 above). Can you generalize your results so that you can use the properties of $f(x) = b^x$ to determine the properties of $f(x) = -b^x$?

6   Can an exponential function be even? Can an exponential function be odd? Explain.

7   Let $f(x) = 3^x$ and $g(x) = 5^x$. Find

a) $(f \circ g)(2)$ b) $(g \circ f)(2)$

c) $(f \circ g)(x)$ d) $(g \circ f)(x)$

e) $(g \circ f)(0)$

8 Let $f(x) = 3^x + 3^{-x}$ and $g(x) = 3^x - 3^{-x}$. Find

a) $f + g$ b) $f \cdot g$

c) f/g d) $[f(x)]^2 - [g(x)]^2$

e) $f(x^2) - g(x^2)$

9 Suppose that a biologist grows a colony of a certain kind of bacteria. Assume that in an experiment, $N = x_0 3^n$ represents the number of bacteria present at the end of n days, where x_0 is the number of bacteria which are initially present. Suppose there are 333,000 bacteria present at the end of 2 days.

a) Find the number of bacteria present at the end of 4 days.

b) What is the number of days at the end of which there are 111,000 bacteria present?

4 Logarithmic Functions and Their Properties

The exponential function $f(x) = b^x$ is either an increasing or decreasing function if $b \neq 1$. We know (Chapter 2, Section 6) that such a function is one-to-one and consequently has an inverse. This inverse function is called the *logarithmic function*. More formally, we define the logarithmic function as follows.

4.1   Definition

The function $f^{-1}(x) = \log_b x$, the *logarithmic function with base b*, is the inverse function of the exponential function $f(x) = b^x$, where $b \neq 1$.   ☐

Using set notation, $f(x) = b^x$ can be written as

$$f = \{(x,y) | y = b^x\}$$

The inverse f^{-1} is formed from f merely by "reversing" the roles of the members of the ordered pairs of f to get

$$f^{-1} = \{(y,x) | y = b^x\}$$

By convention, the symbol x is usually used to represent the domain variable; hence, f^{-1} is written as $f^{-1} = \{(x,y) | x = b^y\}$. But we have defined f^{-1} as $f^{-1}(x) = \log_b x$, so that we also have

$$f^{-1} = \{(x,y)\,|\,y = \log_b x\}$$

Now, if the latter two representations of f^{-1} are compared, it becomes apparent that

$$y = \log_b x \qquad \text{is equivalent to} \qquad x = b^y$$

For example,

$$3 = \log_2 8 \qquad \text{is equivalent to} \qquad 8 = 2^3$$

and

$$x = \log_3 64 \qquad \text{is equivalent to} \qquad 64 = 3^x$$

Since the graph of the inverse f^{-1} is a reflection of the graph of f across the line $y = x$, the graph of $f^{-1}(x) = \log_b x$ is a reflection of the graph of $f(x) = b^x$, $b \neq 1$, across the line $y = x$, as shown in the example of Figure 1.

Figure 1

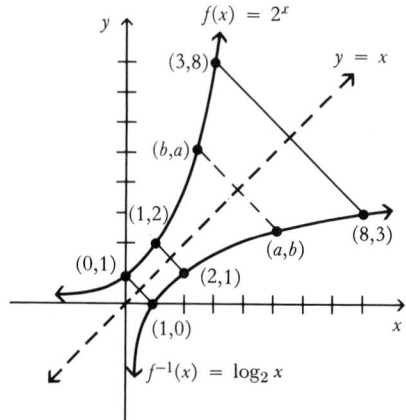

In general, the domain of f^{-1} is the range of f, and the range of f^{-1} is the domain of f. Consequently, since the domain of the exponential function $f(x) = b^x$ is the set of all real numbers, the range of $g(x) = \log_b x$ is also the set of all real numbers; and, since the range of $f(x) = b^x$ is the set of all positive real numbers whenever $b \neq 1$, the domain of $g(x) = \log_b x$ is also the set of all positive real numbers.

EXAMPLES

1   Discuss the properties of $f(x) = \log_3 x$.

SOLUTION.   We know that $f(x) = \log_3 x$ is the inverse of $g(x) = 3^x$. Hence, the domain of $g(x) = 3^x$ is the range of $f(x) = \log_3 x$ and the range of $g(x) = 3^x$ is the domain of $f(x) = \log_3 x$, that is, the domain of $f(x) = \log_3 x$ is the set of all positive real numbers and the range is R. The graph can be determined by expressing $f(x) = \log_3 x$ as $3^{f(x)} = x$, and then using our knowledge of exponents to plot some points. The function $f(x) = \log_3 x$ is continuous and increasing (Figure 2).

Figure 2

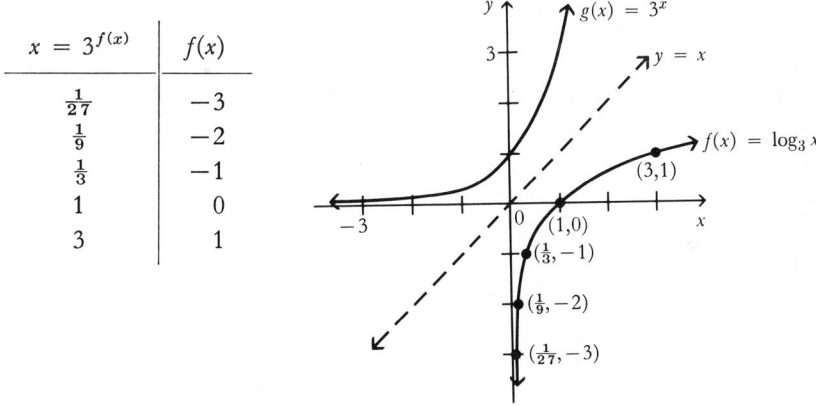

$x = 3^{f(x)}$	$f(x)$
$\frac{1}{27}$	-3
$\frac{1}{9}$	-2
$\frac{1}{3}$	-1
1	0
3	1

2   Discuss the properties of $f(x) = \log_{1/4} x$.

SOLUTION.   The domain of f, as with all logarithmic functions, is the set of all positive real numbers and the range is R. The graph can be determined by considering $f(x) = \log_{1/4} x$ as $(\frac{1}{4})^{f(x)} = x$ to plot some points (Figure 3). $f(x) = \log_{1/4} x$ is continuous and decreasing.

Figure 3

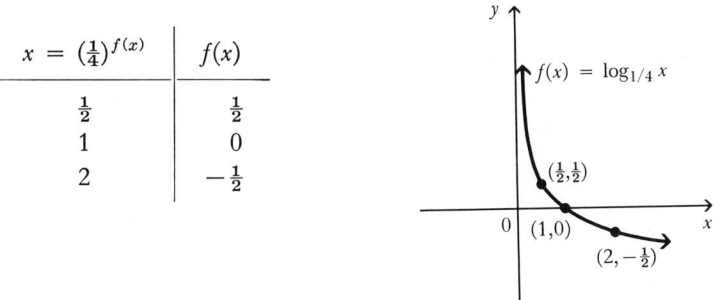

$x = (\frac{1}{4})^{f(x)}$	$f(x)$
$\frac{1}{2}$	$\frac{1}{2}$
1	0
2	$-\frac{1}{2}$

3   Indicate the domain of $f(x) = \log_8 (1 - 2x)$.

SOLUTION.   Since $f(x) = \log_8 (1 - 2x)$ is equivalent to $8^{f(x)} = 1 - 2x$, and, since $8^{f(x)}$ is positive, $1 - 2x > 0$, so that $x < \frac{1}{2}$. Hence the domain is $(-\infty, \frac{1}{2})$.

PROBLEM SET 3

1   Discuss the properties of each of the following functions. Indicate the domain and range. Graph the function. Is the function increasing or decreasing? What is the inverse?

a) $f(x) = \log_2 x$ b) $f(x) = \log_5 x$
c) $f(x) = \log_{1/2} x$ d) $f(x) = \log_4 x$
e) $f(x) = \log_\pi x$

2   Use the graph of $f(x) = \log_{10} x$ to approximate each of the following values.

a) $\log_{10} \frac{1}{2}$ b) $\log_{10} 2$
c) $\log_{10} \pi$ d) $\log_{10} \sqrt{2}$
e) $\log_{10} 0.1$

3   Graph $f(x) = \log_b x$ where $b = 2, 3, 4, 5$ on the same coordinate system. How do the graphs compare?

4   Graph $f(x) = \log_2 x$ and $g(x) = 2^x$ on the same coordinate system. Explain the symmetry with respect to the line $y = x$. (*Hint:* If $(x,y) \in f$, then $(y,x) \in f^{-1}$.)

5   Compare the functional properties of $f(x) = \log_3 x$ to the functional properties of $f(x) = \log_{1/3} x$. How are they the same? How are they different? In general, how do the logarithmic functions with base less than 1 compare to the logarithmic functions with base greater than 1?

6   Let $f(x) = 10^x$ and $g(x) = \log_{10} x$. Find $f \circ g$ and $g \circ f$. Simplify your answer by using the fact that $f(x) = \log_{10} x$ is equivalent to $10^{f(x)} = x$.

7   Graph $y = \log_{10} x$.

a) For what values of x is $y < 0$?
b) For what values of x is $y > 0$?
c) For what value of x is $y = 0$?
d) If $x_1 < x_2$, how does $\log_{10} x_1$ compare to $\log_{10} x_2$?

8   What is the domain of each of the following functions?

a) $f(x) = \log_{10} x^2$ b) $f(x) = \log_{10} |x + 1|$
c) $f(x) = \log_{10} (-x)$ d) $f(x) = \log_{10} (5x - 1)$
e) $f(x) = \log_{10} (x^2 - 4)$

9   Compare the properties of $f(x) = \log_{10} |x|$ to $g(x) = |\log_{10} x|$ by examining their graphs.

5 Properties of Logarithms

Since $y = \log_b x$ is equivalent to $b^y = x$, it follows that the properties of logarithms can be derived from the properties of exponents (see Theorem 1 of Section 2).

THEOREM 1

Suppose that x_1, x_2, and b are positive real numbers such that $b \neq 1$ and that k is any real number. Then

   i $\log_b (x_1 x_2) = \log_b x_1 + \log_b x_2$

  ii $\log_b (x_1^k) = k \log_b x_1$

 iii $\log_b \left(\dfrac{x_1}{x_2} \right) = \log_b x_1 - \log_b x_2$

 iv $b^{\log_b x_1} = x_1$

PROOF OF (i). Let $f(z) = b^z$ and $f(w) = b^w$; then $f(z + w) = f(z) f(w)$ (see Example 3, Section 3); hence, $f^{-1}[f(z + w)] = f^{-1}[f(z)f(w)]$; that is,

(1)
$$z + w = f^{-1}[f(z) f(w)]$$

Suppose that $x_1 = f(z)$ and suppose that $x_2 = f(w)$; then $z = f^{-1}(x_1)$, and $w = f^{-1}(x_2)$, so that, after substituting into Eq. (1), we get

$$f^{-1}(x_1) + f^{-1}(x_2) = f^{-1}(x_1 x_2)$$

Finally, after replacing $f^{-1}(x)$ by $\log_b x$, it follows that

$$\log_b x_1 + \log_b x_2 = \log_b (x_1 x_2)$$

PROOF OF (ii). Let $f(z) = b^z$. Then $[f(z)]^k = (b^z)^k = b^{zk} = f(zk)$, so that $f^{-1}\{[f(z)]^k\} = f^{-1}[f(zk)]$, that is

(2)
$$f^{-1}\{[f(z)]^k\} = zk$$

Suppose that $x_1 = f(z)$; then, $z = f^{-1}(x_1)$. Consequently, by substitution into (2),

$$f^{-1}(x_1^k) = kf^{-1}(x_1)$$

that is,

$$\log_b x_1^k = k \log_b x_1$$

PROOF OF (iii)

$$\log_b \left(\frac{x_1}{x_2}\right) = \log_b (x_1 x_2^{-1})$$

$$\begin{aligned}
&= \log_b x_1 + \log_b x_2^{-1} &&\text{(Theorem 1, i)}\\
&= \log_b x_1 + (-1) \log_b x_2 &&\text{(Theorem 1, ii)}\\
&= \log_b x_1 - \log_b x_2
\end{aligned}$$

PROOF OF (iv).   (See Problem 1b.)

EXAMPLES

1   Evaluate $\log_b b$, $\log_b 1$, and $\log_b b^p$.

SOLUTION.   If $\log_b b = t$, then $b^t = b$, so that $t = 1$. Hence, $\log_b b = 1$. Also, $\log_b 1 = t$ implies $b^t = 1$, so that $t = 0$, that is, $\log_b 1 = 0$. Finally, $\log_b b^p = p \log_b b = p \cdot 1 = p$.

2   Let $f(x) = \log_b x$, $f(2) = 0.35$, $f(3) = 0.55$, and $f(5) = 0.82$. Use Theorem 1 to find each of the following values.

a) $f(\frac{2}{3})$ b) $f(2^3)$ c) $f(2)/f(3)$
d) $[f(2)]^3$ e) $f(24)$ f) $f(\sqrt{\frac{2}{3}})$
g) $f(60/b)$ h) $f(0.6)$

SOLUTIONS

a) $f(\frac{2}{3}) = \log_b (\frac{2}{3}) = \log_b 2 - \log_b 3 = 0.35 - 0.55 = -0.20$
b) $f(2^3) = \log_b 2^3 = 3 \log_b 2 = 3(0.35) = 1.05$
c) $f(2)/f(3) = 0.35/0.55 = \frac{7}{11}$
d) $[f(2)]^3 = (\log_b 2)^3 = (0.35)^3$
e) $f(24) = \log_b 24 = \log_b (2^3 \cdot 3) = \log_b 2^3 + \log_b 3$
     $= 3 \log_b 2 + \log_b 3 = 3(0.35) + 0.55 = 1.6$
f) $f(\sqrt{\frac{2}{3}}) = \log_b (\frac{2}{3})^{1/2} = \frac{1}{2} \log_b (\frac{2}{3}) = \frac{1}{2}(\log_b 2 - \log_b 3)$
     $= \frac{1}{2}(0.35 - 0.55) = -0.10$
g) $f(60/b) = \log_b (60/b) = \log_b 60 - \log_b b$
     $= \log_b (2^2 \cdot 3 \cdot 5) - \log_b b$
     $= 2 \log_b 2 + \log_b 3 + \log_b 5 - \log_b b$
     $= 2(0.35) + 0.55 + 0.82 - 1$
     $= 0.70 + 0.55 + 0.82 - 1 = 1.07$
h) $f(0.6) = \log_b (0.6) = \log_b (\frac{3}{5}) = \log_b 3 - \log_b 5$
     $= 0.35 - 0.82 = -0.47$

3   Solve for x if $\log_3 (x + 1) + \log_3 (x + 3) = 1$.

SOLUTION. $\log_3 (x + 1) + \log_3 (x + 3) = \log_3 [(x + 1)(x + 3)] = 1$. (Why?) Hence, $x^2 + 4x + 3 = 3$. (Why?) Now $\{x | x^2 + 4x + 3 = 3\} =$

$\{x|x^2 + 4x = 0\} = \{0, -4\}$; however, -4 does not satisfy the original equation (Why?), so that $x = 0$ is the only solution.

4   Solve for x if $\log_4 (x + 3) - \log_4 x = 1$.

SOLUTION. $\log_4 (x + 3) - \log_4 x = \log_4 [(x + 3)/x] = 1$; therefore, $(x + 3)/x = 4^1 = 4$, from which it follows that $x = 1$.

PROBLEM SET 4

1 a)   Prove that $\log_b (xyz) = \log_b x + \log_b y + \log_b z$, where b, x, y, and z are positive numbers, with $b \neq 1$. (*Hint:* Use Theorem 1, i.)
   b)   Prove Theorem 1, iv, directly by using an argument similar to the one used in i.

2 Let $f(x) = \log_{10} x$. If $f(2) = 0.3010$ and $f(3) = 0.4771$, find
   a) $f(4)$ b) $f(18)$
   c) $f(1000)$ d) $f(\sqrt[5]{2})$
   e) $f(3000)$ f) $f(5)$
   g) $f(60)$ h) $f(0.5)$
   i) $f(\frac{1}{3})$ j) $f(x^0)$, $x \neq 0$

3 Give specific counterexamples to disprove each of the following statements.
   a) $\log_b (x_1/x_2) = (\log_b x_1)/(\log_b x_2)$
   b) $(\log_b x_1)/(\log_b x_2) = \log_b x_1 - \log_b x_2$
   c) $\log_b x_1 \cdot \log_b x_2 = \log_b x_1 + \log_b x_2$
   d) $\log_b (x_1 x_2) = \log_b x_1 \cdot \log_b x_2$
   e) $\log_b (x_1^p) = (\log_b x_1)^p$
   f) $(\log_b x_1)^p = p \log_b x_1$

4 Solve each of the following equations.
   a) $\log_{10} x = 5$ b) $\log_2 2^4 = x$
   c) $\log_4 x = \frac{3}{2}$ d) $\log_x 4 = \frac{2}{5}$
   e) $\log_3 3^x = 1$ f) $\log_3 x = -2$
   g) $\log_{10} x = 1$ h) $\log_x 5 = 1/(\log_5 x)$
   i) $\log_3 27 = x$ j) $x^{\log_x 2} = 2$

5 Solve each of the following equations.
   a) $\log_2 (x^2 - 9) - \log_2 (x + 3) = 2$
   b) $\log_{10} (x + 1) - \log_{10} x = 1$
   c) $\log_3 (x^2 + 3) = -2$
   d) $[\log_{10} (7x - 12)]/(\log_{10} x) = 2$
   e) $\log_5 \sqrt{(3x + 4)/x} = 0$
   f) $\log_4 x + \log_4 (6x + 11) = 1$
   g) $\log_3 x + \log_3 (x - 6) = \log_3 7$

6 Use Theorem 1 to simplify each of the following expressions.

a) $\log (a^2 - ab) - \log (2a - 2b)$

b) $3 \log (a^2b/c^2) + 2 \log (bc^2/a^4) + 2 \log (abc/2)$

c) $\log [(3x^2 - x)/3] + \log [10/(4x^2 - 8x)]$

$$+ \log (x - 2) - \log (3x - 1)$$

d) $\log (\tfrac{1}{4} - 1/x^2) - \log (\tfrac{1}{2} - 1/x)$

e) $\log (a + a/b) - \log (c + c/b)$

6 Computation of Logarithms

The two logarithmic bases used most often are base 10 and base e, where e, an irrational number, is approximately equal to 2.718. We will see how base 10 can be used to simplify certain computations, such as determining approximations to roots of numbers, and to solve certain types of equations, such as $2^x = 3$ and $5^{x-2} = 8$, equations that cannot be solved by the usual methods of algebra. Base 10 is called the *common base*. By convention, we usually do not write the index 10 when using logarithmic notation so that $\log x$ is the abbreviated way of writing $\log_{10} x$. Base e occurs in many of the formulas that are used in applied mathematics. Base e is called the *natural base*, and *the natural logarithm*, $\log_e x$, *is usually written* $\ln x$.

6.1 Logarithms — Base 10

For certain values of x it is easy to determine $\log x$. For example, $\log 10 = 1$ (Why?)   and $\log 100 = \log 10^2 = 2$ (Why?);   in   fact, $\log 10^n = n$. (Why?)

For other values of x it is *not* easy to determine $\log x$. Let us examine two such values to see how far we could get in computing $\log x$.

Suppose that $x = 5340$. Clearly, we could represent x as $5.34 \cdot 10^3$, so that

$$\log 5340 = \log (5.34 \cdot 10^3)$$
$$= \log 5.34 + \log 10^3$$
$$= \log 5.34 + 3$$

Hence, the problem has been reduced to finding $\log 5.34$.

Suppose that $x = 0.000234$. Then

$$\log 0.000234 = \log (2.34 \cdot 10^{-4})$$
$$= \log 2.34 + \log (10^{-4})$$
$$= \log 2.34 + (-4)$$

Here the problem is reduced to finding log 2.34. In both cases, the computation has been reduced to the computation of the logarithm of a number between 1 and 10. The procedure which is suggested by the two examples can be generalized.

Any positive number x can be represented as $x = s \cdot 10^n$, where $1 \le s < 10$ and n is an integer. This form is called the *scientific notation* for x; n is called the *characteristic* of x.

But $\log x = \log s \cdot 10^n = \log s + \log 10^n = (\log s) + n$ so that $\log x = (\log s) + n$. This latter form is called the *standard form* of $\log x$ and $\log s$ is called the *mantissa*. Note that since $y = \log x$ is increasing (see Problem Set 3, Problem 7d) and since $1 \le s < 10$, we have the fact that $\log 1 \le \log s < \log 10$, that is, $0 \le \log s < 1$. In other words, the mantissa is always a number between 0 and 1, possibly equal to 0.

Hence, the task of determining $\log x$ is reduced to determining $\log s$, where s is always between 1 and 10; but $\log s$ can be determined from the *common log table* (Table I in Appendix A), which gives us *approximations* to the values of the logarithms.

EXAMPLES

In each of the following parts, express the number in scientific notation, and then determine the common logarithm. Indicate the characteristic and the mantissa.

1 53900

SOLUTION. $53900 = 5.39 \cdot 10^4$, so that

$$
\begin{aligned}
\log 53900 &= \log 5.39 + 4 \\
&= 0.7316 + 4 \\
&= 4.7316.
\end{aligned}
$$

Hence, $10^{4.7316} = 53900$. The mantissa is 0.7316 and the characteristic is 4.

2 0.0035

SOLUTION. $0.0035 = 3.5 \cdot 10^{-3}$, so that

$$
\begin{aligned}
\log 0.0035 &= \log 3.5 - 3 \\
&= 0.5441 - 3 \\
&= -2.4559
\end{aligned}
$$

Hence, $10^{-2.4559} = 0.0035$. The mantissa is 0.5441 and the characteristic is -3.

The process of determining logarithm values can be "reversed." Given a number r, the task is to determine the value of x such that $\log x = r$. This number x is called the *antilogarithm* of r and is sometimes written as $x = \text{antilog } r$.

As with finding the logarithm, it is easy to determine x for some values of r, but not so easy for others. For example, if $\log x = -3$, $x = 10^{-3} = 0.001$; if $\log x = 5$, $x = 10^5 = 100,000$; however, if $\log x = 4.4969$, the value of x is not so easy to determine.

The antilog 4.4964, or the solution of $\log x = 4.4969$, can be determined by reversing the process of determining the logarithm. First, we write $\log x = 4.4969$ in standard form, that is, as the sum of a number between 0 and 1 and an integer.

$$\log x = 4.4969$$
$$= 0.4969 + 4$$

Second, use Table I to find a value s such that $\log s = 0.4969$. Here, $s = 3.14$. Hence,

$$\log x = 4.4969$$
$$= 0.4969 + 4$$
$$= \log 3.14 + 4$$
$$= \log 3.14 + \log 10^4$$
$$= \log (3.14 \cdot 10^4)$$

so that $x = 31400$

EXAMPLES

1   Solve $\log x = 2.7210$.

SOLUTION

$$\log x = 0.7210 + 2$$
$$= \log s + 2$$
$$= \log 5.26 + 2$$
$$= \log (5.26 \cdot 10^2)$$

so that $x = 526$

2   Find $10^{-2.0804}$.

SOLUTION.   Let $x = 10^{-2.0804}$, so that

$$\log x = -2.0804$$
$$= (-2.0804 + 3) - 3$$
$$= 0.9196 - 3$$
$$= \log 8.31 - 3$$
$$= \log (8.31 \cdot 10^{-3})$$

Hence,

$$x = 0.00831$$

6.2   Interpolation

The logarithms and antilogarithms which we computed in Section 6.1 were special in the sense that we were able to find the necessary numbers in the logarithm Table I. But what if this were not the case? Suppose, for example, that we wanted to find log 1.234 or suppose that we wanted to find the antilog 0.2217. We would not be able to find log 1.234 or mantissa 0.2217 in Table I. This problem can be resolved by using an approximation method called *linear interpolation*.

Let us investigate the meaning of linear interpolation by determining log 1.234.

$$\log 1.24 = 0.0934$$

and

$$\log 1.23 = 0.0899$$

Next let us examine that portion of the graph of $y = \log x$, where $x \in [1.23, 1.24]$ (Figure 1). log 1.234 is the length of the ordinate associated with abscissa 1.234, so that $\log (1.234) = 0.0899 + \bar{d}$, where $\bar{d}$ is the "distance" between log 1.234 and 0.0899. $\bar{d}$ is the number which we will approximate. First, we "replace" the arc of the log curve with a line segment (Figure 2). Next, we assume that $\bar{d}$ is approximately the same as d in Figure 2. (The amount of curvature of $y = \log x$ has been exaggerated in Figure 2 for illustrative purposes.)

Figure 1

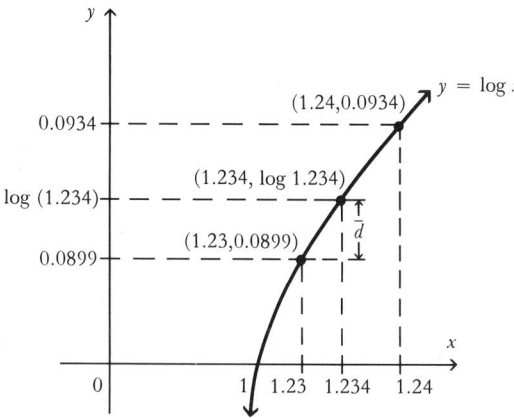

Finally, d can be determined by using the proportionality of the sides of the similar right triangles which have been formed.

$$\frac{d}{0.0035} = \frac{0.004}{0.01}$$

Figure 2

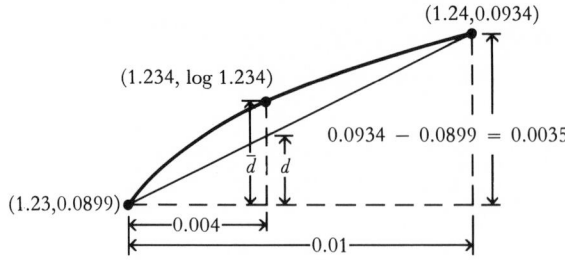

Hence,

$$d = 0.0014$$

so that

$$\log 1.234 = 0.0899 + 0.0014 \qquad \text{(Approximately)}$$
$$= 0.0913$$

EXAMPLE

Find x so that $\log x = 0.2217$, by linear interpolation.

SOLUTION.   From Table **I**, we find

$$\log 1.67 = 0.2227$$

and

$$\log 1.66 = 0.2201$$

As before, we examine the graph (Figure 3) of $y = \log x$ for $x \in [1.66, 1.67]$.

Figure 3

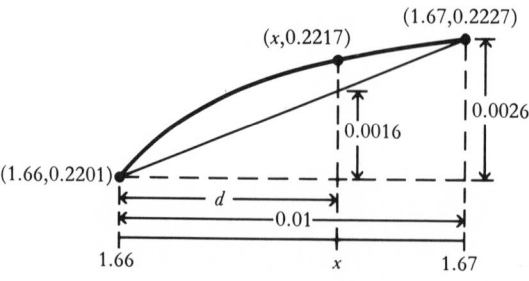

Hence,

$$\frac{d}{0.01} = \frac{0.0016}{0.0026}$$

that is, d is approximately 0.006, so that

$$x = 1.66 + 0.006 \qquad \text{(Approximately)}$$
$$= 1.666$$

Essentially, then, linear interpolation is an approximation method which replaces an arc of a curve with a straight line segment; the accuracy of this method of approximation depends on the "straightness" of the curve between the end points.

The two examples above can be organized in a manner which displays the mechanics involved in linear interpolation as follows.

EXAMPLES

1 Find log 1.234.

SOLUTION

$$0.01 \begin{bmatrix} & \log 1.24 & = 0.0934 \\ 0.004 \begin{bmatrix} \log 1.234 = & ? \\ \log 1.23 & = 0.0899 \end{bmatrix} d \end{bmatrix} 0.0035$$

First,

$$\frac{d}{0.0035} = \frac{0.004}{0.01}$$

so that $d = 0.0014$. Hence,

$$\log 1.234 = 0.0899 + d$$
$$= 0.0899 + 0.0014$$
$$= 0.0913$$

2 Solve log $x = 0.2217$.

SOLUTION

$$0.01 \begin{bmatrix} & \log 1.67 = 0.2227 \\ d \begin{bmatrix} \log x & = 0.2217 \\ \log 1.66 = 0.2201 \end{bmatrix} 0.0016 \end{bmatrix} 0.0026$$

First,

$$\frac{d}{0.01} = \frac{0.0016}{0.0026}$$

so that $d = 0.006$. Hence,

$$x = 1.66 + d$$
$$= 1.66 + 0.006$$
$$= 1.666$$

3   Use logarithms to approximate $\sqrt[5]{17}$.

SOLUTION.   Assume that $x = \sqrt[5]{17}$. Then $x = 17^{1/5}$, so that

$\log x = \frac{1}{5} \log 17$ (Why?)
$= \frac{1}{5}(\log 1.7 + 1)$
$= \frac{1}{5}(0.2304 + 1)$
$= 0.2461$ (Approximately)

Next we can determine x, that is, $\sqrt[5]{17}$, by finding the antilog 0.2461, which after interpolation, gives $x = 1.762$ (approximately).

4   Use logarithms to solve $5^x = 7$.

SOLUTION.   Since $5^x = 7$, we have $\log 5^x = \log 7$, so that $x \log 5 = \log 7$. Hence,

$$x = \frac{\log 7}{\log 5} = \frac{0.8451}{0.699} = \frac{2817}{233}$$

6.3   Logarithms Base e

We can use Table II of Appendix A, together with the general properties of logarithms, to compute natural logarithms.

EXAMPLES

1   Use natural logarithms to solve $e^{-3t} = 0.5$.

SOLUTION.   After taking the natural log of both sides of the equation, we get $\ln e^{-3t} = \ln 0.5$, so that $-3t \ln e = \ln 0.5$; that is, $-3t = \ln 0.5$, from which it follows, by Table II, that

$$t = \frac{-0.693}{-3} = 0.231$$

2   Suppose that the number of bacteria N present after t hours is given by $N = Pe^{2t}$, where P represents the number of bacteria initially present. How long will it take for the number of bacteria to triple?

SOLUTION.   We want $N = 3P$, so that $3P = Pe^{2t}$, that is, $3 = e^{2t}$, from which it follows that $\ln 3 = \ln e^{2t}$ so that $2t \ln e = \ln 3$ or, equivalently, $t = (\ln 3/2) = 1.0986/2 = 0.55$ hours (approximately).

3   *Radium decomposition.* Suppose that the amount of radium R present after t years is given by $R = Pe^{-kt}$, where P represents the number of grams initially present and k is a constant. Find k if 30 percent of the radium disappears in 100 years.

SOLUTION. When $t = 100$, $R = P - 0.3P = 0.7P$. Hence, $0.7P = Pe^{-100k}$, or equivalently, $e^{-100k} = 0.7$, so that $-100k \ln e = \ln 0.7$; that is,

$$k = \frac{\ln 0.7}{-100} = \frac{-0.357}{-100} = 0.0036 \qquad \text{(Approximately)}$$

The next theorem enables us to relate natural and common logarithms.

THEOREM 1

$\log_b x = (\log_a x)/(\log_a b)$, where a and b are positive real numbers different from 1.

PROOF. From Theorem 1, (iv) of Section 5, we know that $b^{\log_b x} = x$, so that $\log_a (b^{\log_b x}) = \log_a x$. Hence, $\log_b x \cdot \log_a b = \log_a x$, from which it follows that

$$\log_b x = \frac{\log_a x}{\log_a b}$$

EXAMPLES

1 Express $\ln x$ in terms of common logarithms.

SOLUTION

$$\ln x = \log_e x = \frac{\log x}{\log e}$$

2 Express $\log_2 10$ in terms of common logarithms.

SOLUTION

$$\log_2 10 = \frac{\log 10}{\log 2} = \frac{1}{\log 2}$$

3 Show that $\log_a b \cdot \log_b a = 1$ for a and b positive numbers different from 1.

SOLUTION

$$\log_a b = \frac{\log_b b}{\log_b a} = \frac{1}{\log_b a}$$

so that

$$\log_a b \cdot \log_b a = 1$$

4 Show that $\ln (\ln x) = \ln (\log x) - \ln (\log e)$.

SOLUTION.   We know that $\ln x = (\log x)/(\log e)$, so that

$$\ln (\ln x) = \ln \left(\frac{\log x}{\log e}\right) = \ln (\log x) - \ln (\log e)$$

PROBLEM SET 5

1 Express each of the following numbers in scientific notation, and then compute the common logarithm. Interpolate if necessary. Indicate the mantissa and characteristic.

a) 0.015
b) 1547
c) $\frac{1}{434}$
d) 795.6
e) 33.33
f) 17
g) 0.00000137
h) 1370000
i) $\frac{100}{5171}$
j) $3^{1/5}$
k) 17^4
l) $171^{1/4}$

2 Find the approximate value of the antilogarithm. Interpolate if necessary.

a) $\log x = 3.1461$
b) $\log x = -1.5050$
c) $\log x = 0.15$
d) $\ln x = 0.1989$
e) $\log x = -9.5031$
f) $\ln x = 2.3$

3 Graph $y = \sqrt{x}$. Use linear interpolation, together with the fact that $\sqrt{1} = 1$ and $\sqrt{4} = 2$, to approximate $\sqrt{2}$. Square your result to see how "close" your approximation is to $\sqrt{2}$.

4 Use common logarithms to approximate each of the following values.

a) $\log_2 5$
b) $\log_{1/10} 10$
c) $\ln 3$
d) $\log_5 \left(\frac{1}{3}\right)$
e) $\log_{1/3} \left(\frac{4}{3}\right)$

5 Use logarithms to solve each of the following equations.

a) $2^x = 7$
b) $e^x = 5$
c) $17^{2x-1} = 4^{-x}$
d) $e^{-4/x} = 0.6$

6 Use logarithms to approximate each of the following values. (Use $\pi = 3.14$.)

a) $\sqrt{11}$
b) e^π
c) $(0.515)^3(4.7)^5/97^2$
d) $\sqrt[3]{731}$
e) $\sqrt{\sqrt{\sqrt{7}}}$

7 Assume that it is known that the number of bacteria N present after t minutes is given by $N = 1000e^{0.25t}$.

a) How many bacteria are present after one-half hour?
b) How long will it take to have 50,000 bacteria?

8 The half-life of radium is defined to be the time required for a given amount of radium to decrease by one-half. Assume that the amount of radium R present after t years is given by $R = Pe^{-kt}$, where P represents the number of grams initially present and k is a constant.

a)   Find k if the half-life is 50 years.

b)   Find the half-life if $k = 0.005$.

9   If interest is compounded continuously, that is, the number of conver-
sions within any year becomes "infinite," the continuously compounded
interest formula

$$A = Pe^{nr}$$

is used, where P represents the principal, r represents the rate of interest
per year expressed as a decimal, A represents the total accumulation
after n years, and e is the natural base. Use this formula to answer the
following questions. Suppose that $1000 is placed at a yearly interest
rate of 6 percent compounded continuously.

a)   How much money is accumulated after 4 years?

b)   In how many years would the $1000 double at this rate?

7   Mathematical Induction

In deductive reasoning, the process usually begins with a basic assumption called the *hypothesis*. Next, established axioms, definitions, and theorems are used to "deduce" from the hypothesis a valid statement. This
latter statement is used in turn to deduce another valid statement and so
on until a sequence of valid statements has been organized that concludes
with the statement to be proven.

The use of the deductive reasoning process is not always apparent
when proving general mathematical statements. Let us consider an example. Suppose we were given the task to prove or disprove the validity
of the following assertion:

$$1 + 2 + 3 + \cdots + n = \frac{n(n + 1)}{2} \qquad \text{for any positive integer } n$$

Observe that if $n = 1$, then $1 = 1(1 + 1)/2$, which is true; if $n = 2$,
then $1 + 2 = 2(2 + 1)/2$, which is also true; if $n = 3$, then $1 + 2 +
3 = 3(3 + 1)/2$, which is again true.

These tested values of n can only give us an *impression* that the equation
is valid. Simply testing these values is not adequate to establish a formal
proof of the equation for all possible values of n.

Let us consider another example. Suppose we were to prove or disprove the following statement:

$$1 + 4 + 7 + \cdots + (3n - 2) = \frac{n(3n - 1)}{2} \qquad \text{for any positive integer } n$$

We can begin to test the equation for specific values of n as we did in the first example. If $n = 1$, then the statement becomes $1 = 1(3 \cdot 1 - 1)/2$, which is true; if $n = 2$, then we have $1 + 4 = 2(3 \cdot 2 - 1)/2$, which is also true; if $n = 3$, then we have $1 + 4 + 7 = 3(3 \cdot 3 - 1)/2$, which is true. Again, however, our testing process is not enough to give us a generalized proof.

In order to establish a formal proof of each of the above statements, we need a method of proof which makes use of the *principle of mathematical induction*.

7.1   Principle of Mathematical Induction

Suppose that S_1, S_2, S_3, ... is a sequence of assertions; that is, suppose that for each positive integer n we have a corresponding assertion S_n. Assume that the following two conditions hold.

i S_1 is true.

ii   For each fixed positive integer k, S_k implies S_{k+1}.

Then it follows that every assertion S_1, S_2, S_3, ... is true, that is, S_n is true for all positive integers.

Let us see how the principle can be applied to prove the first statement above.

S_n is the assertion:

$$1 + 2 + 3 + \cdots + n = \tfrac{1}{2}n(n + 1)$$

So far as we know, S_n may be true for certain values of n and false for other values of n. In order to show that S_n is, in fact, true for all values of n, we need to verify the following conditions:

i S_1 is true.

ii   If S_k is true, then S_{k+1} is also true, where k is a fixed positive integer.

Condition (i) can be verified by direct computation, for S_1 is the assertion which states that $1 = (\tfrac{1}{2})(1)(1 + 1)$, which is clearly true.

To prove condition (2), we must show that S_k implies S_{k+1}; that is, we must show that if S_k is assumed to be true, then S_{k+1} must be true. To this end, assume that S_k is true; that is, assume that

$$1 + 2 + 3 + \cdots + k = (\tfrac{1}{2})k(k + 1)$$

Since S_k is a valid equation, we can add $(k + 1)$ to both sides of this equation, so that

$$
\begin{aligned}
1 + 2 + 3 + \cdots + k + (k + 1) \\
= (\tfrac{1}{2})k(k + 1) + (k + 1) \\
= (\tfrac{1}{2})(k + 1)[(k + 1) + 1]
\end{aligned}
$$

But the latter assertion is precisely S_{k+1}.

Hence, we have proved condition (ii). Thus, by the principle of mathematical induction, we conclude that S_n is true for any positive integer n; therefore, $1 + 2 + 3 + \cdots + n = (\tfrac{1}{2})n(n + 1)$ for any positive integer n.

Let us investigate other examples to see how the principle of mathematical induction is especially valuable in proving certain statements in algebra which are to hold for all positive integers.

EXAMPLES

1   Use mathematical induction to prove that for any positive integer n

$$1 + 4 + 7 + \cdots + (3n - 2) = \frac{n(3n - 1)}{2}$$

PROOF.   Since the principle of mathematical induction will be used, we must prove the two conditions where S_n is the equation

$$1 + 4 + 7 + \cdots + (3n - 2) = \frac{n(3n - 1)}{2}$$

i S_1 becomes $1 = 1(3 \cdot 1 - 1)/2$, which is true.

ii   Assume that S_k is true; that is, assume that for any fixed positive integer k,

$$1 + 4 + 7 + \cdots + (3k - 2) = \frac{k(3k - 1)}{2}$$

We are to prove that S_{k+1} is true; that is, we must prove that for each positive integer k,

$$1 + 4 + 7 + \cdots + (3k - 2) + (3k + 1) = \frac{(k + 1)(3k + 2)}{2}$$

Since S_k is a valid equation, we can add $(3k + 1)$ to each side of this equation, so that

$$1 + 4 + 7 + \cdots + (3k - 2) + (3k + 1) = \frac{k(3k - 1)}{2} + (3k + 1)$$

$$= \frac{3k^2 + 5k + 2}{2}$$

$$= \frac{(k + 1)(3k + 2)}{2}$$

Hence, S_{k+1} is true and we have proved condition (ii). Thus, we conclude that

$$1 + 4 + 7 + \cdots + (3n - 2) = \frac{n(3n - 1)}{2}$$

is true for any positive integer n.

2 Use mathematical induction to prove that $x^n - y^n$ is divisible by $(x - y)$ for any positive integer n whenever $x \neq y$.

PROOF. Using the principle of mathematical induction, we must prove the following two conditions.

i   For $n = 1$, $x^n - y^n = x - y$, which is divisible by $x - y$, so that the assertion S_1 is true.

ii Assume that the assertion S_k is true; that is, for any fixed positive integer k, assume that $x^k - y^k$ is divisible by $(x - y)$. We are to show that S_{k+1} is true; that is, we must show that $x^{k+1} - y^{k+1}$ is divisible by $(x - y)$. Now,

$$x^{k+1} - y^{k+1} = x^{k+1} - xy^k + xy^k - y^{k+1}$$
$$= x(x^k - y^k) + y^k(x - y)$$

so that the right-hand side of the above equation is divisible by $(x - y)$; hence, the left-hand side, $x^{k+1} - y^{k+1}$, is also divisible by $(x - y)$ (Why?); therefore, the assertion S_{k+1} is true and the proof is complete.

Earlier in this chapter in Section 2, we stated Theorem 1. It would be possible to argue the proof of Theorem 1 in an informal way. For example, part (i) of this theorem can be verified by lining up factors in the product $a^m \cdot a^n$ and observing that $m + n$ factors are present:

$$a^n \cdot a^m = \underbrace{(a \cdot a \cdots a)}_{m}\underbrace{(a \cdot a \cdots a)}_{n} = a^{m+n}$$

The formal proof of Theorem 1 (see Problem 2) is based on mathematical induction and the following *recursive definition:*

> *If a is a real number and n is any positive integer, then* $a^1 = a$
> *and* $a^{n+1} = a^n \cdot a^1$.

EXAMPLES

1 Use the recursive definition, together with mathematical induction, to prove that if a is a real number and n is any positive integer, then

$$a^n = \overbrace{a \cdot a \cdot a \cdots a}^{n \text{ factors}}.$$

PROOF

i We have $a^1 = a$ by definition, which shows that S_1 is true.

ii Assume that S_k is true; that is, assume that $a^k = \underbrace{a \cdot a \cdot a \cdots a}_{k \text{ factors}}$.

We must show that S_{k+1} is true. Since $a^{k+1} = a^k \cdot a^1$ by the recursive definition,

$$a^{k+1} = \underbrace{(a \cdot a \cdot a \cdots a)}_{k \text{ factors}} \cdot a$$

so that

$$a^{k+1} = \underbrace{a \cdot a \cdot a \cdots a \cdot a}_{k+1 \text{ factors}}$$

Hence, S_{k+1} is true. Consequently, by induction, S_n is true for any positive integer n; that is,

$$a^n = \underbrace{a \cdot a \cdot a \cdots a}_{n \text{ factors}}$$

2 *Theorem 1, i.* Prove that if a is a real number and m and n are positive integers, then $a^m \cdot a^n = a^{m+n}$.

PROOF. Here again we will use the recursive definition above, together with mathematical induction.

i If we let m represent *any* fixed positive integer, then

$$a^m \cdot a^1 = a^{m+1}$$

by the recursive definition, which shows that the assertion S_1 is true.

ii   Assume that the assertion S_k is true; that is, assume that $a^m \cdot a^k = a^{m+k}$. We must show that S_{k+1} is true; that is, we must show that $a^m \cdot a^{k+1} = a^{m+k+1}$.

By the induction hypothesis, we have

$$a^m \cdot a^k \cdot a^1 = a^{m+k}a$$

Using the recursive definition on each side of equation (1), we find that

$$a^m \cdot a^{k+1} = a^{(m+k)+1}$$
$$= a^{m+(k+1)}$$

which shows that the assertion S_{k+1} is true. Consequently, by induction, S_n is true for any positive integer n; that is, $a^m \cdot a^n = a^{m+n}$.

7.2 Binomial Expansions

The principle of mathematical induction is used to prove a theorem that provides a technique other than repeated multiplication for expanding positive integral powers of binomial expressions, such as $(x + 3)^{10}$ and $(2x - y)^8$. This theorem is called the *binomial theorem*.

Before investigating this theorem, let us consider some examples of expanding the binomial $a + b$ to integral powers.

$$(a + b)^1 = a + b$$
$$(a + b)^2 = a^2 + 2ab + b^2$$
$$(a + b)^3 = a^3 + 3a^2b + 3ab^2 + b^3$$
$$(a + b)^4 = a^4 + 4a^3b + 6a^2b^2 + 4ab^3 + b^4$$
$$(a + b)^5 = a^5 + 5a^4b + 10a^3b^2 + 10a^2b^3 + 5ab^4 + b^5$$

Notice that the following pattern holds for the a and b terms in the expansion of $(a + b)^n$, where n is a positive integer.

i   There are $n + 1$ terms; the "first term" is a^n; the "last term" is b^n.

ii   The power of a decreases by 1 for each term, and the power of b increases by 1 for each term. In any case, the sum of the exponents of a and b is n for each term.

The pattern for the coefficients is easier to detect if the following notation is used. 0! (zero factorial) is defined as 0! = 1. If n is a positive integer, $n!$ (n factorial) is defined as $n! = n(n - 1)(n - 2) \cdots 3 \cdot 2 \cdot 1$. For example,

$$5! = 5 \cdot 4 \cdot 3 \cdot 2 \cdot 1 = 120$$

and

$$7! = 7 \cdot 6 \cdot 5! = (42)(120) = 5040$$

Now, if $0 \le k \le n$, where k and n are integers, then the binomial coefficient, $\binom{n}{k}$, is given by

$$\binom{n}{k} = \frac{n!}{k!(n - k)!}.$$

For example,

$$\binom{5}{3} = \frac{5!}{3!(5 - 3)!} = \frac{5!}{3!2!} = 10$$

$$\binom{17}{14} = \frac{17!}{14!(17 - 14)!} = \frac{17!}{14!3!} = 680$$

$$\binom{5}{2} = \frac{5!}{2!(5 - 2)!} = \frac{5!}{2!3!} = 10$$

The binomial theorem formalizes the patterns that occur in binomial expansions.

THEOREM 1   BINOMIAL THEOREM

Let a and b be real numbers and let n be a positive integer; then

$$(a + b)^n = \binom{n}{0} a^n + \binom{n}{1} a^{n-1}b + \cdots$$
$$+ \binom{n}{k} a^{n-k}b^k + \cdots + \binom{n}{n} b^n$$

PROOF.   Use the principle of mathematical induction. Let S_1 be the statement: $(a + b)^1 = (a^1 + b^1)$.

i S_1 is certainly true. (Why?)

ii   We must show that if S_n is true, then S_{n+1} is also true.
    [Notice that we are using n instead of k for (ii).]

To this end assume that S_n is true; that is, assume that

$$(a + b)^n = \binom{n}{0} a^n + \binom{n}{1} a^{n-1}b + \cdots$$
$$+ \binom{n}{k} a^{n-k}b^k + \cdots + \binom{n}{n} b^n$$

for n a positive integer. After multiplying both sides by $(a + b)$, we obtain

$$
(a + b)^n(a + b)
$$

$$
= (a + b)\left[\binom{n}{0} a^n + \binom{n}{1} a^{n-1}b + \cdots \right.
$$

$$
+ \binom{n}{k} a^{n-k}b^k + \cdots + \left.\binom{n}{n} b^n\right]
$$

$$
= \binom{n}{0}(a^{n+1} + a^n b) + \binom{n}{1}(a^n b + a^{n-1}b^2) + \cdots
$$

$$
+ \binom{n}{k}(a^{n-k+1}b^k + a^{n-k}b^{k+1}) + \cdots
$$

$$
+ \binom{n}{n}(ab^n + b^{n+1})
$$

$$
= \binom{n}{0} a^{n+1} + \left[\binom{n}{0} + \binom{n}{1}\right] a^n b
$$

$$
+ \left[\binom{n}{1} + \binom{n}{2}\right] a^{n-1}b^2 + \cdots
$$

$$
+ \left[\binom{n}{k-1} + \binom{n}{k}\right] a^{n+1-k}b^k + \cdots + \binom{n}{n} b^{n+1}
$$

But,

$$
\binom{n}{k-1} + \binom{n}{k} = \frac{n!}{(k-1)!(n-k+1)!} + \frac{n!}{k!(n-k)!}
$$

$$
= \frac{n!k + n!(n-k+1)}{k!(n-k+1)!}
$$

$$
= \frac{n!(n+1)}{k!(n+1-k)!}
$$

$$
= \frac{(n+1)!}{k!(n+1-k)!}
$$

$$
= \binom{n+1}{k}
$$

so that

$$
(a + b)^{n+1} = \binom{n}{0} a^{n+1} + \binom{n+1}{1} a^n b + \cdots
$$

$$
+ \binom{n+1}{k} a^{n+1-k}b^k + \cdots + \binom{n+1}{n+1} b^{n+1}
$$

But the latter assertion is precisely S_{n+1}, and the proof is complete.

EXAMPLES

Use the binomial theorem to solve each of the following problems.

1   Expand $(x + y)^5$.

SOLUTION. By the binomial theorem,

$$(x + y)^5 = \binom{5}{0} x^5 + \binom{5}{1} x^4 y + \binom{5}{2} x^3 y^2 + \binom{5}{3} x^2 y^3$$
$$+ \binom{5}{4} xy^4 + \binom{5}{5} y^5$$
$$= x^5 + \frac{5!}{1!4!} x^4 y + \frac{5!}{2!3!} x^3 y^2 + \frac{5!}{3!2!} x^2 y^3 + \frac{5!}{4!1!} xy^4 + y^5$$
$$= x^5 + 5x^4 y + 10x^3 y^2 + 10x^2 y^3 + 5xy^4 + y^5$$

2 Expand $(x - 3)^4$.

SOLUTION

$$(x - 3)^4 = (x + (-3))^4$$
$$= \binom{4}{0} x^4 + \binom{4}{1} x^3 (-3) + \binom{4}{2} x^2 (-3)^2$$
$$+ \binom{4}{3} x(-3)^3 + \binom{4}{4} (-3)^4$$
$$= x^4 + 4x^3 (-3) + 6x^2 (-3)^2 + 4x(-3)^3 + (-3)^4$$
$$= x^4 - 12x^3 + 54x^2 - 108x + 81$$

Notice the "symmetry" of the values of the coefficients of the binomial theorem.

$$(a + b)^2 = 1a^2 + 2ab + 1b^2$$
$$(a + b)^3 = 1a^3 + 3a^2 b + 3ab^2 + 1b^3$$

and

$$(a + b)^4 = 1a^4 + 4a^3 b + 6a^2 b^2 + 4ab^3 + 1b^4$$

In general,

$$(a + b)^n = \binom{n}{0} a^n + \binom{n}{1} a^{n-1} b + \binom{n}{2} a^{n-2} b^2 + \cdots + \binom{n}{n-2} a^2 b^{n-2} + \binom{n}{n-1} ab^{n-1} + \binom{n}{n} b^n$$

where

$$\binom{n}{k} = \binom{n}{n-k}$$

since

$$\binom{n}{k} = \frac{n!}{k!(n-k)!}$$

and

$$\binom{n}{n-k} = \frac{n!}{(n-k)!(n-(n-k))!} = \frac{n!}{(n-k)!k!}$$

3   Find the expansion of $(3x^2 - \frac{1}{2}\sqrt{y})^4$.

SOLUTION

$$(3x^2 - \tfrac{1}{2}\sqrt{y})^4 = (3x^2)^4 - 4(3x^2)^3(\tfrac{1}{2}\sqrt{y}) + 6(3x^2)^2(\tfrac{1}{2}\sqrt{y})^2$$
$$- 4(3x^2)(\tfrac{1}{2}\sqrt{y})^3 + (\tfrac{1}{2}\sqrt{y})^4$$
$$= 81x^8 - 54x^6\sqrt{y} + \tfrac{27}{2}x^4 y - \tfrac{3}{2}x^2 y^{3/2} + \tfrac{1}{16}y^2$$

4   Find the sixth term of the expansion of $(2x - y^2)^8$.

SOLUTION.   The sixth term is

$$\binom{8}{5}(2x)^3(-y^2)^5 = -\binom{8}{3}8x^3 y^{10}$$

$$= -\frac{8 \cdot 7 \cdot 6}{3 \cdot 2 \cdot 1}8x^3 y^{10}$$

$$= -448x^3 y^{10}$$

PROBLEM SET 6

1   Prove the following identities by using the principle of mathematical induction.

a) $1 + 3 + 5 + \cdots + (2n - 1) = n^2$
b) $1^2 + 2^2 + 3^2 + \cdots + n^2 = [n(n + 1)(2n + 1)]/6$
c) $1^3 + 2^3 + 3^3 + \cdots + n^3 = [n^2(n + 1)^2]/4$
d) $2 + 4 + 6 + \cdots + 2n = n^2 + n + 1$

2   Use the principle of mathematical induction to prove Theorem 1 of Section 2, parts (ii), (iii), and (iv); that is, prove that if a and b are real numbers and m and n are positive integers, then

a) $(a^n)^m = a^{nm}$ b) $(ab)^n = a^n b^n$
c) $a^m/a^n = a^{m-n}$, $m > n$, $a \neq 0$

(*Hint:* Use either induction on n or induction on m, but not both at once.)

3   Prove that $a^{2n} - b^{2n}$ is divisible by $a + b$, where a and b are real numbers and n is a positive integer.

4   Prove the following identities by using mathematical induction:

a) $\dfrac{1}{1 + 2} + \dfrac{1}{2 + 3} + \dfrac{1}{3 + 4} + \cdots + \dfrac{1}{n(n + 1)} = \dfrac{n}{n + 1}$
b) $4 + 4^2 + 4^3 + \cdots + 4^n = \tfrac{4}{3}(4^n - 1)$

5   Prove that for any number $x \neq 1$

$$x^0 + x^1 + x^2 + \cdots + x^n = \frac{1 - x^{n+1}}{1 - x}$$

6   Prove that $n(n^2 + 5)$ is divisible by 6 for any positive integer n.

7 Evaluate each of the following expressions.

a) $\binom{15}{10}$ b) $\binom{n}{n}$ c) $\binom{6}{2}$

d) $\binom{15}{5}$ e) $\binom{n}{0}$ f) $\binom{6}{5}$

g) $\binom{15}{3}$ h) $\binom{n}{1}$ i) $\binom{6}{4}$

8 a) Show that

$$\binom{n}{r} + \binom{n}{r+1} = \binom{n+1}{r+1}$$

b) Let $a = x = 1$ in the expansion of $(a + x)^n$, and find the sum

$$\binom{n}{0} + \binom{n}{1} + \binom{n}{2} + \cdots + \binom{n}{n}$$

9 Find the first four terms of the following expansions.

a) $(x^2 - 2a)^{10}$ b) $(2a - 1/b)^6$
c) $(\sqrt{x/2} + 2y)^7$ d) $(1/a + x/2)^{11}$
e) $(a^{3/2} - 2x^2)^8$

10 Use the binomial theorem to expand each of the following expressions.

a) $(2z + x)^5$ b) $(x - 3)^4$
c) $(y^2 - 2x)^4$ d) $(1/a + x/2)^3$

11 Find the indicated term for each of the following expressions by using the binomial theorem.

a) $(x^2/2 + a)^{15}$, 4th term b) $(y^2 - 2z)^{10}$, 6th term
c) $(2x^2 - a^2/3)^9$, 7th term d) $(x + \sqrt{a})^{12}$, middle term
e) $(a + x^2/3)^9$, term containing x^{12}
f) $(2\sqrt{y} - x/2)^{10}$, term containing y^4

8 Finite Sums and Series

We shall discover in this section an abbreviated way, called sigma notation, to write finite sums of a recursive nature such as those sums produced by the binomial theorem. Motivated by the notion of finite sums, we will survey geometric series which are, in a sense, special types of "infinite sums."

8.1   Finite Sums

$\sum_{k=1}^{n} a_k$ is called *sigma notation* and is an abbreviated way of writing the finite sum $a_1 + a_2 + \cdots + a_n$, that is, $\sum_{k=1}^{n} a_k = a_1 + a_2 + \cdots + a_n$. Here, a_k represents some function where k, called the *index*, represents the domain variable. For example,

$$\sum_{k=1}^{4} \frac{1}{k} = 1 + \tfrac{1}{2} + \tfrac{1}{3} + \tfrac{1}{4} = \tfrac{25}{12} \qquad \text{with } a_k = \frac{1}{k}$$

EXAMPLES

Evaluate each of the following finite sums in 1, 2, and 3.

1   $\displaystyle\sum_{k=1}^{3} (4k^2 - 3k)$

SOLUTION. $a_k = 4k^2 - 3k$. To find the indicated sum, we substitute the integers 1, 2, and 3 for k in succession, then add the resulting numbers. Thus

$$\sum_{k=1}^{3} (4k^2 - 3k) = (4(1^2) - 3(1)) + (4(2^2) - 3(2)) + (4(3^2) - 3(3))$$
$$= 1 + 10 + 27 = 38$$

2   $\displaystyle\sum_{k=3}^{6} k(k - 2)$

SOLUTION. $a_k = k(k - 2)$. Notice here that the index begins with 3. To find the indicated sum, we substitute the integers 3, 4, 5, and 6 in succession, then add the resulting numbers. Thus

$$\sum_{k=3}^{6} k(k - 2) = (3(3 - 2)) + (4(4 - 2)) + (5(5 - 2)) + (6(6 - 2))$$
$$= 3 + 8 + 15 + 24 = 50$$

3   $\displaystyle\sum_{k=2}^{5} \frac{k - 1}{k + 1}$

SOLUTION.   Here $a_k = (k - 1)/(k + 1)$ so that

$$\sum_{k=2}^{5} \frac{k - 1}{k + 1} = \left(\frac{2 - 1}{2 + 1}\right) + \left(\frac{3 - 1}{3 + 1}\right) + \left(\frac{4 - 1}{4 + 1}\right) + \left(\frac{5 - 1}{5 + 1}\right)$$
$$= \tfrac{1}{3} + \tfrac{2}{4} + \tfrac{3}{5} + \tfrac{4}{6} = \tfrac{21}{10}$$

4   Write each of the following finite sums in sigma notation.

a) $1 + \tfrac{1}{2} + \tfrac{1}{4} + \tfrac{1}{8} + \tfrac{1}{16}$

b)   The binomial theorem formula:

$$(a + b)^n = \binom{n}{0} a^n + \binom{n}{1} a^{n-1}b + \cdots + \binom{n}{k} a^{n-k}b^k + \cdots + \binom{n}{n} b^n$$

SOLUTION.

a) $1 + \frac{1}{2} + \frac{1}{4} + \frac{1}{8} + \frac{1}{16} = (\frac{1}{2})^0 + (\frac{1}{2})^1 + (\frac{1}{2})^2 + (\frac{1}{2})^3 + (\frac{1}{2})^4$

$$= \sum_{k=0}^{4} (\tfrac{1}{2})^k$$

or, equivalently,

$$1 + \tfrac{1}{2} + \tfrac{1}{4} + \tfrac{1}{8} + \tfrac{1}{16} = \sum_{k=1}^{5} (\tfrac{1}{2})^{k-1} \qquad \text{(Why?)}$$

b) $\binom{n}{0} a^n + \binom{n}{1} a^{n-1}b + \cdots + \binom{n}{k} a^{n-k}b^k + \cdots + \binom{n}{n} b^n$

$$= \binom{n}{0} a^n b^0 + \binom{n}{1} a^{n-1}b^1 + \cdots + \binom{n}{k} a^{n-k}b^k + \cdots + \binom{n}{n} a^{n-n}b^n$$

$$= \sum_{k=0}^{n} \binom{n}{k} a^{n-k}b^k$$

so that

$$(a + b)^n = \sum_{k=0}^{n} \binom{n}{k} a^{n-k}b^n$$

8.2   Geometric Series

If a_n determines a sequence (see Chapter 2, Section 4.3) and $s_n = \sum_{k=1}^{n} a_k = a_1 + a_2 + \cdots + a_n$, then the sequence determined by s_n is called an *infinite series* and it is usually written as $\sum_{k=1}^{\infty} a_k$. We will be concerned with determining the "sums" of geometric series.

Geometric series are series of the form $\sum_{k=1}^{\infty} ar^{k-1}$ where a is a constant and $|r| < 1$. For example,

$$\sum_{k=1}^{\infty} (\tfrac{1}{2})^{k-1} = 1 + \tfrac{1}{2} + \tfrac{1}{4} + \tfrac{1}{8} + \cdots + (\tfrac{1}{2})^k + \cdots$$

is a geometric series in which $a = 1$ and $r = \frac{1}{2}$.

The notion of an "infinite sum" is defined as follows.

Suppose that $\sum_{k=1}^{\infty} a_k$ is an infinite series.

First, *partial sums* are formed

$$s_1 = a_1$$
$$s_2 = a_1 + a_2$$
$$s_3 = a_1 + a_2 + a_3$$
$$\cdots \cdots \cdots \cdots \cdots \cdots$$
$$s_n = a_1 + a_2 + \cdots + a_n = \sum_{k=1}^{n} a_k$$

Then the sum S of $\sum_{k=1}^{\infty} a_k$, written $S = \sum_{k=1}^{\infty} a_k$, is defined to be the "limit value" that s_n approaches as "n approaches infinity," if the limit value is finite

Let us use this notion to determine the formula for the sum of a geometric series

$$\sum_{k=1}^{\infty} ar^{k-1}, \qquad |r| < 1$$

Here, $a_k = ar^{k-1}$ so that

$$s_1 = a$$
$$s_2 = a + ar$$
$$s_3 = a + ar + ar^2$$
$$\cdots \cdots \cdots \cdots \cdots \cdots \cdots \cdots \cdots \cdots \cdots$$

(1) $$s_n = a + ar + ar^2 + ar^3 + \cdots + ar^{n-1}$$

Upon multiplying both sides of equation (1) by r, we get

(2) $$rs_n = ar + ar^2 + ar^3 + \cdots + ar^n$$

Next subtract Eq. (2) from Eq. (1) to get

$$s_n - rs_n = a - ar^n$$

so that

$$(1 - r)s_n = a - ar^n$$

Hence,

$$s_n = \frac{a - ar^n}{1 - r} \qquad \text{where } |r| < 1$$

However, this latter equation can be written as

$$s_n = \frac{a}{1 - r} - \frac{ar^n}{1 - r}$$

Intuitively, we can see that as n becomes increasingly large (as n approaches infinity) r^n approaches 0. (Consider what happens for example to the values of $(\frac{1}{2})^n$ as n becomes larger and larger by examining the graph of $f(n) = (\frac{1}{2})^n$.)

Consequently, s_n approaches $a/(1 - r)$ as n approaches infinity so that

$$\sum_{k=1}^{\infty} ar^{k-1} = \frac{a}{1 - r} \qquad \text{where } |r| < 1$$

For example

$$\sum_{k=1}^{\infty} (\tfrac{1}{2})^{k-1} = \frac{1}{1 - \frac{1}{2}} = 2$$

The next example shows that geometric series have an interesting application in connection with the repeating decimals that were introduced in Chapter 1.

EXAMPLE

Use geometric series to find the rational number which corresponds to the following decimals:

a) $0.33\overline{3}$

b) $0.2424\overline{24}$

SOLUTION

a) From the expression $0.33\overline{3}$, we obtain the geometric series

$$0.33\overline{3} = \frac{3}{10} + \frac{3}{100} + \frac{3}{1000} + \frac{3}{10,000} + \cdots + \frac{3}{10^n} + \cdots$$

$$= \tfrac{3}{10} + \tfrac{3}{10}(\tfrac{1}{10}) + \tfrac{3}{10}(\tfrac{1}{10})^2 + \tfrac{3}{10}(\tfrac{1}{10})^3 + \cdots + \tfrac{3}{10}(\tfrac{1}{10})^{n-1} + \cdots$$

$$= \sum_{k=1}^{\infty} \tfrac{3}{10}(\tfrac{1}{10})^{k-1}$$

Here, $a = \tfrac{3}{10}$ and $r = \tfrac{1}{10}$ so that the sum is given by

$$0.33\overline{3} = \frac{\frac{3}{10}}{1 - \frac{1}{10}} = \tfrac{1}{3}$$

b) $0.2424\overline{24}$ can be written as

$$0.2424\overline{24} = \frac{24}{100} + \frac{24}{10,000} + \frac{24}{100,000} + \cdots$$

$$= \sum_{k=1}^{\infty} (\tfrac{24}{100})(\tfrac{1}{100})^{k-1}$$

We have a geometric series in which $a = \tfrac{24}{100}$ and $r = \tfrac{1}{100}$. Hence,

$$0.2424\overline{24} = \frac{\frac{24}{100}}{1 - \frac{1}{100}} = \frac{24}{99} = \frac{8}{33}$$

PROBLEM SET 7

1 Find the numerical values of each of the following finite sums.

a) $\displaystyle\sum_{k=1}^{5} k$

b) $\displaystyle\sum_{k=0}^{4} 3^{2k}$

c) $\displaystyle\sum_{k=1}^{3} (2k + 1)$

d) $\displaystyle\sum_{k=1}^{4} k^k$

e) $\displaystyle\sum_{k=1}^{5} \frac{1}{k(k + 1)}$

f) $\displaystyle\sum_{k=0}^{4} \frac{2^k}{(k + 1)}$

g) $\displaystyle\sum_{k=2}^{5} 2^{k-2}$

h) $\displaystyle\sum_{k=1}^{5} (3k^2 - 5k + 1)$

i) $\displaystyle\sum_{k=1}^{100} 5$

j) $\displaystyle\sum_{k=1}^{4} \frac{3}{k}$

2   Use the principle of mathematical induction to prove each of the following formulas.

a) $\displaystyle\sum_{k=1}^{n} k = \frac{n(n+1)}{2}$

b) $\displaystyle\sum_{k=1}^{n} (2k-1) = n^2$

c) $\displaystyle\sum_{k=1}^{n} k^2 = \frac{n^3}{3} + \frac{n^2}{2} + \frac{n}{6}$

3   Express each of the following finite sums in sigma notation.

a) $1 + 4 + 7 + 10 + 13$

b) $\frac{1}{2} + \frac{1}{4} + \frac{1}{8} + \frac{1}{16} + \frac{1}{32}$

c) $\frac{3}{5} + \frac{9}{25} + \frac{27}{125} + \frac{81}{625}$

d) $\frac{1}{6} + \frac{2}{11} + \frac{3}{16} + \frac{4}{21}$

4   Determine whether each of the following statements is true or false. Give the reason.

a) $\displaystyle\sum_{k=0}^{100} k^3 = \sum_{k=1}^{100} k^3$

b) $\displaystyle\sum_{k=0}^{100} 2 = 200$

c) $\displaystyle\sum_{k=0}^{100} (k+2) = \left(\sum_{k=0}^{100} k\right) + 2$

d) $\displaystyle\sum_{k=0}^{99} (k+1)^2 = \sum_{k=1}^{100} k^2$

e) $\displaystyle\sum_{k=0}^{100} k^2 = \left(\sum_{k=0}^{100} k\right)^2$

5   Find the sum of each of the following geometric series.

a) $\frac{1}{3} + \frac{1}{9} + \frac{1}{27} + \frac{1}{81} + \cdots + (\frac{1}{3})^n + \cdots$

b) $\frac{2}{3} + \frac{4}{9} + \frac{8}{27} + \cdots + (\frac{2}{3})^n + \cdots$

c) $\frac{1}{5} + \frac{1}{25} + \frac{1}{125} + \cdots + (\frac{1}{5})^n + \cdots$

d) $\frac{9}{8} + \frac{9}{64} + \frac{9}{512} + \cdots + (\frac{9}{8})^n + \cdots$

6   Use geometric series to find the rational number that is represented by each of the following decimal numbers.

a) $0.323\overline{232}$

b) $0.04999\overline{9}$

c) $0.4646\overline{46}$

d) $0.072072\overline{072}$

e) $3.561561\overline{561}$

d) $32.421842184\overline{218}$

REVIEW PROBLEM SET

1   Simplify each of the following expressions.

a) $a^{n+4}a^n$

b) $2^n \cdot 4^{n-1} \cdot 8^{n+1}$

c) $x^{n+2} \cdot x^{-n+2}$

d) $(x^{-1})^3$

e) $(4x/y)(\sqrt{y^2/4x})$

f) $\sqrt[3]{\frac{1}{2}x^2} \cdot \sqrt[4]{\frac{1}{3}x^3}$

2 Simplify each of the following expressions:

a) $\dfrac{\log_2 \sqrt{\frac{1}{8}} - \log_2 16^{1/3}}{\log_8 64 \cdot \log_3 3^{1/6}}$

b) $\dfrac{\log_3 \sqrt{243\sqrt{81^3\sqrt{3}}}}{\log_2 \sqrt[4]{64} + \log_e e^{-10}}$

c) $\dfrac{\log_7 7^{4.2} + \log_6 6^{-0.6}}{\log_{25} 5^{3/2} + \log_{0.1} 10}$

d) $\dfrac{\log_\pi \pi^2 + \log_e e^3}{\log_4 16 + \log_2 32}$

3 Determine x in each of the following equations:

a) $6^{\log_6 5} + 7^{\log_7 6} = 3^{\log_3 x}$

b) $9^{\log_x 7} = 7$

c) $\log_x 3^4 = 4$

d) $\log_7 7^4 = x$

e) $\log_3 3^x = 4$

4 Sketch the graph of each of the following functions, and find the domain and the range of each function. Also indicate whether the function is increasing or decreasing.

a) $f(x) = (\frac{1}{2})^x$

b) $f(x) = 2^x + 2^{-x}$

c) $f(x) = 4^x$

d) $f(x) = 2^x - 2^{-x}$

e) $f(x) = 3^{x^2}$

f) $f(x) = 2^{1/x}, \ x \neq 0$

5 Sketch the graph of $f(x) = (\sqrt{3})^x$ and find the domain and the range of f. Use the graph to give an approximation of $(\sqrt{3})^{1/2}$.

6 Find the domains and ranges of f and g, where $f(x) = 5^x$ and $g(x) = \log_5 x$. Also, verify that

$$(f \circ g)(x) = x \quad \text{and} \quad (g \circ f)(x) = x$$

7 Solve each of the following equations:

a) $2^x = 8^{x-1}$

b) $4^{-x} = 8^{x+2}$

c) $3^{2x+2} - 9(3^x) + 9 = 0$

d) $2^{2x+4} - 7(2^{x+2}) + 6 = 0$

8 a) If $\log_b x = 3$, find $\log_{1/b} x$.

b) If $\log_b x = 7$, find $\log_b (1/x)$.

c) Show that $\log_{1/b} x = \log_b (1/x)$.

9 Let $\log_a 2 = 0.69$, $\log_a 3 = 1.10$, $\log_a 5 = 1.62$, and $\log_a 7 = 1.94$. Find each of the following values.

a) $\log_a (3^5 \cdot 3^7)$

b) $\log_a (\sqrt[5]{5^3 \cdot 7^4})$

c) $\log_a \sqrt[3]{16}$

d) $\sqrt[3]{\log_a 16}$

e) $\log_a (2^4/3^4)$

f) $\log_a (\sqrt[3]{\frac{3}{2}})$

g) $\log_a (60/a)$

h) $\log_a \frac{25}{27}$

10 Explain why $f(x) = \log_b x$ is a one-to-one function, where $b \neq 1$, $b > 0$.

11 Find the domain and range of each of the following functions, and then determine the inverse.

a) $f(x) = 5^x$ b) $f(x) = \log_5 x$

c) $f(x) = \log_5 (3x) + \log_5 x$ d) $f(x) = \log_5 (5x + 3)$

12 Solve each of the following equations.

a) $\log_5 (x^2 - 4) = 0$

b) $\log_5 (2x - 1) + \log_5 (2x + 1) = 1$

c) $\log_{1/2} (4x^2 - 1) - \log_{1/2} (2x + 1) = 1$

13 Combine each of the following expressions into a single term.

a) $\log \frac{11}{5} + \log \frac{14}{3} - \log \frac{22}{15}$

b) $\log \frac{6}{7} - \log \frac{27}{4} + \log \frac{21}{16}$

c) $\log x^3 - \log (2/x^4) + \log x^3 + \log (2/x)$

14 Let $\log_b 2 = A$, $\log_b 3 = B$, and $\log_b 5 = C$. Express $\log_b (0.006)$ in terms of A, B, and C.

15 Sketch the graph of each of the following functions.

a) $g(x) = \log_{1/2} x$ b) $g(x) = \log_2 (x + 1)$

c) $f(x) = (\log_2 x)^2$

16 Let $f(x) = \log_{16} x$. Find the domain and the range of f; also find each of the following values.

a) $f(256)$ b) $f(64)$

c) $f(32)$ d) $f(\sqrt[5]{2})$

17 Use $f(x) = \log x$ to solve the equation $2f(x) = 2f(100) - 3$.

18 If the graph of a logarithmic function contains the point $(1000,3)$, what is the base?

19 Solve the equation $\log (\log x) = 0$.

20 Solve each of the following equations:

a) $(\frac{1}{2})^x = 8$ b) $(\frac{2}{3})^x = \frac{1}{5}$

c) $(2.06)^x = 300$ d) $(1.03)^x = 3$

e) $3^x = 7$ f) $10^x = 6$

21 If $S = a[(1 - r^n)/(1 - r)]$, solve for n if $S = 9$, $a = 25$, and $r = \frac{3}{4}$.

22 Let $f(x) = cb^x$, $f(0) = 7$, and $f(1) = 14$. Find b and c.

23 Find the composition $f \circ g$ of each of the following pairs of functions.

a) $f(x) = 5^x$ and $g(x) = x^2 + 1$

b) $f(x) = \log_3 x$ and $g(x) = x$

c) $f(x) = x^2 + 3x - 2$ and $g(x) = 2^x$

d) $f(x) = \log_2 x$ and $g(x) = x^2 + x + 1$

24 Use mathematical induction to prove each of the following equations.

a) $2 + 2^2 + 2^3 + \cdots + 2^n = 2(2^n - 1)$

b) $1 - \frac{1}{2} + \frac{1}{4} + \cdots + (-1)^{n-1}(\frac{1}{2})^{n-1} = \frac{2}{3}[1 - (-\frac{1}{2})^n]$

c) $1 \cdot 3 + 2 \cdot 4 + 3 \cdot 5 + \cdots + n(n + 2) = \frac{1}{6}n(n + 1)(2n + 7)$

25 Use the binomial theorem to expand each of the following expressions.

a) $(3x + y)^4$

b) $(3x + \sqrt{x})^5$

c) $(2x + 1/y)^3$

d) $(x - 1/x)^8$

e) $(3y + 1/3\sqrt{y})^6$

f) $(x^3 - 1/\sqrt{x})^9$

26 a) What amount must have been deposited 20 years ago to amount to $10,000 now at the yearly interest rate of 3 percent compounded continuously?

b) Find the accumulated amount from an initial $1000 after 4 years if the yearly interest rate is 5 percent per year compounded continuously.

27 In the study of probability theory, the normal distribution curve is described by the equation $y = ae^{-cx^2}$. Find the value of c if $a = 2.2$ when $x = 0.5$ and $y = 0.345$.

28 The charge on a condenser is described by $Q = CE(1 - e^{-t/CR})$, where Q is the charge in coulombs, C is the capacity of the condenser in farads, E is the applied voltage, R is the resistance in ohms, and t is the time in seconds after the voltage is applied. Find Q if $C = 7 \cdot 10^{-6}$ farads, $R = 600$ ohms, $E = 130$ volts and $t = 0.025$ seconds.

29 Find the numerical values of each of the following finite sums.

a) $\sum\limits_{k=1}^{5} k(2k - 1)$

b) $\sum\limits_{k=1}^{4} 2k^2(k - 3)$

c) $\sum\limits_{k=2}^{6} (k + 1)(k + 2)$

d) $\sum\limits_{k=5}^{10} (2k - 1)^2$

e) $\sum\limits_{k=1}^{6} 3^{k+1}$

f) $\sum\limits_{k=4}^{7} \frac{1}{k(k - 3)}$

30 Find the sum of each of the following geometric series.

a) $\frac{1}{10} + \frac{1}{100} + \frac{1}{1000} + \cdots + (\frac{1}{10})^n + \cdots$

b) $\frac{3}{5} + \frac{9}{25} + \frac{27}{125} + \cdots + (\frac{3}{5})^n + \cdots$

c) $\frac{3}{4} + \frac{9}{16} + \frac{27}{64} + \cdots + (\frac{3}{4})^n + \cdots$

d) $(\frac{2}{3})^2 + (\frac{2}{3})^4 + (\frac{2}{3})^6 + \cdots + (\frac{2}{3})^{2n} + \cdots$

CHAPTER 5

Circular Functions

5 CIRCULAR FUNCTIONS

1 Introduction

The word "trigonometry" stems from the Greek words for "triangle measurement," and the subject was originally developed to solve geometric problems involving triangles. Today, however, many of the important applications of trigonometry do not involve triangles specifically. The study of periodic phenomena such as sound waves, alternating electric current, and business cycles is based on the principles developed in trigonometry, not from the triangle viewpoint, but rather from the functional approach which is concerned with the properties and applications of "circular functions."

Here, our study of the circular functions will begin by constructing a function called the "wrapping function."

2 The Wrapping Function —
a Periodic Function

The *unit circle* is the circle of radius 1 with center (0,0), whose equation is $x^2 + y^2 = 1$ (see Section 5.4, Chapter 1) (Figure 1). Let us see how it is possible to associate each real number with a point on the unit circle.

Figure 1

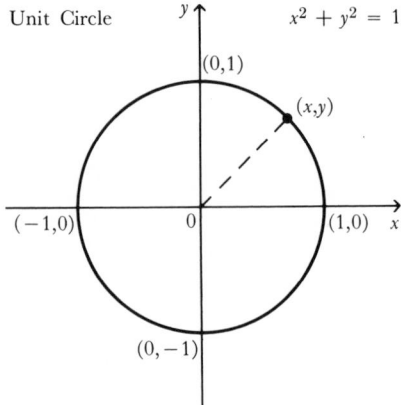

First, associate the set of real numbers with the points on the real line in the usual way (see Section 2.2, Chapter 1):

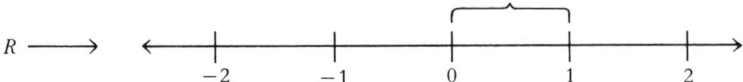

Next, the number line can be "wrapped" around the unit circle using the following scheme. The number 0 on the number line is associated with the point (1,0) on the unit circle; the positive part of the real line is "wrapped around" the circumference of the circle in the counterclockwise sense; the negative part of the real line is "wrapped around" the circumference of the unit circle in the clockwise sense. Hence, if t is any real number, the point on the unit circle associated with t is determined by moving $|t|$ units along the circumference of the unit circle, beginning at the point (1,0) — in the clockwise sense if $t < 0$ or in the counterclockwise sense if $t > 0$ (Figure 2).

Figure 2

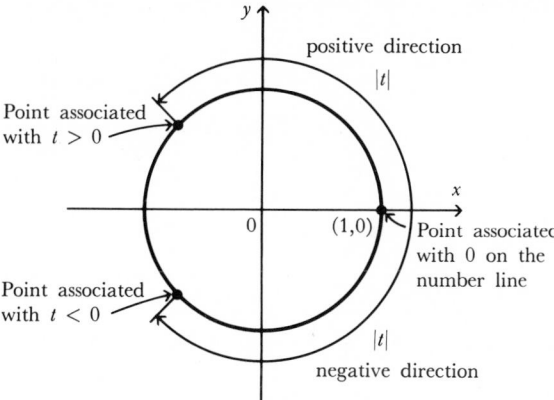

Since the circumference C of a circle is given by $C = 2\pi r$, where r is the radius, the circumference of the unit circle is 2π. Hence, it can be seen (Figure 3) that using this wrapping scheme, the point on the unit circle associated with the real number $\pi/2$ is $(0,1)$; the point associated with π is $(-1,0)$; the point associated with 2π is $(1,0)$; the point associated with $-\pi$ is $(-1,0)$.

Figure 3

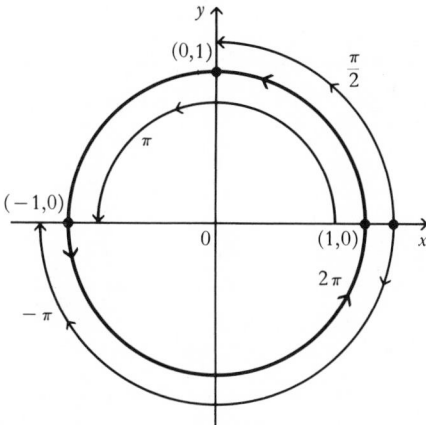

The scheme which has been described here suggests a function, called the *wrapping function P*, which associates each real number t with a point (x,y) on the unit circle (Figure 4). Hence, the example illustrated in Figure 3 can be rewritten as

$$P\left(\frac{\pi}{2}\right) = (0,1) \qquad P(\pi) = (-1,0)$$

$$P(-\pi) = (-1,0) \qquad P(2\pi) = (1,0)$$

Figure 4

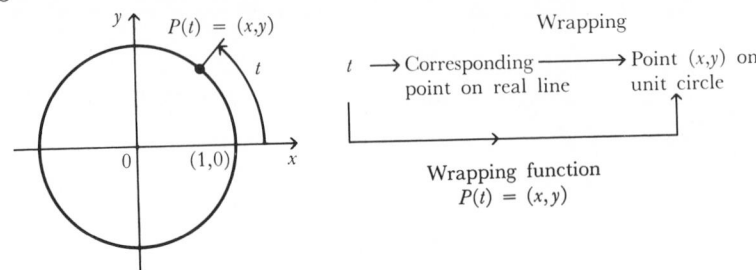

Since the circumference of the unit circle is 2π, we have $P(t) = P(t + 2\pi)$ for any real number t; hence, the wrapping function associates more than one real number with the same point on the unit circle (Figure 5). For example, $P(0) = P(2\pi) = P(4\pi) = P(6\pi) = (1,0)$. In any case, the function values of P repeat every 2π units. This is our first example of a function which has the property that it repeats in value at regular intervals (in this case, in intervals of 2π). A function which has this property is called a *periodic function*.

Figure 5

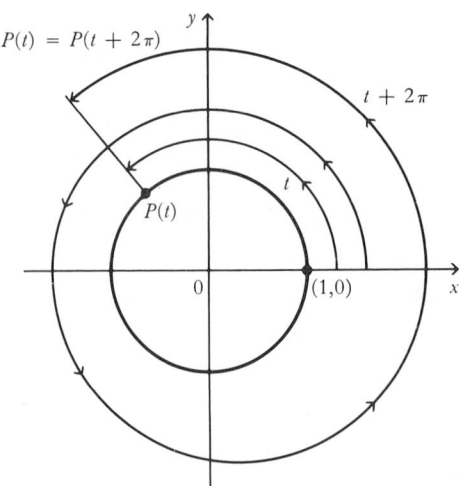

2.1   Definition

A function f is said to be a *periodic function with period a*, where a is a nonzero constant, if, for all x in the domain of f, $x + a$ is also in the domain of f, and

$$f(x + a) = f(x)$$

The smallest *positive* period a is called the *fundamental period of f*.   ☐

If f is a periodic function of period a, we can use the definition repeatedly, so that

$$f(x) = f(x + a) = f[(x + a) + a]$$
$$= f(x + 2a) = f[(x + 2a) + a)$$
$$= f(x + 3a) \quad \text{(and so on)}$$

For example, the wrapping function P is a periodic function of period 2π since $P(t) = P(t + 2\pi)$ for any real number t (Figure 5). Hence,

$$P(t) = P(t + 2\pi) = P(t + 4\pi) = P(t + 6\pi)$$

In general, if f is a periodic function of period a, we have $f(x) = f(x + na)$ for any integer n.

THEOREM 1

If $f(x)$ is a periodic function with fundamental period a, then $f(x + na) = f(x)$, where n is any positive integer.

PROOF. We use mathematical induction to prove this result. Let S_n be the statement that $f(x + na) = f(x)$.

i S_1 is certainly true, since $f(x + a) = f(x)$ by the definition of a periodic function.

ii We must show that if S_n is true, then S_{n+1} is also true. To this end, assume that S_n is true; that is, assume that $f(x + na) = f(x)$; then,

$$f[x + (n + 1)a] = f[(x + na) + a]$$
$$= f(x + na) \quad \text{(Why?)}$$
$$= f(x) \quad \text{(Why?)}$$

But the latter statement is precisely S_{n+1}; hence, by induction, S_n is true for any positive integer n.

Theorem 1 can also be proved when n is a negative integer (see Problem 2). Notice for example, that if f is a periodic function of fundamental period a, then

$$f(x - a) = f[(x - a) + a] = f(x)$$
$$f(x - 2a) = f[(x - 2a) + a] = f(x - a) = f(x)$$
$$f(x - 3a) = f[(x - 3a) + a] = f(x - 2a)$$
$$= f(x) \quad \text{(and so on)}$$

Combining Theorem 1 with the result of Problem 2, we have $f(x + na) = f(x)$ for any integer n.

EXAMPLES

1   Suppose that f is a periodic function with fundamental period 3 and
domain R. Assume also that the function values of f are known for
$[0,3) \subset R$; that is, assume that $S = \{f(x)|x \in [0,3)\}$ is determined. Use
Theorem 1 to express each of the following values as values in S.

a) $f(4)$ b) $f(11)$ c) $f(-3)$
d) $f(7.5)$ e) $f(-7.5)$

SOLUTION

a) $f(4) = f(1 + 3) = f(1)$
b) $f(11) = f(2 + 3 \cdot 3) = f(2)$
c) $f(-3) = f(-3 + 3) = f(0)$
d) $f(7.5) = f(1.5 + 2 \cdot 3) = f(1.5)$
e) $f(-7.5) = f(-7.5 + 3 \cdot 3) = f(1.5)$

This example illustrates that if f is a periodic function of fundamental
period a, we need only know the values of f on $[0,a)$ in order to determine any value of f (Figure 6).

Figure 6

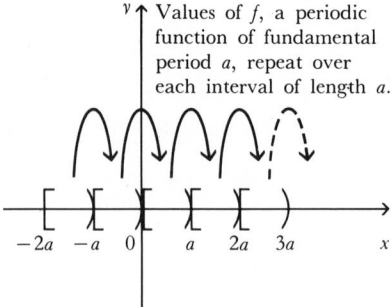

Values of f, a periodic
function of fundamental
period a, repeat over
each interval of length a.

2   If a function f is periodic, then f is not one-to-one. In other words, no
periodic function has an inverse (see Chapter 2, Section 6, Theorem 1).

PROOF.   Suppose that f is a periodic function that has fundamental
period a.
   Since $a \neq 0$, $x + a \neq x$, so that $(x, f(x))$ and $(x + a, f(x + a))$ are
two different members of function f such that $f(x) = f(x + a)$; hence,
f is not one-to-one (Figure 7).

   Returning to the wrapping function, we know that $P(t) = P(t + 2\pi)$.
By examining the unit circle, it can be "seen" that 2π is the fundamental
period of the wrapping function P. Finally, the symmetry of the circle

Figure 7

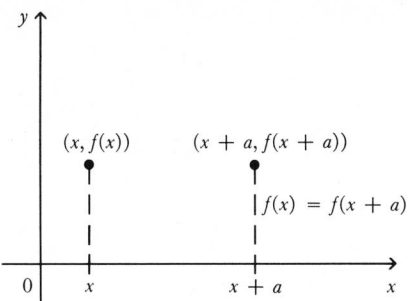

enables us to conclude that if $P(t) = (x,y)$, then $P(-t) = (x,-y)$ (Figure 8). These properties of P, together with some elementary facts from geometry, can be used to evaluate P for special values.

Figure 8

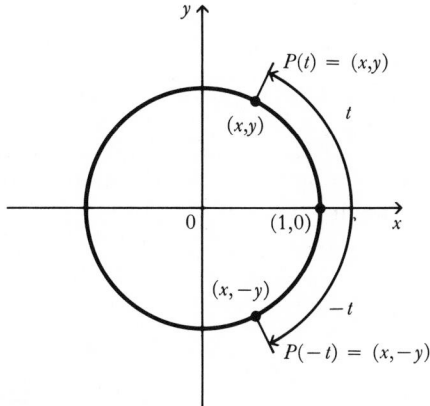

EXAMPLES

1   Determine $P(\pi/4)$, $P(3\pi/4)$, $P(5\pi/4)$, and $P(7\pi/4)$.

SOLUTION.   Let $P(\pi/4) = (x,y)$. Since $P(\pi/4) = P(\frac{1}{2} \cdot \pi/2)$, $P(\pi/4)$ is the midpoint of the arc joining the points $(1,0)$ and $(0,1)$ on the unit circle (Figure 9). Using the symmetry of the circle, we have $x = y$. Since $x^2 + y^2 = 1$, it follows that $x^2 + x^2 = 2x^2 = 1$; that is,

$$x = \frac{1}{\sqrt{2}} \quad \text{or} \quad x = \frac{-1}{\sqrt{2}}$$

But x and y are positive in quadrant I; hence,

$$x = y = \frac{1}{\sqrt{2}}$$

Figure 9

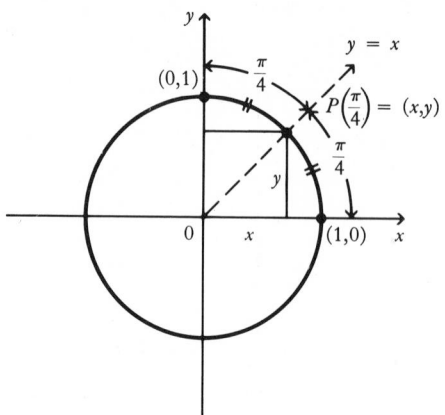

Consequently,

$$P\left(\frac{\pi}{4}\right) = \left(\frac{1}{\sqrt{2}}, \frac{1}{\sqrt{2}}\right)$$

Now the remaining values can be determined by using the symmetry of the circle (Figure 10).

Figure 10

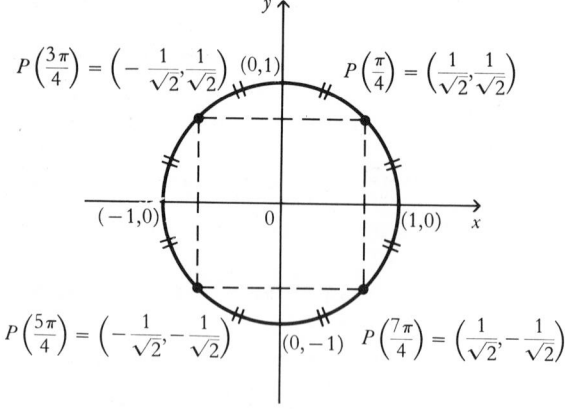

2 Determine $P(\pi/3)$, $P(2\pi/3)$, $P(4\pi/3)$, and $P(5\pi/3)$.

SOLUTION. Let $P(\pi/3) = (x,y)$; then, using the symmetry of the circle,

$$P\left(\frac{2\pi}{3}\right) = (-x,y) \qquad \text{(Figure 11)}$$

Figure 11

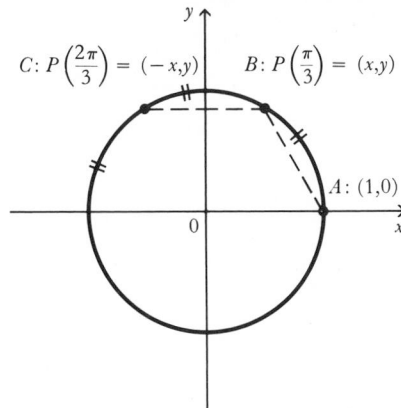

$$C: P\left(\frac{2\pi}{3}\right) = (-x,y) \qquad B: P\left(\frac{\pi}{3}\right) = (x,y)$$

$A: (1,0)$

Since the lengths of arcs $\widehat{AB}$ and $\widehat{BC}$ are equal (each is of length $\pi/3$), it follows from geometry that the chords $\overline{AB}$ and $\overline{BC}$ are equal, so that, using the distance formula, we get

$$\overline{AB} = \overline{BC}$$
$$\overline{AB}^2 = \overline{BC}^2$$
(1) $(x - 1)^2 + y^2 = 4x^2$

But, since $x^2 + y^2 = 1$, $y^2 = 1 - x^2$. By substitution into (1),

$$(x - 1)^2 + (1 - x^2) = 4x^2$$

so that

$$4x^2 + 2x - 2 = 0$$

or, equivalently,

$2(2x - 1)(x + 1) = 0$ from which it follows that $x = \frac{1}{2}$.

(Notice that $x = -1$ is also a root, but since the point $P(\pi/3)$ is in quadrant I, we choose only $x = \frac{1}{2}$.) Hence,

$$y^2 = 1 - \tfrac{1}{4} = \tfrac{3}{4}$$

so that

$$y = \frac{\sqrt{3}}{2} \qquad \text{(Why?)}$$

and

$$P\left(\frac{\pi}{3}\right) = \left(\frac{1}{2}, \frac{\sqrt{3}}{2}\right)$$

Finally, symmetry can be used to determine the remaining values (Figure 12).

Figure 12

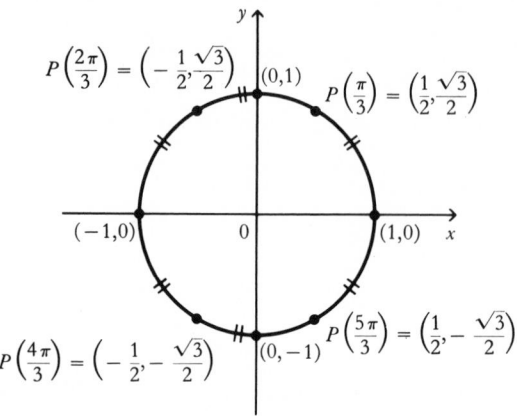

3   Find $P(9\pi/4)$.

SOLUTION.   Using the fact that P is of period 2π and using the results of Example 1 above,

$$P\left(\frac{9\pi}{4}\right) = P\left(\frac{\pi}{4} + 2\pi\right) = P\left(\frac{\pi}{4}\right) = \left(\frac{\sqrt{2}}{2}, \frac{\sqrt{2}}{2}\right)$$

4   Find $P(11\pi/2)$.

SOLUTION.   Again, we can use the fact that P is of period 2π to get

$$P\left(\frac{11\pi}{2}\right) = P\left(\frac{3\pi}{2} + 2\cdot 2\pi\right) = P\left(\frac{3\pi}{2}\right) = (0,-1) \qquad \text{(Figure 13)}$$

Figure 13

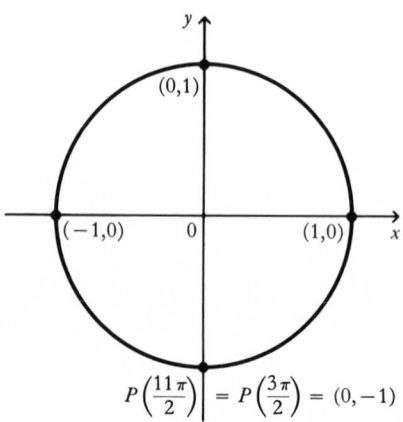

5   Determine each of the following points.

a) $P(-5\pi/4)$

b) $P(-2\pi/3)$

SOLUTION

a) $P\left(\dfrac{-5\pi}{4}\right) = P\left(\dfrac{-5\pi}{4} + 2\pi\right) = P\left(\dfrac{3\pi}{4}\right)$

$\qquad = \left(\dfrac{-1}{\sqrt{2}}, \dfrac{1}{\sqrt{2}}\right)$ (See Example 1 above)

b) $P\left(\dfrac{-2\pi}{3}\right) = P\left(\dfrac{-2\pi}{3} + 2\pi\right) = P\left(\dfrac{4\pi}{3}\right)$

$\qquad = \left(\dfrac{-1}{2}, \dfrac{-\sqrt{3}}{2}\right)$ (See Example 2 above)

PROBLEM SET 1

1   Suppose that $y = f(x)$, a periodic function of fundamental period 2, has been graphed for $x \in [1,3)$ in Figure 14. Graph $y = f(x)$ for $x \in [-3,7]$.

Figure 14

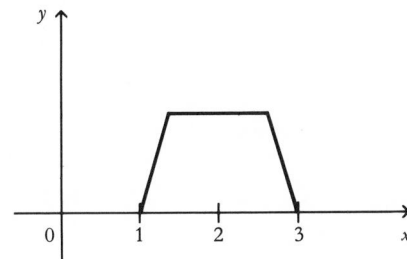

2   Show that if f is a periodic function of fundamental period a, then

$$f(x + na) = f(x) \qquad \text{where } n \text{ is a negative integer}$$

3   Let $y = f(x)$ be a periodic function of fundamental period 6. Express each of the following values in terms of values at $x \in [0,6)$.

a) $f(-5)$

b) $f(10)$

c) $f(51)$

d) $f(-\tfrac{1}{2})$

e) $f(-7.15)$

4   Let f and g be periodic functions with period a. Which of the following functions must be periodic?

a) $f \cdot g$

b) $(f)^2$

c) $f \circ g$

d) f/g

e) $f + g$

5   Let P be the wrapping function. Determine the quadrant in which each of the following points lie.

a) $P(-13)$ b) $P(\frac{29}{3})$ c) $P(6)$

d) $P(3.6)$ e) $P(4.5)$ f) $P(0.8)$

g) $P(-\frac{31}{3})$ h) $P(-3.9)$ i) $P(-7.8)$

6   Determine $P(\pi/6)$, $P(5\pi/6)$, $P(7\pi/6)$, and $P(11\pi/6)$. [*Hint:* If $P(\pi/6) = (x,y)$, then $P(-\pi/6) = (x,-y)$. Notice that $\overset{\frown}{BC} = \overset{\frown}{BA}$, and then use the methods of Example 2 above in which $P(\pi/3)$ was determined (Figure 15).]

Figure 15

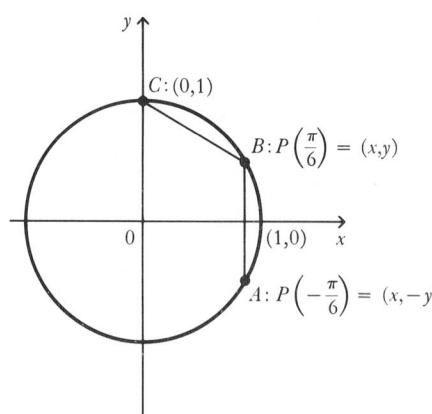

7   Use the properties of the wrapping function P, together with the information in the examples and Problem 6, to determine each of the following values.

a) $P(-\pi/2)$ b) $P(9\pi/2)$

c) $P(-27\pi/2)$ d) $P(85\pi)$

e) $P(77\pi/4)$ f) $P(-11\pi/6)$

g) $P(-22\pi/3)$ h) $P(-11\pi/4)$

8   Let f be a periodic function of fundamental period π; find two values of x, where $0 \leq x \leq \pi$, such that

a) $f(15\pi) = f(x)$ b) $f(-\pi) = f(x)$

9   Suppose that f is a periodic odd function with fundamental period 2 such that $f(\frac{1}{2}) = 3$. Determine each of the following values.

a) $f(\frac{9}{2})$ b) $f(\frac{7}{5})$ c) $f(9) + f(-7)$

3 Circular Functions — Sine and Cosine

For each real number t, the wrapping function P associates an ordered pair of real numbers (x,y) on the unit circle, so that $P:t \rightarrow (x,y)$. Since it is difficult to develop the properties of a function whose range is a set of ordered pairs rather than a set of single numbers (How could we graph such a function so as to "see" many of the functional properties such as increasing, decreasing, and one-to-one?), we will use P to construct two other functions.

3.1   Definition

The *circular functions* — the *cosine* and *sine* — are defined in the following manner.

$$\text{cosine} = \{(t,x)|P(t) = (x,y)\}$$

and

$$\text{sine} = \{(t,y)|P(t) = (x,y)\}$$

Using functional notation, the cosine (t), abbreviated $\cos t$, and the sine (t), abbreviated $\sin t$, are given by

$$\cos t = x \quad \text{and} \quad \sin t = y \quad \text{where } P(t) = (x,y) \quad \square$$

In a certain sense, the cosine and sine functions are constructed by "separating" the ordered pairs in the range of the function P (Figure 1).

Figure 1

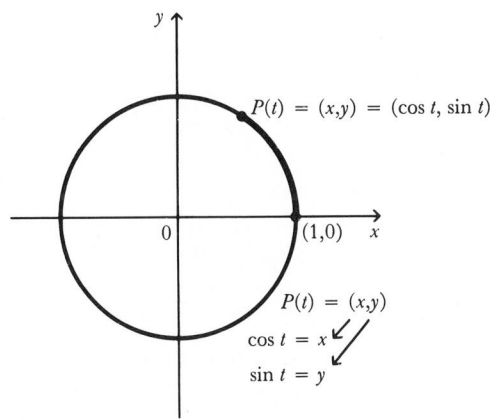

$P(t) = (x,y) = (\cos t, \sin t)$

$(1,0)$

$P(t) = (x,y)$

$\cos t = x$

$\sin t = y$

EXAMPLES

1   Use the results of Section 2 to determine each of the following values.

a) $\sin 0$ and $\cos 0$ b) $\cos (\pi/2)$ and $\sin (\pi/2)$

c) $\cos (7\pi/4)$ and $\sin (7\pi/4)$ d) $\sin (\pi/3)$ and $\cos (\pi/3)$

e) $\sin (4\pi/3)$ and $\cos (4\pi/3)$

SOLUTION

a)   Since $P(0) = (1,0)$ (Why?), $\sin 0 = 0$ (Why?) and $\cos 0 = 1$
     (Why?)

b) $\cos (\pi/2) = 0$ and $\sin \pi/2 = 1$, since $P(\pi/2) = (0,1)$.

c) $\cos (7\pi/4) = 1/\sqrt{2}$ and $\sin (7\pi/4) = -1/\sqrt{2}$, since
     $P(7\pi/4) = (1/\sqrt{2}, -1/\sqrt{2})$.

d) $\sin (\pi/3) = \sqrt{3}/2$ and $\cos (\pi/3) = \frac{1}{2}$, since $P(\pi/3) = (\frac{1}{2}, \sqrt{3}/2)$.

e) $\sin (4\pi/3) = -\sqrt{3}/2$ and $\cos (4\pi/3) = -\frac{1}{2}$, since
     $P(4\pi/3) = (-\frac{1}{2}, -\sqrt{3}/2)$.

2   Suppose $\sin t = \frac{1}{5}$ and $0 < t < \pi/2$. Find $\cos t$.

SOLUTION.   Let $\cos t = x$. Then $P(t) = (x, \frac{1}{5})$ (Why?). But, since
$x^2 + \frac{1}{25} = 1$, $x = \pm 2\sqrt{6}/5$. However, $0 < t < \pi/2$ implies that
$(x, \frac{1}{5})$ is in quadrant I (Figure 2), so that

$$x = \frac{2\sqrt{6}}{5} \qquad \text{that is} \qquad \cos t = \frac{2\sqrt{6}}{5}$$

Figure 2

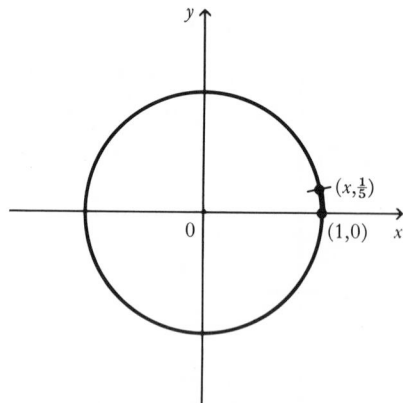

3.2   Properties of the Cosine and Sine

We have seen that if $P(t) = (x,y)$, then $\cos t = x$ and $\sin t = y$. Now,
the properties of P can be used to determine some elementary properties
of the cosine and sine function; in this sense, we sometimes say that

the cosine and sine "inherit" certain properties from the wrapping function P.

Since $P(t) = (x,y)$ is defined for *any* real number t, $\cos t$ and $\sin t$ are defined for any real number; that is, R is the domain for both the cosine and sine functions. Because of the fact that any (x,y) on the unit circle satisfies $-1 \leq x \leq 1$ and $-1 \leq y \leq 1$, $\cos t = x$ has range $[-1,1]$ and $\sin t = y$ has range $[-1,1]$ (Figure 3).

Figure 3

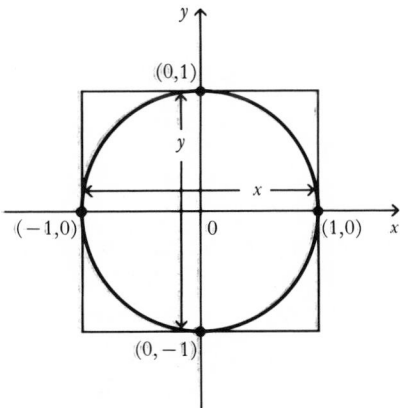

Also, the signs of the values of the cosine and sine functions depend on the quadrant in which the point $P(t)$ is located (Figure 4).

Figure 4

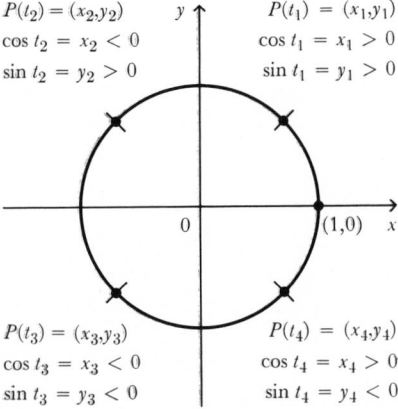

Finally, the cosine and sine are periodic functions with period 2π; for $P(t) = (x,y) = P(t + 2\pi)$ (see Section 2) implies that $\cos t = x = \cos (t + 2\pi)$ and $\sin t = y = \sin (t + 2\pi)$. Hence, if we can determine the values of the cos t and sin t for $t \in [0,2\pi)$, we can use these values to determine cos t and sin t for any real number t.

EXAMPLES

Use the results of Section 2, together with the symmetry of the circle, to determine each of the following values.

1   cos $(25\pi/6)$ and sin $(25\pi/6)$

SOLUTION

$$\cos \frac{25\pi}{6} = \cos \left(\frac{\pi}{6} + 2 \cdot 2\pi \right) = \cos \frac{\pi}{6} = \frac{\sqrt{3}}{2}$$

and

$$\sin \frac{25\pi}{6} = \sin \left(\frac{\pi}{6} + 2 \cdot 2\pi \right) = \sin \frac{\pi}{6} = \frac{1}{2} \qquad \text{(Figure 5)}$$

Figure 5

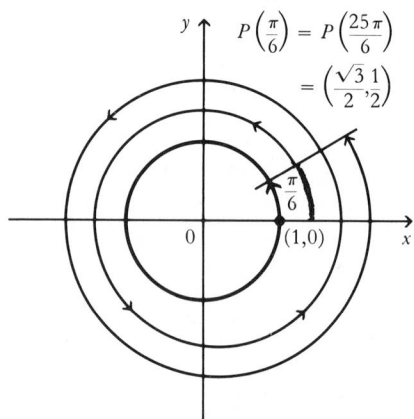

2   cos $(-27\pi/4)$ and sin $(-27\pi/4)$

SOLUTION

$$\cos \left(\frac{-27\pi}{4} \right) = \cos \left(\frac{-27}{4} + 2\pi \cdot 4 \right) = \cos \left(\frac{5\pi}{4} \right) = \frac{-\sqrt{2}}{2}$$

and

$$\sin \left(\frac{-27\pi}{4} \right) = \sin \left(\frac{-27}{4} + 2\pi \cdot 4 \right) = \sin \left(\frac{5\pi}{4} \right) = \frac{-\sqrt{2}}{2}$$

(See Figure 10, Section 2.)

By using the fact that x and y are the coordinates of $P(t)$, we can prove an important theorem about the cosine and sine functions.

THEOREM 1

For any real number t,

i $\cos^2 t + \sin^2 t = 1$

ii $\cos (-t) = \cos t$ (The cosine is an even function)

iii $\sin (-t) = -\sin t$ (The sine is an odd function)

PROOF OF (i).   Assume $P(t) = (x,y)$, so that $\cos t = x$ and $\sin t = y$, where $x^2 + y^2 = 1$. By substituting $\cos t$ for x and $\sin t$ for y, we have $(\cos t)^2 + (\sin t)^2 = 1$ (The power notation for $(\cos t)^n$ is $\cos^n t$ and for $(\sin t)^n$ is $\sin^n t$.), so that

$$\cos^2 t + \sin^2 t = 1$$

PROOF OF (ii) AND (iii). Although we will illustrate this result for a value of t which displays $P(t)$ in quadrant I, it is important to remember that the argument can be used for any real number t. Assume that $P(t) = (x,y)$. Then, by definition, $P(t) = (x,y) = (\cos t, \sin t)$ and $P(-t) = (x,-y) = (\cos (-t), \sin (-t))$ (Figure 6). Hence, by symmetry of the circle, $\cos t = x = \cos (-t)$, and $\sin (-t) = -y = -\sin t$.

Figure 6

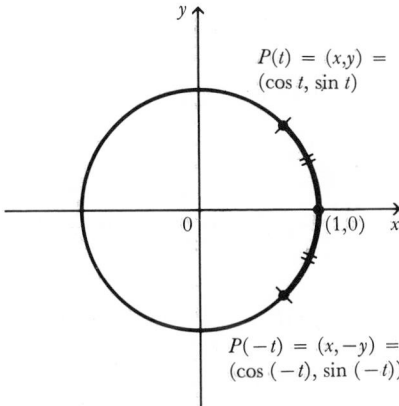

$P(t) = (x,y) =$
$(\cos t, \sin t)$

$(1,0)$

$P(-t) = (x,-y) =$
$(\cos (-t), \sin (-t))$

EXAMPLES

1   If $\sin t = \frac{3}{5}$ and $\pi/2 < t < \pi$, find $\cos t$.

SOLUTION.   Since $\cos^2 t + \sin^2 t = 1$, $\cos t = \pm\sqrt{1 - \sin^2 t}$. But, since $P(t)$ is in quadrant II, we use

$$\cos t = -\sqrt{1 - \sin^2 t} = -\sqrt{1 - \tfrac{9}{25}} = -\tfrac{4}{5}$$

2   Assume that $f(x) = \sin x$ and $g(x) = \cos x$ to evaluate

a) $f(-5\pi)$ b) $g(-10\pi/3)$

SOLUTION

a) $f(-5\pi) = \sin(-5\pi)$
$\qquad\quad = -\sin(5\pi)$
$\qquad\quad = -\sin(\pi + 2 \cdot 2\pi)$
$\qquad\quad = -\sin \pi$
$\qquad\quad = 0 \qquad$ since $P(\pi) = (-1,0)$

b) $g\left(\dfrac{-10\pi}{3}\right) = \cos\left(\dfrac{-10\pi}{3}\right)$

$\qquad\qquad = \cos\left(\dfrac{10\pi}{3}\right)$

$\qquad\qquad = \cos\left(\dfrac{4\pi}{3} + 2\pi\right)$

$\qquad\qquad = \cos\left(\dfrac{4\pi}{3}\right)$

$\qquad\qquad = -\dfrac{1}{2} \qquad$ since $P\left(\dfrac{4\pi}{3}\right) = \left(-\dfrac{1}{2}, \dfrac{-\sqrt{3}}{2}\right)$

3   For what values of t (if any) does $\sin t = \cos t$?

SOLUTION.   Using Theorem 1,

$$1 = \sin^2 t + \cos^2 t = \sin^2 t + \sin^2 t = 2\sin^2 t$$

so that

$$\sin t = \pm\frac{\sqrt{2}}{2} \qquad \text{and} \qquad \cos t = \pm\frac{\sqrt{2}}{2}$$

Hence, from Figure 7 we see that $\sin t = \cos t$ whenever $t \in \{t \mid t = \pi/4 + 2n\pi$, where n is any integer$\} \cup \{t \mid t = 5\pi/4 + 2n\pi$, where n is any integer$\}$.

4   Use the fact that the sine function is a periodic function of period 2π to determine the period of $f(x) = \sin 2x$.

Figure 7

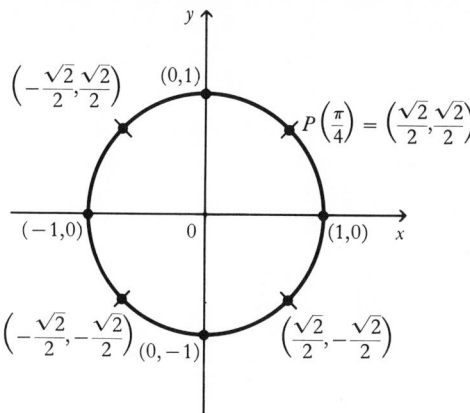

SOLUTION.   Since the sine function has period 2π, it follows that

$$f(x) = \sin 2x$$
$$= \sin (2x + 2\pi)$$
$$= \sin [2(x + \pi)]$$
$$= f(x + \pi)$$

so that $f(x) = \sin 2x$ is a periodic function of period π.

PROBLEM SET 2

1 a) Explain why $P(t) = (\cos t, \sin t)$.

  b) Explain why $P(-t) = (\cos t, -\sin t)$.

2 Use the information given by Figure 8 to complete the given table.

Figure 8

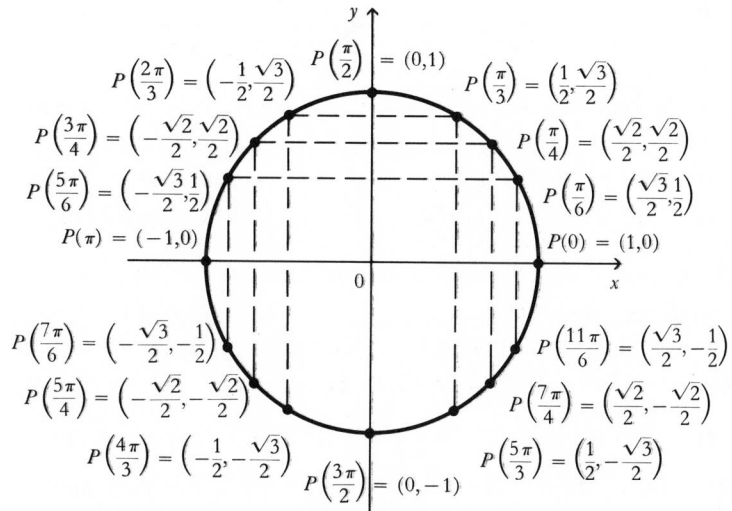

t	$\cos t$	$\sin t$	t	$\cos t$	$\sin t$
0	1	0	π	-1	0
$\dfrac{\pi}{6}$	$\dfrac{\sqrt{3}}{2}$	$\dfrac{1}{2}$	$\dfrac{7\pi}{6}$		
$\dfrac{\pi}{4}$	$\dfrac{\sqrt{2}}{2}$	$\dfrac{\sqrt{2}}{2}$	$\dfrac{5\pi}{4}$		
$\dfrac{\pi}{3}$	$\dfrac{1}{2}$	$\dfrac{\sqrt{3}}{2}$	$\dfrac{4\pi}{3}$		
$\dfrac{\pi}{2}$	0	1	$\dfrac{3\pi}{2}$		-1
$\dfrac{2\pi}{3}$	$-\dfrac{1}{2}$		$\dfrac{5\pi}{3}$		
$\dfrac{3\pi}{4}$		$\dfrac{\sqrt{2}}{2}$	$\dfrac{7\pi}{4}$		
$\dfrac{5\pi}{6}$			$\dfrac{11\pi}{6}$		

3 a) Find a, $\cos t$, and $\sin t$ if $P(t) = (3/a, 4/a)$ is in quadrant I.
   b) Explain why $\sin t > \cos t$ for any $t \in (\pi/2, \pi)$.
   c) Find $\cos t$ if $\sin t = -\frac{5}{6}$ and $P(t)$ is in quadrant IV.
   d) Find $\cos t$ if $\sin t = \frac{3}{10}$ and $\cos t > 0$.
   e) Find $\cos^2 t + \sin^2 t$ if $\sin t = \frac{12}{13}$.
   f) Find $\cos^2 t - \sin^2 t$ in terms of a and b if $\cos t = 2ab/(a^2 + b^2)$.

4 Use the fact that the cosine and sine are periodic functions of fundamental period of 2π to find the period of each of the following functions.
   a) $\sin 4x$ b) $\cos 3x$
   c) $\cos (x/2)$ d) $\sin (x + 1)$

5 Use $f(t) = \cos t$ and $g(t) = \sin t$ to determine each of the following values.
   a) $f(15\pi/6)$ and $g(15\pi/6)$ b) $f(-11\pi/6)$ and $g(-11\pi/6)$
   c) $f(-11\pi/2)$ and $g(-11\pi/2)$ d) $f(89\pi/6)$ and $g(89\pi/6)$

6 Show that $|\sin t| \le 1$ and $|\cos t| \le 1$ for any real number t.

7 Define the function $Q(t) = (\sin t)/(\cos t)$, where $\cos t \ne 0$. Show that Q is an odd function. What can you say about the symmetry of the graph of Q? Define $R(t) = 1/(\cos t)$. Show that R is an even function.

8 Explain why neither $f(x) = \cos x$ nor $f(x) = \sin x$ has an inverse.

9 Explain the difference between $g \circ f$ and $f \circ g$ if $f(x) = \sin x$ and $g(x) = 2x$.

10 Use $f(x) = \cos x$ and $g(x) = 3x$ to answer each of the following parts.

a) Form $g \circ f$, $f \circ g$, and $f \circ f$.

b) Indicate the domain and range of $g \circ f$ and $f \circ g$.

c) Indicate which of the functions of part (a) is even or odd.

11 Show that

$$\begin{vmatrix} \cos t & \sin t \\ -\sin t & \cos t \end{vmatrix} = 1$$

4 Evaluation of Sine and Cosine

Since the cosine and sine functions are periodic functions of period 2π, the evaluation of either the cosine or sine at any given real number t can always be reduced to evaluating the function at a number in $[0, 2\pi)$ (see Section 2). Let us examine a few examples in order to clarify this important fact.

EXAMPLE

In each of the following parts use the fact that the cosine is an even function and the sine is an odd function, together with the fact that the cosine and sine are periodic functions of period 2π, to reduce the evaluation of the given function at the given number to an evaluation of the same function at a number in $[0,2\pi)$. Use 3.14 as the approximate value of π.

a) $\cos(-7)$ b) $\cos 81$ c) $\sin(-15)$

SOLUTION

a) $\cos(-7) = \cos 7$ (Why?)
$= \cos(0.72 + 6.28)$
$= \cos 0.72$ (Why?)

b) $\cos 81 = \cos[5.64 + 12(6.28)]$
$= \cos 5.64$ (Why?)

c) $\sin(-15) = -\sin(15)$ (Why?)
$= -\sin[2.44 + 2(6.28)]$ (Why?)
$= -\sin 2.44$

An alternate method proceeds as follows.

$$\sin(-15) = \sin[-15 + 3(6.28)]$$
$$= \sin 3.84$$

Next, by considering various cases, it can be shown that the evaluation of either the cosine or sine function at $t \in [0,2\pi)$ can be reduced to an evaluation of the function at 0, $\pi/2$, π, $3\pi/2$ or at some number in interval $(0,\pi/2)$ with a possible adjustment in sign.

CASE I. $t \in \{0,\pi/2,\pi,3\pi/2\}$. For these special values, it is easy to evaluate the cosine and sine, since $P(0) = (1,0)$, $P(\pi/2) = (0,1)$, $P(\pi) = (-1,0)$, and $P(3\pi/2) = (0,-1)$ (Figure 1).

Figure 1

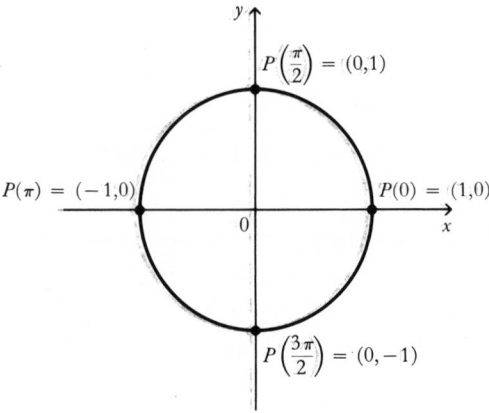

CASE II. $t \in (3\pi/2,2\pi)$ or $P(t)$ is in quadrant IV (Figure 2). First, the "shortest" arc length between $P(t)$ and the x axis is determined. This arc length is called the *reference number*, and it is denoted by t_R. Here, $t_R = 2\pi - t$ (Figure 2).

By the symmetry of the circle, it follows that

$$\cos t = x = \cos t_R \qquad \text{and} \qquad \sin t = -y = -\sin t_R$$

Figure 2

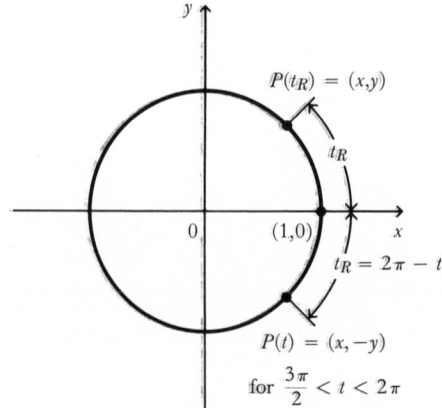

Hence, the evaluation of the cosine and sine at $t \in (3\pi/2, 2\pi)$ has been reduced to an evaluation at the reference number t_R with the sign adjustment for the sine function. In other words, $\cos t$ and $\cos t_R$ are exactly the same, whereas $\sin t$ and $\sin t_R$ agree in absolute value (Why?) but are opposite in sign (Figure 2).

Finally, we will show that $t_R \in (0, \pi/2)$. Since $t \in (3\pi/2, 2\pi)$, $3\pi/2 < t < 2\pi$, from which it follows that

$$\frac{-3\pi}{2} > -t > -2\pi \qquad \text{(Why?)}$$

$$2\pi - \frac{3\pi}{2} > 2\pi - t > 0 \qquad \text{(Why?)}$$

$$0 < 2\pi - t < \frac{\pi}{2}$$

so that

$$0 < t_R < \frac{\pi}{2}$$

CASE III. $t \in (\pi, 3\pi/2)$ or $P(t)$ is in quadrant III (Figure 3). The reference number is determined as before; that is, it is the shortest arc length between $P(t)$ and the x axis. Here, $t_R = t - \pi$ (Figure 3).

Figure 3

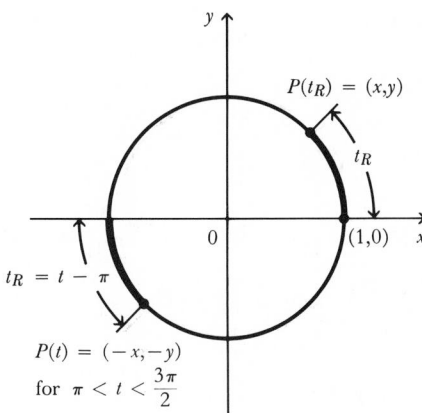

By the symmetry of the circle, we have, for $\pi < t < 3\pi/2$,

$$\cos t = -x = -\cos t_R \qquad \text{and} \qquad \sin t = -y = -\sin t_R$$

Again, $t_R \in (0, \pi/2)$, for $\pi < t < 3\pi/2$ implies that

$$\pi - \pi < t - \pi < \frac{3\pi}{2} - \pi \qquad \text{so that} \qquad 0 < t - \pi < \frac{\pi}{2}$$

that is,

$$0 < t_R < \frac{\pi}{2}$$

Hence, the evaluation at $t \in (\pi, 3\pi/2)$ has been reduced again to an evaluation at $t_R \in (0, \pi/2)$ with the proper adjustment in sign.

CASE IV. $t \in (\pi/2, \pi)$ or $P(t)$ is in quadrant II (Figure 4). As before, we determine the reference number as the shortest arc length between $P(t)$ and the x axis. Here, $t_R = t - \pi$ (Figure 4).

Figure 4

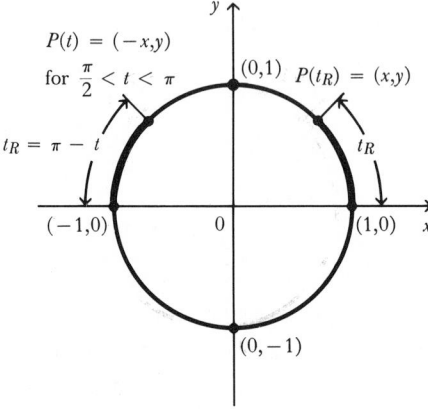

We have, by symmetry, that

$$\cos t = -\cos t_R \qquad \text{and} \qquad \sin t = \sin t_R$$

Again

$$t_R \in \left(0, \frac{\pi}{2}\right) \qquad \text{(Why?)}$$

CASE V. $t \in (0, \pi/2)$ or $P(t)$ is in quadrant I. Here, $t_R = t$ (Figure 5), so that

$$\cos t = \cos t_R \qquad \text{and} \qquad \sin t = \sin t_R$$

Figure 5

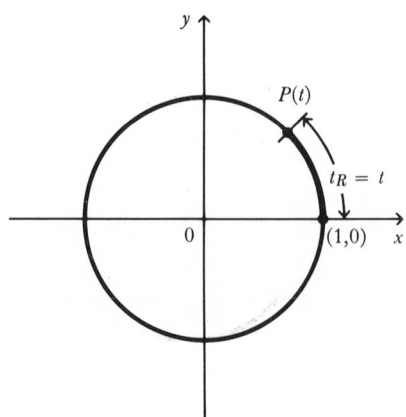

Clearly,

$$t_R \in \left(0, \frac{\pi}{2}\right)$$

EXAMPLES

In each of the following parts, reduce the evaluation of the given function to an evaluation of the same function at a reference number, that is, a number t_R such that $t_R \in (0, \pi/2)$ (use $\pi = 3.14$).

1   sin 2.5 and cos 2.5

SOLUTION.   The reference number is $t_R = 3.14 - 2.50 = 0.64$ (Figure 6). Since $P(2.5)$ is in quadrant **II** where the sine is positive and the cosine is negative,

$$\sin 2.5 = \sin 0.64 \quad \text{and} \quad \cos 2.5 = -\cos 0.64 \quad \text{(Figure 6)}$$

Figure 6

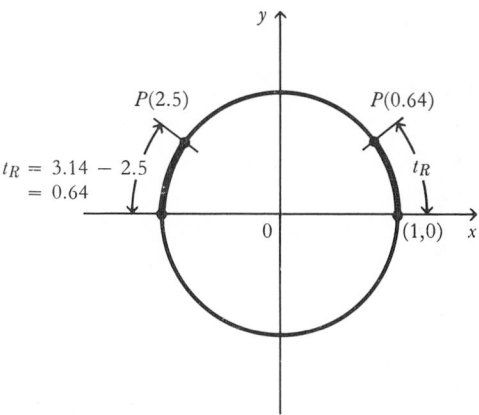

2   sin 6 and cos 6

SOLUTION.   Since $t_R = 6.28 - 6 = 0.28$, and since $P(6)$ is in quadrant **IV** (Figure 7),

$$\sin 6 = -\sin 0.28 \quad \text{and} \quad \cos 6 = \cos 0.28$$

3   cos 29.12 and sin 29.12

SOLUTION.   The periodicity of the cosine and sine can be used to get

$$\cos 29.12 = \cos [4 + 4(6.28)] = \cos 4$$

Figure 7

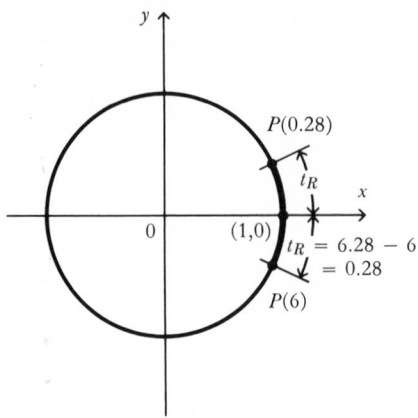

and

$$\sin 29.12 = \sin [4 + 4(6.28)] = \sin 4$$

But the reference number t_R for 4 is

$$t_R = 4 - 3.14 = 0.86$$

Since the cosine and sine are both negative in quadrant III (Figure 8),

$$\cos 4 = -\cos 0.86 \qquad \text{and} \qquad \sin 4 = -\sin 0.86$$

Figure 8

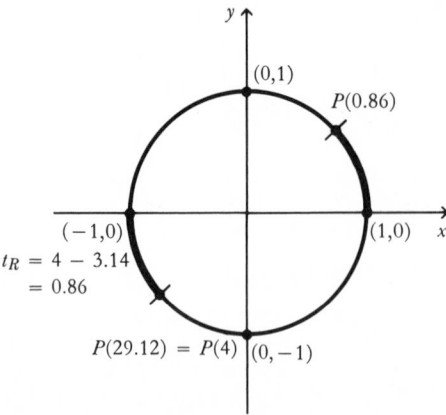

4.1   Tables

The evaluation of the cosine and sine functions can always be reduced to an evaluation at a reference number t, where $t \in (0, \pi/2)$, with the proper adjustment in sign, or at 0, $\pi/2$, π, or $3\pi/2$. The only question that remains is how can we determine the values of $\cos t$ and $\sin t$ for $0 < t < \pi/2$? For certain values, such as $\pi/6$, $\pi/4$, and $\pi/3$, the question has been answered (see Problem set 2, Problem 2). For other values, there is a table (see Table III of Appendix A) which has been constructed using some more advanced techniques of mathematics. As with the logarithmic table, this table gives approximations to the values.

EXAMPLE

Use Table III to determine each of the following values.

a) $\sin 0.65$ b) $\cos 0.65$

c) $\sin 1$ d) $\cos 0.95$

SOLUTION

a) $\sin 0.65 = 0.6052$ b) $\cos 0.65 = 0.7961$

c) $\sin 1 = 0.8415$ d) $\cos 0.95 = 0.5817$

It is obvious that Table III does not contain entries for all values between 0 and $\pi/2$. (For example, $\sin 1.514$ and $\sin 0.005$ cannot be found in Table III.) Fortunately, as we shall see in the example below, *linear interpolation* (see Chapter 4, Section 6.2) can be used to give some reasonably accurate approximations.

Let us summarize the steps for finding $T(t)$, where $T(t)$ is either $\cos t$ or $\sin t$.

1 Locate the quadrant in which $P(t)$ lies.

2 Use the fact that the cosine is even and the sine is odd, together with the fact that the cosine and sine have period 2π, to reduce the evaluation of $T(t)$ to an evaluation at a number in $[0,2\pi)$.

3 Determine the reference number t_R associated with t.

4 Use Table III and linear interpolation if necessary to find $T(t_R) = |T(t)|$.

5 Finally, adjust the sign of $T(t)$ according to the quadrant in which $P(t)$ lies.

EXAMPLES

Use Table III and linear interpolation to approximate each of the following values (use $\pi = 3.14$).

1 $\sin 1.514$

SOLUTION. $P(1.514)$ is in quadrant I, so that the reference number is 1.514. Table III, together with linear interpolation, can be used to approximate sin 1.514 as follows.

$$0.01 \begin{bmatrix} 0.006 \begin{bmatrix} \text{sin } 1.51 & = 0.9982 \\ \text{sin } 1.514 = & ? \\ \text{sin } 1.52 & = 0.9987 \end{bmatrix} d \end{bmatrix} 0.0005$$

$$\frac{0.006}{0.01} = \frac{d}{0.0005}$$

so that

$$d = 0.0003$$

Hence,

$$\begin{aligned} \text{sin } 1.514 &= 0.9987 - 0.0003 \\ &= 0.9984 \qquad \text{(Approximately)} \end{aligned}$$

2   sin (−2.955)

SOLUTION.   Since the sine is an odd function, sin (−2.955) = −sin 2.955. But sin 2.955 = sin 0.185 (Figure 9), since the sine is

Figure 9

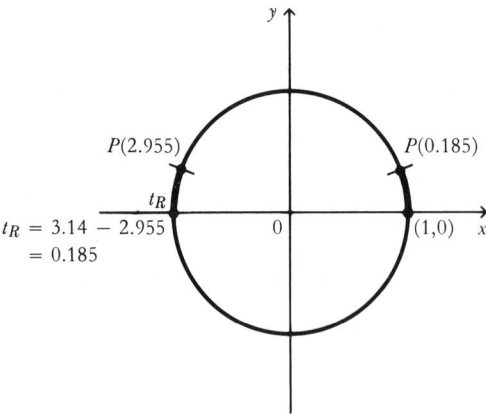

positive in quadrant II and since the reference number for 2.955 is 0.185, so that sin (−2.955) = −sin 0.185. Using linear interpolation, sin 0.185 can be approximated as follows.

$$0.01 \begin{bmatrix} 0.005 \begin{bmatrix} \text{sin } 0.18 & = 0.1790 \\ \text{sin } 0.185 = & ? \\ \text{sin } 0.19 & = 0.1889 \end{bmatrix} d \end{bmatrix} 0.0099$$

$$\frac{0.005}{0.01} = \frac{d}{0.0099}$$

Hence,

$d = 0.005$ (Approximately)

so that

$\sin 0.185 = 0.1889 - 0.005 = 0.1839$

Hence,

$\sin (-2.955) = -0.1839$ (Approximately)

3   $\cos 14.073$

SOLUTION. $P(14.073)$ is in quadrant I, and the reference number for 14.073 is 1.513.

$$\cos 14.073 = \cos [1.513 + 2(6.28)]$$
$$= \cos 1.513$$

Now, linear interpolation can be used to determine $\cos 1.513$ as follows.

$$0.01 \left[0.007 \begin{bmatrix} \cos 1.51 & = 0.0608 \\ \cos 1.513 & = & ? \\ \cos 1.52 & = 0.0508 \end{bmatrix} d \right] 0.01$$

$$\frac{0.007}{0.01} = \frac{d}{0.01}$$

so that

$d = 0.007$

Hence,

$\cos 1.513 = 0.0508 + 0.007 = 0.0578$

[Notice here that d is added to 0.0508. Compare parts (a) and (b) above.] Since $P(14.073)$ is in quadrant I, it follows that

$\cos 14.073 = 0.0578$ (Approximately)

PROBLEM SET 3

1   Use the periodicity, together with the fact that the cosine is an even function and the sine is an odd function, to reduce each of the given evaluations to an evaluation of the same function at a number in $[0,2\pi)$ (use $\pi = 3.14$).

a) $\sin (7\pi/4)$ b) $\cos (-10)$
c) $\sin 7.25$ d) $\cos 8$
e) $\sin (-2.9)$ f) $\cos 19\pi$
g) $\sin (-2\pi/3)$ h) $\cos 1.111$
i) $\cos 1.588$ j) $\sin (-4.232)$
k) $\cos (-2.4)$ l) $\cos (7\pi/6)$

2 Find the reference number for each of the parts of Problem 1 above, and then express the given evaluation in terms of an evaluation at the reference number.

3 Use your results from Problem 2 above, together with Table III and linear interpolation, if necessary, to find each value in Problem 1.

4 a) Follow the path of the point $P(t)$ around the unit circle as t increases from 0 to $\pi/2$. What is the behavior of $\cos t$? Next, examine Table III to see the behavior of $\cos t$ as t increases from 0 to 1.57. What do you notice?
   b) Answer part (a) for $\sin t$.

5 Follow the path of $P(t)$ on the unit circle to determine the behavior of $\cos t$ and $\sin t$ if:

a) t increases from $\pi/2$ to π
b) t increases from π to $3\pi/2$
c) t increases from $3\pi/2$ to 2π

Do the table values show these behaviors? Explain.

5 Graphs of the Sine and Cosine

In this section, we will investigate the graphs of

$$f(x) = \sin x \quad \text{and} \quad g(x) = \cos x$$

Since $f(x) = \sin x$ is a function of period 2π, it is sufficient to restrict our attention to the values of x where $x \in [0,2\pi)$. Then, the graph of $f(x) = \sin x$ for $x \in R$ can be extended as far as we like by repeating the graph, since the graph on interval $[0,2\pi)$ repeats every 2π units (Figure 1).

Figure 1

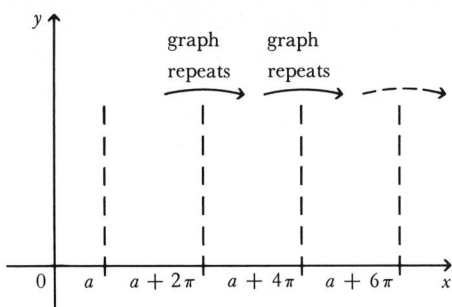

We also know that the range of $f(x) = \sin x$ is $[-1,1]$, so that the graph is "restricted" to a horizontal strip between $y = 1$ and $y = -1$. Combining this restriction with the periodicity, it is enough to graph $f(x) = \sin x$ in the region of Figure 2.

Figure 2

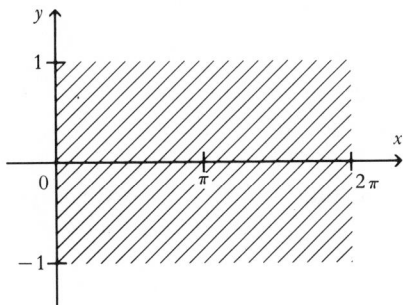

Since we know that $f(x) = \sin x$ is positive for $x \in (0,\pi)$ and negative for $x \in (\pi,2\pi)$ (see Section 3.2, Figure 4), we can further restrict the region (Figure 3).

Figure 3

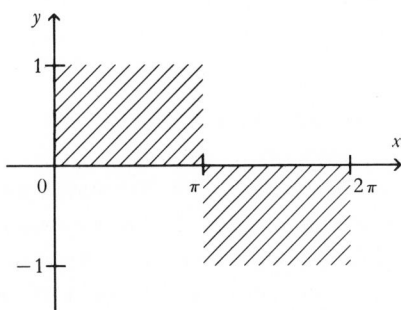

Finally, the known ordered pairs $(x, \sin x)$ can be used, together with the fact that $f(x)$ is increasing in the interval $(0,\pi/2)$, decreasing in the interval $(\pi/2,3\pi/2)$, and again is increasing in the interval $(3\pi/2,2\pi)$ (see Problem set 3, Problem 5) to obtain the graph on $[0,2\pi)$ (Figure 4).

Figure 4

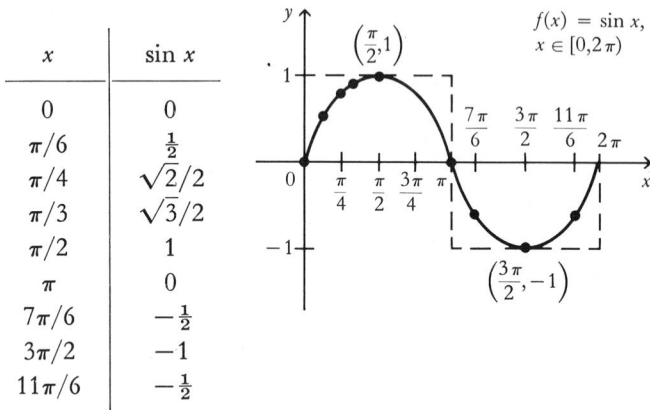

x	$\sin x$
0	0
$\pi/6$	$\frac{1}{2}$
$\pi/4$	$\sqrt{2}/2$
$\pi/3$	$\sqrt{3}/2$
$\pi/2$	1
π	0
$7\pi/6$	$-\frac{1}{2}$
$3\pi/2$	-1
$11\pi/6$	$-\frac{1}{2}$

This graph is sometimes called a *cycle* (see Problem 5) of the sine curve.

Using the periodicity of the sine, the graph of $f(x) = \sin x$ on R is obtained by repeating the cycle every 2π units (Figure 5). Notice that the graph displays the fact that the sine is symmetric with respect to the origin (Why?) and does not have an inverse (Why?).

Figure 5

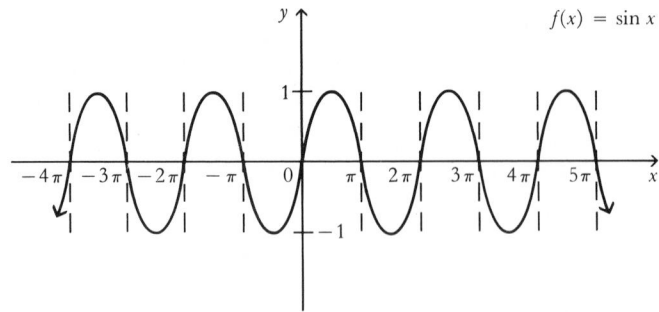

The graph of $f(x) = \cos x$ can be determined in the same way that the graph of the sine function was. Since the cosine is a function of period 2π, it is enough to graph it on $[0,2\pi)$. As with the sine, the range of the cosine is $[-1,1]$, so that we need only consider the graph in the region of Figure 6.

Figure 6

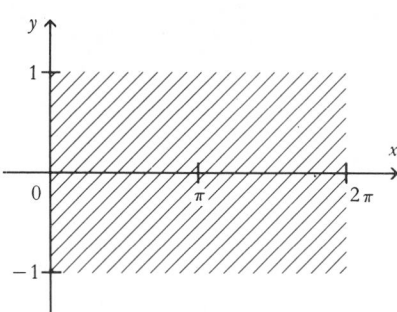

We can further restrict the region which contains the graph by using the fact that $f(x) = \cos x$ is positive for $x \in (0,\pi/2) \cup (3\pi/2,2\pi)$ and negative for $x \in (\pi/2,3\pi/2)$ (see Section 3.2, Figure 4) (Figure 7).

Figure 7

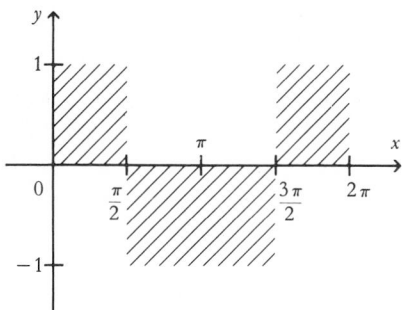

Finally, by using some functional values of the cosine, together with the known behavior of the cosine (see Problem set 3, Problem 5), we get the graph on $[0,2\pi)$, a *cycle* of the cosine curve (Figure 8).

Figure 8

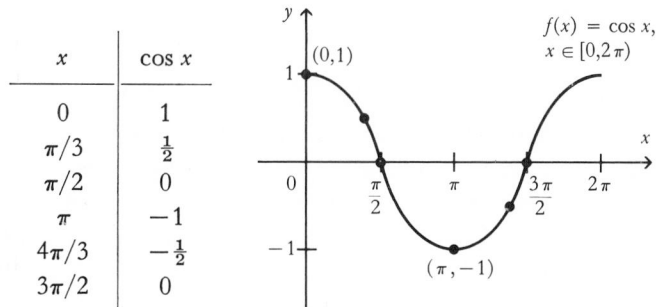

x	$\cos x$
0	1
$\pi/3$	$\frac{1}{2}$
$\pi/2$	0
π	-1
$4\pi/3$	$-\frac{1}{2}$
$3\pi/2$	0

By repeating the cycle every 2π units, we get the graph of $f(x) = \cos x$ on R (Figure 9). Notice that the graph displays the fact that $f(x) = \cos x$ does not have an inverse and that it is an even function.

Figure 9

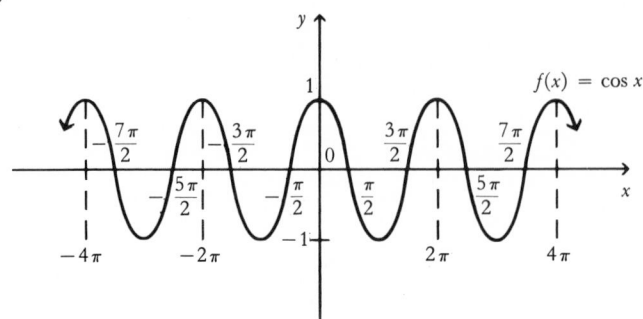

5.1   Graphs of $f(x) = a \sin (kx + b)$

We already sketched the graph of $f(x) = \sin x$ on R (Figure 5). It is worthwhile to investigate the geometric effect on this graph of the constants a, k, and b in graphing functions of the form $f(x) = a \sin (kx + b)$.

First, let us suppose that $k = 1$ and $b = 0$, so that the function takes the form $f(x) = a \sin x$. Since the sine graph $y = \sin x$ contains all points of the form $(x, \sin x)$, the graph of $f(x) = a \sin x$ can be determined from the graph of $f(x) = \sin x$ by multiplying the ordinates by a:

x	$\sin x$	$a \sin x$
$\vdots$	$\vdots$	$\vdots$
x_0	y_0	ay_0
$\vdots$	$\vdots$	$\vdots$

This can be illustrated by examples.

EXAMPLES

In each of the following problems, use the graph of $f(x) = \sin x$ to graph the given function on $[0, 2\pi)$. Explain the relationship between the geometric change of the graph of $f(x) = \sin x$ and the algebraic change of multiplying $\sin x$ by a constant.

1    $f(x) = 3 \sin x$

SOLUTION.   First, we graph one cycle of $f(x) = \sin x$ (Figure 10a). Now the graph of $f(x) = 3 \sin x$ is obtained by plotting the points

$(x, 3 \sin x)$. First, select a value for x, evaluate $\sin x$, and then multiply this latter value by 3:

$$x \to \sin x \to 3 \sin x$$

Geometrically, this means that the ordinate of $(x, \sin x)$ is "stretched" by a multiple of 3 to obtain $(x, 3 \sin x)$ (Figure 10b).

Figure 10

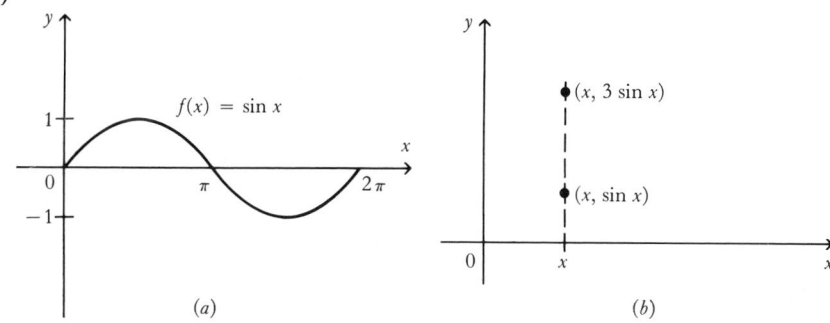

(a)   (b)

The overall geometric effect on the graph of $f(x) = \sin x$, then, is a "vertical stretching" of the sine curve by a multiple of 3 (Figure 11).

Figure 11

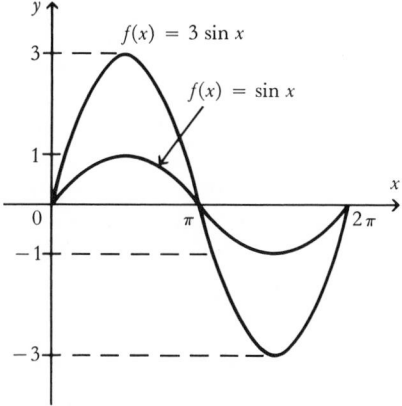

2   $f(x) = \frac{1}{5} \sin x$.

SOLUTION.   First, we graph one cycle of $f(x) = \sin x$ (Figure 12). Now, the graph of $f(x) = \frac{1}{5} \sin x$ is obtained by multiplying the ordinates of the graph of $f(x) = \sin x$ by $\frac{1}{5}$:

$$x \to \sin x \to \frac{1}{5} \sin x$$

Figure 12

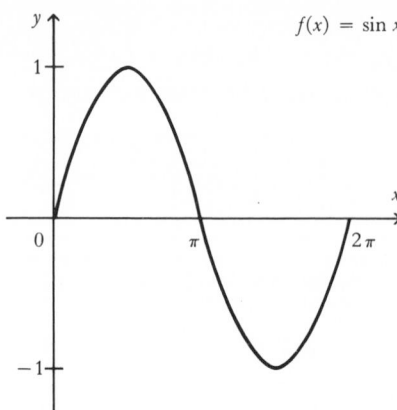

Geometrically, this means that the ordinates of $(x, \frac{1}{5} \sin x)$ are $\frac{1}{5}$ times the ordinates of $(x, \sin x)$. The overall effect on $f(x) = \sin x$ is the "vertical shrinking" of the sine curve by a multiple of $\frac{1}{5}$ (Figure 13).

Figure 13

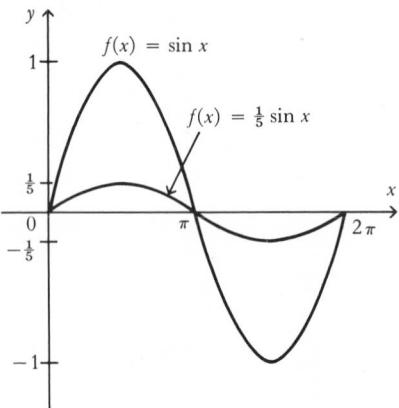

Next, let us consider an example in which $a = 1$, that is, $f(x) = \sin (kx + b)$, by reexamining the graph of $f(x) = \sin x$. We know that when x varies from 0 to 2π, one cycle of the sine function graph is generated. This fact can also be expressed in the following manner.

$f(x) = \sin (\ \ )$ generates one cycle of the sine graph
if ( ) varies from 0 to 2π.

Suppose, for example, that ( ) $= 3x - 1$. Then,

$$f(x) = \sin (3x - 1)$$

generates one cycle of the sine graph if $3x - 1$ varies from 0 to 2π $(0 \leq 3x - 1 < 2\pi)$; that is, if $3x$ varies from 1 to $2\pi + 1$ $(1 \leq 3x < 2\pi + 1)$; that is, if x varies from $\frac{1}{3}$ to $2\pi/3 + \frac{1}{3}$ $(\frac{1}{3} \leq x < 2\pi/3 + \frac{1}{3})$. Hence if x varies from $\frac{1}{3}$ to $2\pi/3 + \frac{1}{3}$, then $3x - 1$ varies from 0 to 2π, so that, in turn, $f(x) = \sin(3x - 1)$ generates one cycle of the sine wave (Figure 14). Using the periodicity of the sine, we get the graph of

Figure 14

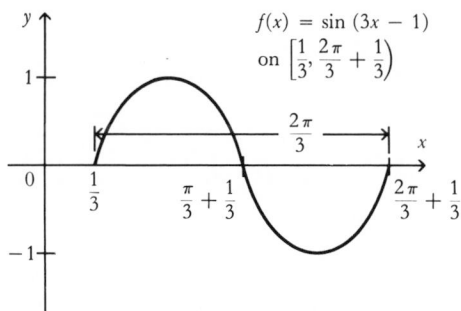

$$f(x) = \sin(3x - 1)$$
$$\text{on } \left[\frac{1}{3}, \frac{2\pi}{3} + \frac{1}{3}\right)$$

$f(x) = \sin(3x - 1)$ over R (Figure 15). Notice here that the sine wave "begins" at $\frac{1}{3}$ (this is called the *phase shift*), and that a cycle covers an interval of length $2\pi/3$ ($2\pi/3$ is the period of $f(x) = \sin(3x - 1)$, and, by contrast, the period of $f(x) = \sin x$ is 2π). The *amplitude* of $y = f(x)$ is defined to be $\frac{1}{2}(M - m)$, where M is the largest value of $f(x)$ and m is the smallest value of $f(x)$; hence, the amplitude of $f(x) = \sin(3x - 1)$ is $\frac{1}{2}[1 - (-1)] = 1$.

Figure 15

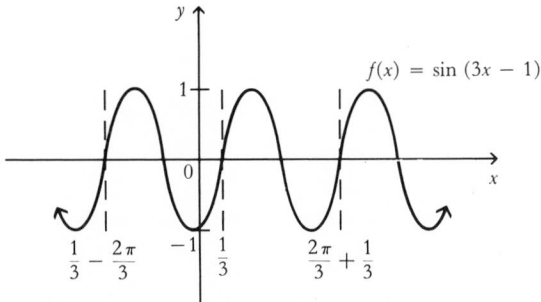

$$f(x) = \sin(3x - 1)$$

EXAMPLES

1   Use the graph of $f(x) = \sin x$ to graph a cycle of $f(x) = 3 \sin(\frac{1}{2}x + 2)$. Indicate the amplitude, period, and phase shift.

SOLUTION. $f(x) = 3 \sin(\frac{1}{2}x + 2)$ generates a cycle of the sine graph if $\frac{1}{2}x + 2$ varies from 0 to 2π $(0 \leq \frac{1}{2}x + 2 < 2\pi)$; that is, if $\frac{1}{2}x$ varies from -2 to $2\pi - 2$ $(-2 \leq \frac{1}{2}x < 2\pi - 2)$; that is; when x varies from -4 to $4\pi - 4$ ($-4 \le x < 4\pi - 4$). Here, the 3 has the effect of "vertically stretching" the graph by a multiple of 3 (Figure 16). The period is 4π; the phase shift is -4; and the amplitude is $\frac{1}{2}[3 - (-3)] = 3$.

Figure 16

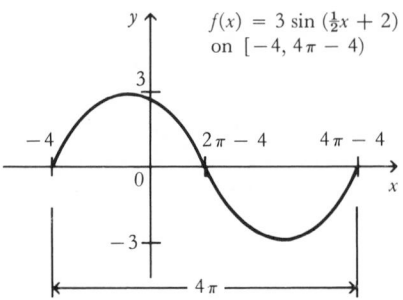

$f(x) = 3 \sin (\frac{1}{2}x + 2)$
on $[-4, 4\pi - 4)$

2 Follow the directions of example 1 for $f(x) = \sin(-x + 1)$.

SOLUTION. $f(x) = \sin(-x + 1) = \sin[-(x - 1)] = -\sin(x - 1)$, since the sine function is an odd function. First, we graph $y = \sin(x - 1)$. Notice that $y = \sin(x - 1)$ generates a sine cycle if $x - 1$ varies from 0 to 2π ($0 \le x - 1 < 2\pi$), that is, when x varies from 1 to $2\pi + 1$ ($1 \le x < 2\pi + 1$) (Figure 17). Finally, we obtain the

Figure 17

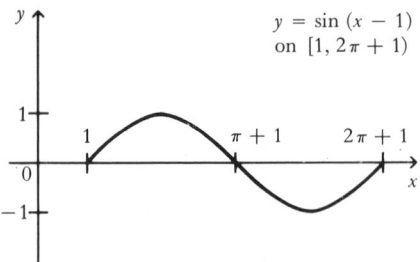

$y = \sin(x - 1)$
on $[1, 2\pi + 1)$

graph of $f(x) = -\sin(x - 1)$ from the graph of $y = \sin(x - 1)$ merely by reflecting the latter curve across the x axis (Figure 18). The period is 2π; the phase shift is 1; the amplitude is 1.

Figure 18

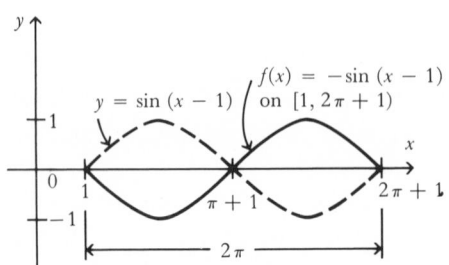

$f(x) = -\sin(x - 1)$
on $[1, 2\pi + 1)$
$y = \sin(x - 1)$

5.2   Graphs of $f(x) = a \cos(kx + b)$

We can use the graph of $f(x) = \cos x$ to obtain the graphs of functions of the form $f(x) = a \cos(kx + b)$ by following the same approach as that which was taken for the sine function. A few examples will clarify the procedure.

EXAMPLES

Use the graph $f(x) = \cos x$ to obtain the amplitude, period, phase shift, and one cycle of the graph of each of the following functions.

1    $f(x) = 4 \cos x$

SOLUTION.   The graph of $f(x) = 4 \cos x$ has the same "horizontal behavior" as $f(x) = \cos x$, although its vertical position differs by a multiple of 4 (Figure 19). The amplitude of $f(x) = 4 \cos x$ is 4; the period is 2π; the phase shift is 0.

Figure 19

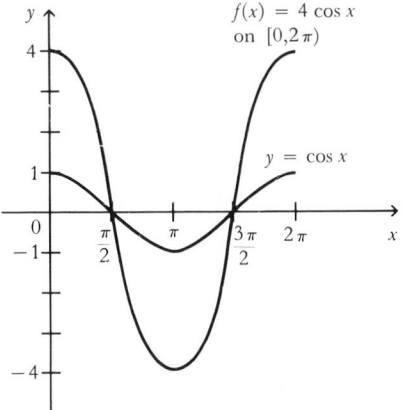

$f(x) = 4 \cos x$
on $[0, 2\pi)$

$y = \cos x$

2    $f(x) = \cos(x/2)$

SOLUTION.   This function generates one cycle of the cosine curve when $x/2$ varies from 0 to 2π $(0 \le x/2 < 2\pi)$, that is, when x varies from 0 to 4π $(0 \le x < 4\pi)$ (Figure 20). The period is 4π; the amplitude is 1; and the phase shift is 0.

3    $f(x) = -3 \cos(x/8 + \pi/2)$

SOLUTION.   First, we will investigate $y = \cos(x/8 + \pi/2)$. This function generates a cosine cycle when $x/8 + \pi/2$ varies from 0 to 2π $(0 \le x/8 + \pi/2 < 2\pi)$, that is, when $x/8$ varies from $-\pi/2$ to $2\pi - \pi/2$ $(-\pi/2 \le x/8 < 2\pi - \pi/2)$, that is, when x varies from -4π to

Figure 20

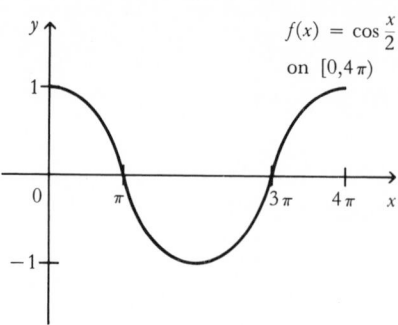

$16\pi - 4\pi$ $(-4\pi \le x < 16\pi - 4\pi)$ (Figure 21). Multiplication of $y = \cos(x/8 + \pi/2)$ by -3 merely stretches the graph by a multiple by 3,

Figure 21

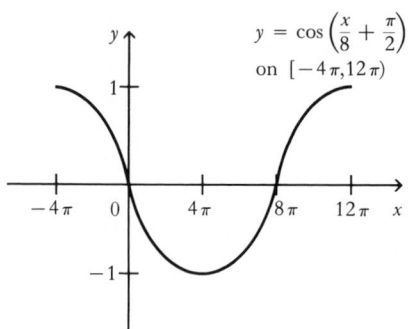

and then reflects this latter graph across the x axis (Why?) (Figure 22). The amplitude is 3; the period is 16π; and the phase shift is -4π.

Figure 22

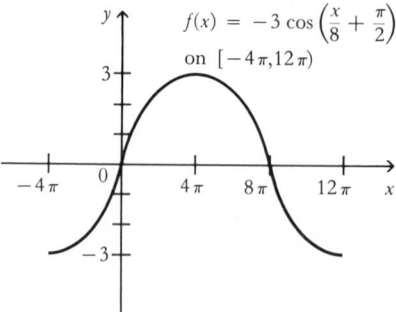

PROBLEM SET 4

1 Use the sine and cosine functions to graph a cycle of each of the following functions. Indicate the period, amplitude, and phase shift.

a) $f(x) = 10 \sin x$ b) $f(x) = \pi \cos x$

c) $f(x) = \frac{1}{3} \sin (x/5)$ d) $f(x) = 3 \cos (-2x)$

e) $f(x) = \sin (\pi x)$ f) $f(x) = 4 \sin (-x/2)$

g) $f(x) = \sin 10x$

2 Follow the directions of problem one for each of the following functions.

    a) $f(x) = 2 \cos (x + \pi)$ b) $f(x) = 5 \sin (x/4 - \pi/2)$

    c) $f(x) = \pi \cos (x/\pi - 1/\pi)$ d) $f(x) = 2 \cos (3 - 2x)$

    e) $f(x) = -\frac{1}{3} \sin (x - 1)$ f) $f(x) = 3 \sin (x + \pi)$

    g) $f(x) = 4 \sin (x/3 + \pi/6)$ h) $f(x) = 3 \cos (x - \pi/6)$

    i) $f(x) = \frac{1}{2} \cos (-x + \pi/12)$ j) $f(x) = 2 \sin (2x/3 + \pi/4)$

3 How does the graph of $f(x) = \cos x$ display the fact that the cosine is symmetric with respect to the y axis?

4 Explain why functions of the form $f(x) = a \sin (kx + b)$ and of the form $f(x) = a \cos (kx + b)$ do not have inverses if $a \neq 0$ and $k \neq 0$.

5 We know that if t varies from 0 to 2π, $P(t)$ transverses the unit circle once, and $\sin t$ varies through all its range values. We know that $f(x) = \sin x$ generates one cycle of the sine curve when x varies from 0 to 2π $(0 \leq x < 2\pi)$. What happens to $\sin t$ when t recycles the unit circle, that is, varies from 2π to 4π $(2\pi \leq x < 4\pi)$? What happens to $\sin x$ when x varies from 2π to 4π? Draw sketches to display these variations. Can you see why the word "cycle" is used to indicate a sine wave? Explain.

6 Consider $f(x) = \sin x - \sin 3x$.

    a) Sketch the graphs of $g(x) = \sin x$ and $h(x) = \sin 3x$ on the same set of axes.

    b) Select appropriate points along the x axis and subtract graphically the ordinates $g(x) - h(x)$ of these points to obtain a sketch of the graph of $f(x) = g(x) - h(x)$.

6 Inverses of the Sine and Cosine

We know from our general study of functions that a function f has an inverse only when f is one-to-one. Geometrically, f^{-1} exists if the graph of $y = f(x)$ intersects any horizontal line in at most one point (see Chapter 2, Section 6).

It is easy to show (see Example 2, Section 2) that the sine and cosine are not one-to-one. For example, $\sin 0 = \sin 2\pi$ and $\cos 0 = \cos 2\pi$; or, using the horizontal line test, we can "see" from the graphs that the functions are not one-to-one, and, consequently, do not have inverses.

Although the sine and cosine functions do not have inverses, it is possible to construct an invertible function from each of the two functions by making suitable restrictions on the domains of the functions.

A one-to-one function can be constructed from $f(x) = \sin x$ in the following manner. The domain of f is R, and the range is $[-1,1]$. From f, define a function $f(x) = \mathrm{Sin}\ x$ (notice that the capital S is used here) by restricting the domain to $[-\pi/2,\pi/2]$ (Figure 1). The range of $f(x) = \mathrm{Sin}\ x$ is $[-1,1]$, and the domain is $[-\pi/2,\pi/2]$. Since $f(x) = \mathrm{Sin}\ x$ is increasing on its domain, $f(x) = \mathrm{Sin}\ x$ has an inverse (see Chapter 2, Section 6).

Figure 1

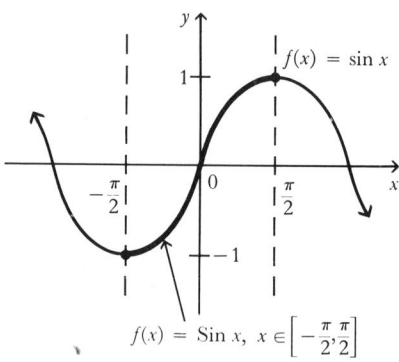

$$f(x) = \mathrm{Sin}\ x, \quad x \in \left[-\frac{\pi}{2}, \frac{\pi}{2}\right]$$

6.1   Definition

The *arcsine function,* denoted by $y = \mathrm{Arcsin}\ x$ or by $y = \sin^{-1} x$, is the inverse function of $f(x) = \mathrm{Sin}\ x$. The domain of the arcsine is $[-1,1]$ and the range is $[-\pi/2,\pi/2]$.

If $f(x) = \mathrm{Sin}\ x$ is denoted by set notation, it follows that

$$f = \{(x,y) \mid y = \mathrm{Sin}\ x\}$$

or, equivalently,

$$f = \left\{(x,y) \mid y = \sin x, \ x \in \left[-\frac{\pi}{2}, \frac{\pi}{2}\right]\right\}$$

so that

$$f^{-1} = \left\{(y,x) \mid y = \sin x, \ x \in \left[-\frac{\pi}{2}, \frac{\pi}{2}\right]\right\}$$
$$= \left\{(x,y) \mid x = \sin y, \ y \in \left[-\frac{\pi}{2}, \frac{\pi}{2}\right]\right\}$$
$$= \{(x,y) \mid \sin^{-1} x = y\}$$

In other words, $\sin^{-1} x = y$ is equivalent to $\sin y = x$, with the restriction that $y \in [-\pi/2, \pi/2]$. $\square$

It should be noted that $\sin^{-1} x \neq (\sin x)^{-1}$; $\sin^{-1} x$ denotes the inverse of the sine function, whereas $(\sin x)^{-1} = 1/(\sin x)$.

EXAMPLES

1 Graph $f(x) = \sin^{-1} x$.

SOLUTION. We must graph $f = \{(x,y) | y = \sin^{-1} x\} = \{(x,y) | \text{Sin } y = x\}$. Since the domain of f is $[-1,1]$ and the range is $[-\pi/2, \pi/2]$, the graph

Figure 2

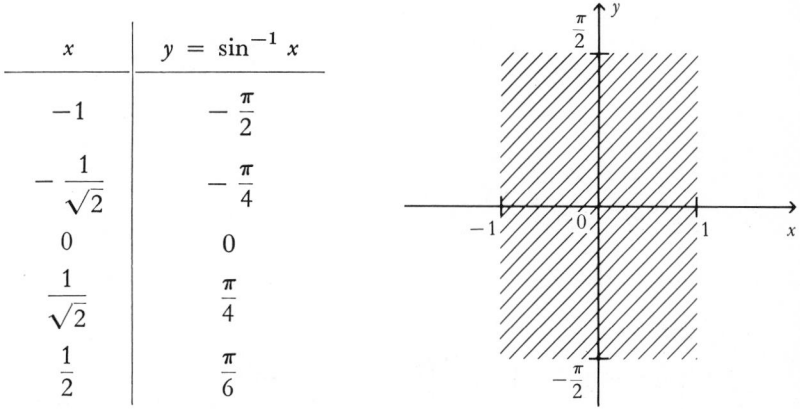

x	$y = \sin^{-1} x$
-1	$-\dfrac{\pi}{2}$
$-\dfrac{1}{\sqrt{2}}$	$-\dfrac{\pi}{4}$
0	0
$\dfrac{1}{\sqrt{2}}$	$\dfrac{\pi}{4}$
$\dfrac{1}{2}$	$\dfrac{\pi}{6}$

is contained in the region of Figure 2. By plotting points, we get the graph of $f(x) = \sin^{-1} x$ (Figure 3).

Figure 3

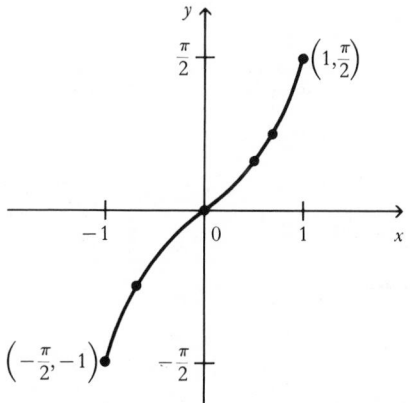

2   Evaluate $\sin^{-1} \frac{1}{2}$.

SOLUTION.   Assume that $\sin^{-1} \frac{1}{2} = x$. Then $\sin x = \frac{1}{2}$, where $x \in [-\pi/2, \pi/2]$, so that $x = \pi/6$.

We can use essentially the same approach for constructing a one-to-one cosine function as that approach which was used above to construct a one-to-one sine function.

From $f(x) = \cos x$, define a function $f(x) = \text{Cos } x$ (notice that capital C is used here), with domain $[0,\pi]$ and range $[-1,1]$ (Figure 4). Since $f(x) = \text{Cos } x$ is decreasing on its domain, $f(x) = \text{Cos } x$ has an inverse.

Figure 4

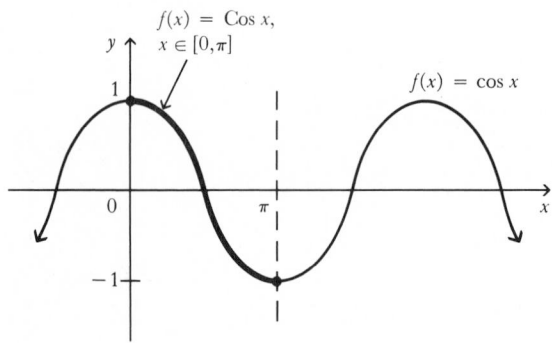

$f(x) = \text{Cos } x,$
$x \in [0,\pi]$

$f(x) = \cos x$

6.2   Definition

The *Arccosine function*, denoted by $y = \text{Arccos } x$ or $y = \cos^{-1} x$, is the inverse function of $f(x) = \text{Cos } x$. The domain of the Arccosine is $[-1,1]$ and the range is $[0,\pi]$.

In set notation, if

$$f = \{(x,y) | y = \text{Cos } x\}$$

then

$$f = \{(x,y) | y = \cos x, x \in [0,\pi]\}$$

so that

$$f^{-1} = \{(y,x) | y = \cos x, x \in [0,\pi]\}$$
$$= \{(x,y) | x = \cos y, y \in [0,\pi]\}$$
$$= \{(x,y) | \cos^{-1} x = y\}$$

Hence, $\cos^{-1} x = y$ is equivalent to $\cos y = x$, where $y \in [0,\pi]$. $\square$

EXAMPLES

1   Evaluate $\cos^{-1} (-\frac{1}{2})$.

SOLUTION.   Let $\cos^{-1} (-\frac{1}{2}) = t$. Then $\cos t = -\frac{1}{2}$, where $t \in [0,\pi]$, so that $t = 2\pi/3$.

2   Find $\cos [\sin^{-1} (-\sqrt{3}/2)]$.

SOLUTION.   Since $\sin^{-1}(-\sqrt{3}/2) = -\pi/3$ (Why?),
$\cos[\sin^{-1}(-\sqrt{3}/2)] = \cos(-\pi/3) = \cos(\pi/3) = \frac{1}{2}$.

3   Show that $\cos(\sin^{-1} x) = \sqrt{1 - x^2}$.

PROOF.   Let $z = \sin^{-1} x$. Then $\sin z = x$, where $z \in [-\pi/2, \pi/2]$,
so that

$$\cos z = \sqrt{1 - \sin^2 z}$$

since the cosine is positive in quadrants I and IV. Hence,
$\cos z = \sqrt{1 - x^2}$. By substitution,

$$\cos\cdot(\sin^{-1} x) = \sqrt{1 - x^2}$$

4   Graph $f(x) = \cos^{-1} x$.

Figure 5

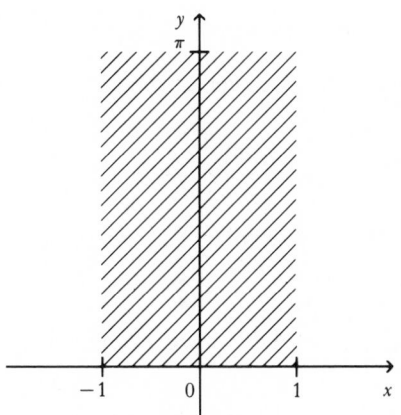

SOLUTION.   The domain and range of f restrict the graph to the region
of Figure 5. Finally, we get the graph of $f(x) = \cos^{-1} x$ by plotting a
few points (Figure 6).

Figure 6

x	$y = \cos^{-1} x$
-1	π
$-\dfrac{1}{2}$	$\dfrac{2\pi}{3}$
0	$\dfrac{\pi}{2}$
$\dfrac{1}{2}$	$\dfrac{\pi}{3}$
1	0

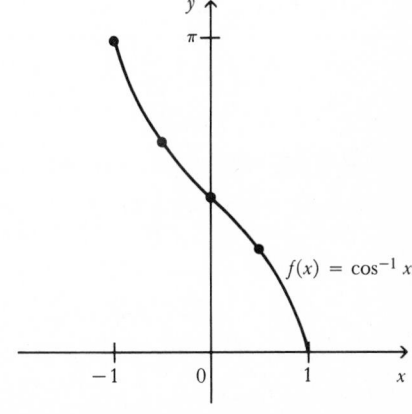

PROBLEM SET 5

1   Determine each of the following values.

a) $\sin^{-1} \frac{1}{2}$

b) $\sin^{-1} 0$

c) $\sin^{-1} (\sqrt{2}/2)$

d) $\cos^{-1} 0$

e) $\cos^{-1} \frac{1}{2}$

f) $\cos^{-1} (-\sqrt{3}/2)$

g) $\sin^{-1} (-\sqrt{2}/2)$

h) $\cos^{-1} (-1)$

i) $\sin^{-1} (-1)$

j) $\sin^{-1} [\sin (\pi/2)]$

k) $\sin^{-1} 0.21$

l) $\cos^{-1} 0.86$

2   Find the exact value of each of the following expressions.

a) $\sin (\cos^{-1} \frac{3}{4})$

b) $\cos [\sin^{-1} (-\frac{35}{37})]$

c) $\cos^{-1} [\cos (-\frac{7}{25})]$

d) $\sin [\cos^{-1} (-1)]$

e) $\sin^{-1} [\sin (-3\pi/2)]$

f) $\cos (\cos^{-1} \frac{7}{12})$

g) $\cos [\sin^{-1} (\sqrt{2}/2)]$

h) $\sin^{-1} [\sin (-\pi/4)]$

i) $\sin^{-1} (\cos \pi)$

j) $\cos^{-1} [\sin (\pi/6)]$

3   For what values of x, if any, is each of the following equations valid?

a) $\sin^{-1} (\sin x) = x$

b) $\sin (\sin^{-1} x) = x$

c) $\cos^{-1} (\cos x) = x$

d) $\cos (\cos^{-1} x) = x$

4   Show that the following statements are valid.

a) $\sin^{-1} x = \cos^{-1} \sqrt{1 - x^2}$ b) $\sin [\sin^{-1} (-x)] = -x$

5   Determine whether each of the following functions is odd or even or neither.

a) $f(x) = \sin^{-1} x$

b) $g(x) = \cos^{-1} x$

6   Define $f(x) = \sin x$, $x \in [\pi/2, 3\pi/2]$. Graph the function. What is the range? Explain why f^{-1} exists. Describe f^{-1}.

7   Discuss the symmetry of the graphs of $f(x) = \sin^{-1} x$ and $f(x) = \cos^{-1} x$.

8   Sketch the graph of each of the following functions.

a) $f(x) = \sin^{-1} \frac{1}{2}x$

b) $f(x) = 2 \cos^{-1} \frac{1}{2}x$

c) $f(x) = \cos^{-1} 3x$

d) $f(x) = \sin^{-1} x + \cos^{-1} x$

7 Other Circular Functions

The sine and cosine functions can be used to define four other functions.

7.1 Definition

The tangent, cotangent, secant, and cosecant functions are defined as follows.

$$\text{tangent} = \left\{ (x,y) \mid y = \frac{\sin x}{\cos x}, \ \cos x \neq 0 \right\}$$

$$\text{cotangent} = \left\{ (x,y) \mid y = \frac{\cos x}{\sin x}, \ \sin x \neq 0 \right\}$$

$$\text{secant} = \left\{ (x,y) \mid y = \frac{1}{\cos x}, \ \cos x \neq 0 \right\}$$

and

$$\text{cosecant} = \left\{ (x,y) \mid y = \frac{1}{\sin x}, \ \sin x \neq 0 \right\}$$

or, more briefly,

$$\tan x = \frac{\sin x}{\cos x} \qquad \cos x \neq 0$$

$$\cot x = \frac{\cos x}{\sin x} \qquad \sin x \neq 0$$

$$\sec x = \frac{1}{\cos x} \qquad \cos x \neq 0$$

and

$$\csc x = \frac{1}{\sin x} \qquad \sin x \neq 0 \quad \square$$

Since this definition expresses each of the four functions in terms of the cosine and/or sine, many of the functional properties of the four functions can be determined by using the known functional properties of the sine and cosine functions.

7.2 Properties of the Tangent, Cotangent, Secant, and Cosecant

Since $\tan x = (\sin x)/(\cos x)$, the domain of the tangent is given by $D_{\text{Tan}} = \{x \mid \cos x \neq 0\}$. However, $\cos x = 0$ for $x = \pi/2 + n\pi$, $n \in I$ (see Section 5, Figure 9). Hence,

$$D_{\text{Tan}} = \left\{ x \mid x \neq \frac{\pi}{2} + n\pi, \ n \in I \right\}$$

Since the domain of the secant is the same as the domain of the tangent (Why?), the domain of the secant is given by

$$D_{\text{Sec}} = \left\{ x \mid x \neq \frac{\pi}{2} + n\pi, \ n \in I \right\}$$

The domain of the cotangent is given by

$$D_{\text{Cot}} = \{x|\sin x \neq 0\}$$

but, since $\sin x = 0$ for $x = n\pi$, $n \in I$ (see Section 5, Figure 5), we have

$$D_{\text{Cot}} = \{x|x \neq n\pi, n \in I\}$$

Since the domain of the cosecant is the same as the domain of the cotangent, the domain of the cosecant is given by

$$D_{\text{Csc}} = \{x|x = n\pi, n \in I\}$$

The ranges of the secant and cosecant are not difficult to determine. We know that $\sec x = 1/(\cos x)$ and that $|\cos x| \leq 1$. Hence,

$$|\sec x| = \left|\frac{1}{\cos x}\right| = \frac{1}{|\cos x|}$$

but,

$$|\cos x| \leq 1 \quad \text{implies} \quad 1 \leq \frac{1}{|\cos x|} \quad \text{whenever } \cos x \neq 0$$

so that

$$1 \leq |\sec x|$$

That is, the range of the secant is given by

$$R_{\text{Sec}} = \{y||y| > 1\} = \{y|y \geq 1\} \cup \{y|y \leq -1\}$$
$$= [1,\infty) \cup (-\infty,-1]$$

Similarly, we can use the fact that $\csc x = 1/(\sin x)$ and $|\sin x| \leq 1$ to conclude that the range of the cosecant is given by

$$R_{\text{Csc}} = \{y||y| \geq 1\} = \{y|y \geq 1\} \cup \{y|y \leq -1\}$$
$$= [1,\infty) \cup (-\infty,-1]$$

The ranges of the tangent and cotangent are not so easy to determine. We will begin by examining the behavior of the tangent for $x \in [0,\pi/2)$.

Figure 1

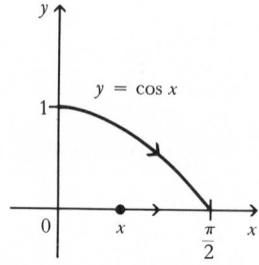

Figure 2

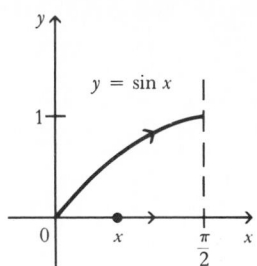

Clearly, as x increases from 0 to $\pi/2$, $y = \cos x$ decreases from 1 to 0 (Figure 1), and $y = \sin x$ increases from 0 to 1 (Figure 2), so that $\tan x = (\sin x)/(\cos x)$ is composed of a ratio of two functions with the function in the denominator decreasing to 0 and the one in the numerator increasing to 1. From the behavior of the sine and cosine function and by examining values in Table 1 (from Table III of Appendix A), we can reasonably conclude that $\tan x$ increases from 0 through all possible real numbers, to "infinity." By a similar argument it can be shown that the tangent assumes all possible negative real values for $x \in (-\pi/2,0]$. Hence, the range of the tangent is R. It can also be shown that the range of the cotangent is R (see Problem 6).

Table 1

x	$\sin x$	$\cos x$	$\tan x = \dfrac{\sin x}{\cos x}$
0	0	1	0
0.11	0.1098	0.9940	0.1104
0.44	0.4259	0.9048	0.4708
0.89	0.7771	0.6294	1.235
1.01	0.8468	0.5319	1.592
1.50	0.9975	0.0707	14.101
1.55	0.9998	0.0208	48.078
1.56	0.9999	0.0108	92.62

It is easy to determine the signs of the tangent, cotangent, secant, and cosecant by using what we know about the signs of the sine and cosine. Table 2, which is self-explanatory, indicates the signs of the function values.

The next theorem uses the properties of the sine and cosine function to determine the periodicity of the tangent, cotangent, secant, and cosecant function and to identify which of the four functions is even and which is odd.

Table 2

$P(x)$ in quadrant:	I	II	III	IV
cos x	+	−	−	+
sin x	+	+	−	−
$\tan x = \dfrac{\sin x}{\cos x}$	$\dfrac{+}{+} = +$	$\dfrac{+}{-} = -$	$\dfrac{-}{-} = +$	$\dfrac{-}{+} = -$
$\cot x = \dfrac{\cos x}{\sin x}$	$\dfrac{+}{+} = +$	$\dfrac{-}{+} = -$	$\dfrac{-}{-} = +$	$\dfrac{+}{-} = -$
$\csc x = \dfrac{1}{\sin x}$	$\dfrac{1}{+} = +$	$\dfrac{1}{+} = +$	$\dfrac{1}{-} = -$	$\dfrac{1}{-} = -$
$\sec x = \dfrac{1}{\cos x}$	$\dfrac{1}{+} = +$	$\dfrac{1}{-} = -$	$\dfrac{1}{-} = -$	$\dfrac{1}{+} = +$

THEOREM 1

i   The tangent, cotangent, secant, and cosecant are periodic functions of period 2π. (Later in Chapter 6, Problem Set 3, we will see that the *fundamental* period of the tangent and cotangent is actually π.)

ii   The secant is an even function.

iii   The tangent, cotangent, and cosecant are odd functions.

PROOF

i $\tan (x + 2\pi) = \dfrac{\sin (x + 2\pi)}{\cos (x + 2\pi)} = \dfrac{\sin x}{\cos x} = \tan x$

and

$\sec (x + 2\pi) = \dfrac{1}{\cos (x + 2\pi)} = \dfrac{1}{\cos x} = \sec x$

(For the cotangent and the cosecant see Problem 1a.)

ii $\sec (-x) = \dfrac{1}{\cos (-x)} = \dfrac{1}{\cos x} = \sec x$

and

iii $\tan (-x) = \dfrac{\sin (-x)}{\cos (-x)} = \dfrac{-\sin x}{\cos x} = -\tan x$

(For the cotangent and the cosecant see Problem 1b.)

Since all four of these functions are periodic functions of period 2π and since these functions are either even or odd, their evaluation at any given number in the domain follows the same procedure as that of the sine and cosine: first, the reference number; next, the given function at the reference number using Table III, together with interpolation if necessary; finally, the evaluation made by adjusting the sign according to the quadrant (Table 2).

EXAMPLES

1 Use the periodicity of the tangent function to simplify $\tan (t - 2\pi)$.

SOLUTION

$$
\begin{aligned}
\tan (t - 2\pi) &= \tan [-(2\pi - t)] \\
&= -\tan (2\pi - t) \\
&= -\tan [(2\pi) + (-t)] \\
&= -\tan (-t) \\
&= -(-\tan t) \\
&= \tan t
\end{aligned}
$$

2 Evaluate $\tan (\pi/4)$ without the use of tables.

SOLUTION

$$
\tan \frac{\pi}{4} = \frac{\sin (\pi/4)}{\cos (\pi/4)} = \frac{1/\sqrt{2}}{1/\sqrt{2}} = 1
$$

3 Evaluate $\tan (-11\pi/6)$ without the use of tables.

Figure 3

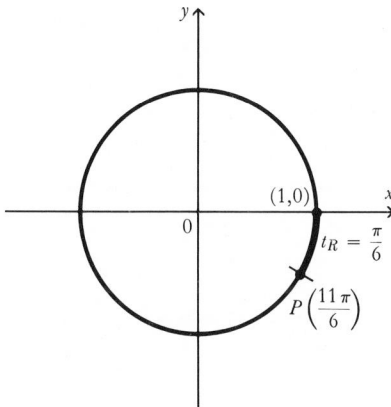

SOLUTION. $\tan (-11\pi/6) = -\tan (11\pi/6)$. But the reference number for $11\pi/6$ is $t_R = \pi/6$ (Figure 3). Since the tangent is negative for

$11\pi/6$, we get

$$-\tan\frac{11\pi}{6} = -\left(-\tan\frac{\pi}{6}\right)$$

$$= \tan\frac{\pi}{6}$$

$$= \frac{\sin(\pi/6)}{\cos(\pi/6)}$$

$$= \frac{\frac{1}{2}}{\sqrt{3}/2}$$

$$= \frac{1}{\sqrt{3}}$$

4   Use Table III to evaluate each of the six circular functions for $x = 4.8$ (use $\pi = 3.14$).

SOLUTION.   The reference number for 4.8 is $t_R = 1.48$, and $P(4.8)$ is in quadrant IV (Figure 4). Hence, by using the known signs of the six functions, together with Table III, we get

$$\sin 4.8 = -\sin 1.48 = -0.9959$$
$$\cos 4.8 = \cos 1.48 = 0.0907$$
$$\tan 4.8 = -\tan 1.48 = -10.983$$
$$\csc 4.8 = -\csc 1.48 = 1.004$$
$$\sec 4.8 = \sec 1.48 = 11.029$$
$$\cot 4.8 = -\cot 1.48 = -0.0910$$

Figure 4

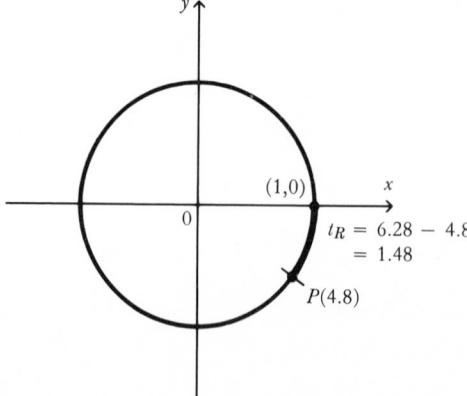

$t_R = 6.28 - 4.8$
$= 1.48$

$P(4.8)$

5   Use Table III and linear interpolation to evaluate tan 3.048 (use $\pi = 3.14$).

SOLUTION. Since the reference number is $t_R = 0.092$ and $P(3.048)$ is in quadrant **II** (Figure 5), we have $\tan 3.048 = -\tan 0.092$. Next, linear interpolation can be used to evaluate $\tan 0.092$.

$$0.01 \left[0.008 \left[\begin{array}{l} \tan 0.09 \ = 0.0902 \\ \tan 0.092 = \\ \tan 0.10 \ = 0.1003 \end{array} \right] d \right] 0.0101$$

$$\frac{d}{0.0101} = \frac{0.008}{0.01}$$

so that

$$d = 0.0081 \qquad \text{(Approximately)}$$

Hence,

$$\tan 0.092 = 0.1003 - 0.0081 = 0.0922$$

so that

$$\tan 3.048 = -0.0922 \qquad \text{(Approximately)}$$

since $P(3.048)$ is in quadrant **II**.

Figure 5

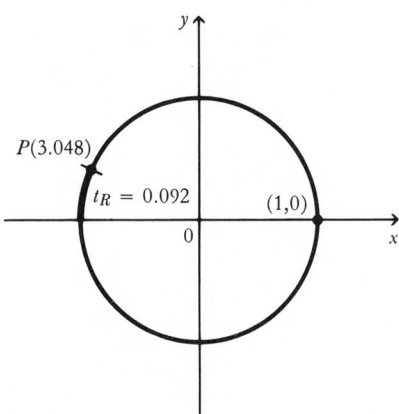

7.3 Graphs of Other Circular Functions

Since $f(x) = \tan x$ is a periodic function of period 2π, it is enough to sketch the graph on $[0,2\pi)$ in order to determine the graph on R.

First, one cycle of $g(x) = \sin x$ and one cycle of $h(x) = \cos x$ is graphed on the same coordinate system. These graphs will be called the *auxiliary graphs* (Figure 6).

Second, the points at which the tan x is undefined are indicated by drawing dotted vertical lines through the values of x at which $\cos x = 0$ (Figure 6).

Next, the points at which $\tan x = 0$ occur where $\sin x = 0$ (Why?) (Figure 6).

Figure 6

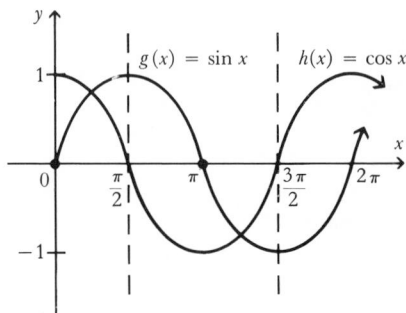

Finally, the sketch of $f(x) = \tan x$ can be determined by examining the auxiliary graphs to determine the behavior of $\tan x = (\sin x)/(\cos x)$ as x increases from 0 to 2π.

i   (See Figure 7.) As x increases from 0 to $\pi/2$, $\sin x$ increases from 0 to 1 and $\cos x$ decreases from 1 to 0 (Figure 7a). Hence, $\tan x = (\sin x)/(\cos x)$, where the numerator is increasing to 1 and the denominator is decreasing to 0; consequently, $\tan x$ is becoming increasingly large in value as x increases to $\pi/2$ (Figure 7b). However, the graph does not cross the line $x = \pi/2$. Because of this behavior, $x = \pi/2$ is called a *vertical asymptote*.

Figure 7

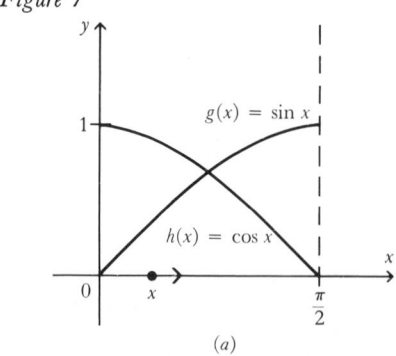

(a)

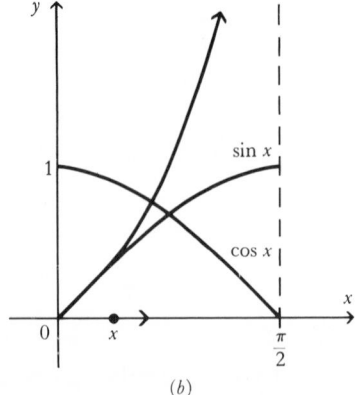

(b)

ii   (See Figure 8.) As x increases from $\pi/2$ to π, $\sin x$ is positive and decreasing from 1 to 0, whereas the $\cos x$ is negative and increasing in *absolute* value. Hence, $\tan x = (\sin x)/(\cos x)$ is negative, with a numerator decreasing in absolute value to 0 and a denominator increasing in absolute value so that the tangent is negative and decreasing in absolute value to 0.

Figure 8

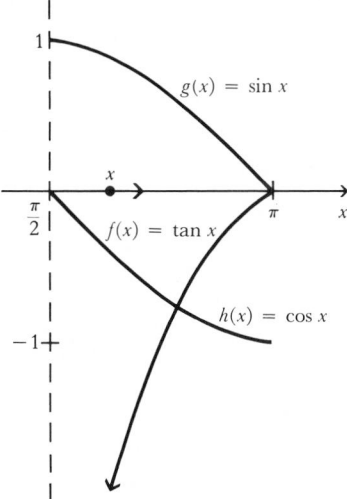

iii   (See Figure 9.) As x increases from π to $3\pi/2$; $\sin x$ is negative and increasing in absolute value to 1, whereas $\cos x$ is negative and decreasing in absolute value to 0; consequently, $\tan x = (\sin x)/(\cos x)$ is positive (Why?) and increasing.

Figure 9

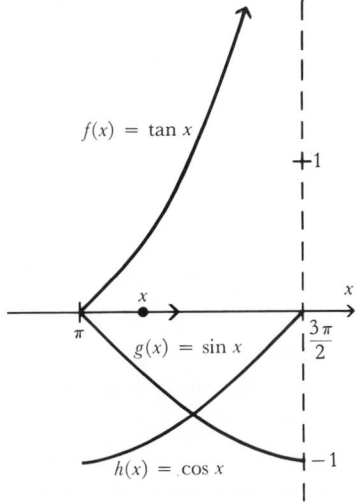

iv   (See Figure 10.) Finally, as x increases from $3\pi/2$ to 2π, $\tan x$ is negative (Why?) and decreasing in absolute value to 0.

Figure 10

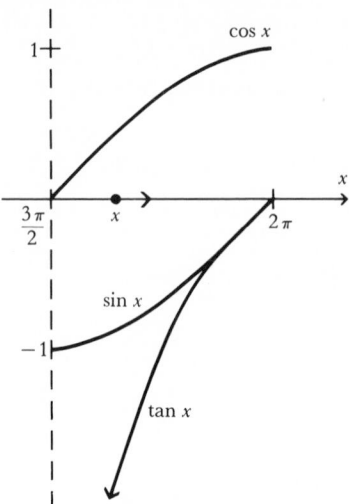

After combining these four results and plotting a few points, we get the graph of $f(x) = \tan x$ on $[0,2\pi)$ (Figure 11). Using the fact that $f(x) = \tan x$ has a period of 2π, we get the graph on R (Figure 12).

Figure 11

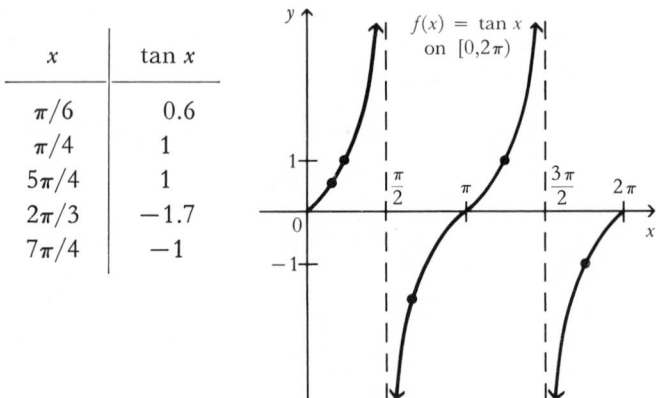

x	$\tan x$
$\pi/6$	0.6
$\pi/4$	1
$5\pi/4$	1
$2\pi/3$	-1.7
$7\pi/4$	-1

Notice that the graph of the tangent displays some of the functional properties of the tangent. For example, the range is R; the tangent is symmetric with respect to the origin; the tangent is not continuous on R; the tangent is not one-to-one. Also, the graph displays the fact that the fundamental period of the tangent function is π, a fact which will be proved later in Chapter 6, Problem Set 3, Problem 11c.

Because the cotangent is a periodic function of period 2π, we will graph $f(x) = \cot x$ on $[0,2\pi)$. The graphs of $g(x) = \cos x$ and $h(x) = \sin x$ can be used as auxiliary graphs to determine the graph of $\cot x = (\cos x)/(\sin x)$.

Figure 12

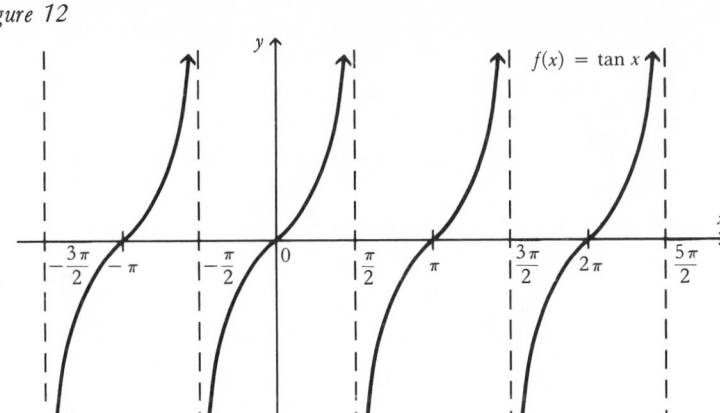

The asymptotes of $f(x) = \cot x$ occur when $\sin x = 0$; the x intercepts of $f(x) = \cot x$ occur when $\cos x = 0$ (Figure 13). Finally, by plotting some points and examining the behavior of $(\cos x)/(\sin x)$ as x increases from 0 to 2π (see Problem 6), we get the graph of $f(x) = \cot x$ on $[0,2\pi)$ (Figure 13).

Figure 13

x	$\cot x$
$\pi/6$	1.7
$\pi/4$	1
$2\pi/3$	-0.6
$5\pi/4$	1
$7\pi/4$	-1

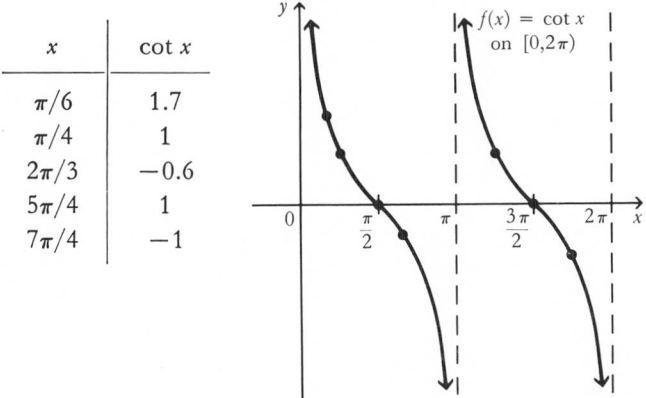

Since the period of $f(x) = \sec x$ is 2π, it is enough to determine the graph on $[0,2\pi)$. Sec $x = 1/(\cos x)$, and sec x has vertical asymptotes wherever $\cos x = 0$ (Figure 14). Finally, we can examine the behavior of sec x and sketch $f(x) = \sec x$ on $[0,2\pi)$ by noting the behavior of $g(x) = \cos x$ as x increases from 0 to 2π (Figure 14).

The graph of $f(x) = \sec x$ reaffirms the fact that the range of $f(x) = \sec x$ is $[1,\infty) \cup (-\infty,-1]$; the secant is not one-to-one; it is not continuous on R.

Figure 14

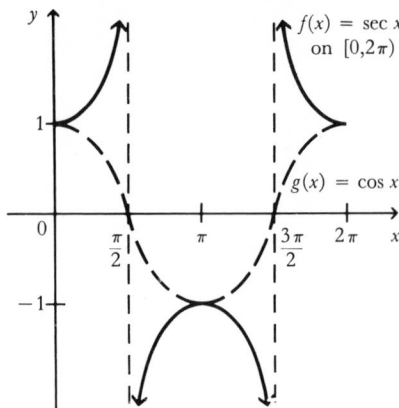

For $f(x) = \csc x = 1/(\sin x)$, the period is 2π and the vertical asymptotes occur when $\sin x = 0$. The graph of $f(x) = \csc x$ can be determined from the auxiliary graph $g(x) = \sin x$ (Figure 15). Here again the graph repeats every 2π units.

Figure 15

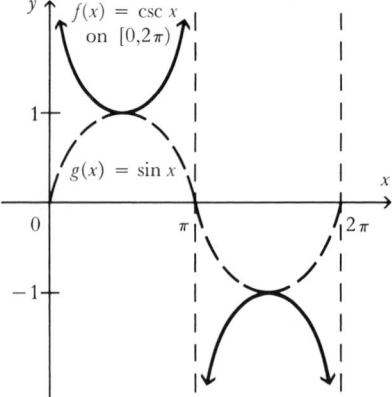

EXAMPLES

1   Use auxiliary graphs to sketch $f(x) = \tan (x - 1)$.

SOLUTION

$$f(x) = \tan (x - 1) = \frac{\sin (x - 1)}{\cos (x - 1)}$$

First, the auxiliary graphs of $g(x) = \sin (x - 1)$ and $h(x) = \cos (x - 1)$ are sketched. Each yields a cycle if $x - 1$ varies from 0 to 2π, that is, when x varies from 1 to $2\pi + 1$ (Figure 16).

Next, we indicate the vertical asymptotes [where $\cos (x - 1) = 0$] and the points where $\tan (x - 1) = 0$ [where $\sin (x - 1) = 0$] (Figure 16).

Finally, we examine the behavior of $\sin (x - 1)$ and $\cos (x - 1)$ to determine the behavior of $\tan (x - 1)$ as x increases from 1 to $2\pi + 1$. Because of periodicity, the graph repeats every 2π units.

Figure 16

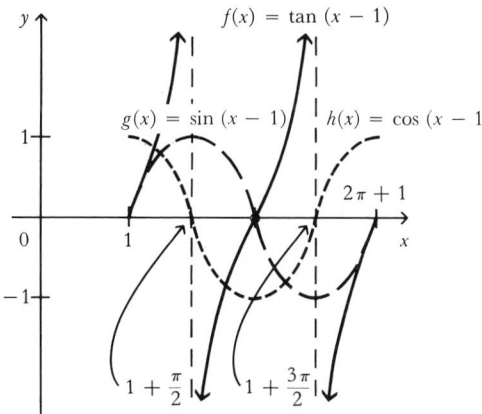

2 Use an auxiliary graph to graph one period of $f(x) = \sec 5x$.

SOLUTION

$$\sec 5x = \frac{1}{\cos 5x}$$

Using the auxiliary graph, we get the graph of $f(x) = \sec 5x$ (Figure 17).

Figure 17

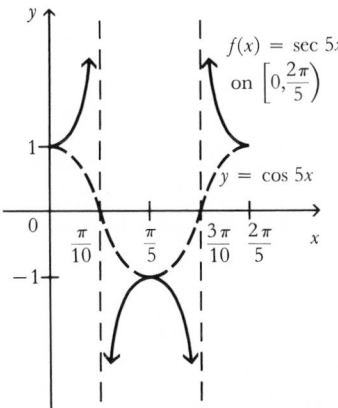

3   Use an auxiliary to sketch one period of $f(x) = \csc(x/4 - 5)$.

SOLUTION.   The auxiliary graph is that of $g(x) = \sin(x/4 - 5)$, since $\csc(x/4 - 5) = 1/[\sin(x/4 + 5)]$. $g(x) = \sin(x/4 - 5)$ generates one sine cycle when $x/4 - 5$ varies from 0 to 2π $(0 \le x/4 - 5 < 2\pi)$, that is, when x varies from 20 to $8\pi + 20$ $(20 \le x < 8\pi + 20)$ (Figure 18).

Figure 18

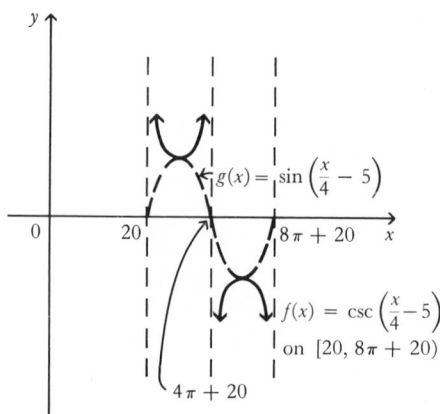

PROBLEM SET 6

1   a)   Complete the proof of Theorem 1, i.
     b)   Complete the proof of Theorem 1, iii.

2   Determine each of the following values without the use of tables.

    a) $\sec(-2\pi/3)$ b) $\tan(3\pi/4)$
    c) $\cot(-11\pi/6)$ d) $\csc(3\pi/4)$
    e) $\sec(-5\pi/6)$ f) $\tan(7\pi/3)$

3   Determine the values of the six circular functions if $\sin x = \frac{3}{5}$.

4   Use Table III and linear interpolation, if necessary, to determine each of the following values (use $\pi = 3.14$).

    a) $\tan 2.1$ b) $\sec 9.5$
    c) $\cot(-10)$ d) $\csc(-1.007)$
    e) $\sec 3.454$

5   a)   Let $f(x) = \tan x$. Use the graph to answer the following questions.

       i   What is the domain?
      ii   What is the range?
     iii   Is the function even or odd? What kind of symmetry does the graph display? Explain.
     iv   Is the function continuous on R?

    v Is the function one-to-one?

    vi What is the fundamental period?

b) Answer (a) for $f(x) = \cot x$.

c) Answer (a) for $f(x) = \sec x$.

d) Answer (a) for $f(x) = \csc x$.

6 Discuss the behavior of $f(x) = \cot x = (\cos x)/(\sin x)$ for $x \in [0,2\pi)$ by examining the auxiliary graphs $g(x) = \cos x$ and $h(x) = \sin x$:

a) As x increases from 0 to $\pi/2$

b) As x increases from $\pi/2$ to π

c) As x increases from π to $3\pi/2$

d) As x increases from $3\pi/2$ to 2π

7 Use auxiliary graphs to graph each of the following functions.

a) $f(x) = 2 \tan 3x$ b) $f(x) = 2 \sec x$

c) $f(x) = 3 \cot x$ d) $f(x) = \frac{1}{3} \csc x$

e) $f(x) = -8 \sec 2x$ f) $f(x) = \cot (2x - 1)$

g) $f(x) = 3 \sec (4 - x)$ h) $f(x) = 2 \tan (x/3 + 5)$

8 Use the graphs to complete the following table.

t increasing from __ to __	$0 \to \dfrac{\pi}{2}$	$\dfrac{\pi}{2} \to \pi$	$\pi \to \dfrac{3\pi}{2}$	$\dfrac{3\pi}{2} \to 2\pi$
$\sin t$	Increasing	Decreasing		
$\cos t$	Decreasing			
$\tan t$	Increasing		Increasing	
$\cot t$		Decreasing		
$\sec t$				Decreasing
$\csc t$				

9 *The arctangent function.*

a) Explain why $f(x) = \tan x$ does not have an inverse.

b) Restrict the domain of $f(x) = \tan x$ to construct $f(x) = \text{Tan } x$ with $x \in (-\pi/2,\pi/2)$. Sketch $f(x) = \tan x$ and $f(x) = \text{Tan } x$ on the same coordinate system.

c) Why is $f(x) = \text{Tan } x$ one-to-one?

d) *Definition.* The Arctangent function, $y = \text{Arctan } x$ or $y = \tan^{-1} x$, is the inverse function of $f(x) = \text{Tan } x$. The domain of the Arctangent is R (Why?) and the range is $(-\pi/2,\pi/2)$ (Why?). Using set notation, if

$$f = \{(x,y) | y = \text{Tan } x\}$$

then

$$f^{-1} = \{(x,y)|\tan^{-1} x = y\} \qquad \text{(Why?)}$$

so that

$\tan^{-1} x = y$ is equivalent to $\tan y = x$ with $x \in (-\pi/2, \pi/2)$.

e) Evaluate $\tan^{-1} (\sqrt{3}/3)$, $\arctan (-1)$, and $\tan^{-1} [\cos (\pi/2)]$.
f) Graph $f(x) = \tan^{-1} x$.

10 a) Define the inverse cotangent function, $y = \text{Arccot } x$ or $y = \cot^{-1} x$ with the equation $x = \cot y$, where $0 < y < \pi$.
b) Evaluate $\cot^{-1} \sqrt{3}$, $\cot^{-1} (-\sqrt{3})$, $\arccot (\sqrt{3}/3)$, and $\cot^{-1} (0.34)$
c) Sketch the graph of $y = \cot^{-1} x$.

11 Express each of the following expressions in terms of x.
a) $\tan (\tan^{-1} x)$ b) $\cos (\tan^{-1} x)$
c) $\sin (\cot^{-1} x)$ d) $\cos (\cot^{-1} 2x)$
e) $\tan [\cot^{-1} (1/x)]$

REVIEW PROBLEM SET

1 Suppose that f is a periodic odd function of period 2 and $f(\tfrac{1}{2}) = 4$. Determine each of the following values.
a) $f(\tfrac{5}{2})$ b) $f(\tfrac{11}{2})$
c) $f(\tfrac{19}{2})$ d) $f(9) + f(-7)$

2 Suppose that f is a periodic function with period 2π; find two values of x in the interval $[0,4\pi)$ such that
a) $f(x) = f(-\pi/2)$ b) $f(x) = f(15\pi)$

3 Consider the function f whose domain is the set of positive integers and for which $f(x)$ is the integer in the xth decimal place in the decimal expansion of $\tfrac{27}{111}$.
a) Find the range of f.
b) Is f periodic? If so, find its fundamental period.
c) Find $f(103)$.

4 Find the domain and range of each of the following functions. Also, graph the function.
a) $f(x) = 3 \sin (5x/2)$ b) $f(x) = 5 \cos (3x/4)$
c) $f(x) = 2 \tan 3x$ d) $f(x) = -\tfrac{1}{2} \sec (x/7)$
e) $f(x) = 5 \csc 4x$ f) $f(x) = \cot (2x/3)$

5 Find the real numbers t such that
a) $\sin t = \cos (-t)$ b) $\sin t = -\cos t$

6 Let $f(x) = \sin x$ and $g(x) = \cos x$. Find each of the following values without tables.

a) $f(17\pi/3)$ b) $f(19\pi/6)$ c) $g(71\pi/2)$
d) $g(-35\pi/6)$ e) $g(22\pi/3)$

7 Determine each of the following values. (Use $\pi = 3.14$.)

a) $\cos 7.6$ b) $\sin 13.4$ c) $\tan 3.77$
d) $\cot 6.37$ e) $\cos 4.73$ f) $\sin 5.37$
g) $\csc 6.91$ h) $\tan (-6.90)$ i) $\cos (-7.5)$
j) $\sin (-4.33)$

8 Assume that t is any real number. Indicate which of the following are true and which are false.

a) $|\cos 2t| \le 1$
b) $|\sin (t/3)| \le \frac{1}{3}$
c) $|\sin^2 t + \cos^2 t| \le 2$
d) $|\sin 5t + \cos 5t + \sin t| \le 3$
e) $|\sqrt{3} \sin t + \cos t| \le 2$

9 Sketch the graphs of $f(x) = \sin x$, $0 \le x < 2\pi$, and $g(x) = \sin 2x$, $0 \le x < 2\pi$. Find the domain and the range of $f + g$ and sketch the graph of $f + g$ on the same coordinate axes as f and g.

10 Determine (i) the symmetry of the function, (ii) the intervals where the function is increasing or decreasing, and (iii) the graph of each of the following functions.

a) $f(x) = \cos 2x$
b) $f(x) = 3 \cot x$
c) $f(x) = \sin (2x - 3\pi/4)$
d) $f(x) = 2 \tan (2x - \pi/8)$
e) $f(x) = 4 \csc x$
f) $f(x) = 3 \sec 4x$
g) $f(x) = 2 \sin 8x$

11 Evaluate each of the following expressions.

a) $\sin [\tan^{-1} (\sqrt{3}/3)]$ b) $\tan [\sin^{-1} (\sqrt{3}/2)]$
c) $\tan^{-1} [\sin (\pi/2)]$ d) $\sin [\tan^{-1} (-\sqrt{3})]$
e) $\sin (\tan^{-1} 1)$ f) $\tan [\tan^{-1} (x + 1)]$
g) $\cos (\sin^{-1} \sqrt{1 - x^2})$ h) $\cot (\tan^{-1} 2x)$
i) $\tan^{-1} 0.933$ j) $\cot^{-1} 0.249$
k) $\sin (\sin^{-1} (1 + x^2))$ l) $\cos^{-1} 0.4536$

12 Graph each of the following functions. Indicate the domain and the range.

a) $f(x) = \sin^{-1} 2x$ b) $f(x) = \cos^{-1} 3x$
c) $f(x) = \sin (\sin^{-1} x)$ d) $f(x) = \sin^{-1} (\cos x)$
e) $f(x) = \tan^{-1} 2x$

CHAPTER 6

Trigonometric Functions

6 TRIGONOMETRIC FUNCTIONS

1 Introduction

This chapter will be devoted to an introduction of the *trigonometric functions* and their relationship to circular functions. The trigonometric functions, are, in a sense, the circular functions applied to angles. The trigonometric functions are defined on angle measurements, whereas the circular functions are defined on real numbers.

We will see that the trigonometric functions are quite useful in solving certain types of geometric problems; for example, the trigonometric functions can be used to find missing parts of triangles.

Let us begin by reviewing some elementary plane geometry.

2 Angles

We know from plane geometry that two distinct points determine a (straight) *line*. A line has no end points. A *ray*, or *half-line*, is a line with one end point, whereas a *line segment* is a line with two distinct end points (Figure 1).

Figure 1

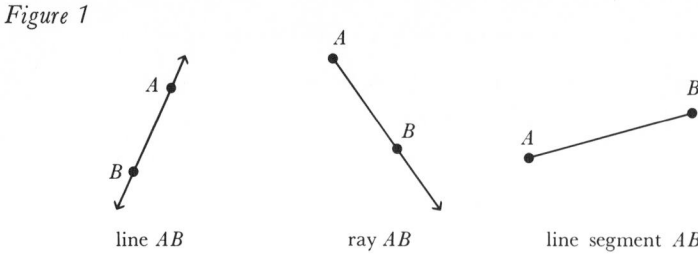

line *AB*   ray *AB*   line segment *AB*

An *angle* is determined by rotating a ray about its end point, the *vertex* of the angle, from some initial position, the *initial side* of the angle, to a terminal position, the *terminal side* of the angle (Figure 2). If the angle is formed by a counterclockwise rotation, the angle is said to be an angle of *positive* sense, whereas if the angle is formed by a clockwise rotation, the angle is of *negative* sense. In Figure 2, the angle determined by Q, P, and R, $\angle QPR$, is a positive angle, whereas $\angle CAB$ is negative.

Figure 2

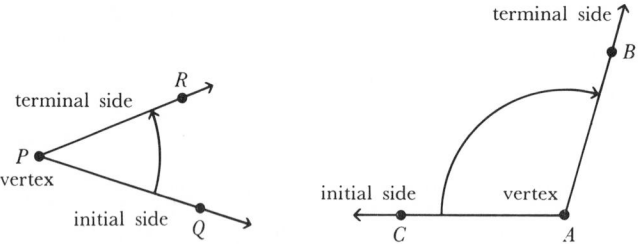

For convenience, Greek letters are often used to label angles. In Figure 3, α is the positive angle $\angle DBC$ whereas θ is the negative angle $\angle ABC$.

Figure 3

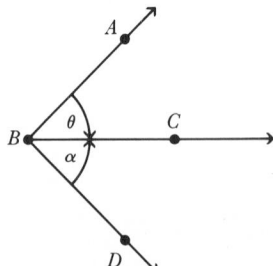

It is important to remember that an angle is determined by the initial side, the terminal side, and the rotation used to form it. For example, the two angles α and β in Figure 4 have the same initial and terminal sides, yet are different angles.

Figure 4

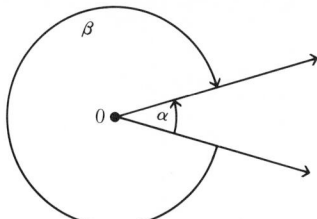

Angles are measured by using either *degrees* or *radians*. *One degree* (1°) is the measure of a positive angle which is formed by $\frac{1}{360}$ of one complete revolution (Figure 5*a*). Furthermore, a degree can be divided into 60 equal parts called *minutes* ('); a minute can be divided into 60 equal parts called *seconds* ("). On the other hand, one *radian* (1) is the measure of a positive angle which intercepts an arc of length 1 on a circle of radius 1 (Figure 5*b*). The angle measure is positive or negative according to whether the angle is formed by a counterclockwise or clockwise rotation. Hence, the radian measure of an angle is the "directed" length of its subtended arc on a circle of radius 1.

Figure 5

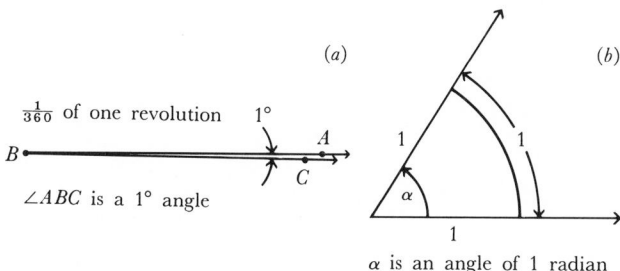

EXAMPLES

1   Indicate both the degree measure and the radian measure of an angle α formed by

a)   1 complete counterclockwise rotation
b) $\frac{1}{4}$ counterclockwise rotation
c) $\frac{1}{8}$ clockwise rotation

SOLUTION

a)   Since 1° is the measure of an angle formed by $\frac{1}{360}$ of one complete revolution, the degree measure of α is $(360)(1°) = 360°$. The radian measure of α is the length of the circumference of a circle of radius 1, 2π (Figure 6).

Figure 6

α is 360° or 2π radians

b) α is either $\frac{1}{4}(360°) = 90°$ or $\frac{1}{4}(2\pi) = \pi/2$ radians (Figure 7a).

c) $\frac{1}{8}(360°) = 45°$ and $\frac{1}{8}(2\pi) = \pi/4$, however, α is a negative angle; hence, α is $-45°$ or $-\pi/4$ radians (Figure 7b).

Figure 7

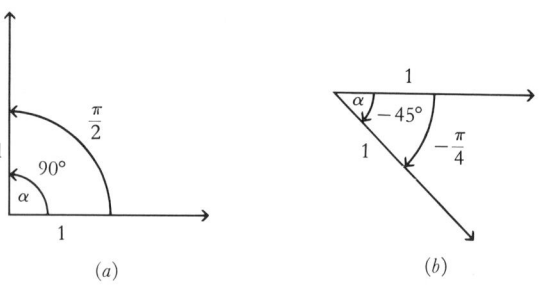

(a)   (b)

2   Express 37.45° in terms of degrees, minutes, and seconds.

SOLUTION. $37.45° = 37° + 0.45°$; however, $0.45° = (0.45)(60') = 27.00'$, so that $37.45° = 37°27'0''$.

3   Derive a formula for converting angle measurements from one measure to the other.

SOLUTION.   First, let us find the radian measure R_1 of a 1° angle. An angle of 1° subtends an arc on the unit circle of length $\frac{1}{360}$ of the circumference of the circle. Using the fact that the radian measure R_1 is the length of the subtended arc, together with the fact that the circumference if 2π, we have $R_1 = \frac{1}{360}(2\pi) = \pi/180$ (Figure 8). Hence, 1° corresponds to $\pi/180$ radians. This means then that an angle of D degrees is $(\pi/180)D$ radians, so that $R = (\pi/180)D$, where R represents the radian measure of any angle and D represents the degree measure of the same angle. Clearly, we could also express the relationship between R and D as $D = (180/\pi)R$. (Why?)

Figure 8

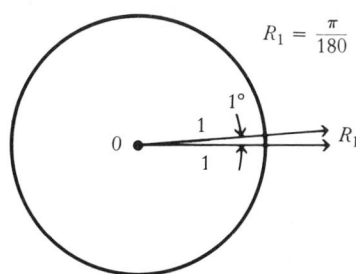

$$R_1 = \frac{\pi}{180}$$

For example, $30°$ corresponds to $(\pi/180)(30) = \pi/6$ radians; an angle of $-12°$ has a radian measure of $(\pi/180)(-12) = -\pi/15$; 2 radians correspond to $(180/\pi)(2) = (360/\pi)°$.

The radian measure of a central angle of a circle can be used to determine both the length of the arc which the angle subtends and the area of the sector determined by the central angle.

Suppose that θ is the central angle of a circle of radius r (Figure 9). Also assume that the angle θ has a radian measure t. (If θ is measured in degrees, we can always convert to radians.)

Figure 9

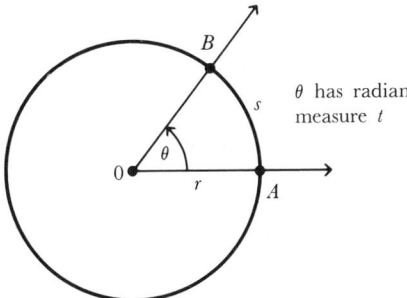

θ has radian measure t

Our task is to determine s, the length of $\overgroup{AB}$. The length of the circumference of the circle is $2\pi r$; but, since θ determines an arc which is "$(t/2\pi)$th" of the circumference (Why?),

$$s = \frac{t}{2\pi}(2\pi r) \qquad \text{that is} \qquad s = tr$$

Hence, we have a formula for determining the length of an arc subtended by a central angle of t radians.

Next, we can determine the area of sector OAB. Since the area of the circle is πr^2 and since θ determines $(t/2\pi)$th of the circle, the area A is determined by

$$A = \frac{t}{2\pi}\pi r^2$$

so that

$$A = \frac{tr^2}{2}$$

Using the fact that $s = tr$, we can also write this latter formula as

$$A = \tfrac{1}{2}sr$$

EXAMPLES

1   Find the length of an arc of a circle of radius 6 inches and with a central angle of

a) 70°   b) $\pi/6$

SOLUTION

a) $s = tr$, where t is the radian measure of the angle. Since 70° corresponds to $70\pi/180 = 7\pi/18$ radians,

$$s = 6\left(\frac{7\pi}{18}\right) = \frac{7\pi}{3} \text{ inches} \qquad (\text{Figure } 10a)$$

b) $s = tr = 6(\pi/6) = \pi$ inches   (Figure 10b)

Figure 10

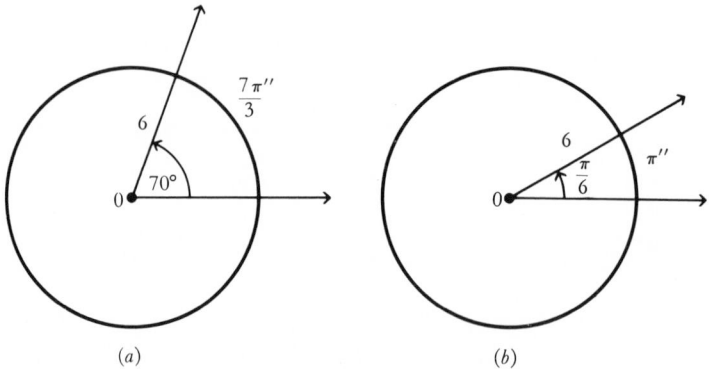

(a)   (b)

2   Find the area of the sector of a circle of radius 6 inches and subtended by a central angle of

a) 65°   b) $\pi/6$

SOLUTION

a) $A = \tfrac{1}{2}r^2t$. Since 65° corresponds to $65\pi/180 = 13\pi/36$ radians,

$$A = \tfrac{1}{2}(36)\left(\frac{13\pi}{36}\right) = \frac{13\pi}{2} \text{ square inches}$$

b) $A = \tfrac{1}{2}(36)(\pi/6) = 3\pi$ square inches

3   The tip of the minute hand of a clock travels $7\pi/10$ inches in 3
minutes. How long is the minute hand?

SOLUTION.   In 3 minutes, the minute hand generates a central angle of
$(3)(\frac{1}{60})(360°) = 18°$. (Why?) But an angle of 18° has a radian measure
of $t = (\pi/180)(18) = \pi/10$, so that $7\pi/10 = r(\pi/10)$. Hence,
$r = 7$ inches (Figure 11).

Figure 11

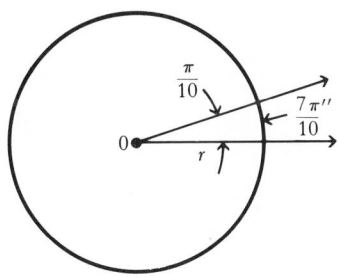

2.1   Functions Defined on Angles

An angle is in *standard position* if it is placed on a Cartesian coordinate
system so that the vertex corresponds to the origin and the initial side
coincides with the positive x axis. For example, an 80° angle in standard
position would have its terminal side in quadrant **I** (Figure 12a), whereas
an angle of radian measure $-3\pi/5$ in standard position has its terminal
side in quadrant **III** (Figure 12b). [Notice that $-3\pi/5$ corresponds to
$(180/\pi)(-3\pi/5) = -108°$.]

Figure 12

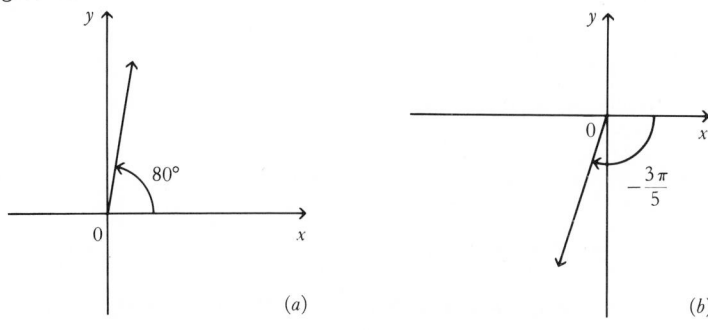

Now, suppose that θ is a 45° angle in standard position and suppose
that (x,y) is any point other than $(0,0)$ on the terminal side of θ (Figure
13). We can compute the distance r between (x,y) and $(0,0)$ by using the
distance formula:

$$r = \sqrt{(x - 0)^2 + (y - 0)^2} = \sqrt{x^2 + y^2}$$

Figure 13

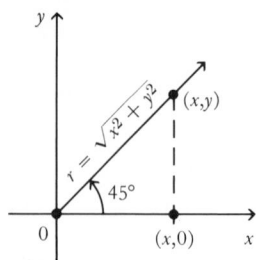

Since the triangle determined by the three points $(0,0)$, (x,y), and $(x,0)$ is isosceles (Why?), we have $x = y$ and $r = \sqrt{2x^2} = \sqrt{2}x$. What we want here are functions which relate θ, r, x, and y. These functions, the *trigonometric functions*, are defined as follows.

2.2   Definition

Let θ be an angle in standard position, let (x,y) be any point other than $(0,0)$ on the terminal side of θ, and let r be the distance between (x,y) and $(0,0)$ (Figure 14).

Figure 14

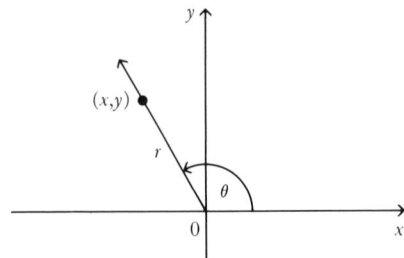

The six *trigonometric* functions are defined in the following manner.

$$\text{sine} = \left\{ (\theta, \sin\theta) \,\middle|\, \sin\theta = \frac{y}{r} \right\}$$

$$\text{cosine} = \left\{ (\theta, \cos\theta) \,\middle|\, \cos\theta = \frac{x}{r} \right\}$$

$$\text{tangent} = \left\{ (\theta, \tan\theta) \,\middle|\, \tan\theta = \frac{y}{x}, \; x \neq 0 \right\}$$

$$\text{cotangent} = \left\{ (\theta, \cot\theta) \,\middle|\, \cot\theta = \frac{x}{y}, \; y \neq 0 \right\}$$

$$\text{secant} = \left\{ (\theta, \sec\theta) \,\middle|\, \sec\theta = \frac{r}{x}, \; x \neq 0 \right\}$$

$$\text{cosecant} = \left\{ (\theta, \csc\theta) \,\middle|\, \csc\theta = \frac{r}{y}, \; y \neq 0 \right\}$$

where $r = \sqrt{x^2 + y^2}$. These functions are usually written in the following abbreviated forms.

$$\sin \theta = \frac{y}{r}$$

$$\cos \theta = \frac{x}{r}$$

$$\tan \theta = \frac{y}{x}, \qquad x \neq 0$$

$$\cot \theta = \frac{x}{y}, \qquad y \neq 0$$

$$\sec \theta = \frac{r}{x}, \qquad x \neq 0$$

and

$$\csc \theta = \frac{r}{y}, \qquad y \neq 0 \quad \square$$

Returning to θ, the 45° angle, it has been noted that $x = y$ for any (x,y) on the terminal side of the angle and that $r = \sqrt{2}\, x$ (Figure 15).

Figure 15

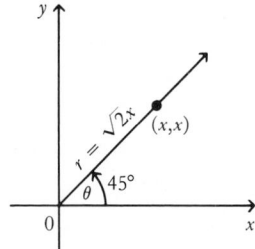

Hence, by Definition 2.2,

$$\sin \theta = \sin 45° = \frac{x}{\sqrt{2}\, x} = \frac{1}{\sqrt{2}}$$

$$\cos \theta = \cos 45° = \frac{x}{\sqrt{2}\, x} = \frac{1}{\sqrt{2}}$$

$$\tan \theta = \tan 45° = \frac{x}{x} = 1$$

$$\cot \theta = \cot 45° = \frac{x}{x} = 1$$

$$\sec \theta = \sec 45° = \frac{\sqrt{2}\, x}{x} = \sqrt{2}$$

and

$$\csc \theta = \csc 45° = \frac{\sqrt{2}\, x}{x} = \sqrt{2}$$

It is important to notice that the values of the six trigonometric functions for the 45° angle depend only on the terminal side of the angle in the sense that no matter what particular point may be selected on the terminal side to evaluate the six functions (other than (0,0) of course) the results are the same. For example, (1,1) with $r = \sqrt{2}$ will yield the same results as (5,5) with $r = 5\sqrt{2}$.

In general, if (x,y) and (x_1,y_1) are two different points on the terminal side of θ other than (0,0), so that $r = \sqrt{x^2 + y^2}$ and $r_1 = \sqrt{x_1^2 + y_1^2}$, we have, because of the similar triangles $\triangle OBP_1$ and $\triangle OAP$ (Figure 16),

$$\frac{|y_1|}{r_1} = \frac{|y|}{r} \qquad \frac{|x_1|}{r_1} = \frac{|x|}{r} \qquad \frac{|y_1|}{|x_1|} = \frac{|y|}{|x|}$$

$$\frac{|x_1|}{|y_1|} = \frac{|x|}{|y|} \qquad \frac{r_1}{|x_1|} = \frac{r}{|x|} \qquad \frac{r_1}{|y_1|} = \frac{r}{|y|}$$

Figure 16

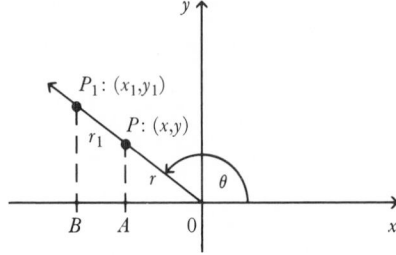

However, since the two points are in the same quadrant, x_1 and x have the same signs and y_1 and y have the same signs so that we get

$$\frac{y_1}{r_1} = \frac{y}{r} \qquad \frac{x_1}{r_1} = \frac{x}{r} \qquad \frac{y_1}{x_1} = \frac{y}{x}$$

$$\frac{x_1}{y_1} = \frac{x}{y} \qquad \frac{r_1}{x_1} = \frac{r}{x} \qquad \frac{r_1}{y_1} = \frac{r}{y}$$

Hence, the values of the trigonometric functions are the same no matter what two points are selected on the terminal side of the angle other than (0,0).

EXAMPLES

1   Evaluate sin 180°, cos 180°, sin $(-\pi/2)$ and cos $(-\pi/2)$.

SOLUTION.   First, select points on the terminal sides of the 180° angle and the $-\pi/2$ angle after the angles are put in standard position (Figure 17). Here $(-3,0)$ is selected on the terminal side of the 180° angle, and $(0,-2)$ is selected on the terminal side of the $-\pi/2$ angle. Hence, sin 180° $= \frac{0}{3} = 0$ and cos 180° $= (-3/3) = -1$; also, sin $(-\pi/2) = (-2/2) = -1$ and cos $(-\pi/2) = \frac{0}{2} = 0$. Notice that the result would be the same if any other points were chosen on these terminal sides.

Figure 17

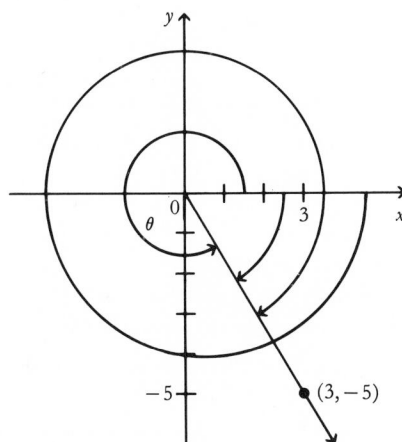

2 Evaluate the trigonometric functions on θ if θ has $(3, -5)$ on its terminal side. Is θ unique?

SOLUTION. Figure 18 suggests the fact that there are infinitely many different angles with this same terminal side. Hence θ is not unique.

Figure 18

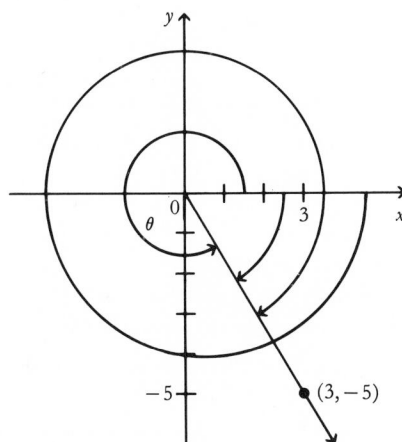

Using the fact that $r = \sqrt{3^2 + (-5)^2} = \sqrt{34}$, we have

$$\sin \theta = \frac{y}{r} = \frac{-5}{\sqrt{34}} \qquad \cos \theta = \frac{x}{r} = \frac{3}{\sqrt{34}}$$

$$\tan \theta = \frac{y}{x} = -\frac{5}{3} \qquad \cot \theta = \frac{x}{y} = -\frac{3}{5}$$

$$\sec \theta = \frac{r}{x} = \frac{\sqrt{34}}{3} \qquad \csc \theta = \frac{r}{y} = \frac{\sqrt{34}}{-5}$$

3   In what quadrant is the terminal side of θ if $\sin \theta = -\frac{7}{9}$? Evaluate $\cos \theta$.

SOLUTION. $\sin \theta = y/r = -\frac{7}{9}$, from which we can deduce the possibilities shown in Figure 19. Since $9 = \sqrt{x^2 + 49}$, $x^2 = 32$. Hence, $x = \pm 4\sqrt{2}$, so that $\cos \theta = 4\sqrt{2}/9$ if θ has a terminal side in quadrant IV or $\cos \theta = -4\sqrt{2}/9$ if θ has terminal side in quadrant III. Notice that there are actually infinitely many different possible values for θ; however, any such θ must have one of the two terminal sides shown in Figure 19.

Figure 19

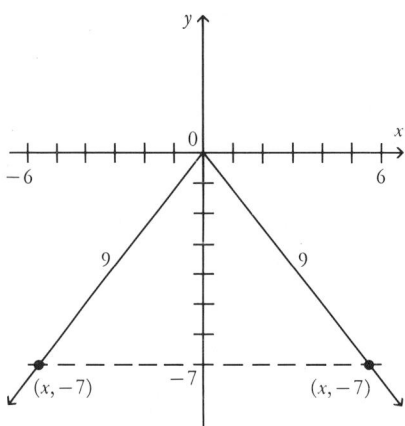

PROBLEM SET 1

1   In each of the following problems, sketch the angle in standard position. If the angle is given in radian measure, convert to degree measure; or, if the measure is given in degree measure, convert to radian measure.

a)   40°   b) $-7\pi/2$ c)   444°
d) $-95°$ e) 7π f)   330°
g) $-30°$ h) $11\pi/6$ i)   2.61
j) -8.43

2   Find the arc length of the arc of a circle of radius r which is subtended by a central angle θ for each of the following situations.

a) $r = 7$ inches and $\theta = 3\pi/14$ b) $r = 4$ inches and $\theta = 2\pi/5$
c) $r = 6$ inches and $\theta = 50°$ d) $r = 9$ inches and $\theta = 275°$
e) $r = 7$ inches and $\theta = \pi°$

3 Find the area of the sector of a circle of radius r which is subtended by a central angle of θ for each of the following situations.

a) $r = 8$ inches and $\theta = 3\pi/22$ b) $r = 5$ inches and $\theta = 2\pi/25$
c) $r = 11$ inches and $\theta = 45°$ d) $r = 14$ inches and $\theta = 245°$
e) $r = 4$ inches and $\theta = 180°$

4 Explain why an angle of 1 radian is larger in measure than an angle of 1°.

5 Draw a 60° angle in standard position, and then use Figure 20 to evaluate the trigonometric functions on 60°. Would the value differ if the angle were 420°? $-300°$? $\pi/3$? Explain.

Figure 20

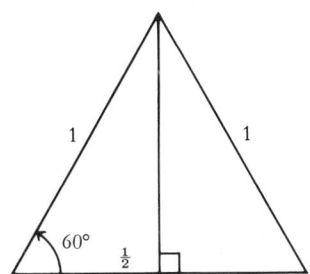

6 Determine the values of the trigonometric functions on θ in each of the following cases.

a) θ has $(-5,0)$ on its terminal side. What is the measure of θ?
b) θ has $(-3,-4)$ on its terminal side.
c) θ has $(7,-10)$ on its terminal side.
d) θ has $(0,1)$ on its terminal side. What is the measure of θ?
e) θ has $(-1,\sqrt{3})$ on its terminal side. What is the measure of θ?
f) $(x,-4)$ is 11 units from $(0,0)$ and is on the terminal side of θ.
g) $\cos \theta = \frac{5}{6}$.
h) $(3x,x)$ is on the terminal side of θ and $x \neq 0$.

7 Use Definition 2.2 to prove each of the following identities.

a) $\tan \theta = (\sin \theta)/(\cos \theta)$ b) $\cot \theta = (\cos \theta)/(\sin \theta)$
c) $\sec \theta = 1/(\cos \theta)$ d) $\csc \theta = 1/(\sin \theta)$
e) $\sin^2 \theta + \cos^2 \theta = 1$

3 Trigonometric and Circular Functions

Suppose that t is a real number. If the wrapping function P gives $P(t) = (x, y)$, then the *circular* functions yield $\cos t = x$ and $\sin t = y$ (Figure 1).

Figure 1

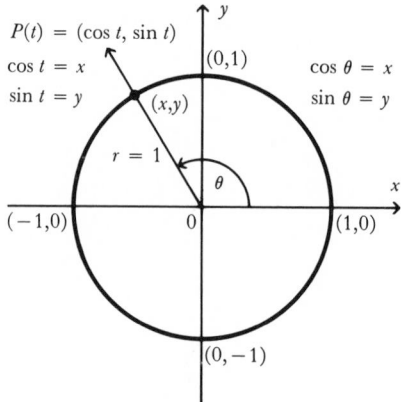

By Definition 2.2, the *trigonometric* functions on θ yield $\cos \theta = x/r$ and $\sin \theta = y/r$, where $(x, y) \neq (0, 0)$ is a point on the terminal side of θ and $r = \sqrt{x^2 + y^2}$. In particular, if we select (x, y) so that $r = 1$, we have $\cos \theta = x/1 = x$ and $\sin \theta = y/1 = y$ (Figure 1). Hence, if t is considered to be the radian measure of angle θ, we have the results

$$\cos \theta = \cos t$$

and

$$\sin \theta = \sin t$$

Here, $\cos \theta$ and $\sin \theta$ are the values of the trigonometric functions, whereas $\cos t$ and $\sin t$ are the values of the circular functions.

In other words, the circular sine and cosine functions can be thought of as the trigonometric sine and cosine functions defined on angles, and, conversely, the trigonometric sine and cosine functions defined on angles can be thought of as the circular sine and cosine functions defined on radian measures of the angles.

Finally, since the other four trigonometric functions can be expressed in terms of the sine and cosine (see Problem Set 1, Problem 7) in the same way the circular functions can be expressed in terms of the sine and cosine, we have

$$\tan \theta = \frac{\sin \theta}{\cos \theta} = \frac{\sin t}{\cos t} = \tan t$$

$$\cot \theta = \frac{\cos \theta}{\sin \theta} = \frac{\cos t}{\sin t} = \cot t$$

$$\sec \theta = \frac{1}{\cos \theta} = \frac{1}{\cos t} = \sec t$$

and

$$\csc \theta = \frac{1}{\sin \theta} = \frac{1}{\sin t} = \csc t$$

where t is the radian measure of θ, we have the following result:

> If T is any one of the six trigonometric functions and C is the corresponding circular function, then
>
> $$T(\theta) = C(t)$$
>
> where θ is an angle with radian measure t.

Hence it follows that all the properties of the circular functions become properties of the trigonometric functions. (See Problems 2, 3, 4 and 5.)

EXAMPLES

1 Find $\sin 60°$ and $\cos 60°$.

SOLUTION. An angle of $60°$ is $60(\pi/180) = \pi/3$ radians; hence (Figure 2),

$$\sin 60° = \sin \frac{\pi}{3} = \frac{\sqrt{3}}{2} \qquad \text{and} \qquad \cos 60° = \frac{\pi}{3} = \frac{1}{2}$$

Figure 2

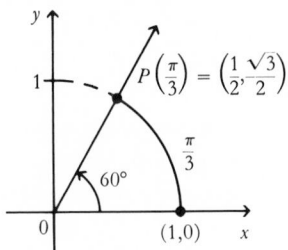

2 Find $\cos 150°$ and $\sin 150°$.

SOLUTION.   An angle of 150° is $150(\pi/180) = 5\pi/6$ radians, so that (Figure 3)

$$\cos 150° = \cos \tfrac{5}{6}\pi = -\frac{\sqrt{3}}{2}$$

and

$$\sin 150° = \sin \frac{5\pi}{6} = \frac{1}{2}$$

Figure 3

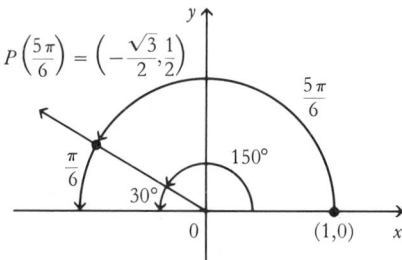

3   Simplify $\sec^2 45° \sin 60° - 3 \tan 120°$.

SOLUTION. $\sec^2 45° \sin 60° - 3 \tan 120° = 2(\sqrt{3}/2) + 3\sqrt{3} = 4\sqrt{3}$.

3.1   Reference Angles

Since $T(\theta) = C(t)$, where t is the radian measure of angle θ, it follows that the trigonometric functions are periodic functions of period 2π if radian measure is used or of 360° if degree measure is used (see Problem 5a) and that the evaluations of the trigonometric functions parallel the evaluations of the circular functions.

Given any angle, we can find another angle with the same terminal side as the given angle so that the new angle is between 0° and 360° (or 0 and 2π). If the angle is 0°, 90°, 180°, or 270° the evaluation is not difficult; if not, we can find a *reference angle* as we found a reference number. For example, the reference angle for 300° is 60°; for −200° it

Figure 4

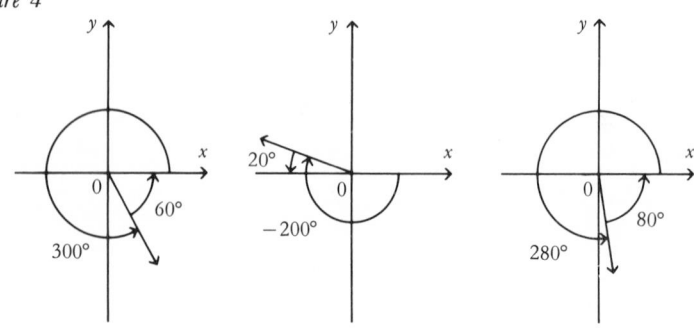

is 20°; and for 280° it is 80° (Figure 4). Notice that the reference angle of a given angle is an *acute angle* formed by the terminal side of the given angle and the x axis.

As with the circular functions, the value of the given trigonometric function on the given angle agrees in absolute value with the value of the function on the reference angle; hence, we can compute $T(\theta)$ as follows.

1   Locate the quadrant where the terminal side of θ lies.

2   Determine the reference angle θ_R, an acute angle formed by the terminal side of θ and the x axis.

3   Use Table IV if degrees are used or Table III if radians are used, and linear interpolation if necessary, to find $T(\theta_R) = |T(\theta)|$.

4   Finally, adjust the sign to get $T(\theta)$ according to which quadrant contains the terminal side of θ.

EXAMPLES

1   Use linear interpolation and Table IV to compute $\sin(-27°43')$.

SOLUTION.   The reference angle $\theta_R = 27°43'$ (Figure 5); $27°43'$ is between $27°40'$ and $27°50'$; hence, by linear interpolation,

$$10'\left[3'\begin{bmatrix}\sin 27°40' = 0.4643 \\ \sin 27°43' = \quad ? \\ \sin 27°50' = 0.4669\end{bmatrix}d\right]0.0026$$

Therefore, $d/0.0026 = \frac{3}{10}$, so that $d = 0.3(0.0026) = 0.00078 = 0.0008$ (Approximately). Hence, $\sin 27°43' = 0.4643 + 0.0008 = 0.4651$, but since $-27°43'$ is in quadrant IV, we have

$$\sin(-27°43') = -0.4651 \qquad \text{(Approximately)}$$

Figure 5

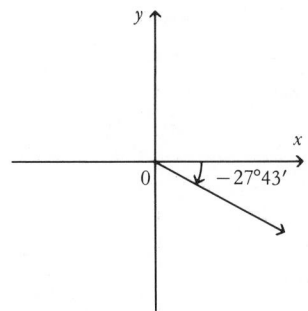

2   Find sin 480°.

SOLUTION.   Since 480° = 360° + 120°, sin 480° = sin 120°. The terminal side of a 120° angle in standard position lies in the second
quadrant, and the reference angle θ_R = 60°. Thus, sin 480° =
sin 120° = sin 60° = $\sqrt{3}/2$ since the sine is positive in quadrant II
(Figure 6).

Figure 6

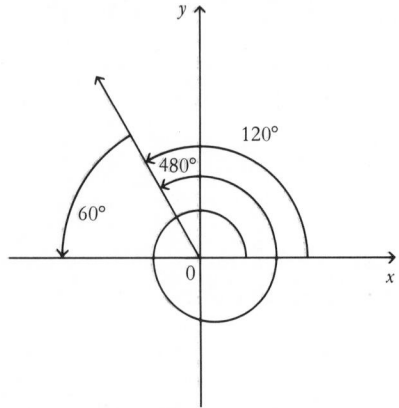

3   Use Table IV and linear interpolation if necessary to determine
tan 200°45′.

SOLUTION.   An angle of 200°25′ in standard position has its terminal
side in quadrant III. The reference angle is 20°25′ (Figure 7). Since
the tangent is positive in quadrant III, we have tan 200°25′ =
tan 20°25′. But tan 20°25′ can be approximated by linear interpolation
as follows:

$$10'\left[5'\begin{bmatrix}\tan 20°20' = 0.3706 \\ \tan 20°25' = \quad ? \\ \tan 20°30' = 0.3739\end{bmatrix}d\right]0.0033$$

Figure 7

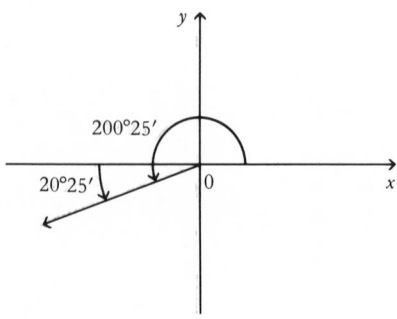

Therefore,

$$\frac{d}{0.0033} = \frac{5}{10}$$

so that

$$d = 0.0017 \qquad \text{(Approximately)}$$

Hence,

$$\begin{aligned} \tan 20°25' &= 0.3706 + 0.0017 \\ &= 0.3723 \qquad \text{(Approximately)} \end{aligned}$$

PROBLEM SET 2

1 Complete the following table:

θ Measure		$\sin \theta$	$\cos \theta$	$\tan \theta$	$\cot \theta$	$\sec \theta$	$\csc \theta$
Degree	Radian						
0°							
	$\dfrac{\pi}{6}$						
45°		$\dfrac{\sqrt{2}}{2}$					
60°							
	$\dfrac{\pi}{2}$						
135°							
150°							
	π						

2 Determine the domain of each of the trigonometric functions by examining Definition 2.2. Describe the domains in terms of the degree measures of the angles. Describe the domains in terms of the radian measures of the angles. How do these domains compare to the domains of the corresponding circular functions?

3 a) Assume that angle θ has a terminal side in quadrant I. Indicate the sign of the value of each of the trigonometric functions, then compare your results to the results in Chapter 5.

  b) Do part (a) for θ in quadrant II.

  c) Do part (a) for θ in quadrant III.

  d) Do part (a) for θ in quadrant IV.

4 Use Definition 2.2 to determine the ranges of the trigonometric functions, and then compare your results to the circular function ranges.

5 a) Show that the trigonometric functions are periodic functions of period $360°$ (or 2π radians).

  b) Explain why the trigonometric sine, tangent, cotangent, and cosecant functions are odd and the trigonometric cosine and secant functions are even.

6 Without the use of the tables, determine each of the following values.

  a) $\cos 150°$ b) $\sec (-120°)$ c) $\sin 135°$

  d) $\cot (-330°)$ e) $\cos (-300°)$ f) $\csc (-750°)$

7 Express each of the following trigonometric functions in terms of the same function of the reference angle.

  a) $\sin 1059°$ b) $\cos 235°$

  c) $\tan 325°$ d) $\csc 320°$

  e) $\sin (-37°45')$ f) $\sec (-100°)$

  g) $\cot 102°$

8 Use Table IV, and linear interpolation if necessary, to find each of the values of Problem 7.

4 Trigonometric and Circular Function Identities

In this section some of the standard formulas or identities that enable us to express the cosine or sine of a sum or difference of two numbers or two angles in terms of cosines and sines of the two numbers or the two angles will be derived. For example, suppose that $\cos (t + s)$ were to be computed, using the values $\cos t$, $\cos s$, $\sin t$, and $\sin s$. The first response might be to say the $\cos (t + s) = \cos t + \cos s$, however, this is *not* the case in general. For example, $\cos (\pi/2 + \pi/2) = \cos \pi = -1 \neq \cos (\pi/2) + \cos (\pi/2) = 0$ and $\cos (45° + 45°) = \cos 90° \neq \cos 45° + \cos 45° = \sqrt{2}$. Notice here that although the proofs of the following theorems are given in terms of real numbers s and t, the results are also valid if s and t are interpreted as angles. In other words, use s and t to represent real numbers and angles interchangeably.

THEOREM 1

If t and s are any real numbers, then

i $\cos (t - s) = \cos t \cos s + \sin t \sin s$

ii $\cos (t + s) = \cos t \cos s - \sin t \sin s$

PROOF

i   Although this identity holds for all real numbers t and s, we will assume for definiteness that $s > 0$, $t > 0$, and $t > s$ as illustrated in Figure 1. Since the arc $\overset{\frown}{P_0 P_3}$ is equal to the arc $\overset{\frown}{P_1 P_2}$ (Why?), it follows from geometry that the chord $\overline{P_0 P_3}$ is equal to the chord $\overline{P_1 P_2}$. Using the distance formula, we obtain

$$\overline{P_1 P_2}^2 = (\cos t - \cos s)^2 + (\sin t - \sin s)^2$$

and

$$\overline{P_0 P_3}^2 = [\cos (t - s) - 1]^2 + [\sin (t - s) - 0]^2.$$

Figure 1

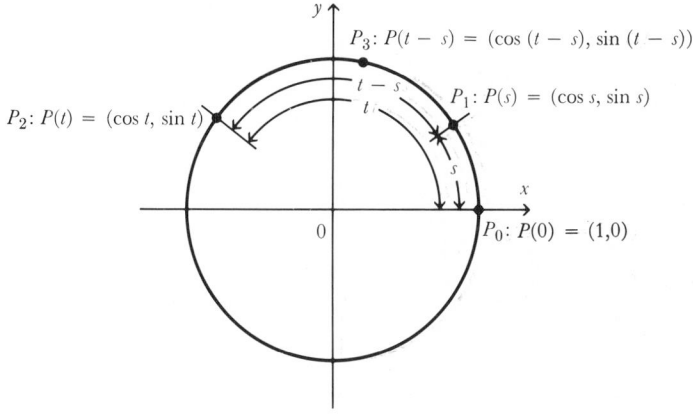

$P_3: P(t - s) = (\cos (t - s), \sin (t - s))$

$P_1: P(s) = (\cos s, \sin s)$

$P_2: P(t) = (\cos t, \sin t)$

$P_0: P(0) = (1,0)$

Equating $\overline{P_1 P_2}^2$ with $\overline{P_0 P_3}^2$, we have

$$(\cos t - \cos s)^2 + (\sin t - \sin s)^2$$
$$= [\cos (t - s) - 1]^2 + \sin^2 (t - s)$$

The left-hand side of this equation simplifies to $2 - 2(\cos t \cos s + \sin t \sin s)$, and the right-hand side simplifies to $2 - 2 \cos (t - s)$ (Why?), so that

$$2 - 2(\cos t \cos s + \sin t \sin s) = 2 - 2 \cos (t - s)$$

Hence,

$$\cos (t - s) = \cos t \cos s + \sin t \sin s \qquad \text{(Why?)}$$

ii $\cos (t + s) = \cos [t - (-s)] = \cos t \cos (-s) + \sin t \sin (-s)$
because of the identity in (i) above; however, the latter expression
can be written as $\cos t \cos s - \sin t \sin s$ since

$$\cos (-s) = \cos s \qquad \text{and} \qquad \sin (-s) = -\sin s$$

Hence,

$$\cos (t + s) = \cos t \cos s - \sin t \sin s$$

THEOREM 2

If t is any real number, then

i $\cos \left(\dfrac{\pi}{2} - t \right) = \sin t$

ii $\sin \left(\dfrac{\pi}{2} - t \right) = \cos t$

PROOF.   Apply Theorem 1, i to get

i $\cos \left(\dfrac{\pi}{2} - t \right) = \cos \dfrac{\pi}{2} \sin t + \sin \dfrac{\pi}{2} \sin t$

$$= 0 + \sin t = \sin t$$

ii $\sin \left(\dfrac{\pi}{2} - t \right) = \cos \left[\dfrac{\pi}{2} - \left(\dfrac{\pi}{2} - t \right) \right] \qquad \text{(Theorem 2, i)}$

$$= \cos \left(\dfrac{\pi}{2} - \dfrac{\pi}{2} + t \right)$$

$$= \cos t$$

Notice that if Theorem 2 is applied to angles measured in degrees,
then the identities would be written as $\cos (90° - \theta) = \sin \theta$ and
$\sin (90° - \theta) = \cos \theta$.

THEOREM 3

If t and s are any real numbers, then

i $\sin (t + s) = \sin t \cos s + \cos t \sin s$

ii $\sin (t - s) = \sin t \cos s - \cos t \sin s$

PROOF

i $\sin (t + s) = \cos \left[\dfrac{\pi}{2} - (t + s) \right] \qquad \text{(Why?)}$

$$= \cos \left[\left(\dfrac{\pi}{2} - t \right) - s \right]$$

$$= \cos \left(\dfrac{\pi}{2} - t \right) \cos s + \sin \left(\dfrac{\pi}{2} - t \right) \sin s \qquad \text{(Why?)}$$

$$= \sin t \cos s + \cos t \sin s$$

ii $\quad \sin (t - s) = \sin [t + (-s)]$
$$= \sin t \cos (-s) + \sin (-s) \cos t$$
$$= \sin t \cos s - \sin s \cos t \qquad \text{(Why?)}$$

THEOREM 4

If t is any real number, then

i $\quad \cos 2t = \cos^2 t - \sin^2 t$
$$= 2 \cos^2 t - 1$$
$$= 1 - 2 \sin^2 t$$

ii $\quad \sin 2t = 2 \sin t \cos t.$

PROOF

i $\quad \cos 2t = \cos (t + t)$
$$= \cos t \cos t - \sin t \sin t \qquad \text{(Theorem 1, ii)}$$
$$= \cos^2 t - \sin^2 t$$

However, since $\cos^2 t + \sin^2 t = 1$, we also have

$$\cos 2t = (1 - \sin^2 t) - \sin^2 t = 1 - 2 \sin^2 t$$

or

$$\cos 2t = \cos^2 t - (1 - \cos^2 t) = 2 \cos^2 t - 1$$

ii $\quad \sin 2t = \sin (t + t)$
$$= \sin t \cos t + \cos t \sin t \qquad \text{(Why?)}$$
$$= 2 \sin t \cos t$$

THEOREM 5

If t is any real number, then

i $\quad \cos^2 \left(\dfrac{t}{2} \right) = \dfrac{1 + \cos t}{2}$

ii $\quad \sin^2 \left(\dfrac{t}{2} \right) = \dfrac{1 - \cos t}{2}$

PROOF

i From Theorem 4, i, we have, upon substituting t for $2t$,

$$\cos t = 2 \cos^2 \left(\frac{t}{2} \right) - 1$$

so that

$$\frac{\cos t + 1}{2} = \cos^2 \left(\frac{t}{2} \right)$$

ii (See Problem 1.)

EXAMPLES

Use the identities to solve each of the following problems.

1   Prove that $\cos(\pi/2 + t) = -\sin t$ and that $\sin(90° + t) = \cos t$.

PROOF

$$\cos\left(\frac{\pi}{2} + t\right) = \cos\frac{\pi}{2}\cos t - \sin\frac{\pi}{2}\sin t \qquad \text{(Theorem 1, ii)}$$

$$= 0 - \sin t$$

$$= -\sin t$$

and

$$\sin(90° + t) = \sin 90° \cos t + \cos 90° \sin t \qquad \text{(Theorem 3, i)}$$

$$= \cos t$$

2   Use the fact that $7\pi/12 = \pi/3 + \pi/4$ to evaluate $\cos(7\pi/12)$.

SOLUTION

$$\cos\frac{7\pi}{12} = \cos\left(\frac{\pi}{3} + \frac{\pi}{4}\right)$$

$$= \cos\frac{\pi}{3}\cos\frac{\pi}{4} - \sin\frac{\pi}{3}\sin\frac{\pi}{4}$$

$$= \frac{1}{2}\frac{\sqrt{2}}{2} - \frac{\sqrt{3}}{2}\frac{\sqrt{2}}{2}$$

$$= \frac{\sqrt{2}}{4} - \frac{\sqrt{6}}{4}$$

3   Determine the value of $\sin(t + s)$ if $\cos s = \frac{4}{5}$, where $0 < s < \pi/2$, and $\sin t = \frac{3}{5}$, where $\pi/2 < t < \pi$.

SOLUTION

$$\sin s = \sqrt{1 - \cos^2 s} = \sqrt{1 - \tfrac{16}{25}} = \tfrac{3}{5}$$

and, since t indicates an angle with terminal side in quadrant II,

$$\cos t = -\sqrt{1 - \sin^2 t} = -\sqrt{1 - \tfrac{9}{25}} = -\tfrac{4}{5}$$

Hence,

$$\sin(t + s) = \sin t \cos s + \cos t \sin s$$

$$= (\tfrac{3}{5})(\tfrac{4}{5}) + (-\tfrac{4}{5})(\tfrac{3}{5})$$

$$= 0$$

4   Use the fact that $\frac{1}{2}(30°) = 15°$ to evaluate $\sin 15°$.

SOLUTION

$$\sin 15° = \sqrt{\frac{1 - \cos 30°}{2}} \qquad \text{(Theorem 5, ii)}$$

$$= \frac{\sqrt{2 - \sqrt{3}}}{2}$$

5   Prove that $[\sin (t/2) + \cos (t/2)]^2 - \sin t = 1$ for any real number t.

PROOF

$$\left[\sin\left(\frac{t}{2}\right) + \cos\left(\frac{t}{2}\right)\right]^2 - \sin t$$

$$= \sin^2\left(\frac{t}{2}\right) + 2 \sin\left(\frac{t}{2}\right) \cos\left(\frac{t}{2}\right) + \cos^2\left(\frac{t}{2}\right) - \sin t$$

$$= 1 + 2 \sin\left(\frac{t}{2}\right) \cos\left(\frac{t}{2}\right) - \sin t$$

$$= 1 + \sin t - \sin t \qquad \text{(Theorem 4, ii)}$$

$$= 1$$

6   Prove that if t is a real number in the domains of the given functions, then

a) $\tan^2 t + 1 = \sec^2 t$ b) $\cot^2 t + 1 = \csc^2 t$

PROOF

a) $\tan^2 t + 1 = \dfrac{\sin^2 t}{\cos^2 t} + 1 = \dfrac{\sin^2 t + \cos^2 t}{\cos^2 t}$

$$= \frac{1}{\cos^2 t} = \sec^2 t$$

b) $\cot^2 t + 1 = \dfrac{\cos^2 t}{\sin^2 t} + 1 = \dfrac{\cos^2 t + \sin^2 t}{\sin^2 t}$

$$= \frac{1}{\sin^2 t} = \csc^2 t$$

7   Prove that $1 - \tan^4 t = 2 \sec^2 t - \sec^4 t$ if t is in the domain of the tangent and secant.

PROOF

$$1 - \tan^4 t = (1 - \tan^2 t)(1 + \tan^2 t)$$
$$= (1 - \tan^2 t) \sec^2 t \qquad \text{(See Example 6a)}$$
$$= (1 - \sec^2 t + 1) \sec^2 t$$
$$= (2 - \sec^2 t) \sec^2 t$$
$$= 2 \sec^2 t - \sec^4 t$$

8   Prove that $\tan (t + s) = (\tan t + \tan s)/[1 - (\tan t \tan s)]$ if t, s, and $t + s$ are in the domain of the tangent function.

PROOF

$$\tan (t + s) = \frac{\sin (t + s)}{\cos (t + s)}$$

$$= \frac{\sin t \cos s + \sin s \cos t}{\cos t \cos s - \sin t \sin s}$$

Dividing both the numerator and the denominator of the right-hand side by cos s cos t, we get

$$\tan (t + s) = \frac{(\sin t \cos s)/(\cos t \cos s) + (\sin s \cos t)/(\cos s \cos t)}{(\cos t \cos s)/(\cos t \cos s) - (\sin t \sin s)/(\cos t \cos s)}$$

so that, after simplifying the above expression, we have

$$\tan (t + s) = \frac{\tan t + \tan s}{1 - \tan t \tan s}$$

PROBLEM SET 3

1 Complete the proof of Theorem 5, ii.

2 Given $\tan t = -\frac{5}{12}$, find sin t and cos t. Are the answers unique? (*Hint:* Use Example 6a to find sec t first.)

3 Use the identities to simplify each of the following expressions.

a) $(\cos t + \sin^2 t \sec t)/(\sec t)$ b) $(\sec t \csc t)/(\tan t + \cot t)$
c) $\cos^6 t + \sin^6 t$ d) $(\tan t + \cot t)/(\sec t \csc t)$

4 a) Suppose that $\tan t = \frac{3}{4}$; find sin 2t and cos 2t.
     b) If $\csc t = \frac{4}{3}$, find the values tan 2t and cot 2t.

5 Suppose that $\sin t = \frac{3}{5}$, where $0 < t < \pi/2$. Evaluate each of the following expressions.

a) sin 2t   b) cos 2t
c) sin 3t   d) cos 3t

6 Give two specific examples to prove that each of the following equations does *not* always hold.

a) $\cos (t + s) = \cos t + \cos s$
b) $\sin (t - s) = \sin t - \sin s$

7 Find the exact value of each of the following expressions by using the identities.

a) $\sin (\pi/8)$ b) $\cos (\pi/12)$
c) $\sin (5\pi/12)$ d) $\cos (5\pi/8)$
e) $\sin (7\pi/12)$

8 Prove each of the following identities.

    a) $\sin (u + v) + \sin (u - v) = 2 \sin u \cos v$

    b) $\sin (u + v) - \sin (u - v) = 2 \cos u \sin v$

    c) $\cos (u - v) + \cos (u + v) = 2 \cos u \cos v$

    d) $\cos (u - v) - \cos (u + v) = 2 \sin u \sin v$

9 Use the results of Problem 8 to prove each of the following identities. (*Hint:* Using Problem 8, let $s = u + v$ and $t = u - v$; therefore, $u = (s + t)/2$ and $v = (s - t)/2$. Substitute for u and v in terms of s and t.)

    a) $\sin s + \sin t = 2 \sin [(s + t)/2] \cos [(s - t)/2]$

    b) $\sin s - \sin t = 2 \cos [(s + t)/2] \sin [(s - t)/2]$

    c) $\cos s + \cos t = 2 \cos [(s + t)/2] \cos [(s - t)/2]$

    d) $\cos t - \cos s = 2 \sin [(s + t)/2] \sin [(s - t)/2]$

10 If $\sin t = \frac{1}{2}$ and $\cos s = -\sqrt{3}/2$, evaluate each of the following expressions where $\pi/2 < t < \pi$ and $\pi < s < 3\pi/2$.

    a) $\sin (\pi + t)$ b) $\cos (s + t)$

    c) $\sin (s - t)$ d) $\cos (4\pi - t)$

    e) $\sin (2t)$ f) $\sin (t/2)$

11 a)   Use the identity for $\tan (t + s)$ (see Example 8), together with the fact that the tangent is an odd function, to prove that

$$\tan (t - s) = \frac{\tan t - \tan s}{1 + \tan t \tan s}$$

    b)   Use the identity for $\tan (t + s)$ to prove that

$$\tan 2t = \frac{2 \tan t}{1 - \tan^2 t}$$

    c)   Prove that $f(x) = \tan x$ is a periodic function of fundamental period π.

12 a)   Develop an identity for $\cot (t + s)$. (*Hint:* Follow the procedure of Example 8.)

    b)   Use part (a) to derive the identity for $\cot 2t$.

    c)   Prove that $f(x) = \cot x$ is a periodic function of fundamental period π.

13 Express each of the following functions in terms of the sine and/or cosine.

    a) $(\sec t + \csc t)^2 \tan t$ b) $(\csc t + \cot t)^2$

    c) $1/(1 + \tan^2 t)$ d) $1/(\sec^2 x) - 1/(\tan^2 x)$

    e) $\tan^2 x$ f) $(1 - \sin^2 x)/\cos x$

    g) $\cot (t - \pi/2)$ h) $[\sin (t/2) + \cos (t/2)]^2$

14 Prove each of the following identities.

a) $\cot t + \tan t = \sec t \csc t$

b) $\dfrac{\sin 3t}{\sin t} = 2 \cos 2t + 1$

c) $\sec^4 t - \sec^2 t = \dfrac{\sin^2 t}{\cos^4 t}$

d) $1 - \tan^4 t = 2 \sec^2 t - \sec^4 t$

e) $(\cot t + \csc t)^2 = \dfrac{1 + \cos t}{1 - \cos t}$

f) $\tan^2 t - \sin^2 t = \dfrac{\sin^4 t}{\cos^2 t}$

g) $\dfrac{\cos^2 t}{1 + \sin t} = 1 - \sin t$

h) $\dfrac{1 - \tan^2 t}{1 + \tan^2 t} = 1 - 2 \sin^2 t$

i) $\cot t - \tan t = 2 \cot 2t$

j) $\cos^2 t(1 - \tan^2 t) = \cos 2t$

k) $\dfrac{\tan s + \tan t}{\tan s - \tan t} = \dfrac{\sin (s + t)}{\sin (s - t)}$

l) $\dfrac{\tan (s - t) + \tan t}{1 - \tan (s - t) \tan t} = \tan s$

m) $\tan \left(t + \dfrac{\pi}{3} \right) = \dfrac{\tan t + \sqrt{3}}{1 - \sqrt{3} \tan t}$

n) $\cot \left(t + \dfrac{\pi}{4} \right) + \tan \left(t - \dfrac{\pi}{4} \right) = 0$

o) $\dfrac{1 + \cos 2t}{\sin 2t} = \cot t$

p) $\tan t = \dfrac{\sin 2t}{1 + \cos 2t}$

q) $2 \csc 2t = \csc t \sec t$

r) $\dfrac{\sin 4t}{\sin 2t} = 2 \cos 2t$

s) $\dfrac{\sin 5t}{\sin t} - \dfrac{\cos 5t}{\cos t} = 4 \cos 2t$

t) $\dfrac{\cos 2t}{1 + \sin 2t} = \dfrac{1 - \tan t}{1 + \tan t}$

u) $4 \sin^2 t \cos^2 t + \cos^2 2t = 1$

v) $\sec t \csc t - 2 \cos t \csc t = \tan t - \cot t$

w) $\tan t + \cot t = 2 \csc 2t$

x) $\dfrac{\sin 3t}{\sin t} - \dfrac{\cos 3t}{\cos t} = 2$

y) $3 - 4 \cos 2t + \cos 4t = 8 \sin^4 t$

15 Express each of the following expressions as a trigonometric function of θ.

a) $\sin (90° - \theta)$

b) $\cos (\pi - \theta)$

c) $\tan (270° - \theta)$

d) $\tan (3\pi/2 + \theta)$

e) $\cos (180° + \theta)$

f) $\sec (90° - \theta)$

g) $\csc (90° - \theta)$

h) $\cot (\pi/2 - \theta)$

i) $\cos (90° - \theta)$

j) $\sin (270° + \theta)$

k) $\sin (10\pi - \theta)$

l) $\cos (7\pi/2 - \theta)$

m) $\sin (11\pi/2 - \theta)$

n) $\cos (-\pi - \theta)$

16 Solve each of the following equations for a value of θ, without the use of the tables.

a) $\sin \theta = \cos (45° - 2\theta)$

b) $\tan \theta/2 = \cot 2\theta$

c) $\sin (\theta + 15°) = \cos (\theta - 30°)$

17 Prove each of the following identities.

a) $-\sin^2 \theta(1 - \csc^2 \theta) = \cos^2 \theta$

b) $\cot^2 \theta \sec^2 \theta = 1 + \cot^2 \theta$

c) $\sec^2 \theta \cot^2 \theta - \cos^2 \theta \csc^2 \theta = 1$

d) $\cos^4 \theta - \sin^4 \theta = \cos 2\theta$

e) $4 \sin^2 \theta \cos^2 \theta = 1 - \cos^2 2\theta$

f) $2 \cos \theta - \sin 2\theta \csc \theta = 0$

g) $\cos 2\theta + 2 \sin^2 \theta = 1$

5 Trigonometric Equations

Now we can use the properties of the trigonometric functions, together with the trigonometric identities, to solve equations containing trigonometric functions. In solving a trigonometric equation, we are always looking for the set of *all* angles which make the given equation valid.

EXAMPLES

Solve each of the following trigonometric equations.

1 $\sin t = \frac{1}{2}$, where t is a real number.

SOLUTION.   (See Figure 1.) We know that $\sin (\pi/6) = \frac{1}{2}$ because $P(\pi/6) = (\sqrt{3}/2, \frac{1}{2})$. Here, $\pi/6$ is the reference angle, and, since the sine is positive also in quadrant II, we have $\sin (5\pi/6) = \frac{1}{2}$. Finally, using the fact that the sine has period 2π, we have

$$t \in \left\{ t \,\middle|\, t = \frac{\pi}{6} + 2\pi k, \ k \in I \right\} \cup \left\{ t \,\middle|\, t = \frac{5\pi}{6} + 2\pi k, \ k \in I \right\}$$

Figure 1

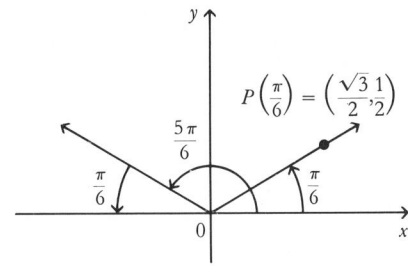

$$P\left(\frac{\pi}{6}\right) = \left(\frac{\sqrt{3}}{2}, \frac{1}{2}\right)$$

2   $\sin t = -0.8$, where t is a real number (use $\pi = 3.142$).

SOLUTION.   (See Figure 2.) We can find the reference angle t_R by using linear interpolation to solve $\sin t_R = 0.8$.

$$0.01 \left[d \begin{bmatrix} \sin 0.92 = 0.7956 \\ \sin t\quad = 0.8000 \\ \sin 0.93 = 0.8016 \end{bmatrix} 0.0016 \right] 0.0060$$

$$\frac{d}{0.01} = \frac{0.0016}{0.006}$$

so that

$$d = 0.003 \qquad \text{(Approximately)}$$

Hence,

$$t_R = 0.927 \qquad \text{(Approximately)}$$

Since the sine is negative in quadrants III and IV, we have

$$t \in \{t | t = 4.069 + 2\pi k, \ k \in I\} \cup \{t | t = 5.357 + 2\pi k, \ k \in I\}$$

Figure 2

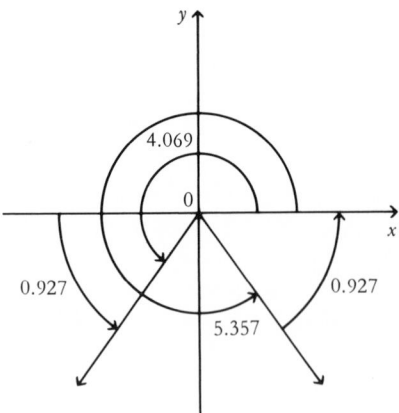

3   $\sin x = 1$, where x is a real number.

SOLUTION.   (See Figure 3.) One number in the solution set is $\pi/2$, since $\sin \pi/2 = 1$. $f(x) = \sin x$ is periodic with period 2π; therefore, the solution set is

$$\left\{ x | x = \frac{\pi}{2} + 2\pi k, \ k \in I \right\}$$

Figure 3

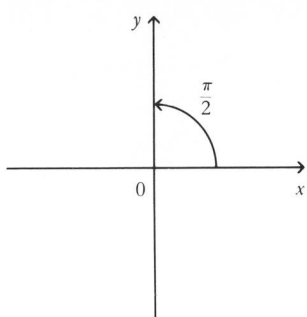

4   $\sin x + \cos x = 1$, where x is a real number.

SOLUTION.   Since $\sin x + \cos x = 1$, $\sin x = 1 - \cos x$. Now, square both sides (realizing that we must later check for extraneous roots) to get

$$\sin^2 x = (1 - \cos x)^2$$

but,

$$\sin^2 x = 1 - \cos^2 x = (1 - \cos x)(1 + \cos x)$$

so that

$$(1 - \cos x)(1 + \cos x) = (1 - \cos x)^2$$

that is,

$$(1 - \cos x)[(1 + \cos x) - (1 - \cos x)] = 0$$

from which we get

$$2(1 - \cos x)(\cos x) = 0$$

But, the solution set of the latter equation is

$$\{x | 1 - \cos x = 0\} \cup \{x | \cos x = 0\}$$
$$= \{x | x = 2\pi k, \, k \in I\} \cup \left\{x \Big| x = \pm \frac{\pi}{2} + 2\pi k, \, k \in I\right\}$$

Checking back in the original equation, we find the solution set to be

$$\{x | x = 2\pi k, \, k \in I\} \cup \left\{x \Big| x = \frac{\pi}{2} + 2\pi k, \, k \in I\right\}$$

Notice here that $-\pi/2$ is an extraneous root.

5    $2 \sin^4 x - 9 \sin^2 x + 4 = 0$, for $0 \le x < 2\pi$.

SOLUTION.   (See Figure 4.)   This equation can be factored as

$$(2 \sin^2 x - 1)(\sin^2 x - 4) = 0$$

Figure 4

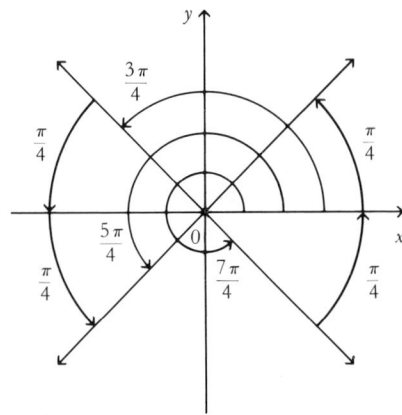

The solution set, then, is

$$\{x | 2 \sin^2 x - 1 = 0\} \cup \{x | \sin^2 x - 4 = 0\} \qquad \text{for} \quad 0 \le x < 2\pi$$

or, equivalently,

$$\{x | \sin^2 x = \tfrac{1}{2}\} \cup \{x | \sin^2 x = 4\}$$

$$= \left\{x \Big| \sin x = \frac{\pm\sqrt{2}}{2}\right\} \cup \{x | \sin x = \pm 2\} \qquad \text{where } 0 \le x < 2\pi$$

Since the sine function has range $[-1,1]$, $\sin x = \pm 2$ has no solution; therefore, the solution set is

$$\left\{x \Big| x = \frac{(2k + 1)\pi}{4}, \ k = 0, 1, 2, 3\right\}$$

6    $\sin 2x - 2 \sin x = 0$, for $0 \le x < 2\pi$.

SOLUTION.   First we use the identity for $\sin 2x$ to rewrite the equation as $2 \sin x \cos x - 2 \sin x = 0$, so that the solution set is

$$\{x | 2 \sin x (\cos x - 1) = 0\} = \{x | \sin x = 0\} \cup \{x | \cos x - 1 = 0\}$$

$$= \{0, \pi\} \qquad \text{for } 0 \le x < 2\pi \qquad \text{(Why?)}$$

7   $\cos 2\theta + \sin^2 \theta = 1$, for $0° \leq \theta < 360°$.

SOLUTION.   Since $\cos 2\theta = \cos^2 \theta - \sin^2 \theta$,

$\cos 2\theta + \sin^2 \theta = \cos^2 \theta$

so that the solution set is

$\{\theta | \cos^2 \theta = 1\} = \{0°, 180°\}$ for $0° \leq \theta < 360°$

PROBLEM SET 4

1   Solve each of the following trigonometric equations.

a) $\sin t = 1/\sqrt{2}$ b) $\cos t = 2$
c) $\cos t = \frac{1}{2}$ d) $\sin t = -0.7033$
e) $\cos t = 1$ f) $\cos t = -0.6675$
g) $\sin t = 0.7$ h) $\cos t = 0.555$
i) $\sin t = 0$ j) $\cos t = 10.62$

2   Solve each of the following trigonometric equations for x.

a) $\sin x - \cos x = 0$ b) $4 \sin^2 x - 1 = 0$
c) $3 \tan x - \sqrt{3} = 0$ d) $2 \cos x + \sqrt{3} = 0$

3   Solve for x and y, if $0 \leq x \leq \pi/2$ and $0 \leq y \leq \pi/2$, when
$\tan (x - y) = 1$ and $\sin (x + y) = 1$.

4   Solve each of the following equations for x if $0 \leq x < 2\pi$.

a) $2 \cos x - \sin x = 1$ b) $\sin^2 x - 2 \sin x + 1 = 0$
c) $2 - \sin x = 2 \cos^2 x$ d) $4 \cos^2 x - 5 \sin x \cot x - 6 = 0$
e) $2 \sin^2 x - \sin x - 1 = 0$ f) $4 \csc x - 8 = 0$
g) $2 \sec x + 4 = 0$ h) $3 \cot^2 x - 1 = 0$
i) $\sin x + \cos x \tan x = 3$

5   Solve each of the following equations for θ if $0 \leq \theta < 360°$.

a) $\sin \theta = -\sqrt{3}/2$ b) $\cos \theta = -0.8880$
c) $2 \cos^2 \theta - \cos \theta = 0$ d) $\tan^2 \theta + \sec \theta - 3 = 0$
e) $\tan^2 \theta - 2 \tan \theta + 1 = 0$ f) $\cot^2 \theta - 5 \cot \theta + 4 = 0$
g) $2 \cos^2 \theta + \cos \theta = 0$ h) $2 \cos^2 \theta - \sin \theta = 1$
i) $\tan \theta - 3 \cot \theta = 0$ j) $\cos 2\theta + \sin 2\theta = 0$

6 Triangle Trigonometry

We conclude this chapter with a study of applications of the trigonometric functions in determining missing parts of triangles.

Two standard formulas of trigonometry, the *law of sines* and *law of cosines*, will be derived. Before deriving the formulas, it is convenient to establish some standard notation for representing the angles and corresponding sides of triangles. If a triangle is determined by points A, B, and C ($\triangle ABC$), the angle at vertex A is denoted by α; the angle at vertex B is denoted by β; the angle at vertex C is denoted by γ; the side opposite angle α is a; the side opposite angle β is b; the side opposite angle γ is c (Figure 1).

Figure 1

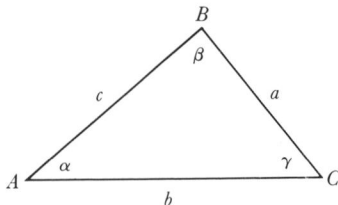

6.1 Right Triangles

Suppose we are given a right triangle $\triangle ABC$, with $\gamma = 90°$ (Figure 2). If we consider $\triangle ABC$ to be on a coordinate system with α in standard position, then it is not difficult to describe the values of the six trigonometric functions in terms of the sides of the right triangle:

$$\sin \alpha = \frac{a}{c} = \frac{\text{length of side opposite } \alpha}{\text{length of hypotenuse}}$$

$$\cos \alpha = \frac{b}{c} = \frac{\text{length of adjacent side of } \alpha}{\text{length of hypotenuse}}$$

$$\tan \alpha = \frac{\sin \alpha}{\cos \alpha} = \frac{a}{b} = \frac{\text{length of side opposite } \alpha}{\text{length of adjacent side of } \alpha}$$

$$\csc \alpha = \frac{1}{\sin \alpha} = \frac{c}{a} = \frac{\text{length of hypotenuse}}{\text{length of side opposite } \alpha}$$

$$\sec \alpha = \frac{1}{\cos \alpha} = \frac{c}{b} = \frac{\text{length of hypotenuse}}{\text{length of adjacent side of } \alpha}$$

and

$$\cot \alpha = \frac{\cos \alpha}{\sin \alpha} = \frac{b}{a} = \frac{\text{length of adjacent side of } \alpha}{\text{length of side opposite } \alpha}$$

Figure 2

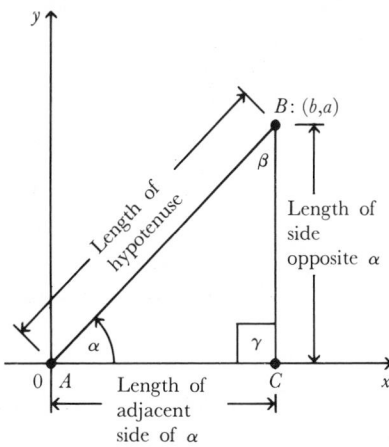

EXAMPLES

1 Determine the missing parts of the right triangle in Figure 3.

SOLUTION. $\tan \alpha = \frac{1}{2}$, so that α is approximately $26°34'$ and β is approximately $63°26'$. Finally, we can use the Pythagorean theorem to determine c as $c = \sqrt{5}$.

Figure 3

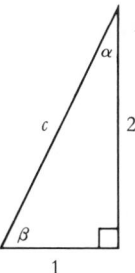

2 From a mountaintop 10,000 feet above a horizontal plane two towns were observed with angles of depression (acute angle formed by the line of sight and a horizontal line passing through the position of the sighting) are $60°$ and $45°$, respectively, as given in Figure 4. How far apart are the two towns?

SOLUTION. In Figure 4, A represents the position of the observer, C represents the position of the first town, and D the position of the second town. The angles of depression are $\angle DAE$ and $\angle CAE$. Using the fact that alternate interior angles formed by the transversal of two parallel lines are equal, we have

$$\angle BCA = \angle CAE = 60° \qquad \text{and} \qquad \angle BDA = \angle DAE = 45°$$

Figure 4

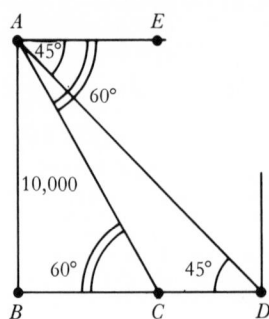

Hence, $\overline{BC} = 10000 \cot 60° = (10000/\sqrt{3})$ feet, and $\overline{BD} = 10000 \cot 45° = 10000$ feet, so that the distance between C and D is

$$\overline{BD} - \overline{BC} = 10000 - \frac{10000}{\sqrt{3}}$$

We have seen above how it is possible to use the trigonometric functions to relate the sides and angles of right triangles. Now, let us use the trigonometric functions to derive two formulas which relate the sides and angles of triangles that are not necessarily right triangles.

THEOREM 1   (LAW OF SINES)

In any $\triangle ABC$,

$$\frac{\sin \alpha}{a} = \frac{\sin \beta}{b} = \frac{\sin \gamma}{c}$$

PROOF.   (See Figure 5.) We can use the fact that the area of a triangle is equal to the product of one-half the base and altitude, together with the fact that the sine of an acute angle of a right triangle is equal to the ratio of the length of the side opposite the angle to the length of the hypotenuse of the right triangle. First, draw altitudes h_1 and h_2.

Figure 5

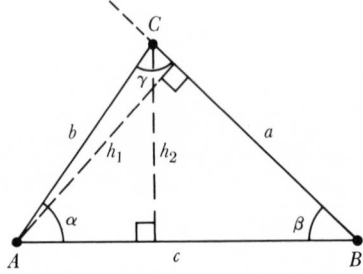

The area of $\triangle ABC = \frac{1}{2}ch_2 = \frac{1}{2}ah_1$; but,

$$\frac{1}{2}ch_2 = \frac{1}{2}c\,(a \sin \beta) \qquad \text{since} \qquad \sin \beta = \frac{h_2}{a}$$

and

$$\frac{1}{2}ch_2 = \frac{1}{2}c\,(b \sin \alpha) \qquad \text{since} \qquad \sin \alpha = \frac{h_2}{b}$$

Also,

$$\frac{1}{2}ah_1 = \frac{1}{2}a\,(b \sin \gamma) \qquad \text{since} \qquad \sin \gamma = \frac{h_1}{b}$$

Hence,

$$\frac{1}{2}ca \sin \beta = \frac{1}{2}cb \sin \alpha = \frac{1}{2}ab \sin \gamma$$

so that

$$ca \sin \beta = cb \sin \alpha = ab \sin \gamma$$

After dividing by abc, we get

$$\frac{\sin \beta}{b} = \frac{\sin \alpha}{a} = \frac{\sin \gamma}{c}$$

If any two angles and a side of a triangle are known (denoted by ASA), the law of sines can be used to determine either of the two remaining sides. Let us consider a few examples of this situation.

EXAMPLES

1   In $\triangle ABC$, $a = 12$, $\alpha = 45°$, and $\beta = 105°$. Find c.

SOLUTION.   (See Figure 6.)   Since $\alpha + \beta + \gamma = 180°$, $\gamma = 30°$. Using the law of sines,

$$\frac{\sin 45°}{12} = \frac{\sin 30°}{c}$$

so that

$$c = \frac{12 \sin 30°}{\sin 45°} = 6\sqrt{2}$$

Figure 6

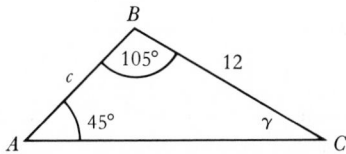

2   If in $\triangle ABC$, $a = 20$, $\gamma = 51°$, and $\beta = 42°$, find b.

SOLUTION.   (See Figure 7.) Since $\alpha + \beta + \gamma = 180°$, $\alpha = 87°$. Using the law of sines,

$$\frac{\sin 87°}{20} = \frac{\sin 42°}{b}$$

so that

$$b = \frac{20 \sin 42°}{\sin 87°} = 13.4 \qquad \text{(Approximately)}$$

Figure 7

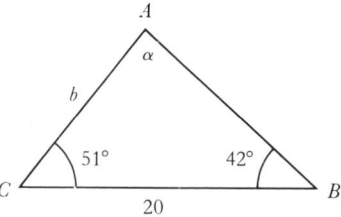

Let us examine the various cases which may occur if we are given two sides and an angle opposite one of them (denoted by *SSA*). It may be that there is no possible triangle with these parts (Figure 8*a*); there may be two different triangles with these parts (Figure 8*b*); or there

Figure 8

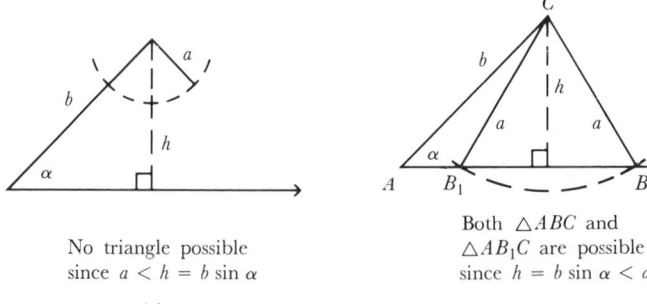

No triangle possible
since $a < h = b \sin \alpha$

(a)

Both $\triangle ABC$ and
$\triangle AB_1C$ are possible
since $h = b \sin \alpha < a < b$

(b)

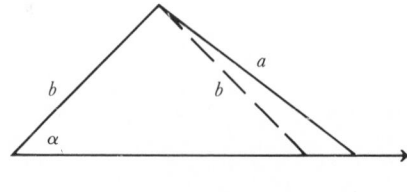

Only one triangle is
possible since $a > b$

(c)

may be only one triangle with these parts (Figure 8c). Because there are three different possibilities here, we sometimes refer to this situation as the *ambiguous case*. In the next example, we will see how the law of sines can be used to solve any situation which may occur in the ambiguous case.

EXAMPLES

1   In each of the following problems, find the indicated missing parts of all possible triangles.

a)   If $a = 20$, $b = 15$, and $\alpha = 30°$, find β to the nearest degree.
b)   If $a = 5$, $b = 20$, and $\alpha = 30°$, find β to the nearest degree.
c)   If $a = 30$, $b = 50$, and $\alpha = 30°$, find β and γ to the nearest minute.

SOLUTION

a)   We will attempt to find β, keeping in mind that there may be zero, one, or two triangles. If we assume that at least one triangle exists, then, by the law of sines,

$$\frac{\sin \beta}{15} = \frac{\sin 30°}{20}$$

so that

$$\sin \beta = \tfrac{3}{8}$$

Since β must be less than 180° (it is an angle of a triangle) and since the sine is positive for acute (first quadrant) and obtuse (second quadrant) angles, β is approximately 22° or 158°. (Why?) Since it is impossible to have a 158° angle in a triangle which is already known to have a 30° angle, there is only one triangle possible, and $\beta = 22°$ (Figure 9).

Figure 9

b)   Here again we assume that at least one such triangle exists, so that

$$\frac{\sin \beta}{20} = \frac{\sin 30°}{5}$$

Hence

$$\sin \beta = 2$$

But, since $|\sin \theta| \le 1$, no such β exists; therefore, no triangle exists with the given parts (Figure 10).

Figure 10

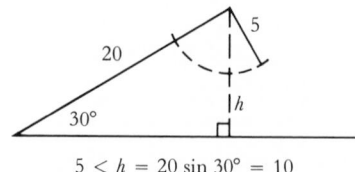

$$5 < h = 20 \sin 30° = 10$$

c) If we assume at least one such triangle exists, we have

$$\frac{\sin \beta}{50} = \frac{\sin 30°}{30}$$

so that $\sin \beta = \frac{5}{6}$.

Hence, β is approximately 56°26′ or 123°34′. Since either value of β satisfies $\alpha + \beta < 180°$, we have two possible triangles. One of the two possible triangles $\triangle ABC$ has angles 30°, 56°26′, and 93°34′, whereas the other triangle $\triangle ABD$ has angles 30°, 123°34′, and 26°26′ (Figure 11).

Figure 11

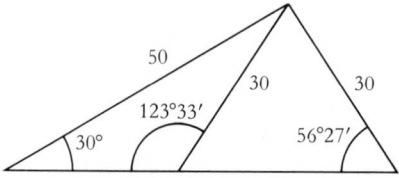

2   A tower is 125 feet high on a mountain on the bank of a river. It is observed that the angle of depression from the top of the tower to a point on the opposite shore is 28°40′ and the angle of depression from the base of the tower to the same point on the shore is 18°20′. How wide is the river and how high is the mountain?

SOLUTION.   In Figure 12, $\overline{BC}$ represents the height of the tower, $\overline{BD}$ represents the height of the mountain, and A is the point on the opposite shore. $\overline{BC} = 125$ feet. In $\triangle ABC$,

$$\gamma = 90° - 28°40' = 61°20'$$
$$\beta = 90° + 18°20' = 108°20'$$
$$\alpha = 180° - (\beta + \gamma) = 10°20'$$

Figure 12

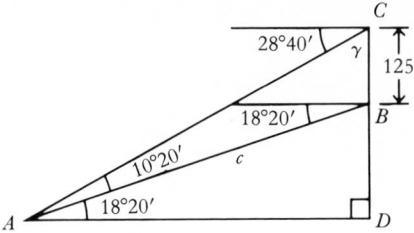

By the law of sines,

$$c = \frac{125 \sin 61°20'}{\sin 10°20'} = \frac{125(0.8774)}{0.1794} = 611 \text{ feet} \qquad \text{(Approximately)}$$

so that

$$\overline{BD} = c \sin 18°20' = 611(0.3145) = 192 \text{ feet} \qquad \text{(Approximately)}$$

and

$$\overline{AD} = c \cos 18°20' = 611(0.9492) = 580 \text{ feet} \qquad \text{(Approximately)}$$

Therefore, the river is 580 feet wide and the mountain is 192 feet high.

Now let us derive another formula which relates the sides and the angles of triangles, the *law of cosines*.

THEOREM 2 (LAW OF COSINES)

In any $\triangle ABC$,

i $c^2 = a^2 + b^2 - 2ab \cos \gamma$

ii $b^2 = a^2 + c^2 - 2ac \cos \beta$

iii $a^2 = b^2 + c^2 - 2bc \cos \alpha$

That is, the square of the length of any side of a triangle is equal to the sum of the squares of the lengths of the other two sides minus twice their product times the cosine of the angle included between these other two sides.

PROOF.   First, consider $\triangle ABC$ on a Cartesian coordinate system with γ in standard position (Figure 13). A has coordinates $(b \cos \gamma, b \sin \gamma)$ (Why?) and B has coordinates $(a,0)$ (Why?), so that, by the distance formula, we have

$$
\begin{aligned}
c^2 &= (b \cos \gamma - a)^2 + (b \sin \gamma - 0)^2 \\
&= b^2 \cos^2 \gamma - 2ab \cos \gamma + a^2 + b^2 \sin^2 \gamma \\
&= b^2 \cos^2 \gamma + b^2 \sin^2 \gamma + a^2 - 2ab \cos \gamma \\
&= a^2 + b^2 (\cos^2 \gamma + \sin^2 \gamma) - 2ab \cos \gamma \\
&= a^2 + b^2 - 2ab \cos \gamma
\end{aligned}
$$

Figure 13

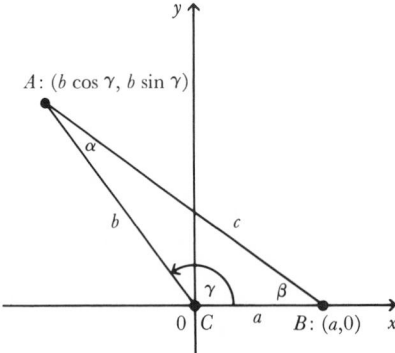

In view of the fact that the location of the coordinate axes in the plane is merely a matter of convenience, the other two formulas are obtained in a similar manner.

If two sides and an included angle of a triangle are known (*SAS*), the law of cosines can be used to determine the third side (see Example 1 below), or, if the three sides of a triangle are known (*SSS*), any of the angles can be found by using the law of cosines (see Example 2 below).

EXAMPLES

1   In $\triangle ABC$, $a = 8$, $b = 6$, and $\gamma = 60°$. Find c.

Figure 14

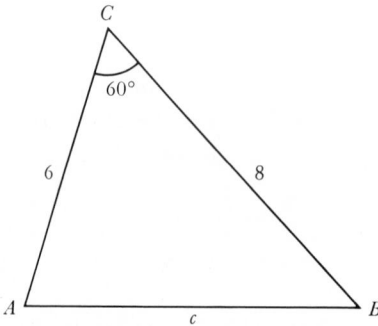

SOLUTION.   (See Figure 14.) Using the law of cosines,

$$c^2 = a^2 + b^2 - 2ab \cos \gamma$$
$$= 64 + 36 - 2(8)(6)(\tfrac{1}{2})$$
$$= 100 - 48 = 52$$

so that

$$c = \sqrt{52} = 2\sqrt{13}$$

2   In $\triangle ABC$, $a = 5$, $b = 10$, and $c = 8$. Find α.

SOLUTION.   (See Figure 15.)   Using the law of cosines,

$$a^2 = b^2 + c^2 - 2bc \cos \alpha$$
$$25 = 100 + 64 - 2(10)(8) \cos \alpha$$

so that

$$\cos \alpha = \tfrac{139}{160} = 0.8688 \qquad \text{(Approximately)}$$

Using Table IV and linear interpolation, we find that α is approximately 29°41'.

Figure 15

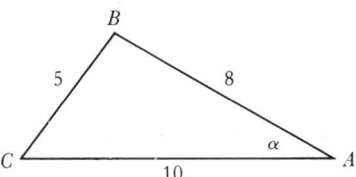

3   A motorboat is moving west and is propelled 30 feet per second. Find the strength of the tide which alters the course of the boat 20° south of west and reduces the speed to 25 feet per second.

SOLUTION.   (See Figure 16.) Let $\overline{AB}$ represent the strength of the tide in feet per second. Using the law of cosines, we have

$$\overline{AB}^2 = \overline{OA}^2 + \overline{OB}^2 - 2\overline{OA} \cdot \overline{OB} \cdot \cos 20°$$
$$= (30)^2 + (25)^2 - 2(30)(25)(0.9397)$$
$$= 900 + 625 - 1500(0.9397)$$
$$= 1525 - 1409.6$$
$$= 115.4 \qquad \text{(Approximately)}$$

Therefore, $\overline{AB} = \sqrt{115.4}$ feet per second.

Figure 16

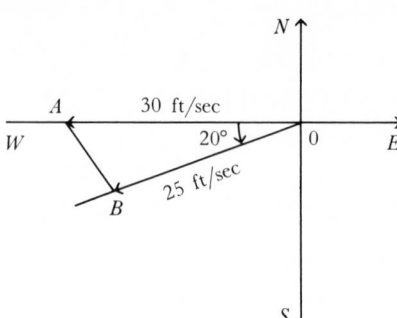

PROBLEM SET 5

1 Assume that $\triangle ABC$ is a right triangle, with the parts as labeled in Figure 17. Find the missing parts, given the following parts.

a) $a = 5,\ b = 3$ b) $a = 10,\ \alpha = 30°$
c) $a = 17,\ \beta = 43°$ d) $a = 7,\ c = 12$
e) $b = 8,\ \beta = 15°$ f) $b = 3a$
g) $a = b$

Figure 17

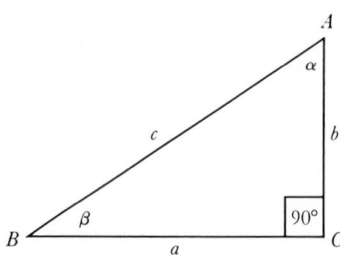

2 Use the law of sines to determine whether there is one triangle, two triangles, or no triangle in each of the following cases. Find the missing parts of all possible triangles.

a) $b = 17.5,\ c = 15.2,$ and $\gamma = 45°$
b) $a = 10,\ b = 50,$ and $\alpha = 22°$
c) $c = 18.9,\ a = 10.4,$ and $\gamma = 65°$
d) $a = 182.5,\ b = 82.5,$ and $\alpha = 72°$
e) $b = 17.41,\ c = 19.32,$ and $\gamma = 45°$

3 Use the law of cosines to find the indicated missing part of each of the following triangles.

a) $\alpha = 60°,\ b = 20,\ c = 6;$ find a.
b) $a = 3,\ b = 4,\ c = 6;$ find α.
c) $a = 4,\ b = 7,\ c = 5;$ find $\alpha,\ \beta,$ and γ.

d) $a = 5$, $b = 8$, $c = 10$; find β.

e) $c = 39$, $b = 98$, and $\alpha = 17°$; find a.

f) $a = 144$, $b = 180$, $c = 108$; find β.

4 Find the indicated missing part of each of the following triangles.

a) If $b = 4$, $c = 6$, $\beta = 30°$; find $\sin \gamma$.

b) $\alpha = 56°$, $b = 7$, $c = 12$; find a.

c) $a = 20$, $b = 4$, $c = 18$; find α.

d) If $\alpha = 60°$, $\beta = 75°$, $a = 10\sqrt{3}$; find b.

e) $a = 12$, $b = \sqrt{109}$, $c = 5$; find α, γ, and β.

5 While flying at a height of 1,000 feet, a pilot observes that the angle of depression of an airport is 15°. At that moment what is the distance between the plane and the airport?

6 A ladder is placed against a building with its foot 10 feet away from the building, on level ground. If it just reaches a window 20 feet above the ground, what angle will the ladder make with the ground?

7 A man standing 10 feet from a wall in an art gallery observes that the angle of elevation (acute angle between the line of sight and the horizontal line through the position of sighting) of the top of a picture in the art gallery is 30° and the angle of elevation of the bottom of the picture is 15°. What is height of the picture?

8 From a tower 108 feet high, a man observed that the angles of depression of a street light and its base are respectively 30° and 60°. How high is the light above the ground?

9 a) Prove Hero's formula: The area of a triangle $\triangle ABC$, with sides a, b, and c and semiperimeter $s = \frac{1}{2}(a + b + c)$, is

$$A = \sqrt{s(s - a)(s - b)(s - c)}$$

(*Hint:* Use the Law of Sines.)

b) Use part (a) to find the area of $\triangle ABC$ with

i $a = 810$, $b = 990$, and $c = 360$

ii $a = 492$, $b = 369$, and $c = 246$

iii Vertices $A:(2,3)$, $B:(5,7)$, and $C:(6,1)$

10 An airplane heads directly east with an airspeed of 170 miles per hour, while a wind is blowing 30° south of east. Find the speed of the wind after two hours if the plane has traveled 600 miles.

11 A balloon is rising vertically at the rate of 15 feet per second; and at the same time it is blown horizontally by a wind of 20 feet per second. Find the angle its path makes with the horizon after three seconds.

12 Two railroads meet at an angle of 35°20′. If two trains leave from the railway station (where the two railroads meet) at the same time and if the speed of the first is 30 miles per hour, find the speed of the second train if they are 50 miles apart after $2\frac{1}{2}$ hours from their departure.

13 An observer on the ground views a kite from the east with an angle of elevation of 59°20′. Another person observes that its angle of elevation from the west is 34°15′. If the observers are 200 feet apart, how high is the kite?

14 Assume that the diagonal of a parallelogram is 80 inches long and at one end makes angles measuring 35° and 27° with the sides of the parallelogram. Find the lengths of the sides of the parallelogram.

15 Prove the following identities for $\triangle ABC$.

a) If $\beta = 2\alpha$, then $\cos \alpha = b/2a$.
b) $b^2 - c^2 = a(b \cos \gamma - c \cos \beta)$

REVIEW PROBLEM SET

1 Change the following radian measures to degree measures.

a) $5\pi/3$ b) $-3\pi/4$ c) $5\pi/16$
d) $11\pi/6$ e) $13\pi/6$ f) $-13\pi/4$
g) $8\pi/3$ h) $-18\pi/7$ i) $17\pi/5$
j) $27\pi/6$ k) $33\pi/4$ l) $-41\pi/4$

2 Change the following degree measures to radian measures.

a) 290°   b) −70°   c) 135°
d) 460°   e) 190°   f) −105°
g) 820°   h) −30°   i) 12°

3 Find the length of the circular arc and the area of the circular sector that is generated by a central angle θ in a circle of radius r if

a) $r = 7$ and $\theta = 75°$ b) $r = 2$ and $\theta = 160°$
c) $r = 10$ and $\theta = 700°$ d) $r = 4$ and $\theta = -30°$
e) $r = 6$ and $\theta = 36°$

4 a) A circle of radius 4 inches contains a central angle θ that intercepts an arc 10 inches long. What size is θ in radians? In degrees? Find the area of the sector whose central angle is θ.

b) A central angle is 310° and has an intercepted arc of 35π inches. Find the radius of the circle and the area of the sector.

5 Find the values of the six trigonometric functions for each of the following angles without using a table.

a) −330°   b) 270°   c) 180°
d) 150°   e) 210°   f) 135°
g) −120°   h) −225°   i) −45°

6 Find the values of all six trigonometric functions of the angle θ if the terminal side of θ in its standard position contains the following given points.

a) (3,4)   b) (5,12)   c) (7,25)
d) (6,8)   e) (8,17)   f) $(-3,4)$
g) $(-4,3)$ h) (5,6)

7 Given an angle θ whose terminal side does not lie either along the x axis or the y axis, prove that the functions $f(\theta) = \tan \theta$ and $g(\theta) = \cot \theta$ are defined and $f(\theta)g(\theta) = 1$.

8 Let $f(\theta) = \cot \theta + 4$.

a) Find the domain of f.   b) Find the range of f.
c) Is $f(\theta)$ an even or odd function?

9 Let $\csc \theta = -\frac{7}{4}, 0° < \theta < 360°$. Find

a) $\sin \theta$ b) $\cos \theta$ c) $\tan \theta$
d) $\cot \theta$ e) $\sec \theta$

10 Use the trigonometric identities to evaluate each of the following expressions.

a) $\sin 330° \cos 180° - \cos 330° \sin 180°$
b) $\cos 270° \cos 150° + \sin 270° \sin 150°$
c) $\sin 120° \cos 30° + \cos 120° \sin 30°$
d) $\cos 60° \cos 30° - \sin 60° \sin 30°$

11 Prove each of the following equations by using the identities.

a) $\cos (90° - \theta) \tan (90° - \theta) = \cos \theta$
b) $\tan \theta + \cot \theta = \csc (90° - \theta) \csc \theta$
c) $[(\sin 62°)/(\sec 62°)][(\cot 28°)/(\cos 28°)] = \sin 62°$
d) $\cot 67° \cot 23° \cos 67° \tan 67° = \cos 23°$
e) $\cos 13° \tan 13° \tan 77° \csc 77° = 1$
f) $\sin^2 \theta \csc (90° - \theta) - \cot^2 (90° - \theta) \cos \theta = 0$

12 Find the measure of θ in each of the following equations if $0° \le \theta < 360°$.

a) $\sin \theta = -1$ b) $\cos \theta = \sqrt{3}/2$
c) $\tan \theta = \sqrt{3}$ d) $\cos \theta = -\sqrt{2}/2$
e) $\csc \theta = -2$ f) $\cot \theta = \sqrt{3}/3$
g) $\sin \theta = \cos 2\theta$ h) $\tan (\theta - 30°) = \cot 2\theta$
i) $\sin (\theta + 16°) = \cos 2\theta$

13 Solve the following trigonometric equations for $0 \le t < 2\pi$.

a) $\sin t = \sqrt{2}/2$ b) $4 \sin^2 t - 3 = 0$
c) $2 \cos^2 t - \cos t - 1 = 0$ d) $2 \sin^2 t + \sqrt{2} \sin t = 0$

e) $\tan^2 t + (1 - \sqrt{3}) \tan t - \sqrt{3} = 0$
f) $\sin^2 t - 2 \sin t + 1 = 0$
g) $3 \tan^2 t - \sqrt{3} \tan t = 0$
h) $\cos t \cot^2 t - 3 \cos t = 0$

14 Rewrite each of the following expressions in the form of $y = A \cos(\pi t - \alpha)$ for some appropriate real numbers A and α.

a) $y = -4 \cos \pi t + 3 \sin \pi t$ b) $y = 5 \cos \pi t + 12 \sin \pi t$
c) $y = 6 \cos \pi t + 8 \sin \pi t$ d) $y = -3 \cos \pi t - 4 \sin \pi t$

15 Use appropriate trigonometric identities to determine each of the following values.

a) $\sin 15°$ b) $\cos 15°$
c) $\tan 75°$ d) $\sec 75°$

16 Suppose that $\sin t = \frac{4}{5}$ and $\cos s = \frac{4}{5}$, where $0 < s < t < \pi/2$. Evaluate each of the following trigonometric functions.

a) $\sin(t + s)$ b) $\cos(t + s)$
c) $\sin(t - s)$ d) $\cos(t - s)$
e) $\tan(t + s)$ f) $\cot(t - s)$
g) $\sec(t + s)$ h) $\csc(t - s)$

17 Prove or disprove whether the first expression is equal to the second expression in each of the following problems.

a) $(1 + \tan t)^2/(1 + \tan^2 t)$ and $\sin 2t + 1$
b) $\cot 4t + \tan 2t$ and $\csc 4t$
c) $\tan 4t - \tan 2t$ and $\tan 2t \sec 4t$
d) $\tan 2t - \tan t$ and $\tan t \sec 2t$
e) $\tan(t/2 + \pi/4)$ and $(1 + \sin t)/(\cos t)$
f) $(\sin 5t)/(\sin t) - (\cos 5t)/(\cos t)$ and $\cos 2t$
g) $\sin t + \cos t \tan s$ and $\sec s \sin(t + s)$
h) $(4 \tan t - 4 \tan^3 t)/(1 - 6 \tan^2 t + \tan^4 t)$ and $\tan 4t$
i) $\tan(t + \pi/3) + \tan(t - \pi/3)$ and $(\tan t)/[1 - (3 \tan^2 t)]$
j) $\cos 2t \sin 3t + \cos 3t \sin 2t$ and $\sin 5t$
k) $\sin 5t \cos t - \cos 5t \sin t$ and $2 \sin 2t (\cos^2 t - \sin^2 t)$
l) $\sin 4t + \sin 2t$ and $\sin 2t(2 \cos 2t + 1)$

18 Solve for the missing parts of $\triangle ABC$ if $\gamma = 90°$.

a) $a = 5$ and $b = 12$ b) $c = 15$ and $\alpha = 37°$
c) $b = 25$ and $\beta = 65°$ d) $a = 5$ and $c = 14$
e) $a = 17$ and $\beta = 51°$ f) $\sin \alpha = \frac{4}{5}$ and $c = 25$
g) $\tan \alpha = \frac{3}{4}$ and $a = 12$ h) $a = 6$ and $b = 8$

19 Find the remaining parts of each of the following triangles.

a) $a = 5$, $b = 7$, and $\gamma = 30°$
b) $\alpha = 120°$, $c = 8$, and $b = 3$

c) $c = 10$, $\alpha = 45°$, and $\beta = 75°$
d) $a = 162$, $b = 215$, and $\beta = 110°$
e) $b = 4$, $c = 6$, and $\beta = 30°$
f) $a = 13.6$, $b = 7.82$, and $\alpha = 60°$
g) $a = 4.8$, $c = 4.3$, and $\alpha = 115°$
h) $b = 66.2$, $c = 42.3$, and $\alpha = 30°$
i) $a = 10$, $\beta = 42°$, and $\gamma = 51°$
j) $a = 4$, $c = 10$, and $\beta = 150°$

20   Two men 600 feet apart observe a balloon in the sky between them. The respective angles of elevation of the balloon are 75° and 48°. Find the height of the balloon above the ground.

CHAPTER 7

Vectors in the Plane

7 VECTORS IN THE PLANE

1 Introduction

Vectors can be used to explain and integrate many of the basic notions of algebra, geometry, and trigonometry. Here, we shall investigate vectors in the plane from both a geometric and algebraic viewpoint. Also, we shall survey the applications of vectors to solve problems in geometry. By defining rotations as functions of vectors, we shall see how it is possible to use vectors to prove the trigonometric identities for $\cos (s + t)$ and $\sin (s + t)$.

2 Geometric Approach to Vectors in the Plane

Suppose we are given the task of categorizing air trips within the United States according to the following scheme. Each category is determined by both the distance traveled and the direction in which the distance is traveled, and two trips are considered equivalent if they are in the same category. One such category would be a 100 mile trip north; another category would be a 435 mile trip southwest; a third category would be a 535 mile trip northeast (Figure 1).

Figure 1

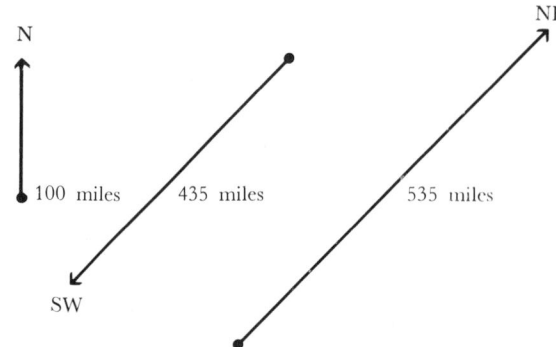

Notice that a 100 mile trip north from Detroit, *according to this scheme,* is considered to be equivalent to a 100 mile trip north from Cleveland (Figure 2). Here, the equivalence of trips does not depend on where the

Figure 2

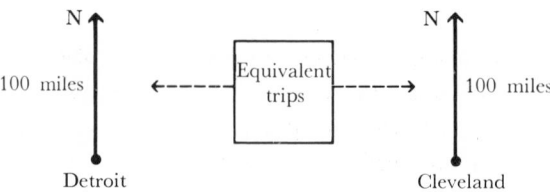

trip originates but only on the direction and length of the trip. For example, a 100 mile trip south is not considered to be equivalent to a 100 mile trip north because the directions are different (Figure 3).

Figure 3

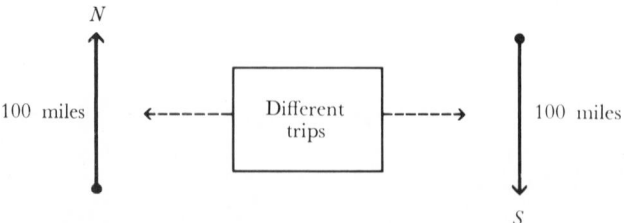

A 100 mile trip north is not considered to be equivalent to a 200 mile trip north according to this scheme because the lengths are different (Figure 4). The trips must agree both in length and direction in order to be considered equivalent.

Figure 4

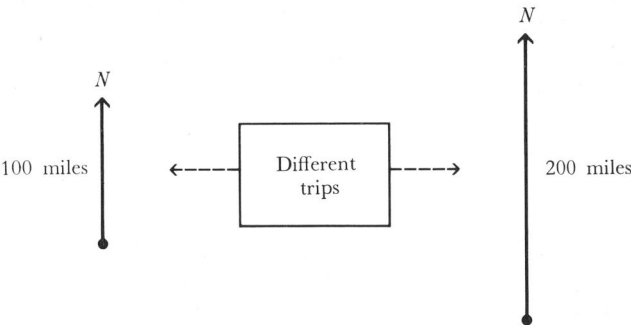

This illustration is a specific example of a situation that can be modeled by *vectors* in the plane.

A *vector* in the plane is a line segment with a direction usually denoted by an arrowhead at the end of the segment (Figure 5). The length of the line segment is called the *length or magnitude* of the vector, and the direction of the line segment is called the *direction* of the vector. The end point of the vector containing the arrowhead is called the *terminal point* of the vector, and the other end point is called the *initial point* of the vector (Figure 5). A *zero vector*, denoted by $\overline{\mathbf{0}}$, is a vector whose initial and terminal

Figure 5

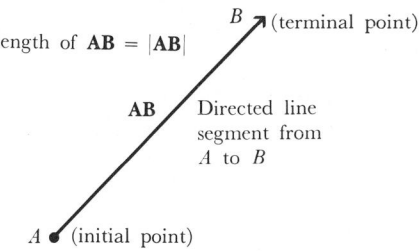

points coincide. In the example above, a 100 mile trip north is represented by a vector of length 100 pointing north (Figure 6). If a vector is determined by a directed line segment with the initial point A and the terminal point B, then it is denoted by $\mathbf{AB}$; its magnitude is denoted by $|\mathbf{AB}|$ (Figure 5). Notice that $|\overline{\mathbf{0}}| = 0$. (Why?)

Figure 6

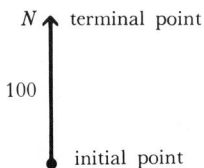

The notation **AB** suggests that the vector is determined by line segment *AB* from point *A* to point *B* (Figure 7*a*). **BA**, on the other hand,
represents a vector with the same end points as vector **AB** but is in the
opposite direction (Figure 7*b*).

Figure 7

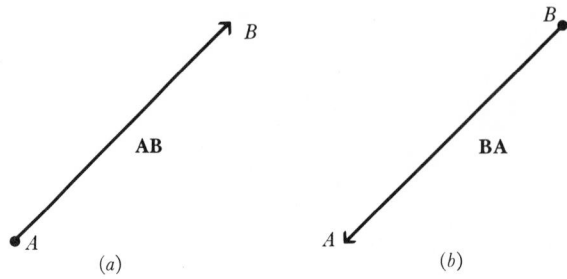

(*a*)   (*b*)

As in the example, two vectors are considered to be equal if the vectors
agree both in magnitude and in direction; for instance, **AB** and **BA**
(Figure 7) are not equal (even though their lengths are the same) because they are opposite in direction; that is,

$$|\mathbf{AB}| = |\mathbf{BA}| \quad \text{but} \quad \mathbf{AB} \neq \mathbf{BA}$$

Finally, lowercase boldface letters with a bar on top are also used to
denote vectors. Hence, we speak of "vector u" and write it as $\bar{\mathbf{u}}$.

2.1   Addition of Vectors

Suppose we are given two vectors $\bar{\mathbf{u}}$ and $\bar{\mathbf{v}}$ (Figure 8). First, we "shift" or
"translate" $\bar{\mathbf{v}}$, so that the initial point of $\bar{\mathbf{v}}$ coincides with the terminal

Figure 8

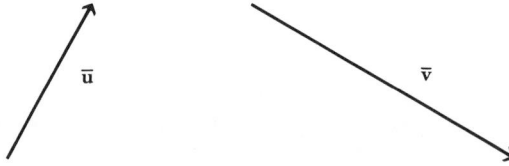

point of $\bar{\mathbf{u}}$ (Figure 9). The vector having the same initial point as $\bar{\mathbf{u}}$ and
the same terminal point as $\bar{\mathbf{v}}$ is defined to be the sum $\bar{\mathbf{u}} + \bar{\mathbf{v}}$ (Figure 9).

Figure 9

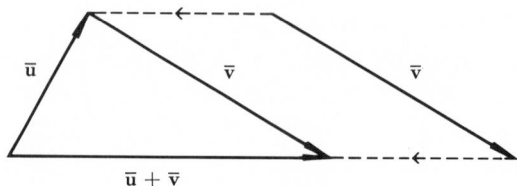

$\bar{\mathbf{u}} + \bar{\mathbf{v}}$

EXAMPLE

Use the geometry of vector addition to show that vector addition is commutative; that is, show that $\bar{u} + \bar{v} = \bar{v} + \bar{u}$, where $\bar{u}$ and $\bar{v}$ are given in Figure 10.

Figure 10

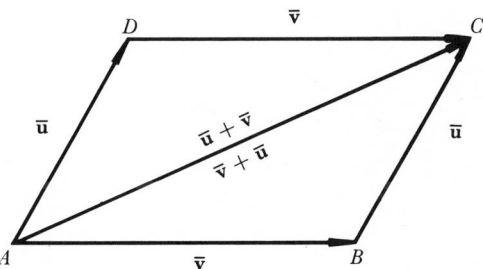

SOLUTION. (Figure 10) Here, $\bar{u}$ and $\bar{v}$ determine parallelogram $ABCD$, with $\bar{u} + \bar{v}$ and $\bar{v} + \bar{u}$ coinciding with the same diagonal vector **AC**. Hence, $\bar{u} + \bar{v} = \bar{v} + \bar{u}$.

2.2 Scalar Multiplication and Subtraction of Vectors

Suppose we are given a real number a and a vector $\bar{u}$. The real number a in this context is called a *scalar*; $a\bar{u}$ is defined to be a vector with magnitude $|a|\,|\bar{u}|$, with the same direction as $\bar{u}$ if $a > 0$ and with opposite direction as $\bar{u}$ if $a < 0$ (Figure 11). If $a = 0$, $a\bar{u} = \bar{0}$, the zero vector. In other words, $a\bar{u}$ is a vector collinear with vector $\bar{u}$ and $|a\bar{u}| = |a|\,|\bar{u}|$. If $0 < |a| < 1$ and $\bar{u} \neq \bar{0}$, $|a\bar{u}| < |\bar{u}|$; if $|a| > 1$, $|a\bar{u}| > |\bar{u}|$; if $|a| = 1$, $|a\bar{u}| = |\bar{u}|$.

Figure 11

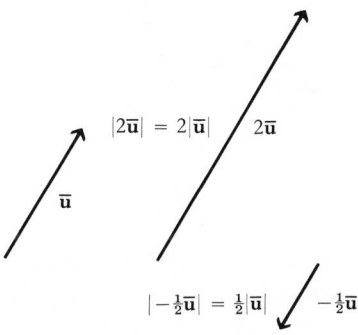

For example, **AB** $= -$**BA**. (Why?) $5\bar{u}$ is a vector in the direction of $\bar{u}$, with magnitude five times the magnitude of $\bar{u}$; $-\frac{1}{3}\bar{u}$ is opposite in direction to $\bar{u}$ and has a length $\frac{1}{3}$ that of $\bar{u}$.

Now we can use vector addition and scalar multiplication to define *vector subtraction* as $\bar{\mathbf{u}} - \bar{\mathbf{v}} = \bar{\mathbf{u}} + (-\bar{\mathbf{v}})$ (Figure 12).

Figure 12

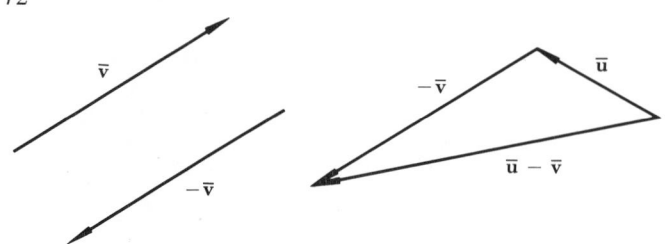

EXAMPLES

1   Compare $\bar{\mathbf{u}} + \bar{\mathbf{v}}$ to $\bar{\mathbf{u}} - \bar{\mathbf{v}}$ geometrically.

SOLUTION. $\bar{\mathbf{u}} + \bar{\mathbf{v}}$ and $\bar{\mathbf{u}} - \bar{\mathbf{v}}$ are opposite diagonals of the parallelogram determined by $\bar{\mathbf{u}}$ and $\bar{\mathbf{v}}$ (Figure 13).

Figure 13

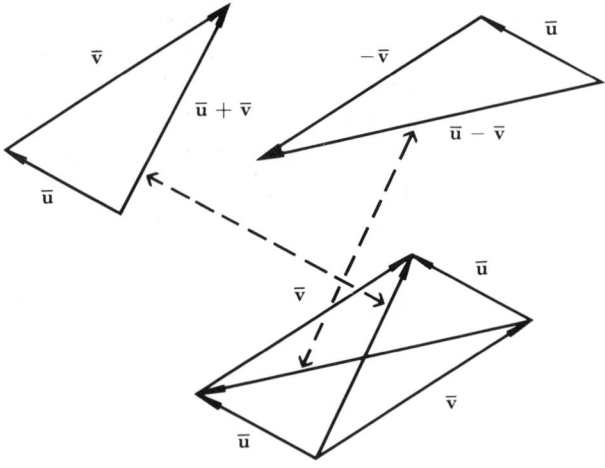

2   Show geometrically that $2(\bar{\mathbf{u}} + \bar{\mathbf{v}}) = 2\bar{\mathbf{u}} + 2\bar{\mathbf{v}}$.

SOLUTION.   First sketch $\bar{\mathbf{u}} + \bar{\mathbf{v}}$ (Figure 14a). Then construct triangle $\triangle EKL$ similar to the original triangle $\triangle CDF$ such that $\mathbf{EK} = 2\bar{\mathbf{u}}$ and $\mathbf{KL} = 2\bar{\mathbf{v}}$, so that $\mathbf{EL} = 2\bar{\mathbf{u}} + 2\bar{\mathbf{v}}$ by vector addition, and $\mathbf{EL} = 2\mathbf{CF} = 2(\bar{\mathbf{u}} + \bar{\mathbf{v}})$ by the similarity of the triangles (Figure 14b).

Figure 14

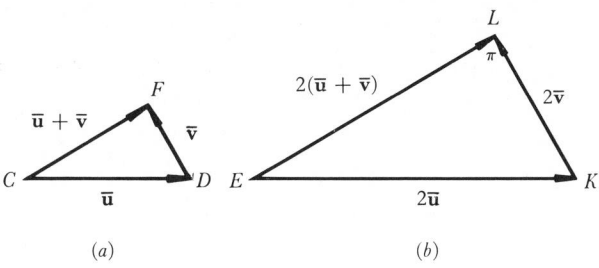

(a)   (b)

3 Let *ABCD* be a parallelogram. Use vectors to prove that the diagonals *AC* and *BD* bisect each other (Figure 15).

Figure 15

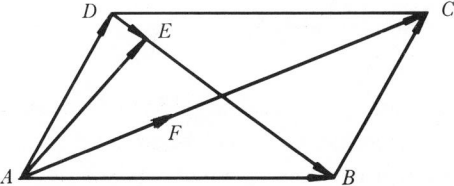

SOLUTION. Assume that E is the midpoint of BD and F is the midpoint of AC. We wish to show that E and F coincide, that is, we wish to show that $\mathbf{AF} = \mathbf{AE}$.

$$\mathbf{AF} = \tfrac{1}{2}(\mathbf{AC}) \quad \text{and} \quad \mathbf{AC} = \mathbf{AB} + \mathbf{BC}$$

so that

$$\mathbf{AF} = \tfrac{1}{2}(\mathbf{AB} + \mathbf{BC})$$

Also,

$$\mathbf{AE} = \mathbf{AD} + \mathbf{DE}$$

but,

$$\mathbf{DE} = \tfrac{1}{2}(\mathbf{DB}) \quad \text{where} \quad \mathbf{DB} = \mathbf{AB} - \mathbf{AD}$$

Hence,

$$\mathbf{DE} = \tfrac{1}{2}(\mathbf{AB} - \mathbf{AD})$$

so that

$$\mathbf{AE} = \mathbf{AD} + \tfrac{1}{2}(\mathbf{AB} - \mathbf{AD}) = \tfrac{1}{2}(\mathbf{AB} + \mathbf{AD}) = \tfrac{1}{2}(\mathbf{AB} + \mathbf{BC}) = \mathbf{AF}.$$

Hence, F and E coincide.

3 Analytic Representation of Vectors in the Plane

Suppose that vector $\bar{\mathbf{u}}$ is positioned on a plane with a Cartesian coordinate system so that the initial point of $\bar{\mathbf{u}}$ is the origin and the terminal point is point (a,b) (Figure 1). $\bar{\mathbf{u}}$ is called a *radius vector* or *position vector*, and we identify such a vector $\bar{\mathbf{u}}$ as $\bar{\mathbf{u}} = \langle a,b \rangle$. a and b are called the *x component and y component* of $\bar{\mathbf{u}}$, respectively.

Figure 1

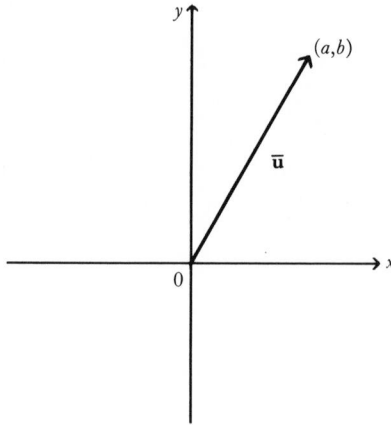

For example, $\bar{\mathbf{0}} = \langle 0,0 \rangle$; $\bar{\mathbf{u}} = \langle -4,5 \rangle$ has x component -4 and y component 5 (Figure 2); all vectors with x component 0 have terminal points on the y axis. (Why?) For example, $\bar{\mathbf{v}} = \langle 0,-3 \rangle$.

We will see that the components of position vectors completely characterize these types of vectors in the sense that the determination of the magnitude of a position vector, the addition of position vectors, the scalar

Figure 2

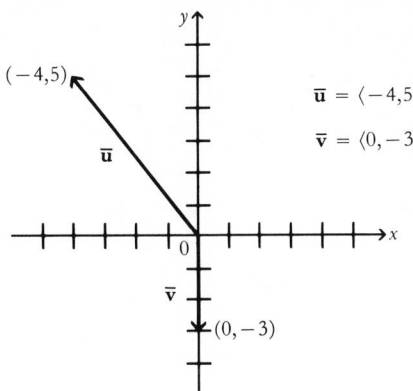

$\bar{\mathbf{u}} = \langle -4,5 \rangle$

$\bar{\mathbf{v}} = \langle 0,-3 \rangle$

multiplication of position vectors, and the subtraction of position vectors can be performed by using the components.

3.1   Vector Equality in Terms of Components

We have already seen that $\bar{\mathbf{u}} = \bar{\mathbf{v}}$ whenever $|\bar{\mathbf{u}}| = |\bar{\mathbf{v}}|$ and $\bar{\mathbf{u}}$ and $\bar{\mathbf{v}}$ have the same direction. If $\bar{\mathbf{u}}_1$ and $\bar{\mathbf{u}}_2$ are position vectors, they have the same initial point $(0,0)$, and the question of equality is reduced to a comparison of the components; that is, if $\bar{\mathbf{u}}_1 = \langle a_1,b_1 \rangle$ and $\bar{\mathbf{u}}_2 = \langle a_2,b_2 \rangle$, then $\bar{\mathbf{u}}_1 = \bar{\mathbf{u}}_2$ whenever $a_1 = a_2$ and $b_1 = b_2$.

3.2   Magnitude in Terms of Components

The magnitude or length of a position vector $\bar{\mathbf{u}}$, $|\bar{\mathbf{u}}|$, can be determined by using the components and the distance formula, for if $\bar{\mathbf{u}} = \langle a,b \rangle$, then

$$|\bar{\mathbf{u}}| = \sqrt{a^2 + b^2} \qquad \text{(Figure 3)}$$

Figure 3

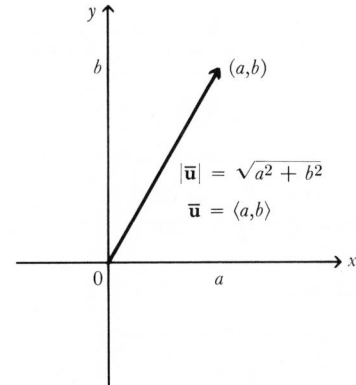

$|\bar{\mathbf{u}}| = \sqrt{a^2 + b^2}$

$\bar{\mathbf{u}} = \langle a,b \rangle$

3.3   Vector Algebra in Terms of Components

Addition and scalar multiplication of position vectors can be accomplished by using the components. Assume that $\bar{\mathbf{u}}_1 = \langle a_1, b_1 \rangle$, $\bar{\mathbf{u}}_2 = \langle a_2, b_2 \rangle$, and c is a scalar; then $\bar{\mathbf{u}}_1 + \bar{\mathbf{u}}_2$ and $c\bar{\mathbf{u}}_1$ can be represented geometrically as in Figures 4a and b. Hence,

$$\bar{\mathbf{u}}_1 + \bar{\mathbf{u}}_2 = \langle a_1, b_1 \rangle + \langle a_2, b_2 \rangle = \langle a_1 + a_2, b_1 + b_2 \rangle$$

and

$$c\bar{\mathbf{u}}_1 = c\langle a_1, b_1 \rangle = \langle ca_1, cb_1 \rangle$$

Figure 4

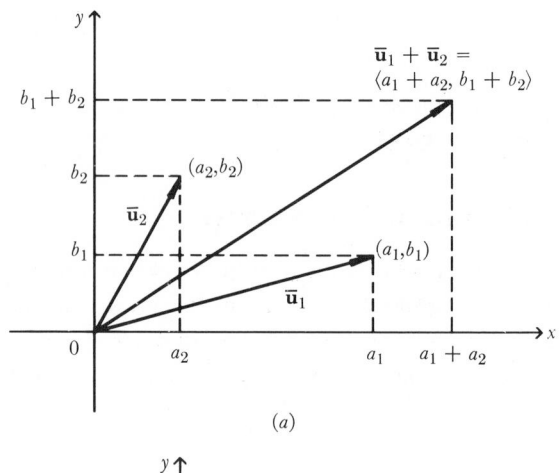

(a)

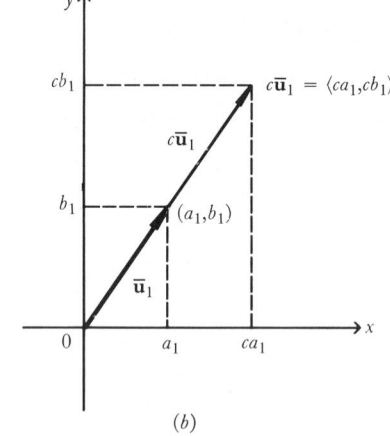

(b)

As before, $\bar{\mathbf{u}} - \bar{\mathbf{v}} = \bar{\mathbf{u}} + (-\bar{\mathbf{v}})$, so that if $\bar{\mathbf{u}} = \langle a_1, b_1 \rangle$ and $\bar{\mathbf{v}} = \langle a_2, b_2 \rangle$,

$$\begin{aligned}
\bar{\mathbf{u}} - \bar{\mathbf{v}} &= \bar{\mathbf{u}} + (-\bar{\mathbf{v}}) \\
&= \langle a_1, b_1 \rangle + (-\langle a_2, b_2 \rangle) \\
&= \langle a_1, b_1 \rangle + \langle -a_2, -b_2 \rangle \\
&= \langle a_1 - a_2, b_1 - b_2 \rangle \quad \text{(Figure 5)}
\end{aligned}$$

Figure 5

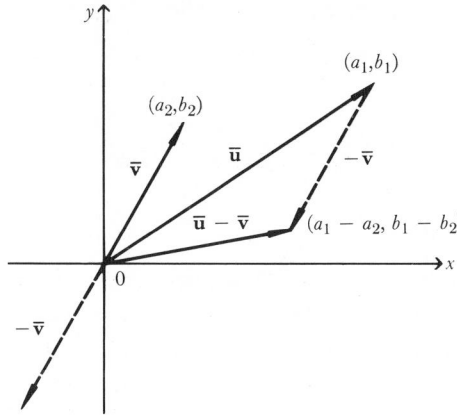

EXAMPLES

1   Characterize all position vectors $\bar{\mathbf{u}}$ such that $|\bar{\mathbf{u}}| = 1$.

SOLUTION.   Assume that $\bar{\mathbf{u}} = \langle x, y \rangle$, so that $|\bar{\mathbf{u}}| = \sqrt{x^2 + y^2} = 1$; that is, $x^2 + y^2 = 1$. Hence, all such vectors have their terminal points on the unit circle (Figure 6).

Figure 6

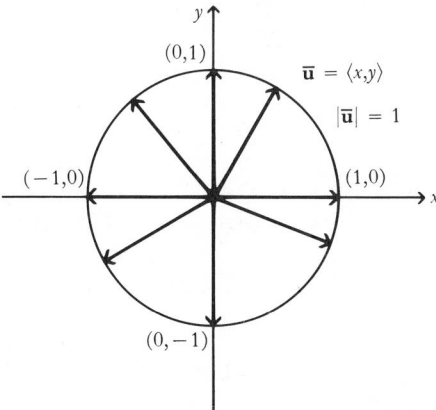

2   Let $\bar{\mathbf{u}}_1 = \langle 3, 4 \rangle$ and $\bar{\mathbf{u}}_2 = \langle 5, 6 \rangle$. Find

    a) $\bar{\mathbf{u}}_1 + \bar{\mathbf{u}}_2$ b) $\bar{\mathbf{u}}_1 - \bar{\mathbf{u}}_2$

    c) $5\bar{\mathbf{u}}_1$ d) $|\bar{\mathbf{u}}_2|$

    e) $4\bar{\mathbf{u}}_1 - 3\bar{\mathbf{u}}_2$ f) $\left|(1/|\bar{\mathbf{u}}_1|)\bar{\mathbf{u}}_1\right|$

SOLUTION

    a) $\bar{\mathbf{u}}_1 + \bar{\mathbf{u}}_2 = \langle 3, 4 \rangle + \langle 5, 6 \rangle = \langle 8, 10 \rangle$

    b) $\bar{\mathbf{u}}_1 - \bar{\mathbf{u}}_2 = \langle 3, 4 \rangle - \langle 5, 6 \rangle = \langle -2, -2 \rangle$

c) $5\bar{u}_1 = 5\langle 3,4 \rangle = \langle 15,20 \rangle$

d) $|\bar{u}_2| = \sqrt{25 + 36} = \sqrt{61}$

e) $4\bar{u}_1 - 3\bar{u}_2 = 4\langle 3,4 \rangle - 3\langle 5,6 \rangle$
$$= \langle 12,16 \rangle + \langle -15,-18 \rangle$$
$$= \langle -3,-2 \rangle$$

f) $\left| (1/|\bar{u}_1|)\bar{u}_1 \right| = \left| (1/|\langle 3,4 \rangle|)\langle 3,4 \rangle \right| = |\tfrac{1}{5}\langle 3,4 \rangle| = |\langle \tfrac{3}{5},\tfrac{4}{5} \rangle| = 1$

3.4   Basis Vectors

A vector of length 1 is called a *unit vector;* hence, if $\bar{u} = \langle a,b \rangle$ is a unit vector, $|\bar{u}| = \sqrt{a^2 + b^2} = 1$ (see Example 1 above). For example, $\bar{u}_1 = \langle 1,0 \rangle$, $\bar{u}_2 = \langle 0,1 \rangle$, $\bar{u}_3 = \langle -\tfrac{1}{2}, \sqrt{3}/2 \rangle$, $\bar{u}_4 = \langle -1/\sqrt{2}, -1/\sqrt{2} \rangle$, and $\bar{u}_5 = \langle \tfrac{3}{5}, -\tfrac{4}{5} \rangle$ are unit vectors (Figure 7).

Figure 7

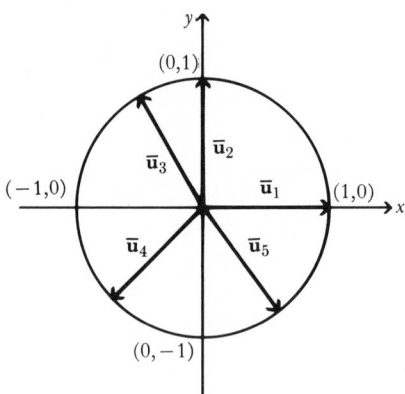

If $\bar{u}$ is not a unit vector and if $\bar{u} \neq \bar{0}$, we can form a unit vector in the same direction as $\bar{u}$ by multiplying $\bar{u}$ by $1/|\bar{u}|$ (see Example 2f above).

THEOREM 1

If $\bar{u} \neq \bar{0}$, $(1/|\bar{u}|)\bar{u}$ is a unit vector in the same direction as $\bar{u}$.

PROOF.   Suppose that $\bar{u} = \langle a,b \rangle$. Then $|\bar{u}| = \sqrt{a^2 + b^2}$, so that

$$\frac{1}{|\bar{u}|}\bar{u} = \frac{1}{\sqrt{a^2 + b^2}} \langle a,b \rangle = \left\langle \frac{a}{\sqrt{a^2 + b^2}}, \frac{b}{\sqrt{a^2 + b^2}} \right\rangle$$

Hence,

$$\left| \frac{1}{|\bar{u}|}\bar{u} \right| = \sqrt{\frac{a^2}{a^2 + b^2} + \frac{b^2}{a^2 + b^2}} = \sqrt{\frac{a^2 + b^2}{a^2 + b^2}} = 1$$

Since $1/|\bar{u}| > 0$, $(1/|\bar{u}|)\bar{u}$ has the same direction as $\bar{u}$. $(1/|\bar{u}|)\bar{u}$ is often called the *normalized* $\bar{u}$ vector.

Next, we define the vectors $\mathbf{i} = \langle 1,0 \rangle$ and $\mathbf{j} = \langle 0,1 \rangle$. $\mathbf{i}$ and $\mathbf{j}$ are unit vectors (Why?) and are in the direction of the positive x axis and y axis, respectively (Figure 8). $\mathbf{i}$ and $\mathbf{j}$ form a *basis* for the system of vectors in the plane in the sense that each vector in the plane can be written in terms of $\mathbf{i}$ and $\mathbf{j}$ as follows.

If $\bar{\mathbf{u}}$ is a radius vector, then $\bar{\mathbf{u}}$ is of the form $\bar{\mathbf{u}} = \langle x, y \rangle$, so that

$$\begin{aligned}
\bar{\mathbf{u}} = \langle x, y \rangle &= \langle x,0 \rangle + \langle 0,y \rangle \qquad \text{(Figure 8)} \\
&= x \langle 1,0 \rangle + y \langle 0,1 \rangle \\
&= x\mathbf{i} + y\mathbf{j}
\end{aligned}$$

Figure 8

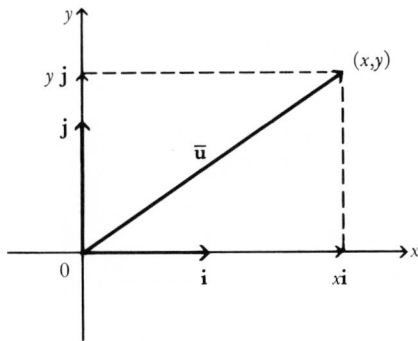

$x\mathbf{i}$ and $y\mathbf{j}$ are called the vector *projections* of $\bar{\mathbf{u}}$ along the x axis and the y axis, respectively.

On the other hand, if $\bar{\mathbf{u}}$ is not a radius vector, then $\bar{\mathbf{u}}$ is of the form $\bar{\mathbf{u}} = \mathbf{P}_1\mathbf{P}_2$, where $P_1 = (x_1, y_1)$ and $P_2 = (x_2, y_2)$ are any two points

Figure 9

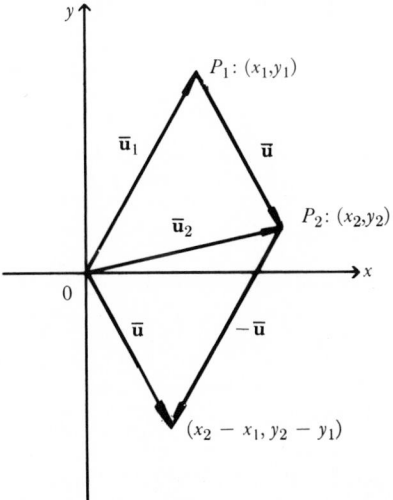

in the plane. But $\bar{u} = \bar{u}_2 - \bar{u}_1$, where $\bar{u}_1$ and $\bar{u}_2$ are the radius vectors determined by P_1 and P_2 (Figure 9). Since we have $\bar{u}_1 = \langle x_1, y_1 \rangle$ and $\bar{u}_2 = \langle x_2, y_2 \rangle$,

$$\bar{u} = \langle x_2, y_2 \rangle - \langle x_1, y_1 \rangle = \langle x_2 - x_1,\ y_2 - y_1 \rangle$$

so that

$$\bar{u} = (x_2 - x_1)\mathbf{i} + (y_2 - y_1)\mathbf{j}$$

where (x_1, y_1) is the initial point of $\bar{u}$ and (x_2, y_2) is the terminal point of $\bar{u}$. Notice that $|\bar{u}| = \sqrt{(x_1 - x_2)^2 + (y_1 - y_2)^2}$.

EXAMPLES

1   Let $\bar{u}$ be the vector with initial point $(-1,3)$ and terminal point $(2,7)$.

a)   Write $\bar{u}$ in the form $u_x\mathbf{i} + u_y\mathbf{j}$.
b)   Find $|\bar{u}|$.
c)   Find $\bar{u}_N$, the normalized $\bar{u}$.

Figure 10

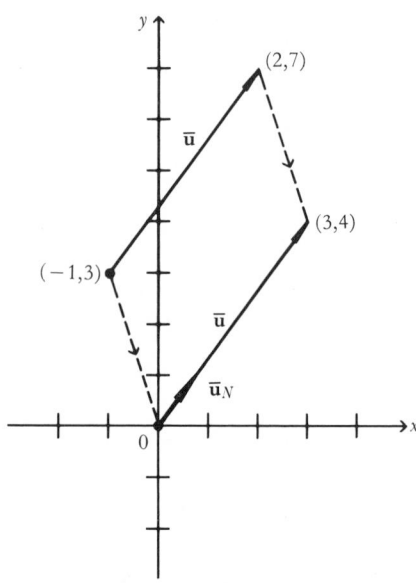

SOLUTION.   (See Figure 10.)

a) $\bar{u} = (x_2 - x_1)\mathbf{i} + (y_2 - y_1)\mathbf{j} = 3\mathbf{i} + 4\mathbf{j}$
b) $|\bar{u}| = \sqrt{u_x^2 + u_y^2} = \sqrt{9 + 16} = \sqrt{25} = 5$
c) $\bar{u}_N = (1/|\bar{u}|)\bar{u} = \frac{3}{5}\mathbf{i} + \frac{4}{5}\mathbf{j}$.

2   Find a point $\frac{1}{3}$ of the way from $(1,4)$ to $(6,6)$.

SOLUTION.   (See Figure 11.) Let $P = (x, y)$ be $\frac{1}{3}$ of the way from A to B; then $\mathbf{AP} = (x - 1)\mathbf{i} + (y - 4)\mathbf{j} = \frac{1}{3}(5\mathbf{i} + 2\mathbf{j})$, from which it follows that $x - 1 = \frac{5}{3}$ and $y - 4 = \frac{2}{3}$, or $x = \frac{8}{3}$ and $y = \frac{14}{3}$. There-fore, the coordinates of P are given by $\left(\frac{8}{3}, \frac{14}{3}\right)$.

Figure 11

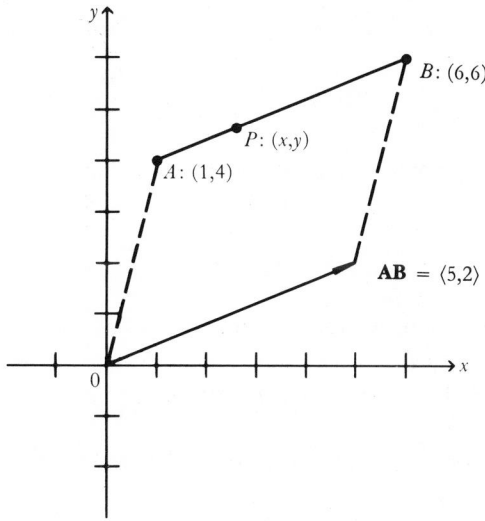

ALTERNATE SOLUTION.   (See Figure 12.) Let $\bar{\mathbf{v}} = \langle x, y \rangle$, where $P = (x, y)$ is on the vector from A to B. $\bar{\mathbf{v}} = \mathbf{0A} + \mathbf{AP}$, but $\mathbf{AP} = \frac{1}{3}\mathbf{AB}$. Therefore,

$$\bar{\mathbf{v}} = \langle 1, 4 \rangle + \frac{1}{3}\langle 5, 2 \rangle$$
$$= \langle 1, 4 \rangle + \langle \frac{5}{3}, \frac{2}{3} \rangle$$
$$= \langle \frac{8}{3}, \frac{14}{3} \rangle$$

so that $x = \frac{8}{3}$ and $y = \frac{14}{3}$.

Figure 12

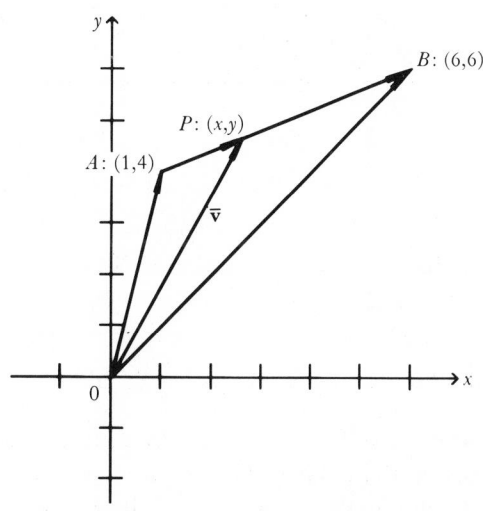

PROBLEM SET 1

1 Let $\bar{u}$ be a vector in the positive direction of the x axis and $\bar{v}$ be a vector that makes an angle of 30° with the vector $\bar{u}$ by a counterclockwise rotation from the positive x axis; assume that $|\bar{u}| = 3$ and $|\bar{v}| = 5$. Draw a diagram of each of the following vectors.

a) $2\bar{u} + \bar{v}$ b) $2\bar{u} + \frac{1}{2}\bar{v}$

c) $\frac{1}{2}\bar{u} - 2\bar{v}$ d) $-\bar{u} - 3\bar{v}$

2 Use the geometry of vector addition to show that vector addition is associative; that is, show $(\bar{u} + \bar{v}) + \bar{w} = \bar{u} + (\bar{v} + \bar{w})$.

3 If $|\bar{u}| = |\bar{v}|$, does it follow that $\bar{u} = \bar{v}$? Explain.

4 Use vectors to prove that the line segment joining the midpoints of two sides of a triangle in the plane is parallel to the third side and has a length equal to one-half the length of the third side.

5 Let $PQRS$ be a parallelogram as shown in Figure 13.

  a) Find $\bar{w}$ in terms of

      i $\bar{u}_1$ and $\bar{v}_1$

      ii $\bar{u}_2$ and $\bar{v}_1$

      iii $\bar{u}_2$ and $\bar{v}_2$

  b) Sketch $\bar{v}_2 + \bar{w} + \bar{u}_2$.

  c) Sketch $\bar{u}_1 + \bar{v}_1 + \bar{u}_2 + \bar{v}_2$.

Figure 13

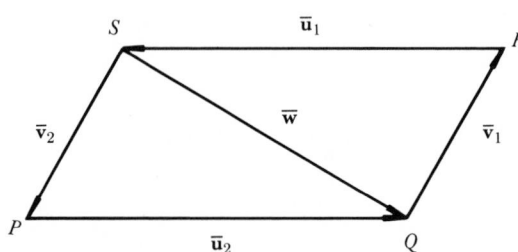

6 Use $\bar{u}_1 = \langle 3,4 \rangle$, $\bar{u}_2 = \langle -2,4 \rangle$, and $\bar{u}_3 = \langle 7,8 \rangle$ to determine each of the following vectors.

a) $2\bar{u}_1 + 3\bar{u}_2$ b) $3\bar{u}_2 - \bar{u}_1$

c) $\bar{u}_1 + (\bar{u}_2 + \bar{u}_3)$ d) $(\bar{u}_1 + \bar{u}_2) + \bar{u}_1$

e) $2\bar{u}_1 - 3\bar{u}_2$ f) $\bar{u}_2 - \bar{u}_1 - \bar{u}_3$

Represent all of the above vectors graphically.

7 Write $\bar{u}$ in the form $\bar{u} = u_x \mathbf{i} + u_y \mathbf{j}$, find $|\bar{u}|$, and normalize $\bar{u}$ if $\bar{u}$ is a vector whose initial point is the first point and whose terminal point is the second point given in each of the following parts.

a) (8,6), (3,4)   b) (7,6), (2,3)
c) (−2,6), (3,−5)   d) (−3,2), (1,−3)
e) (3,7), (−3,1)   f) (1,−3), (5,−1)

8   Let $P_1 = (−6,−10)$ and $P_2 = (8,8)$ be two points in the plane.

a) Use vectors to find the point that is $\frac{2}{3}$ of the way from P_1 to P_2.
b) Use vectors to find the point that is 4 units from P_1 along the directed line from P_1 to P_2.

9   a) Sketch V where $V = \{\bar{u}|\bar{u} = t\langle−1,2\rangle, t \in R\}$.
b) Sketch V where $V = \{\bar{u}|\bar{u} = (1 − t)\langle 0,2\rangle + t\langle 3,4\rangle, t \in [0,1]\}$.
c) Sketch the graph determined by the terminal points of vectors $\bar{u}$ where $\bar{u} = (5\mathbf{i} − \mathbf{j})t + (4\mathbf{i} + 2\mathbf{j})$, where t is any real number.

4 Inner Product

In this section, we will examine a multiplicative operation between two vectors that results in a scalar. This multiplication, called *inner product* or *dot product*, will enable us to study the notion of orthogonality (perpendicularity) from an algebraic viewpoint. If $\bar{u}$ and $\bar{v}$ are two vectors in the plane, we define the *inner product* or *dot product* of $\bar{u}$ and $\bar{v}$, denoted by $\bar{u} \cdot \bar{v}$, as $\bar{u} \cdot \bar{v} = |\bar{u}|\,|\bar{v}| \cos \theta$, $0 \le \theta \le \pi$, where θ is the angle between $\bar{u}$ and $\bar{v}$. The product $|\bar{u}| \cos \theta$ is called the *scalar projection of $\bar{u}$ on $\bar{v}$*. A geometric interpretation is given in Figure 1. Notice that if $\bar{v} \ne \bar{0}$, it follows from

$$\bar{u} \cdot \bar{v} = |\bar{u}|\,|\bar{v}| \cos \theta$$

Figure 1

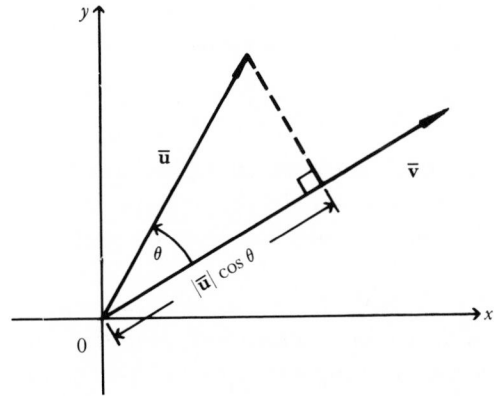

that

$$|\bar{\mathbf{u}}| \cos \theta = \frac{\bar{\mathbf{u}} \cdot \bar{\mathbf{v}}}{|\bar{\mathbf{v}}|}$$

EXAMPLES

1   Find $\bar{\mathbf{u}} \cdot \bar{\mathbf{v}}$ if $\bar{\mathbf{u}}$ and $\bar{\mathbf{v}}$ are unit vectors and $\theta = 30°$ is the angle between $\bar{\mathbf{u}}$ and $\bar{\mathbf{v}}$. What is the scalar projection of $\bar{\mathbf{u}}$ on $\bar{\mathbf{v}}$?

SOLUTION. $\bar{\mathbf{u}} \cdot \bar{\mathbf{v}} = |\bar{\mathbf{u}}| \, |\bar{\mathbf{v}}| \cos 30° = \cos 30° = \sqrt{3}/2$ so that the scalar projection of $\bar{\mathbf{u}}$ on $\bar{\mathbf{v}}$ is

$$\frac{\bar{\mathbf{u}} \cdot \bar{\mathbf{v}}}{|\bar{\mathbf{v}}|} = \frac{\sqrt{3}/2}{1} = \frac{\sqrt{3}}{2}$$

2   What can be concluded about the size of the angle between $\bar{\mathbf{u}}$ and $\bar{\mathbf{v}}$ if $\bar{\mathbf{u}} \cdot \bar{\mathbf{v}} < 0$?

SOLUTION.   Since $\bar{\mathbf{u}} \cdot \bar{\mathbf{v}} = |\bar{\mathbf{u}}| \, |\bar{\mathbf{v}}| \cos \theta$, $|\bar{\mathbf{u}}| > 0$, and $|\bar{\mathbf{v}}| > 0$, we have $\cos \theta < 0$, so that $90° < \theta \leq 180°$.

3   Suppose that $\bar{\mathbf{u}} \neq 0$, $\bar{\mathbf{v}} \neq 0$, and $\bar{\mathbf{u}}$ is parallel to $\bar{\mathbf{v}}$. Find $\bar{\mathbf{u}} \cdot \bar{\mathbf{v}}$.

SOLUTION.   Since $\bar{\mathbf{u}}$ is parallel to $\bar{\mathbf{v}}$, the angle between $\bar{\mathbf{u}}$ and $\bar{\mathbf{v}}$ is $0°$ or $180°$. Hence,

$$\bar{\mathbf{u}} \cdot \bar{\mathbf{v}} = |\bar{\mathbf{u}}| \, |\bar{\mathbf{v}}| \quad (\pm 1)$$
$$= \pm |\bar{\mathbf{u}}| \, |\bar{\mathbf{v}}|$$

Now the dot product can be used to characterize orthogonality or perpendicularity.

THEOREM 1

Two nonzero vectors $\bar{\mathbf{u}}$ and $\bar{\mathbf{v}}$ are orthogonal (perpendicular) if and only if $\bar{\mathbf{u}} \cdot \bar{\mathbf{v}} = 0$.

PROOF.   Assume that $\bar{\mathbf{u}}$ is orthogonal to $\bar{\mathbf{v}}$; then

$$\bar{\mathbf{u}} \cdot \bar{\mathbf{v}} = |\bar{\mathbf{u}}| \, |\bar{\mathbf{v}}| \cos 90° = |\bar{\mathbf{u}}| \, |\bar{\mathbf{v}}| \cdot 0 = 0$$

Conversely, assume that $\bar{\mathbf{u}} \cdot \bar{\mathbf{v}} = 0$; then $0 = |\bar{\mathbf{u}}| \, |\bar{\mathbf{v}}| \cos \theta$, where θ is the angle between $\bar{\mathbf{u}}$ and $\bar{\mathbf{v}}$. But $\bar{\mathbf{u}}$ and $\bar{\mathbf{v}}$ are nonzero, so that $\cos \theta = 0$. This implies $\theta = 90°$; that is, $\bar{\mathbf{u}}$ is orthogonal to $\bar{\mathbf{v}}$.

It is easy to find $\bar{\mathbf{u}} \cdot \bar{\mathbf{v}}$ if $\bar{\mathbf{u}}$, $\bar{\mathbf{v}}$, and θ are known; however, if $\bar{\mathbf{u}}$ and $\bar{\mathbf{v}}$ are known, the ease of the computation of $\bar{\mathbf{u}} \cdot \bar{\mathbf{v}}$ depends on how difficult it is to find θ. It is our purpose here to derive a *second* method of computing $\bar{\mathbf{u}} \cdot \bar{\mathbf{v}}$, a method that depends only on the components of $\bar{\mathbf{u}}$ and $\bar{\mathbf{v}}$.

THEOREM 2

If $\bar{\mathbf{u}} = u_x\mathbf{i} + u_y\mathbf{j}$ and $\bar{\mathbf{v}} = v_x\mathbf{i} + v_y\mathbf{j}$, then $\bar{\mathbf{u}} \cdot \bar{\mathbf{v}} = u_xv_x + u_yv_y$.

PROOF.   Suppose that θ is the angle between $\bar{\mathbf{u}}$ and $\bar{\mathbf{v}}$ (Figure 2). By the law of cosines,

$$L^2 = |\bar{\mathbf{u}}|^2 + |\bar{\mathbf{v}}|^2 - 2|\bar{\mathbf{u}}|\,|\bar{\mathbf{v}}|\cos\theta$$

so that

(1) $$L^2 = |\bar{\mathbf{u}}|^2 + |\bar{\mathbf{v}}|^2 - 2\bar{\mathbf{u}}\cdot\bar{\mathbf{v}} \qquad \text{(Why?)}$$

Figure 2

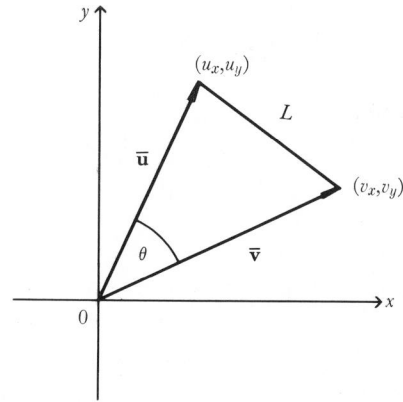

But, by the distance formula,

(2) $$L^2 = (u_x - v_x)^2 + (v_y - u_y)^2$$

Also

$$|\bar{\mathbf{u}}|^2 = u_x^2 + u_y^2 \qquad \text{and} \qquad |\bar{\mathbf{v}}|^2 = v_x^2 + v_y^2$$

so that, after equating (2) to (1) ,we have

$$(u_x - v_x)^2 + (u_y - v_y)^2 = u_x^2 + u_y^2 + v_x^2 + v_y^2 - 2\bar{\mathbf{u}}\cdot\bar{\mathbf{v}}$$

After simplifying this expression, we get

$$-2u_xv_x - 2u_yv_y = -2\bar{\mathbf{u}}\cdot\bar{\mathbf{v}}$$

that is,

$$u_xv_y + u_yv_y = \bar{\mathbf{u}}\cdot\bar{\mathbf{v}}$$

EXAMPLES

1   Compute each of the following values.

a) $\mathbf{i}\cdot\mathbf{j}$ b) $\mathbf{i}\cdot\mathbf{i}$ c) $\mathbf{j}\cdot\mathbf{j}$

SOLUTION

a) $\mathbf{i} \cdot \mathbf{j} = (1\mathbf{i} + 0\mathbf{j}) \cdot (0\mathbf{i} + 1\mathbf{j}) = 1 \cdot 0 + 0 \cdot 1 = 0$; $\mathbf{i}$ and $\mathbf{j}$ are orthogonal.

b) $\mathbf{i} \cdot \mathbf{i} = (1\mathbf{i} + 0\mathbf{j}) \cdot (1\mathbf{i} + 0\mathbf{j}) = 1 \cdot 1 + 0 \cdot 0 = 1$

c) $\mathbf{j} \cdot \mathbf{j} = (0\mathbf{i} + 1\mathbf{j}) \cdot (0\mathbf{i} + 1\mathbf{j}) = 0 \cdot 0 + 1 \cdot 1 = 1$

2 Show that $u_x = \bar{\mathbf{u}} \cdot \mathbf{i}$ and $u_y = \bar{\mathbf{u}} \cdot \mathbf{j}$, where $\bar{\mathbf{u}} = u_x\mathbf{j} + u_y\mathbf{j}$.

SOLUTION

$$\bar{\mathbf{u}} \cdot \mathbf{i} = (u_x\mathbf{i} + u_y\mathbf{j}) \cdot (1\mathbf{i} + 0\mathbf{j}) = u_x \cdot 1 + 0 = u_x$$

and

$$\bar{\mathbf{u}} \cdot \mathbf{j} = (u_x\mathbf{i} + u_y\mathbf{j}) \cdot (0\mathbf{i} + 1\mathbf{j}) = 0 + u_y = u_y$$

3 Determine the following dot products.

a) $\langle 2,3 \rangle \cdot \langle 4,5 \rangle$ b) $\langle \sqrt{2}, \sqrt{8} \rangle \cdot \langle \sqrt{8}, \sqrt{2} \rangle$

c) $\langle 3,-2 \rangle \cdot \langle 1,3 \rangle$ d) $\langle -2,-2 \rangle \cdot \langle 3,2 \rangle$

SOLUTION

a) $\langle 2,3 \rangle \cdot \langle 4,5 \rangle = 2 \cdot 4 + 3 \cdot 5 = 8 + 15 = 23$

b) $\langle \sqrt{2}, \sqrt{8} \rangle \cdot \langle \sqrt{8}, \sqrt{2} \rangle = \sqrt{2} \cdot \sqrt{8} + \sqrt{8} \cdot \sqrt{2} = 4 + 4 = 8$

c) $\langle 3,-2 \rangle \cdot \langle 1,3 \rangle = 3 \cdot 1 + (-2) \cdot 3 = 3 - 6 = -3$

d) $\langle -2,-2 \rangle \cdot \langle 3,2 \rangle = (-2) \cdot 3 + (-2) \cdot 2 = -6 - 4 = -10$

4 Let $\bar{\mathbf{u}} = \langle 2,-4 \rangle$ and $\bar{\mathbf{v}} = \langle 6,3 \rangle$. Show that $\bar{\mathbf{u}}$ and $\bar{\mathbf{v}}$ are orthogonal.

PROOF. (See Figure 3.)

$$\bar{\mathbf{u}} \cdot \bar{\mathbf{v}} = \langle 2,-4 \rangle \cdot \langle 6,3 \rangle = 12 - 12 = 0$$

Figure 3

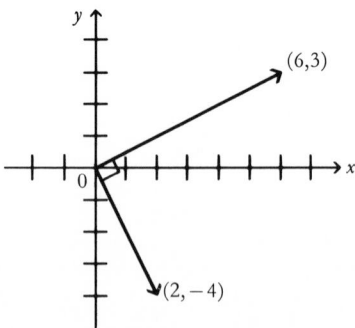

5 Find the angle θ between $\bar{\mathbf{u}} = 3\mathbf{i} + 5\mathbf{j}$ and $\bar{\mathbf{v}} = 2\mathbf{i} - 7\mathbf{j}$.

SOLUTION. Since $\bar{\mathbf{u}} \cdot \bar{\mathbf{v}} = 3 \cdot 2 - 7 \cdot 5 = -29$, $|\bar{\mathbf{u}}| = \sqrt{34}$, and $|\bar{\mathbf{v}}| = \sqrt{53}$, it follows from $\bar{\mathbf{u}} \cdot \bar{\mathbf{v}} = |\bar{\mathbf{u}}|\, |\bar{\mathbf{v}}| \cos \theta$ that

$-29 = \sqrt{34}\,\sqrt{53}\cos\theta$, so that

$$\theta = \cos^{-1}\left(\frac{-29}{\sqrt{1802}}\right)$$

6 Find $\cos\alpha$ in the triangle with vertices $A = (-2,0)$, $B = (4,3)$, and $C = (5,-1)$.

SOLUTION. From Figure 4,

$$\mathbf{AB} = [4 - (-2)]\mathbf{i} + (3 - 0)\mathbf{j} = 6\mathbf{i} + 3\mathbf{j}$$

and

$$\mathbf{AC} = [5 - (-2)]\mathbf{i} + (-1 - 0)\mathbf{j} = 7\mathbf{i} - \mathbf{j}$$

Figure 4

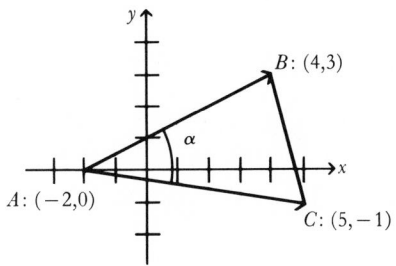

Hence,

$$\cos\alpha = \frac{(\mathbf{AB})\cdot(\mathbf{AC})}{|\mathbf{AB}|\,|\mathbf{AC}|} = \frac{(6\mathbf{i} + 3\mathbf{j})\cdot(7\mathbf{i} - \mathbf{j})}{\sqrt{45}\cdot\sqrt{50}} = \frac{39}{15\sqrt{10}} = \frac{13}{5\sqrt{10}}$$

7 Prove that $|\bar{\mathbf{u}}| = \sqrt{\bar{\mathbf{u}}\cdot\bar{\mathbf{u}}}$.

PROOF. Assume $\bar{\mathbf{u}} = \langle u_x, u_y\rangle$; then

$$\bar{\mathbf{u}}\cdot\bar{\mathbf{u}} = u_x^2 + u_y^2 = |\bar{\mathbf{u}}|^2$$

so that

$$|\bar{\mathbf{u}}| = \sqrt{\bar{\mathbf{u}}\cdot\bar{\mathbf{u}}}$$

PROBLEM SET 2

1 Find the dot product and the angle between each of the following pairs of vectors.

a) $\langle 4,3\rangle$, $\langle -3,2\rangle$ b) $\langle 3,1\rangle$, $\langle 1,3\rangle$

c) $\langle 1,2\rangle$, $\langle 1,-1\rangle$ d) $\langle 7,0\rangle$, $\langle 0,9\rangle$

2   Let $\bar{u} = \langle 2,3 \rangle$, $\bar{v} = \langle 1,4 \rangle$, and $\bar{w} = \langle -3,-1 \rangle$. Show by direct computation that each of the following properties hold.

a) $\bar{u} \cdot \bar{u} = |\bar{u}|^2$ b) $\bar{u} \cdot \bar{v} = \bar{v} \cdot \bar{u}$

c) $8(\bar{u} \cdot \bar{v}) = (8\bar{u}) \cdot \bar{v}$ d) $\bar{u} \cdot (\bar{v} + \bar{w}) = \bar{u} \cdot \bar{v} + \bar{u} \cdot \bar{w}$

3   Find the scalar projection of $\bar{u}$ on $\bar{v}$ if

a) $\bar{u} = 3i + 2j$ and $\bar{v} = 6i + 4j$

b) $\bar{u} = 4i + 3j$ and $\bar{v} = 6j$

c) $\bar{u} = -3i + j$ and $\bar{v} = 5i + 3j$

4   Find x such that the given vectors are orthogonal.

a) $\langle x,3 \rangle$ and $\langle -4,2 \rangle$ b) $\langle 2,x \rangle$ and $\langle -8,x \rangle$

c) $\langle 3,x \rangle$ and $\langle 0,5 \rangle$ d) $\langle 3,x \rangle$ and $\langle 7,5 \rangle$

5   Let $\bar{u}$ and $\bar{v}$ be two orthogonal vectors in the plane. Express each of the following values in terms of $|\bar{u}|$ and $|\bar{v}|$.

a) $|4\bar{u} + 5\bar{v}|$ b) $\big||\bar{u}|\bar{v} + |\bar{v}|\bar{u}\big|$

c) $|2\bar{u} - 3\bar{v}|$ d) $\big|\bar{u}/|\bar{u}|\big| \cdot |\bar{u}|$

6   Show that if $\bar{u}$ is orthogonal to $\bar{v}$, then $|\bar{u} + \bar{v}| = |\bar{u} - \bar{v}|$.

7   Assume that $\bar{u}$, $\bar{v}$, and $\bar{w}$ are vectors in the plane. Prove the following assertions (use Theorem 2 to compute the dot products).

a) $\bar{u} \cdot \bar{v}$ is a scalar.   b) $\bar{u} \cdot \bar{v} = \bar{v} \cdot \bar{u}$

c) $a(\bar{u} \cdot \bar{v}) = (a\bar{u}) \cdot \bar{v} = \bar{u} \cdot (a\bar{v})$

d) $\bar{u} \cdot (\bar{v} + \bar{w}) = (\bar{u} \cdot \bar{v}) + (\bar{u} \cdot \bar{w})$

e) $\bar{u} \cdot \bar{u} > 0$ if $\bar{u} \neq 0$

5 Applications

In this section, let us consider a few examples of the application of vectors to solving problems in geometry and trigonometry.

5.1 Rotations

A rotation about the origin can be considered as a function which maps position vectors into position vectors by "turning" the given vectors through the *angle of rotation*. For example, a 90° rotation f maps position vectors into other position vectors by a "90° counterclockwise turn" about the origin (Figure 1). In the figure $f(\bar{u}) = \bar{v}$ where $\bar{u}$ and $\bar{v}$ determine a 90° angle, and $|\bar{u}| = |\bar{v}|$.

Figure 1

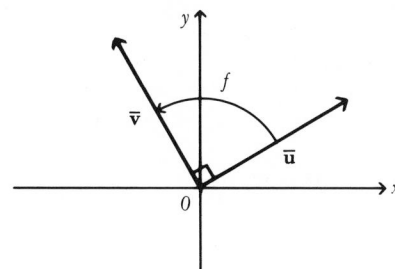

If f is a 90° rotation, then

$$f(\mathbf{i}) = \mathbf{j} \qquad f(-\mathbf{i}) = f(-\mathbf{j}) \qquad f(-\mathbf{j}) = \mathbf{i} \qquad \text{(Figure 2)}$$

Figure 2

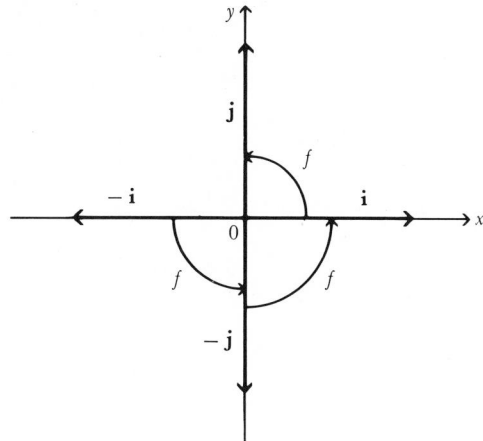

Suppose that f is a rotation through angle θ such that $f(\bar{\mathbf{u}}) = \bar{\mathbf{v}}$ (Figure 3).

Figure 3

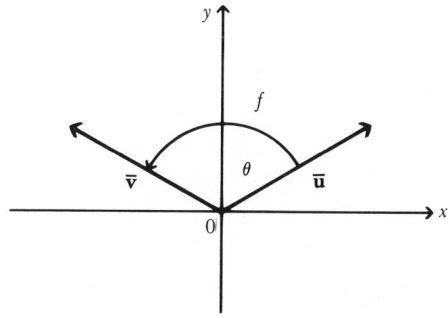

The rotation f has the following two properties:

1   The rotation of $a\bar{\mathbf{u}}$ by f is equivalent to the rotation of $\bar{\mathbf{u}}$ by f with
    the result multiplied by a; that is,

$$f(a\bar{\mathbf{u}}) = af(\bar{\mathbf{u}})   \text{(Figure 4)}$$

Figure 4

(a) Multiply $\bar{\mathbf{u}}$ by a to get
$a\bar{\mathbf{u}}$, and then rotate the
result through θ to get $f(a\bar{\mathbf{u}})$.

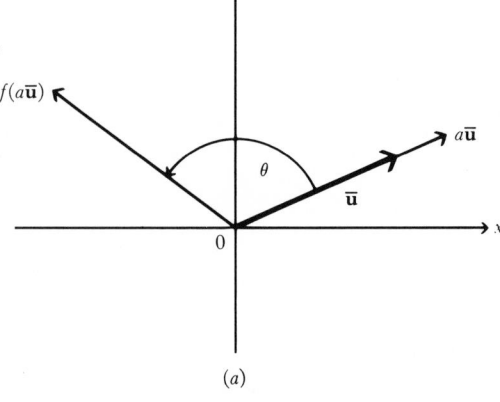

(a)

$$f(a\bar{\mathbf{u}}) = af(\bar{\mathbf{u}})$$

(b) Rotate $\bar{\mathbf{u}}$ through θ to
get $f(\bar{\mathbf{u}})$, and then multiply
the result by a to get $af(\bar{\mathbf{u}})$.

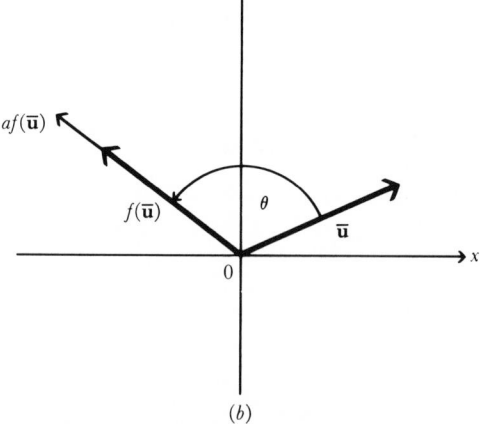

(b)

2   Another important property of rotations is that the rotation of the
    sum of two vectors is equivalent to the sum of the rotations; that is,

$$f(\bar{\mathbf{u}} + \bar{\mathbf{v}}) = f(\bar{\mathbf{u}}) + f(\bar{\mathbf{v}})   \text{(Figure 5)}$$

Figure 5

(a) Add $\bar{\mathbf{u}}$ and $\bar{\mathbf{v}}$ to get $\bar{\mathbf{u}} + \bar{\mathbf{v}}$, then rotate the result through θ to get $f(\bar{\mathbf{u}} + \bar{\mathbf{v}})$.

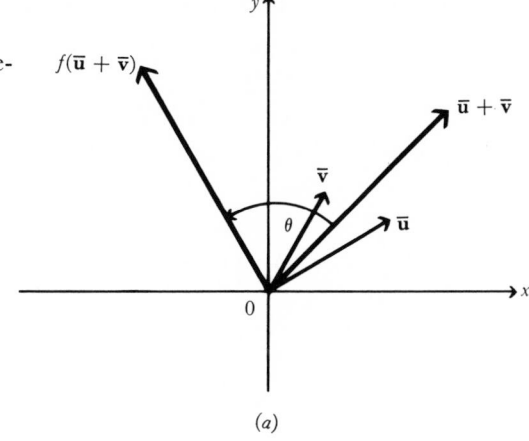

(a)

$$f(\bar{\mathbf{u}} + \bar{\mathbf{v}}) = f(\bar{\mathbf{u}}) + f(\bar{\mathbf{v}})$$

(b) Rotate $\bar{\mathbf{v}}$ and $\bar{\mathbf{u}}$ through θ to get $f(\bar{\mathbf{u}})$ and $f(\bar{\mathbf{v}})$, and then add the results to get $f(\bar{\mathbf{u}}) + f(\bar{\mathbf{v}})$.

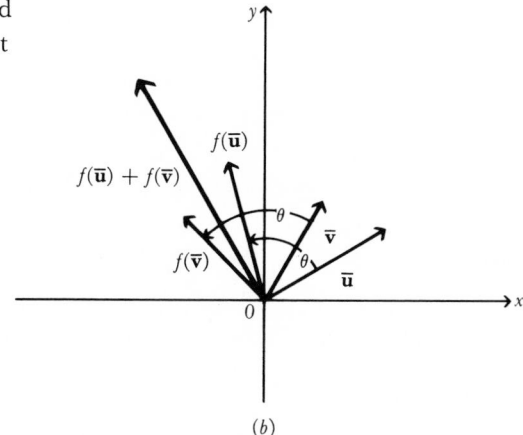

(b)

If any function satisfies the above two properties, then f is called a *linear transformation;* hence, the operation of rotation is a linear transformation. The two properties above tell us that if we know what a rotation f does to $\mathbf{i}$ and $\mathbf{j}$, then we can find the rotation on any vector $\bar{\mathbf{u}}$; for, if $\bar{\mathbf{u}} = u_x\mathbf{i} + u_y\mathbf{j}$, then

$$\begin{aligned} f(\bar{\mathbf{u}}) &= f(u_x\mathbf{i} + u_y\mathbf{j}) \\ &= f(u_x\mathbf{i}) + f(u_y\mathbf{j}) \quad \text{(Property 2)} \\ &= u_x f(\mathbf{i}) + u_y f(\mathbf{j}) \quad \text{(Property 1)} \end{aligned}$$

For example, if f is a rotation such that

$$f(\mathbf{i}) = \frac{1}{\sqrt{2}}\mathbf{i} + \frac{1}{\sqrt{2}}\mathbf{j} \quad \text{and} \quad f(\mathbf{j}) = \frac{-1\mathbf{i}}{\sqrt{2}} + \frac{1\mathbf{j}}{\sqrt{2}}$$

then

$$f(3\mathbf{i} + 4\mathbf{j}) = 3f(\mathbf{i}) + 4f(\mathbf{j})$$

$$= 3\left(\frac{1\mathbf{i}}{\sqrt{2}} + \frac{1\mathbf{j}}{\sqrt{2}}\right) + 4\left(\frac{-1\mathbf{i}}{\sqrt{2}} + \frac{1\mathbf{j}}{\sqrt{2}}\right)$$

$$= \frac{-1\mathbf{i}}{\sqrt{2}} + \frac{7\mathbf{j}}{\sqrt{2}} \qquad \text{(Figure 6)}$$

Figure 6

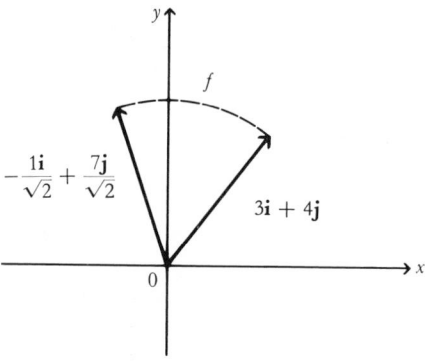

Notice that if g is a rotation function through an angle α and f is a rotation function through an angle β, then we may consider the composite mappings $(f \circ g)$ or $(g \circ f)$ as a rotation function through $\alpha + \beta$ radians. Also, if $f(\mathbf{i}) = x\mathbf{i} + y\mathbf{j}$, then, by using Properties 1 and 2, we have

$$(g \circ f)(\mathbf{i}) = g[f(\mathbf{i})] = g(x\mathbf{i} + y\mathbf{j}) = xg(\mathbf{i}) + yg(\mathbf{j})$$

EXAMPLE

Use rotations of vectors to prove the identities

$$\cos (t + s) = \cos t \cos s - \sin t \sin s$$

and

$$\sin (t + s) = \sin t \cos s + \cos t \sin s$$

where s and t are real numbers.

PROOF.   Let f be a rotation which maps $\mathbf{i}$ through an angle of t radians to the vector $x\mathbf{i} + y\mathbf{j}$ (Figure 7). By the definition of circular functions (see Chapter 5, Section 3), $x = \cos t$ and $y = \sin t$, so that

$$f(\mathbf{i}) = x\mathbf{i} + y\mathbf{j} = (\cos t)\mathbf{i} + (\sin t)\mathbf{j}$$

Figure 7

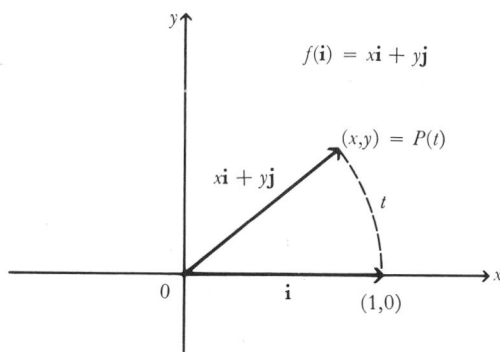

$$f(\mathbf{i}) = x\mathbf{i} + y\mathbf{j}$$

By symmetry (Figure 8),

$$f(\mathbf{j}) = -y\mathbf{i} + x\mathbf{j} = (-\sin t)\mathbf{i} + (\cos t)\mathbf{j}$$

Figure 8

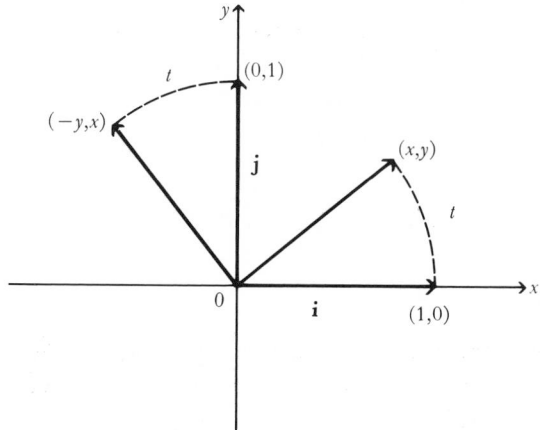

Similarly, if g is a rotation through s radians

$$g(\mathbf{i}) = (\cos s)\mathbf{i} + (\sin s)\mathbf{j} \qquad \text{and} \qquad g(\mathbf{j}) = (-\sin s)\mathbf{i} + (\cos s)\mathbf{j}$$

Hence,

$$
\begin{aligned}
(g \circ f)(\mathbf{i}) &= g[f(\mathbf{i})] \\
&= g(x\mathbf{i} + y\mathbf{j}) \\
&= x g(\mathbf{i}) + y g(\mathbf{j}) \\
&= \cos t((\cos s)\mathbf{i} + (\sin s)\mathbf{j}) + \sin t((-\sin s)\mathbf{i} + (\cos s)\mathbf{j}) \\
&= (\cos t \cos s - \sin t \sin s)\mathbf{i} + (\cos t \sin s + \sin t \cos s)\mathbf{j}
\end{aligned}
$$

Furthermore, $(g \circ f)$ can be regarded as a single rotation through $(t + s)$ radians, so that

$$(g \circ f)(\mathbf{i}) = \cos (t + s)\mathbf{i} + \sin (t + s)\mathbf{j} \qquad \text{(Figure 9)}$$

Figure 9

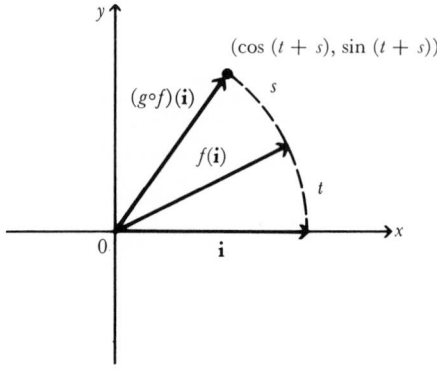

By comparing the two representations for $(g \circ f)(\mathbf{i})$, we get

$$\cos (t + s) = \cos t \cos s - \sin t \sin s$$

and

$$\sin (t + s) = \cos t \sin s + \sin t \cos s$$

5.2   Vector Equation of a Line

It is possible to use vectors to write the equation of a line. Assume that $P_1 = (x_1, y_1)$ and $P_2 = (x_2, y_2)$ are two points on a line. Let $\overline{\mathbf{b}}$ be the position vector $\mathbf{OP_1}$ and let $\overline{\mathbf{m}}$ be the vector $\mathbf{P_1P_2}$, so that

$$\overline{\mathbf{b}} = \langle x_1, y_1 \rangle \qquad \text{and} \qquad \overline{\mathbf{m}} = \langle x_2 - x_1,\ y_2 - y_1 \rangle$$

Now if t is any real number, then $\overline{\mathbf{m}}t$ denotes all vectors parallel to $\overline{\mathbf{m}}$, so that $\overline{\mathbf{u}} = \overline{\mathbf{m}}t + \overline{\mathbf{b}}$ denotes all vectors with terminal points on the given line. The equation $\overline{\mathbf{u}} = \overline{\mathbf{m}}t + \overline{\mathbf{b}}$, where t is any real number, is called the *vector equation* of the line (Figure 10).

Since $\overline{\mathbf{m}} = \langle x_2 - x_1,\ y_2 - y_1 \rangle$ and $\overline{\mathbf{b}} = \langle x_1, y_1 \rangle$, we can also write the vector equation as

$$\begin{aligned}
\overline{\mathbf{u}} &= \langle x_2 - x_1,\ y_2 - y_1 \rangle t + \langle x_1, x_2 \rangle \\
&= \langle t(x_2 - x_1),\ t(y_2 - y_1) \rangle + \langle x_1, x_2 \rangle \\
&= \langle t(x_2 - x_1) + x_1,\ t(y_2 - y_1) + x_2 \rangle
\end{aligned}$$

Figure 10

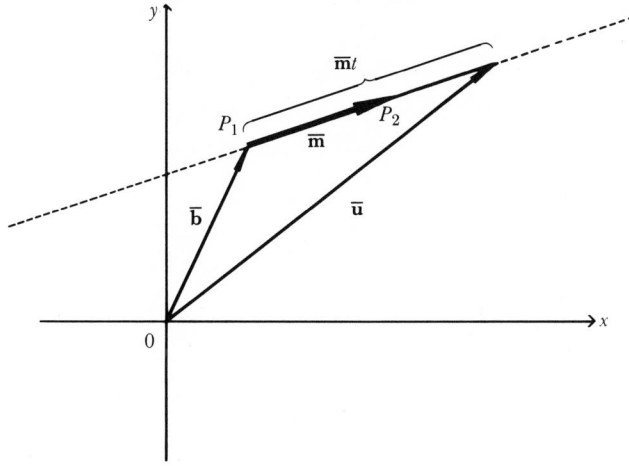

EXAMPLES

1 Find the vector equation of the line containing points (3,4) and (−1,2).

SOLUTION. The form of the equation is $\bar{\mathbf{u}} = \bar{\mathbf{m}}t + \bar{\mathbf{b}}$, where $\bar{\mathbf{b}}$ is a position vector with terminal point on the line and $\bar{\mathbf{m}}$ is a position vector parallel to the line, so that we can let $\bar{\mathbf{b}} = \langle -1,2 \rangle$ and $\bar{\mathbf{m}} = \langle 3 - (-1), 4 - 2 \rangle = \langle 4,2 \rangle$ (Figure 11). Hence,

$$\begin{aligned}
\bar{\mathbf{u}} &= \langle 4,2 \rangle t + \langle -1,2 \rangle \\
&= \langle 4t,2t \rangle + \langle -1,2 \rangle \\
&= \langle 4t - 1, 2t + 2 \rangle
\end{aligned}$$

where t is any real number.

Figure 11

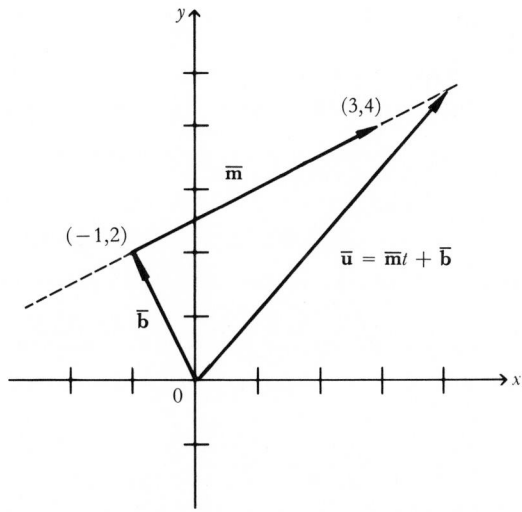

2   Find the vector equation of the line $y = 3x + 2$.

SOLUTION.   Here, we can use the two points on the line (0,2) and (1,5) to define $\overline{b}$ and $\overline{m}$ as $\overline{b} = \langle 0,2 \rangle$ and $\overline{m} = \langle 1,3 \rangle$ (Figure 12). Hence, the vector equation of the line is given by

$$\overline{u} = \langle 1,3 \rangle t + \langle 0,2 \rangle$$
$$= \langle t, 3t + 2 \rangle$$

where t is any real number.

Figure 12

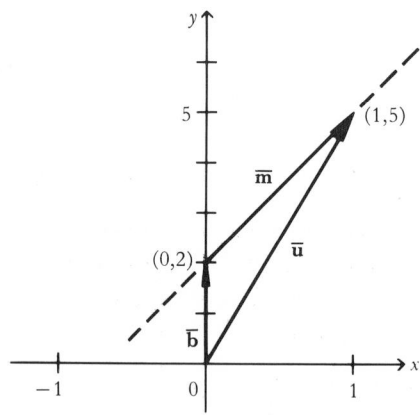

We conclude this section with a few more examples displaying the use of vectors in solving problems in geometry and trigonometry.

EXAMPLES

1   Prove that the diagonals of a rhombus *ADCB* (Figure 13) (parallelogram with equal sides) are perpendicular to each other.

Figure 13

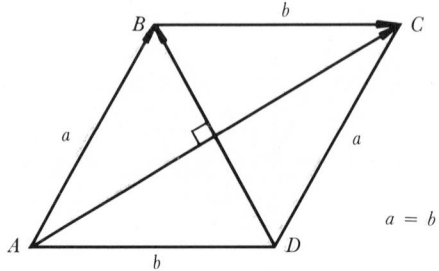

PROOF. Let $|\mathbf{AB}| = a$ and $|\mathbf{BC}| = b$. We see from Figure 13 that $\mathbf{AC} = \mathbf{AB} + \mathbf{BC}$ and $\mathbf{DB} = \mathbf{AB} - \mathbf{BC}$. Using the results of Problem set 2, Problem 7,

$$
\begin{aligned}
(\mathbf{AC} \cdot \mathbf{DB}) &= (\mathbf{AB} + \mathbf{BC}) \cdot (\mathbf{AB} - \mathbf{BC}) \\
&= (\mathbf{AB}) \cdot (\mathbf{AB}) + (\mathbf{BC}) \cdot (\mathbf{AB}) - (\mathbf{AB}) \cdot (\mathbf{BC}) - (\mathbf{BC}) \cdot (\mathbf{BC}) \\
&= |\mathbf{AB}|^2 - |\mathbf{BC}| \\
&= a^2 - b^2
\end{aligned}
$$

Since $a = b$, $\mathbf{AC} \cdot \mathbf{DB} = 0$, so that $\mathbf{AC}$ is orthogonal (perpendicular) to $\mathbf{DB}$.

2 Prove that the three altitudes of any triangle intersect.

PROOF. Suppose that altitudes $\overline{AE}$ and $\overline{BD}$ intersect at 0 as shown in Figure 14. We must show that the line segment CF formed by extending $\overline{OC}$ through O to F is orthogonal (perpendicular) to $\overline{AB}$.

Figure 14

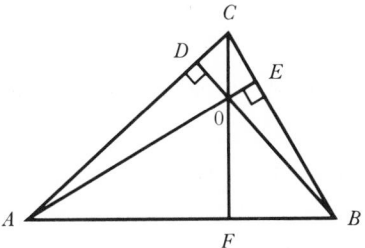

We know that $\mathbf{CB} \cdot \mathbf{OA} = 0$ and $\mathbf{AC} \cdot \mathbf{OB} = 0$; but $\mathbf{CB} = (\mathbf{OB} - \mathbf{OC})$ and $\mathbf{AC} = (\mathbf{OC} - \mathbf{OA})$, so that $(\mathbf{OB} - \mathbf{OC}) \cdot \mathbf{OA} = 0$ and $(\mathbf{OC} - \mathbf{OA}) \cdot \mathbf{OB} = 0$. Hence,

$$(\mathbf{OB} \cdot \mathbf{OA}) - (\mathbf{OC} \cdot \mathbf{OA}) + (\mathbf{OC} \cdot \mathbf{OB}) - (\mathbf{OA} \cdot \mathbf{OB}) = 0$$

that is,

$$(\mathbf{OB} - \mathbf{OA}) \cdot \mathbf{OC} = 0$$

However, since $\mathbf{OB} - \mathbf{OA} = \mathbf{AB}$, this means that $\mathbf{AB} \cdot \mathbf{OC} = 0$, so that $\overline{CF}$ is perpendicular to $\overline{AB}$.

3 Use the inner product to derive the law of cosines.

PROOF.   Let $|\mathbf{AB}| = c$, $|\mathbf{AC}| = b$, and let θ be the angle between $\mathbf{AC}$ and $\mathbf{AB}$ as shown in Figure 15. $\mathbf{BC} = \mathbf{AC} - \mathbf{AB}$. Hence,

$$
\begin{aligned}
|\mathbf{BC}|^2 = \mathbf{BC} \cdot \mathbf{BC} &= (\mathbf{AC} - \mathbf{AB}) \cdot (\mathbf{AC} - \mathbf{AB}) \\
&= |\mathbf{AC}|^2 - [(\mathbf{AC}) \cdot (\mathbf{AB})] - [(\mathbf{AB}) \cdot (\mathbf{AC})] + |\mathbf{AB}|^2 \\
&= b^2 - 2(\mathbf{AC}) \cdot (\mathbf{AB}) + c^2 \\
&= b^2 + c^2 - 2bc \cos \theta
\end{aligned}
$$

Figure 15

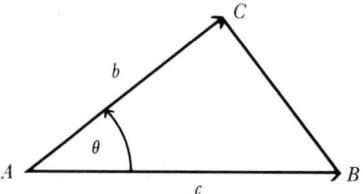

4   Let $\bar{\mathbf{u}}$ and $\bar{\mathbf{v}}$ be unit radius vectors that make angles θ and ϕ with the x axis, respectively. Use the inner product to prove that $\cos(\theta - \phi) = \cos \theta \cos \phi + \sin \theta \sin \phi$.

SOLUTION.   First, we can use trigonometry to write

$$\bar{\mathbf{u}} = \langle u_x, u_y \rangle = \langle \cos \theta, \sin \theta \rangle$$

and

$$\bar{\mathbf{v}} = \langle v_x, v_y \rangle = \langle \cos \phi, \sin \phi \rangle \qquad \text{(Figure 16)}$$

so that

$$\bar{\mathbf{u}} \cdot \bar{\mathbf{v}} = \cos \theta \cos \phi + \sin \theta \sin \phi$$

Also,

$$
\begin{aligned}
\bar{\mathbf{u}} \cdot \bar{\mathbf{v}} &= |\bar{\mathbf{u}}| \, |\bar{\mathbf{v}}| \cos(\theta - \phi) \\
&= 1 \cdot 1 \cos(\theta - \phi)
\end{aligned}
$$

since $\bar{\mathbf{u}}$ and $\bar{\mathbf{v}}$ are unit vectors. Hence,

$$\cos(\theta - \phi) = \cos \theta \cos \phi + \sin \phi \sin \theta$$

Figure 16

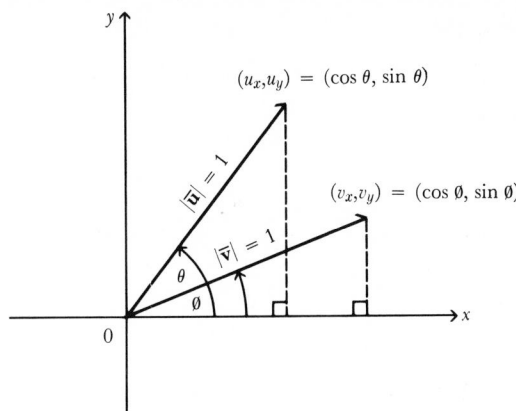

PROBLEM SET 3

1 Let f be a rotation through $30°$.

a) Use trigonometry to find $f(\mathbf{i})$.
b) Use symmetry to find $f(\mathbf{j})$ from part (a).
c) Use Properties 1 and 2 in Section 5.1 to find $f(4\mathbf{i})$, $f(-7\mathbf{i} + 5\mathbf{j})$, $f(-8\mathbf{j})$, and $f(\mathbf{i} - \mathbf{j})$.
d) Does f^{-1} exist? Explain.

2 Assume that f is a rotation through a positive angle of measure less than $360°$ such that $f(\mathbf{i}) = -\mathbf{i}$.

a) What is the angle of rotation of f?
b) What is $f(\mathbf{j})$?
c) If g is a $45°$ rotation, describe the rotations $g \circ f$ and $f \circ g$.

3 Assume that

$$f(\mathbf{i}) = \left(\frac{1}{\sqrt{2}}\right)\mathbf{i} + \left(\frac{1}{\sqrt{2}}\right)\mathbf{j}$$

We know that

$$f(\mathbf{j}) = \left(\frac{-1}{\sqrt{2}}\right)\mathbf{i} + \left(\frac{1}{\sqrt{2}}\right)\mathbf{j}$$

(Why?) Use $\bar{\mathbf{u}} = \mathbf{i} + 2\mathbf{j}$ and $\bar{\mathbf{v}} = -3\mathbf{i} + \mathbf{j}$ to demonstrate each of the following statements.

a) $f(\bar{\mathbf{u}} + \bar{\mathbf{v}}) = f(\bar{\mathbf{u}}) + f(\bar{\mathbf{v}})$
b) $f(8\bar{\mathbf{u}}) = 8f(\bar{\mathbf{u}})$
c) $f(5\bar{\mathbf{u}} - 7\bar{\mathbf{v}}) = 5f(\bar{\mathbf{u}}) - 7f(\bar{\mathbf{v}})$

4   Use vectors to prove that the median to the base of an isosceles triangle is perpendicular to the base.

5   Use vectors to prove that if the midpoints of the consecutive sides of any quadrilateral are joined, the resulting quadrilateral is a parallelogram.

6   If $\bar{u} = 3\mathbf{i} - 6\mathbf{j}$ and $\bar{v} = 4\mathbf{i} + 2\mathbf{j}$ are the sides of a right triangle, prove that the midpoint of the hypotenuse is equidistant from the vertices.

7   Use vectors to derive the formula for the distance between points (x_1, y_1) and (x_2, y_2).

8   Find a vector equation and graph each of the following lines.
a)   A line containing points $(1,4)$ and $(4,3)$
b)   The line $y = 3$
c)   The line $x = 2$
d)   The line $y = -3x - 1$
e)   The line containing point $(1,2)$ and parallel to the line $y = -\frac{1}{2}x$

REVIEW PROBLEM SET

1   Let O, A, and B be collinear points. Find n such that $\mathbf{OB} = n\mathbf{OA}$ if
a) B is the midpoint of $\mathbf{OA}$
b) A is the midpoint of $\mathbf{OB}$
c) O is the midpoint of $\mathbf{AB}$
d) B is $\frac{3}{4}$ of the way from O to A

2   Let $\bar{u} = \langle 3,4 \rangle$ and $\bar{v} = \langle 4,3 \rangle$. Find each of the following vectors and represent them graphically.
a) $3\bar{u}$ b) $\bar{v} - \bar{u}$ c) $-2\bar{u} + \bar{v}$
d) $3\bar{u} + 2\bar{v}$ e) $\bar{u} - 2\bar{v}$

3   Let $\bar{u} = \langle -3,4 \rangle$, $\bar{v} = \langle 4,3 \rangle$, and $\bar{w} = \langle 1,-3 \rangle$; find each of the following expressions:
a) $|\bar{u}| - |\bar{v}|$ b) $|3\bar{u}| + |5\bar{v}|$
c) $|\bar{u}|^2 + |\bar{v}|^2$ d) $|\bar{u} + \bar{v}|^2$
e) $|\bar{u} - \bar{v} - \bar{w}|^2 - |\bar{u}|^2$ f) $|2\bar{u} + 3\bar{v} + 4\bar{w}|^2$
g) $|\bar{u}|^2 + |\bar{v}|^2 + |\bar{w}|^2$ h) $2|\bar{u}|^2 + 3|\bar{u}|\,|\bar{v}| + 6|\bar{v}|^2$

4   Assume that $\bar{u} \neq 0$, $\bar{v} \neq 0$, and $c \neq 0$. Show that $\bar{u}$ is collinear with $\bar{v}$ if and only if $\bar{u} = c\bar{v}$.

5   Let $\bar{u} = \langle 1,1 \rangle$, $\bar{v} = \langle 1,1 \rangle$, and $\bar{w} = \langle 1,-1 \rangle$. Determine s, t, and r such that $\langle 4,6 \rangle = s\bar{u} + t\bar{v} + r\bar{w}$.

6   Write $f(\mathbf{i})$ in the form $x\mathbf{i} + y\mathbf{j}$ if f corresponds to a rotation through each of the following angles.

a) $2\pi/3$ b) π

c) $-45°$ d) $100°$

7 Suppose that f and g are rotations of the plane about the origin. Show that $f \circ g = g \circ f$.

8 If $|\bar{u}| = 4$, determine $|3\bar{u}|$, $|-5\bar{u}|$, $5|\bar{u}|$, and $-3|\bar{u}|$.

9 Determine $\bar{u}$ in each of the following cases if θ is the angle that $\bar{u}$ makes with the positive x axis.

a) $|\bar{u}| = 5$ and $\theta = 30°$

b) $|\bar{u}| = 6$ and $\theta = 45°$

c) $|\bar{u}| = 8$ and $\theta = 60°$

10 Find the three angles of a triangle whose vertices are $(2,-1)$, $(1,-3)$, and $(3,-4)$.

11 Let $\bar{u} = \langle 2,3 \rangle$, $\bar{v} = \langle -1,4 \rangle$, and $\bar{w} = \langle 4,5 \rangle$. Determine $\bar{z}$ in each of the following parts.

a) $\bar{u} + \bar{v} = \bar{w} + \bar{z}$ b) $2(\bar{u} - \bar{v}) = 3(\bar{w} - \bar{z})$

c) $3(\bar{z} + \bar{v}) = 5(\bar{z} - \bar{w})$ d) $\bar{z} + 3(\bar{z} + \bar{u}) + 4(\bar{z} + \bar{v}) = \bar{0}$

12 Use $\bar{u}$, $\bar{v}$, and $\bar{w}$ of Problem 11 to find

a) $\bar{v} \cdot \bar{u}$ b) $3\bar{u} \cdot 2\bar{v}$

c) $4\bar{u} \cdot (\bar{v} + \bar{w})$ d) $2\bar{v} \cdot (3\bar{u} + 2\bar{w})$

e) $(\bar{u} - \bar{v}) \cdot 6(\bar{u} + \bar{v})$ f) $(4\bar{v} + 3\bar{w}) \cdot (4\bar{v} - 3\bar{w})$

g) $(\bar{u} + \bar{v} - \bar{w}) \cdot (\bar{u} + \bar{v} + \bar{w})$

13 Let $\bar{u} = \mathbf{AB}$ and $\bar{v} = \mathbf{AD}$, where AB and AD are adjacent sides of parallelogram $ABCD$. Show that $\bar{u} + \bar{v} = \mathbf{AC}$.

14 Show that the line that joins one vertex of a parallelogram to the midpoint of an opposite side divides the diagonal in the ratio $2:1$.

15 Let $\bar{u}$ and $\bar{v}$ be vectors in the plane with $|\bar{u}| = a$ and $|\bar{v}| = b$. Show that

a) $(a\bar{v} + b\bar{u}) \cdot (a\bar{v} - b\bar{u}) = 0$

b) $(\bar{u} + \bar{v}) \cdot (\bar{u} - \bar{v}) = a^2 - b^2$

16 Use vectors to prove the Pythagorean theorem for a right triangle $\triangle ABC$.

17 Let $\bar{u}$ and $\bar{v}$ be vectors in the plane. Solve for x if $(\bar{u} + x\bar{v}) \cdot \bar{u} = 0$. Is there always a solution? Is it unique?

18 Use vectors to prove that the median to the base of an isosceles triangle bisects the vertex angle.

19 Use $|\bar{u} + \bar{v}|^2 = (\bar{u} + \bar{v}) \cdot (\bar{u} + \bar{v})$ to establish the triangle inequality $|\bar{u} + \bar{v}| \leq |\bar{u}| + |\bar{v}|$. When does the equality hold?

20 Let $\bar{\mathbf{u}} = \langle x_1, y_1 \rangle$ and $\bar{\mathbf{v}} = \langle x_2, y_2 \rangle$ be unit vectors and let θ be the angle between the vectors $\bar{\mathbf{u}}$ and $\bar{\mathbf{v}}$, where $0 \leq \theta \leq \pi$. Show that $\frac{1}{2}|\bar{\mathbf{v}} - \bar{\mathbf{u}}| = \sin(\theta/2)$.

21 Show that

a) $\bar{\mathbf{u}} \cdot \bar{\mathbf{v}} = \frac{1}{2}\{|\bar{\mathbf{u}} + \bar{\mathbf{v}}|^2 - (|\bar{\mathbf{u}}|^2 + |\bar{\mathbf{v}}|^2)\}$

b) $\bar{\mathbf{u}} \cdot \bar{\mathbf{v}} = \frac{1}{4}\{|\bar{\mathbf{u}} + \bar{\mathbf{v}}|^2 - |\bar{\mathbf{u}} - \bar{\mathbf{v}}|^2\}$

22 Let $\bar{\mathbf{u}}$ be the vector **OP**, where $P = (\frac{1}{2}, \sqrt{3}/2)$.

a) Write $\bar{\mathbf{u}}$ in the form $x\mathbf{i} + y\mathbf{j}$.

b) If $\bar{\mathbf{u}} = f(\mathbf{i})$, where f is a rotation, find the angle of rotation.

c) Determine $f(\mathbf{j})$.

d) Use the results of parts (b) and (c) to determine $f(2\mathbf{i} - 5\mathbf{j})$.

CHAPTER 8

Complex Numbers and Theory of Equations

8 COMPLEX NUMBERS AND THEORY OF EQUATIONS

1 Introduction

In Chapter 3, Section 5, we discussed the solution of a quadratic equation, an equation which has an equivalent form $ax^2 + bx + c = 0$, where $a \neq 0$ and a, b, and c are real numbers. The solution of such an equation is real if the discriminant, $b^2 - 4ac$, is nonnegative. If the discriminant is negative, it is impossible to solve the quadratic equation *in the real number system*. For example, $\{x \mid x^2 + 1 = 0\} = \emptyset$ if we restrict ourselves to R. Our purpose here is to extend the real number system to a "new" system — the *complex number system* — which contains numbers that satisfy the equations such as $x^2 + 1 = 0$.

2 Complex Numbers

An ordered pair of real numbers (a,b), which shall be denoted as $a + bi$, is called a *complex number*. The algebra of complex numbers is defined in terms of the albegra of real numbers as follows.

Assume that $z_1 = a_1 + b_1 i$ and $z_2 = a_2 + b_2 i$ are complex numbers. Then:

1   *Equality.* $z_1 = z_2$ if and only if $a_1 = a_2$ and $b_1 = b_2$.

2   *Addition.* $z_1 + z_2 = (a_1 + a_2) + (b_1 + b_2)i$.

3   *Multiplication.* $z_1 \cdot z_2 = (a_1a_2 - b_1b_2) + (a_1b_2 + a_2b_1)i$.

For $z = a + bi$, a is called the *real part* of z and b is called the *imaginary part* of z. It would perhaps be better to identify a as the "non-i part" and b as the "i part" of the complex number, but the choice of words "real part" and "imaginary part" is accepted today for historical reasons. Hence, two complex numbers are equal if and only if the real and imaginary parts are equal; the real part of the sum of two complex numbers is the sum of the real parts and the imaginary part of the sum of two complex numbers is the sum of the imaginary parts.

The set of complex numbers will be denoted by C, so that in set notation, we have $C = \{a + bi | a, b \in R\}$.

If the imaginary part of a complex number is 0, we will consider the number to be real; hence, $a + 0i$ will be considered to be the real number a; and, in this sense, R can be considered to be a proper subset of C.

EXAMPLES

Find the sum and product of each of the following pairs of complex numbers and identify the real and imaginary parts of each result.

1   i, i

2   $5 + 6i, 9 + 3i$

3   $4 - 2i, -3 + i$

SOLUTION

1   $i + i = 2i$, so that the real part of $2i$ is 0 and the imaginary part is 2.

$$i \cdot i = i^2 = (0 + 1i)(0 + 1i)$$
$$= (0 \cdot 0 - 1 \cdot 1) + (0 \cdot 1 + 1 \cdot 0)i \qquad \text{(Why?)}$$
$$= -1$$

Hence, the symbol i in $z = a + bi$ is sometimes denoted as $\sqrt{-1}$. The real part of -1 is -1 and the imaginary part is 0.

2   $(5 + 6i) + (9 + 3i) = 14 + 9i$; 14 is the real part and 9 is the imaginary part of $14 + 9i$.

$$(5 + 6i)(9 + 3i) = (45 - 18) + (54 + 15)i$$
$$= 27 + 69i$$

27 is the real part and 69 is the imaginary part of $27 + 69i$.

3 $(4 - 2i) + (-3 + i) = 1 - i$; here, 1 is the real part and -1 is the imaginary part of $1 - i$.

$$(4 - 2i)(-3 + i) = (-12 + 2) + (6 + 4)i$$
$$= -10 + 10i$$

The real part is -10 and the imaginary part is 10.

We have in Example 1 one of the properties which does not hold in R but holds in C: If $x \in R$, $x^2 \geq 0$, whereas it is possible to have $z \in C$ such that $z^2 < 0$ ($i^2 = -1$).

If the order properties of R did hold in C, then, by trichotomy,

$$i = 0 \quad \text{or} \quad i < 0 \quad \text{or} \quad i > 0$$

But, if $i = 0$, then $i \cdot i = 0$ implies that $-1 = 0$; hence, $i \neq 0$. On the other hand, if $i > 0$, then $i^2 > 0$ implies that $-1 > 0$ since $i^2 = -1$; hence, $i \not> 0$. Finally, if $i < 0$, then $i^2 > 0$, so that $-1 > 0$ since $i^2 = -1$; hence, $i \not< 0$. Consequently, trichotomy does *not* hold in C; that is, the order relation which exists in R does not exist in C.

The domain of functions can be extended to the set of complex numbers. For example, consider the function f whose domain is the set of complex numbers and whose rule of correspondence is $f(z) = 3z + 1$; then $f(i) = 3i + 1$ and $f(1 - i) = 3(1 - i) + 1 = 4 - 3i$.

2.1 Properties of Addition and Multiplication

Since we defined the operations of addition and multiplication on C in terms of the corresponding operations on R, it is not surprising that the properties of addition and multiplication on C are the same as the properties of addition and multiplication on R. (These properties are listed in Appendix B.)

Assume that z_1, z_2, $z_3 \in C$; then the following properties hold.

1 CLOSURE OF ADDITION AND MULTIPLICATION:

i $z_1 + z_2 \in C$
ii $z_1 \cdot z_2 \in C$

2 COMMUTATIVITY OF ADDITION AND MULTIPLICATION:

i $z_1 + z_2 = z_2 + z_1$
ii $z_1 z_2 = z_2 z_1$

3 ASSOCIATIVITY OF ADDITION AND MULTIPLICATION:

i $z_1 + (z_2 + z_3) = (z_1 + z_2) + z_3$
ii $z_1 \cdot (z_2 \cdot z_3) = (z_1 \cdot z_2) \cdot z_3$

4   DISTRIBUTIVE PROPERTIES:

i $z_1 \cdot (z_2 + z_3) = (z_1 \cdot z_2) + (z_1 \cdot z_3)$

ii $(z_1 + z_2) \cdot z_3 = (z_1 \cdot z_3) + (z_2 \cdot z_3)$

5   IDENTITY:

i   There exists $0 \in C$ such that $z + 0 = 0 + z = z$ for every $z \in C$.

ii There exists $1 \in C$ such that $z \cdot 1 = 1 \cdot z = z$ for every $z \in C$.

6   INVERSE:

i   If $z \in C$, then there exists $-z \in C$ such that
$z + (-z) = (-z) + z = 0$.

ii If $z \in C$, $z \neq 0$, then there exists $z^{-1} \in C$ such that
$z \cdot z^{-1} = z^{-1} \cdot z = 1$.

PROOF OF PROPERTY 6, i: Suppose that $z = a + bi$. Then, by letting
$-z = -a - bi$, we have $(a + bi) + (-a - bi) = 0 + 0i = 0$.

For the proofs of the other properties, see Problem 6.

2.2   Subtraction of Complex Numbers

If $z_1, z_2 \in C$, then $z_1 - z_2$, that is, the *difference* of z_1 and z_2, is defined
as $z_1 - z_2 = z_1 + (-z_2)$.

EXAMPLES

1   If $z_1 = 7 + 4i$ and $z_2 = 3 + 5i$, then

$$z_1 - z_2 = (7 + 4i) - (3 + 5i) = (7 + 4i) + (-3 - 5i)$$
$$= 4 - i$$

2   If $z_1 = 4 - 5i$ and $z_2 = -5 + 7i$, then

$$z_1 - z_2 = (4 - 5i) - (-5 + 7i) = (4 - 5i) + (5 - 7i)$$
$$= 9 - 12i$$

2.3   Division of Complex Numbers

The *conjugate* of a complex number $z = a + bi$, written $\bar{z}$ (read "z bar"),
is defined as $\bar{z} = a - bi$. If $z_1 = a_1 + b_1i$, $z_1 \neq 0$, and $z_2 = a_2 + b_2i$,
then the *quotient* $z_2 \div z_1$ is given by

$$\frac{z_2}{z_1} = \frac{z_2 \cdot \bar{z_1}}{z_1 \cdot \bar{z_1}}$$

or, equivalently,

$$\frac{a_2 + b_2 i}{a_1 + b_1 i} = \frac{(a_2 + b_2 i)(a_1 - b_1 i)}{(a_1 + b_1 i)(a_1 - b_1 i)}$$

$$= \frac{(a_2 a_1 + b_2 b_1) + (a_1 b_2 - b_1 a_2)i}{a_1^2 + b_1^2}$$

Notice that the result is a complex number of the form $x + yi$, with

$$x = \frac{a_2 a_1 + b_2 b_1}{a_1^2 + b_1^2} \quad \text{and} \quad y = \frac{a_1 b_2 - b_1 a_2}{a_1^2 + b_1^2}$$

Notice also that the denominator is a real number.

EXAMPLES

1   Find the conjugate of each of the following complex numbers.

a) $3 + 3i$ b) -4
c) $5i$ d) $-1 - i$

SOLUTION

a) $3 - 3i$ b) -4
c) $-5i$ d) $-1 + i$

2   Show that $z\bar{z} \in R$ and $z\bar{z} \geq 0$.

SOLUTION.   Let $z = a + bi$; then $\bar{z} = a - bi$, so that

$$z\bar{z} = (a + bi)(a - bi)$$
$$= (a^2 + b^2) + (ab - ab)i$$
$$= (a^2 + b^2) + (0 \cdot i)$$
$$= a^2 + b^2 \in R$$

Since $a^2 \geq 0$ and $b^2 \geq 0$ for any $a, b \in R$, we have $a^2 + b^2 \geq 0$.

3   Write each of the following quotients in the form $a + bi$.

a) $1/(3 - 2i)$ b) $(1 + i)/(1 - i)$ c) $(6 + 9i)/(1 - 2i)$

SOLUTION

a) $\dfrac{1}{3 - 2i} = \dfrac{1}{3 - 2i} \cdot \dfrac{3 + 2i}{3 + 2i} = \dfrac{3 + 2i}{9 + 4} = \dfrac{3}{13} + \dfrac{2i}{13}$

b) $\dfrac{1 + i}{1 - i} = \dfrac{1 + i}{1 - i} \cdot \dfrac{1 + i}{1 + i} = \dfrac{(1 + i)^2}{2} = \dfrac{2i}{2} = i$

c) $\dfrac{6 + 9i}{1 - 2i} = \dfrac{6 + 9i}{1 - 2i} \cdot \dfrac{1 + 2i}{1 + 2i} = \dfrac{-12 + 21i}{5} = \dfrac{-12}{5} + \dfrac{21}{5}i$

4   Show that if z is a complex number, $z + \bar{z}$ is a real number.

SOLUTION.   Let $z = a + bi$. Then $\bar{z} = a - bi$, so that

$$z + \bar{z} = (a + a) + (b - b)i$$
$$= 2a \in R$$

5   Let $z = 3 + 5i$. Find $\bar{z}$, $\bar{z} + z$, and $(z - \bar{z})/i$.

SOLUTION.   Since $z = 3 + 5i$, $\bar{z} = 3 - 5i$, so that

$$\bar{z} + z = (3 - 5i) + (3 + 5i) = 6$$

and

$$\frac{z - \bar{z}}{i} = \frac{(3 + 5i) - (3 - 5i)}{i} = \frac{10i}{i} = 10$$

6   If $z \neq 0$, show that $1/z$ is the multiplicative inverse of z; that is, $z \cdot z^{-1} = 1$, where $z^{-1} = 1/z$.

SOLUTION.   If $z = a + bi \neq 0$, then

$$\frac{1}{z} = \frac{1}{a + bi} \cdot \frac{a - bi}{a - bi} = \frac{a - bi}{a^2 + b^2}$$

so that

$$z \cdot \frac{1}{z} = (a + bi) \cdot \frac{a - bi}{a^2 + b^2} = \frac{a^2 + b^2}{a^2 + b^2} = 1$$

PROBLEM SET 1

1   Perform the indicated operations, writing the answer in the form $a + bi$.

a) $(5 + 6i) + (3 - 4i) - (2 + 7i)$
b) $(6 + i)(5 - 3i)$
c) $(3 + 2i)(2 - 5i)(1 - i)$
d) $(3 - 2i)/(2 - i)$
e) $(5 - i)^2/(1 + i)$
f) $i^{27} + i^5 - i^9$
g) $(-1 - \sqrt{2}\,i)^3/(5 - 3i)$
h) $(3 + \sqrt{2}\,i)(3 - \sqrt{2}\,i)$
i) $6/7i$
j) $(3 + i)^3$
k) $(4 + 3i)^{-1}$
l) $(3 + 2i) - (7 - 3i)$
m) $(7 - 3i)/5i$
n) $4/(3 + 2i)$
o) $(35 + 8i)/4i$
p) $(3 - i)/(2 + 3i)$
q) $-3/5i^3$

r) $(2 - 3i)^4$ s) $(2 - 7i)(2 + 3i)$
t) $4i^{-13}$ u) $2i/(1 + i)^4$
v) $i^{18} - 3i^7$ w) $(3 + 5i)/(4 - 3i)$

2   Find the real numbers x and y to satisfy each of the following equations.

a) $x - 3 + 2iy = 8i$
b) $3x - y + ix - 2iy = 6 - 3i$
c) $3x + 2yi = 6 + 11i$

3   Find $\bar{z}$, the real part of z, the imaginary part of z, and $1/z$ for each of the following numbers.

a) $z = 2 + \sqrt{3}\, i$ b) $z = 1 - \frac{1}{2}i$
c) $z = (2 + \sqrt{3}\, i)(1 - \frac{1}{2}i)^2$ d) $z = 2i$

4   Prove each of the following statements.

a) If $\bar{z} = z$, then z is real.
b) $z + \bar{z} = 0$ if and only if the real part of z is 0.
c) $\overline{z_1 + z_2} = \bar{z}_1 + \bar{z}_2$
d) $\overline{z_1 z_2} = \bar{z}_1 \bar{z}_2$
e) $\overline{z_1/z_2} = \bar{z}_1/\bar{z}_2,\ z_2 \neq 0$
f) $\bar{\bar{z}} = z$

5   Let z_1 and z_2 be complex numbers. Show that

$$\text{Re}\left(\frac{z_1}{z_1 + z_2}\right) + \text{Re}\left(\frac{z_2}{z_1 + z_2}\right) = 1$$

where Re (z) indicates the real part of z.

6   Assume the properties of addition and multiplication on R that are listed in Appendix B.

a) Prove that C is closed under addition and multiplication.
b) Prove the commutativity of addition and multiplication on C.
c) Prove the associativity of addition and multiplication on C.
d) Prove the distributive properties on C.
e) Prove the identity properties of addition and multiplication on C.

7   Let f be a function whose domain is the set of complex numbers and whose rule of correspondence is given by $f(z) = z^2 + 5z + i$. Find

a) $f(2 - i)$ b) $f(2 + i)$
c) $f(1 - i)$ d) $f(1 + i)$

8   We are given the set $T = \{1, -1, i, -i\}$.

a)   Construct a *multiplication* table as shown:

·	1	−1	i	−i
1				
−1				
i				
−i				

b)   Is the set T closed under multiplication?
c)   Is multiplication on T commutative?
d)   Is multiplication on T associative?
e)   What is the identity element?
f)   What are the reciprocals of each of the elements of T? (Two elements are reciprocals of each other if their product equals 1.)

3   Geometric Representation of Complex Numbers

Each ordered pair of real numbers (a,b) can be associated with the complex number $z = a + bi$, and each complex number $z = a + bi$ can be associated with the ordered pair of real numbers (a,b). Because of this one-to-one correspondence between the set of complex numbers and the set of ordered pairs of real numbers, we use the points in the plane associated with the ordered pairs of real numbers to represent the complex numbers. For example, the ordered pairs $(2,-3)$, $(5,2)$, and (e,π) are used to represent complex numbers $z_1 = 2 - 3i$, $z_2 = 5 + 2i$, and $z_3 = e + \pi i$, respectively as points in the plane (Figure 1). The plane on which the complex numbers are represented is called the *complex plane*; the horizontal axis (x axis) is called the *real axis*, and the vertical axis (y axis) is called the *imaginary axis*. Thus, complex numbers of the form $z = bi$ are represented by points of the form $(0,b)$, that is, by points on the imaginary axis, whereas complex numbers of the form $z = a$ are represented by points of the form $(a,0)$, that is, by points on the real axis.

Figure 1

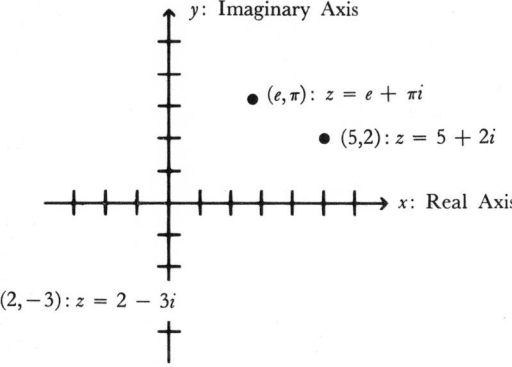

y: Imaginary Axis

(e, π): $z = e + \pi i$

$(5,2)$: $z = 5 + 2i$

x: Real Axis

$(2, -3)$: $z = 2 - 3i$

3.1 The Modulus of a Complex Number

If $z = a + bi$, then the *absolute value* or *length* or *modulus* of z, written $|z|$, is defined by

$$|z| = \sqrt{a^2 + b^2}$$

The modulus of $z = a + bi$ is the distance between the origin and the point (a,b) (Figure 2). Notice that $|z| = \sqrt{z \cdot \bar{z}}$ (see Problem 4).

Figure 2

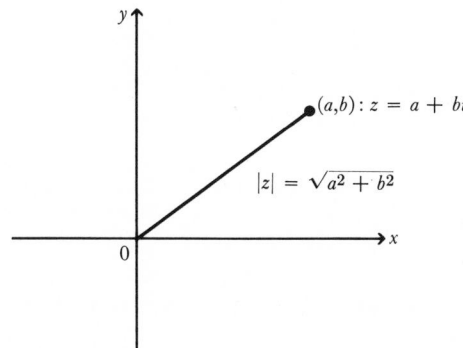

(a,b): $z = a + bi$

$|z| = \sqrt{a^2 + b^2}$

EXAMPLES

1   Let $z = 1 + \sqrt{3}\, i$. Find $|z|$ and show that $z\bar{z} = |z|^2$.

SOLUTION

$$|z| = \sqrt{1^2 + (\sqrt{3})^2} = \sqrt{1 + 3} = \sqrt{4} = 2$$

also

$$z\bar{z} = (1 + \sqrt{3}\, i)(1 - \sqrt{3}\, i) = 1^2 + (\sqrt{3})^2 = 4 = |z|^2 \qquad \text{(Figure 3)}$$

Figure 3

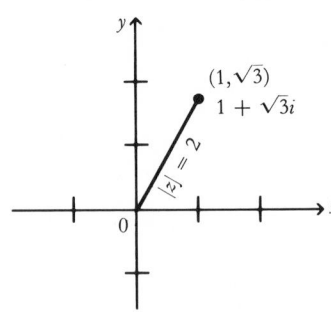

2   Let $z_1 = 4 + 3i$ and $z_2 = \sqrt{3} - i$. Find

   a) $|z_1|$ b) $|z_2|$ c) $|z_1z_2|$

   SOLUTION

   a) $|z_1| = \sqrt{16 + 9} = \sqrt{25} = 5$

   b) $|z_2| = \sqrt{(\sqrt{3})^2 + (-1)^2} = \sqrt{4} = 2$

   c) $|z_1z_2| = |(4 + 3i)(\sqrt{3} - i)|$

   $= |(4\sqrt{3} + 3) + (3\sqrt{3} - 4)i|$

   $= \sqrt{(4\sqrt{3} + 3)^2 + (3\sqrt{3} - 4)^2} = 10$

3   Let z_1 and z_2 be complex numbers; then $|z_1z_2| = |z_1|\,|z_2|$.

   PROOF.   (This is a generalization of our result in Example 2 above.)

   $|z_1z_2| = \sqrt{(z_1z_2)(\overline{z_1z_2})} = \sqrt{(z_1\overline{z_1})(z_2\overline{z_2})}$ (Problem 4)

   $= \sqrt{|z_1|^2|z_2|^2} = |z_1|\,|z_2|$

4   Let $z = x + iy$. Describe geometrically the set of all complex numbers z such that $|z - 1| = 1$.

   SOLUTION

   $|z - 1| = |(x + iy) - 1| = |(x - 1) + iy|$

   $= \sqrt{(x - 1)^2 + y^2} = 1$

   so that

   $(x - 1)^2 + y^2 = 1$

   which is a circle with center $(1,0)$ and radius 1 (Figure 4).

Figure 4

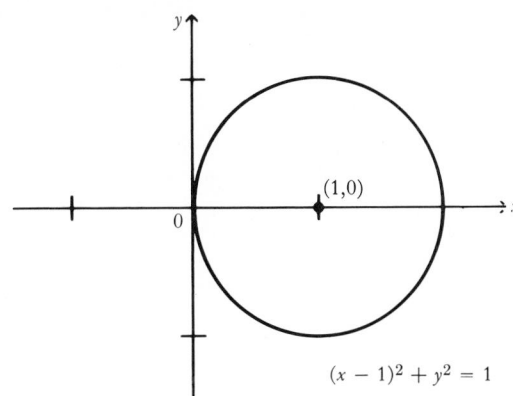

$(x - 1)^2 + y^2 = 1$

4   Polar Coordinates

We have seen that points in the plane can be referenced or associated with pairs of real numbers by using the Cartesian coordinate system. In this section, we will investigate another way of associating pairs of numbers with points in the plane based upon a "grid" composed of concentric circles and rays emanating from the common center of the circles (Figure 1).

Figure 1

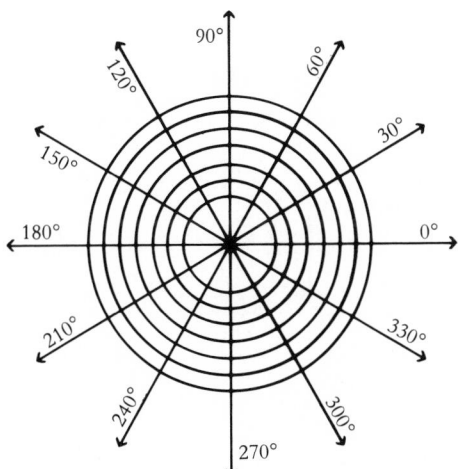

Such a system is called a *polar coordinate system*. The frame of reference for this coordinate system consists of a fixed point O, called the *pole*, and a fixed ray called the *polar axis*. The position of a point P is uniquely determined by r and θ, where θ is any angle in standard position having the ray $\overline{OA}$ as its initial side and a ray on line OP as its terminal side, and r is the directed distance along the terminal side of θ between P and the pole. The pair (r,θ) is called *the polar coordinates* of P (Figure 2).

Figure 2

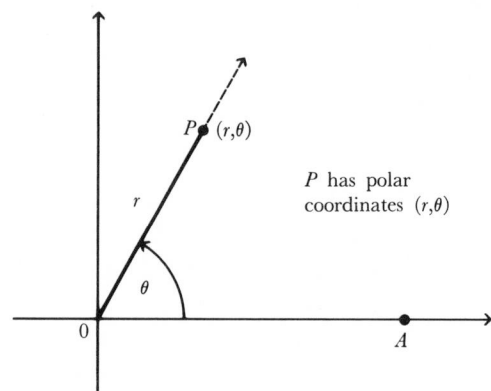

P has polar coordinates (r,θ)

If the angle θ is measured in degrees, then (r,θ) clearly indicates that the ordered pair represents polar coordinates. On the other hand, if θ is given in radians, then the ordered pair of real numbers (r,θ) is in-distinguishable from the notation used in Cartesian coordinates. For example, clearly $(2,30°)$ represents polar coordinates, whereas $(2,3)$ could be rectangular or 3 could be the radian measure of an angle

Figure 3a

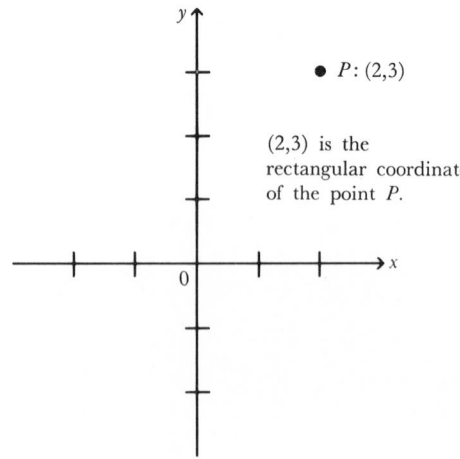

$P: (2,3)$

$(2,3)$ is the rectangular coordinate of the point P.

Figure 3b

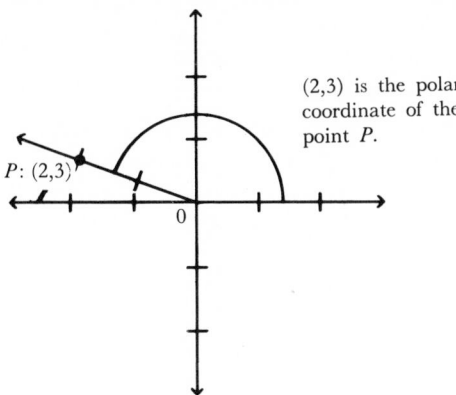

(2,3) is the polar coordinate of the point *P*.

(Figures 3*a* and *b*). If the context does not make clear that these are polar coordinates, we will assume that they are rectangular coordinates.

It is important to observe that a polar coordinate system does not establish a one-to-one correspondence between points in a plane and ordered pairs (*r*,*θ*). In fact, each point can be represented by infinitely many ordered pairs of numbers. For example, (2,30°), (2,390°), and (2,−330°) each represent the same point (Figure 4).

Figure 4

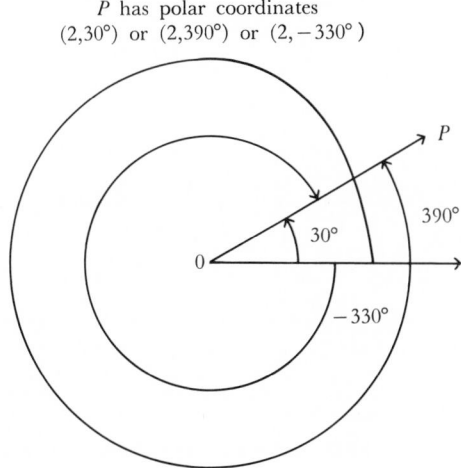

P has polar coordinates
(2,30°) or (2,390°) or (2,−330°)

Also, *r* need not be positive. If *r* < 0, the point (*r*,*θ*) is determined by plotting (|*r*|, *θ* + 180°) or (|*r*|, *θ* + *π*), depending on whether *θ* is measured in degrees or radians. For example, (−2,30°) is the same as (2,210°) (Figure 5).

Figure 5

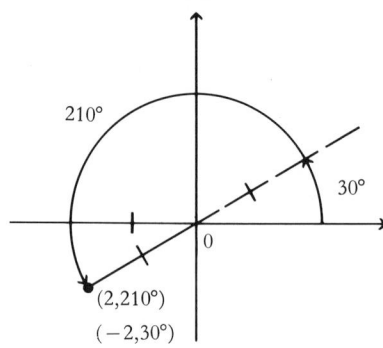

EXAMPLES

1   Plot the points which have the following polar coordinates.

a) $(3,70°)$ b) $(0,0)$ c) $(7,7\pi/5)$

d) $(3,100°)$ e) (π,π) f) $(3,5)$

g) $(5,0)$

SOLUTION.   The points are shown in Figure 6.

Figure 6

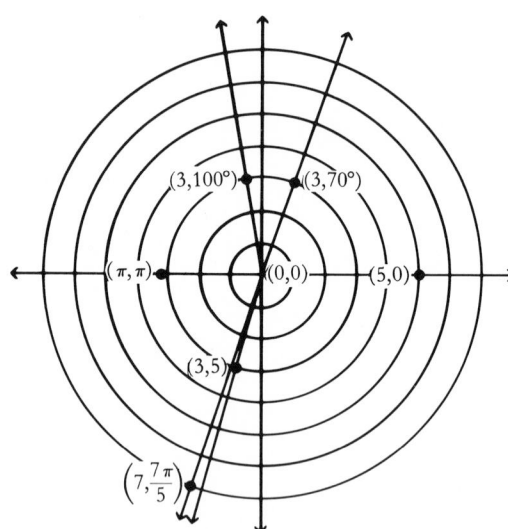

2   Plot polar point $(4,45°)$, and then give five other polar representations of the same point.

SOLUTION. $(4,-315°)$, $(4,405°)$, $(-4,-135°)$, $(-4,225°)$, and $(4, \pi/4)$ are other polar representations of the same point (Figure 7).

Figure 7

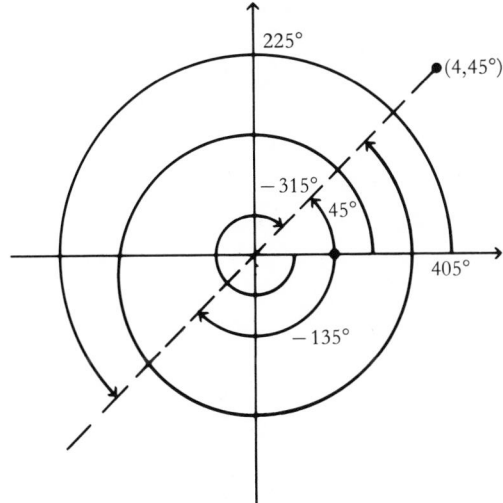

4.1   Conversion of Coordinates

If (r,θ) is a polar representation of a point P, the trigonometric functions can be used to find the rectangular coordinates (x,y) of the same point (Figure 8). We know from trigonometry that $\sin \theta = y/r$ and $\cos \theta = x/r$; hence,

$$y = r \sin \theta \quad \text{and} \quad x = r \cos \theta$$

These formulas are often referred to as the *transformation* or *conversion* formulas; they enable us to convert from *polar to rectangular coordinates.*

Figure 8

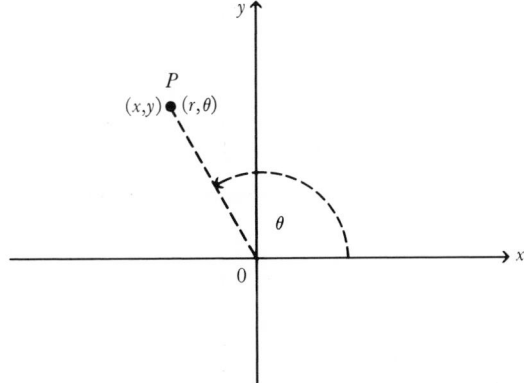

EXAMPLES

Convert the given polar coordinates to rectangular coordinates.

1   $(3,60°)$

2   $(-2,180°)$

3   $(4,-150°)$

4   (π,π)

SOLUTION.

1   $x = r\cos\theta = 3\cos 60° = \frac{3}{2}$ and $y = r\sin\theta = 3\sin 60° = 3\sqrt{3}/2$.
    Hence, the rectangular coordinates are $(\frac{3}{2}, 3\sqrt{3}/2)$ (Figure 9).

Figure 9

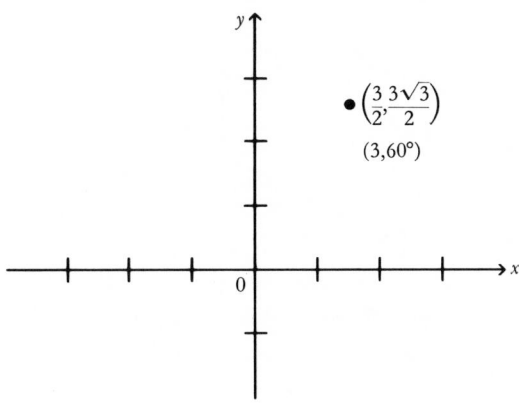

2   $x = r\cos\theta = -2\cos 180° = 2$ and $y = r\sin\theta = -2\sin 180° = 0$.
    Hence the rectangular coordinates are $(2,0)$ (Figure 10).

Figure 10

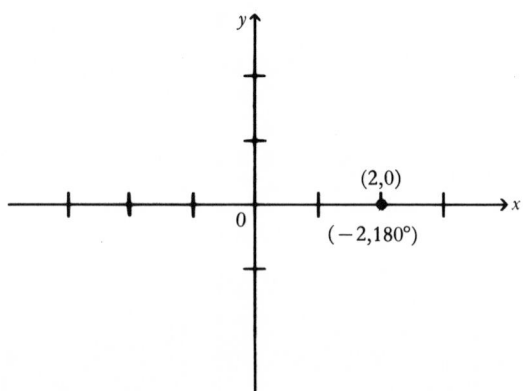

3   $x = r\cos\theta = 4\cos(-150°) = 4(-\sqrt{3}/2) = -2\sqrt{3}$ and
    $y = r\sin\theta = 4\sin(-150°) = 4(-\frac{1}{2}) = -2$. Hence the rectangular
    coordinates are $(-2\sqrt{3}, -2)$ (Figure 11).

Figure 11

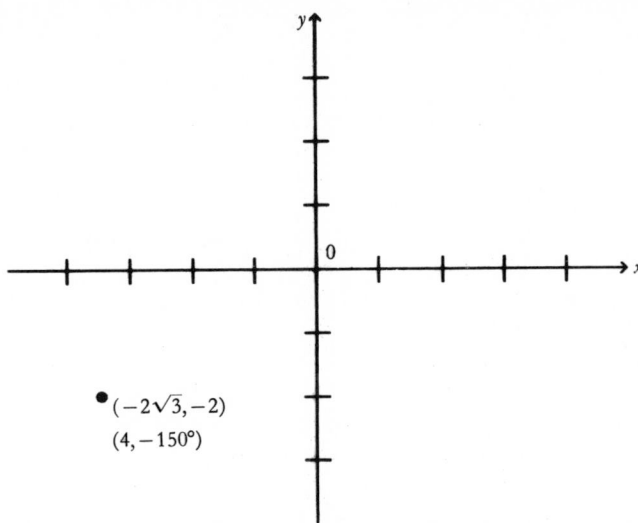

$(-2\sqrt{3},-2)$
$(4,-150°)$

4    $x = r \cos \theta = \pi \cos \pi = -\pi$ and $y = r \sin \theta = \pi \sin \pi = 0$. Hence the rectangular coordinates are $(-\pi,0)$ (Figure 12).

Figure 12

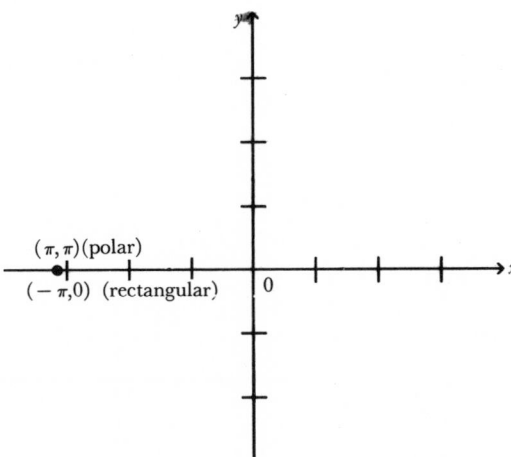

(π,π)(polar)
$(-\pi,0)$ (rectangular)

Now, assume that the rectangular coordinates of a point P are given by (x,y). Then the tangent function can be used to find polar coordinates (r,θ) of the same point (Figure 13). Hence, $r = \sqrt{x^2 + y^2}$ and $\tan \theta = y/x$ can be used to transform the rectangular coordinates to polar coordinates.

Figure 13

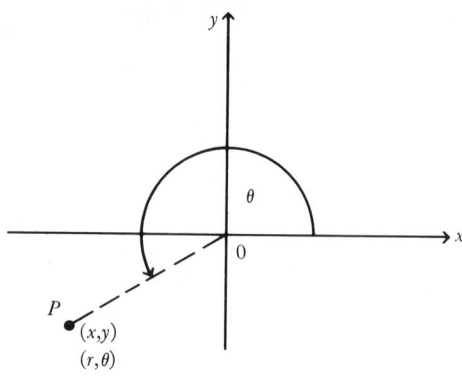

EXAMPLES

Convert the given rectangular coordinates to polar coordinates.

1   $(-1,1)$

2   $(3,-3/\sqrt{3})$

3   $(-3,4)$

SOLUTION

1   $r = \sqrt{x^2 + y^2} = \sqrt{(-1)^2 + 1} = \sqrt{2}$, and, since the point is in quadrant II, $\tan \theta = -1$ implies that $\theta = 135°$; hence, one pair of polar coordinates is $(\sqrt{2},135°)$ (Figure 14).

Figure 14

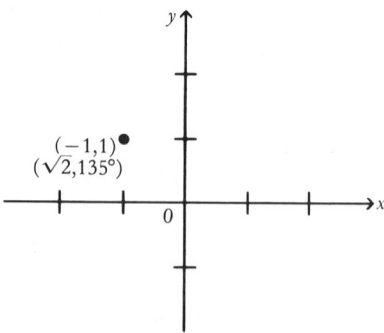

2   $r = \sqrt{3^2 + (-3/\sqrt{3})^2} = \sqrt{9 + 3} = \sqrt{12} = 2\sqrt{3}$ and $\tan \theta = -\sqrt{3}/3 = -1/\sqrt{3}$, so that $\theta = -30°$, since the point is in quadrant IV. Hence, one possible pair of polar coordinates is given by $(2\sqrt{3}, -30°)$ (Figure 15).

Figure 15

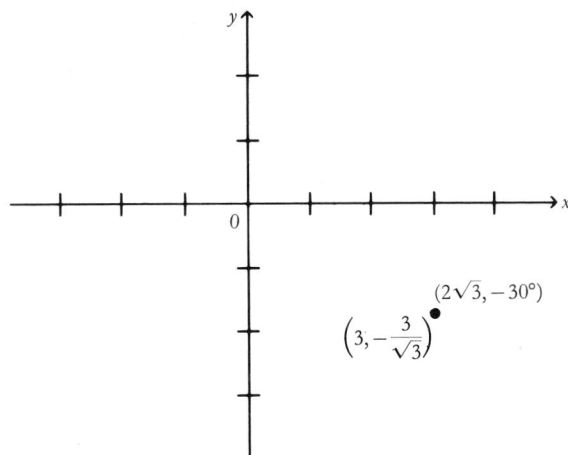

3   $r = \sqrt{(-3)^2 + 4^2} = 5$ and $\tan \theta = -\frac{4}{3} = -1.333\overline{3}$. From Table IV, we find that θ is approximately equal to 127°, so that (5, 127°) is one pair of polar coordinates (Figure 16).

Figure 16

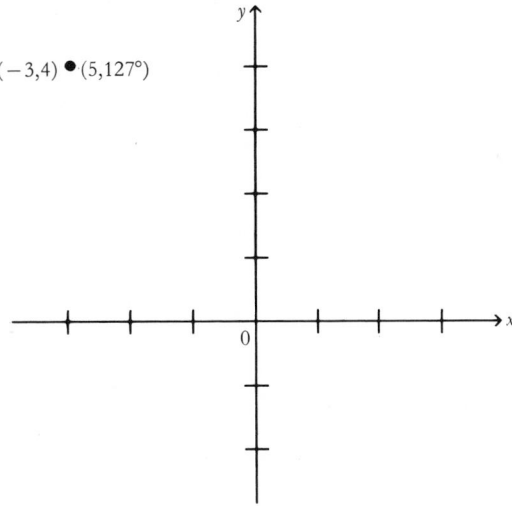

4.2   Polar Form of Complex Numbers

A complex number $z = x + iy$ can be written in the form $z = r \cos \theta + ir \sin \theta$, where $x = r \cos \theta$, $y = r \sin \theta$, and r is the modulus of z (Figure 17). $r(\cos \theta + i \sin \theta)$ is called the *polar form* or *trigonometric form* of the complex number z. The number θ in this representation is called an *argument* of the complex number z. Notice that θ is not unique, since

$$r(\cos \theta + i \sin \theta) = r(\cos \theta_1 + i \sin \theta_1)$$

holds whenever $\theta - \theta_1$ is an integral multiple of 2π. Hence, *two complex numbers are equal if and only if their moduli are equal and their arguments differ by a multiple of 2π*. Thus, we can write the complex number z in the form
$z = x + iy = r[\cos(\theta + 2\pi k) + i \sin(\theta + 2\pi k)], k \in I$.

Figure 17

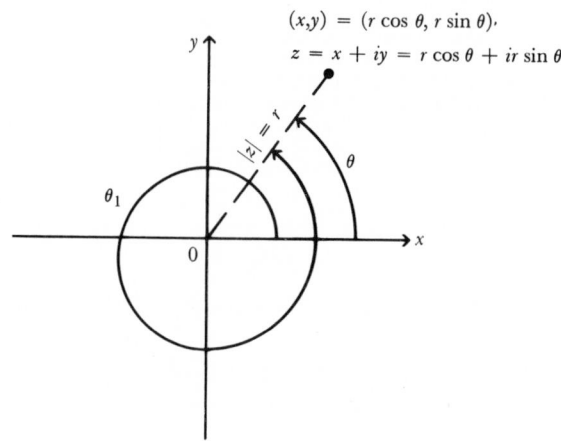

$(x,y) = (r \cos \theta, r \sin \theta)$.

$z = x + iy = r \cos \theta + ir \sin \theta$

For example, the complex number $z = 1 + i$ can be represented in the polar form as $z = \sqrt{2}[\cos(\pi/4) + i \sin(\pi/4)]$, or as $z = \sqrt{2} \times [\cos(9\pi/4) + i \sin(9\pi/4)]$, since $r = \sqrt{1^2 + 1^2} = \sqrt{2}$ and since $\pi/4$ and $9\pi/4$ have the same terminal sides and satisfy $\tan \theta = 1$. Also, z can be represented in the polar form by

$$z = \sqrt{2}\left(\cos \frac{-7\pi}{4} + i \sin \frac{-7\pi}{4}\right)$$
$$= \sqrt{2}\left(\cos \frac{7\pi}{4} - i \sin \frac{7\pi}{4}\right) \qquad \text{(Figure 18)}$$

Figure 18

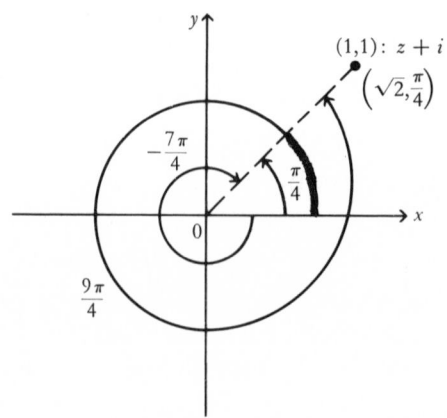

$(1,1): z + i$

$\left(\sqrt{2}, \frac{\pi}{4}\right)$

Notice that $(\sqrt{2}, 9\pi/4)$ and $(\sqrt{2}, -7\pi/4)$ are possible polar coordinates of $(1,1)$.

EXAMPLES

1 Change each of the following complex numbers from polar form to rectangular form.

   a) $z = 2[\cos(\pi/3) + i\sin(\pi/3)]$
   b) $z = 4[\cos(-\pi/6) + i\sin(-\pi/6)]$
   c) $z = 8[\cos(\pi/2) + i\sin(\pi/2)]$

SOLUTION.

   a) $z = x + iy = 2\cos\dfrac{\pi}{3} + i2\sin\dfrac{\pi}{3} = 2\cdot\frac{1}{2} + i\cdot 2\,\dfrac{\sqrt{3}}{2} = 1 + i\sqrt{3}$

   b) $z = x + iy = 4\cos\left(-\dfrac{\pi}{6}\right) + i4\sin\left(-\dfrac{\pi}{6}\right) = 4\,\dfrac{\sqrt{3}}{2} + i\cdot 4(-\frac{1}{2})$

        $= 2\sqrt{3} - 2i$

   c) $z = x + iy = 8\cos\dfrac{\pi}{2} + 8i\sin\dfrac{\pi}{2} = 8\cdot 0 + i8\cdot 1 = 8i$

2 Change each of the following complex numbers from rectangular form to polar form.

   a) $z = 2 + 0i$
   b) $z = -\sqrt{3} - i$

SOLUTION. (See Figure 19.)

   a) $2 + 0i = r(\cos\theta + i\sin\theta)$, where $r = \sqrt{2^2 + 0^2} = 2$ and an argument is $\theta = 0$, so that $z = 2(\cos 0 + i\sin 0)$.

   b) $z = r(\cos\theta + i\sin\theta)$, where $r = \sqrt{(-\sqrt{3})^2 + (-1)^2} = 2$, and θ satisfies $\tan\theta = 1/\sqrt{3}$ with θ in quadrant **III**, so that one value of θ is $\theta = 7\pi/6$. Hence, $z = 2[\cos(7\pi/6) + i\sin(7\pi/6)]$.

Figure 19

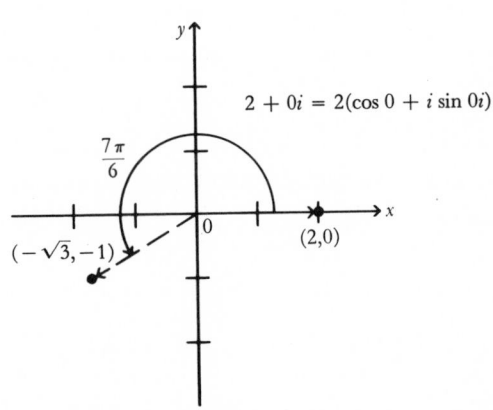

3 Consider the complex numbers $z_1 = 1 + i$ and $z_2 = 1 + \sqrt{3}\,i$. The polar representation of z_1 and z_2 can be given by

$$z_1 = \sqrt{2}\left(\cos\frac{\pi}{4} + i\sin\frac{\pi}{4}\right) \quad \text{and} \quad z_2 = 2\left(\cos\frac{\pi}{3} + i\sin\frac{\pi}{3}\right)$$

The modulus of z_1 is $r = \sqrt{2}$ and an argument is $\pi/4$; and the modulus of z_2 is $r_2 = 2$ and an argument is $\pi/3$. By multiplication, we find that

$$z_1 z_2 = 2\sqrt{2}\left[\left(\cos\frac{\pi}{4}\cos\frac{\pi}{3} - \sin\frac{\pi}{4}\sin\frac{\pi}{3}\right)\right.$$
$$\left. + i\left(\sin\frac{\pi}{4}\cos\frac{\pi}{3} + \sin\frac{\pi}{3}\cos\frac{\pi}{4}\right)\right]$$

This product can be simplified by using the trigonometric identities:

$$2\sqrt{2}\left[\cos\left(\frac{\pi}{4} + \frac{\pi}{3}\right) + i\sin\left(\frac{\pi}{4} + \frac{\pi}{3}\right)\right] = 2\sqrt{2}\left(\cos\frac{7\pi}{12} + i\sin\frac{7\pi}{12}\right)$$

(Figure 20)

Figure 20

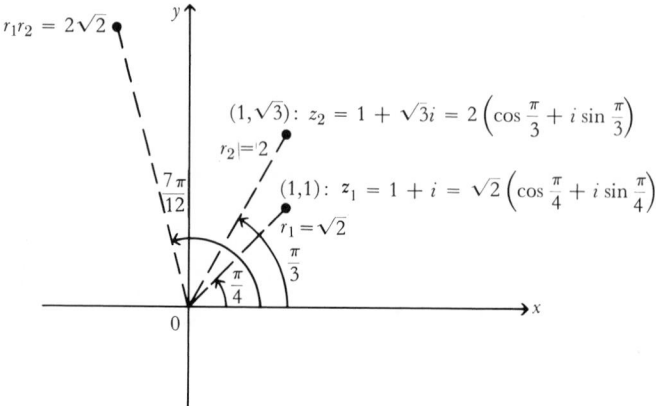

Notice in Example 3 above that the modulus of the product $z_1 z_2$ satisfies $|z_1 z_2| = |z_1|\,|z_2| = r_1 r_2 = 2\sqrt{2}$ and an argument of $z_1 z_2$ is $\pi/4 + \pi/3 = 7\pi/12$. The following theorem generalizes the results of this example.

THEOREM 1

Suppose that z_1 and z_2 are complex numbers in polar form; that is,

$$z_1 = r_1(\cos\theta_1 + i\sin\theta_1)$$

and

$$z_2 = r_2(\cos \theta_2 + i \sin \theta_2)$$

Then

$$z_1 z_2 = r_1 r_2[\cos (\theta_1 + \theta_2) + i \sin (\theta_1 + \theta_2)]$$

(This theorem states that the product of two complex numbers is the complex number whose modulus is the product of the moduli of the two complex numbers, and with an argument which is the sum of the arguments of the two complex numbers.)

PROOF

$$\begin{aligned} z_1 z_2 &= r_1(\cos \theta_1 + i \sin \theta_1)r_2(\cos \theta_2 + i \sin \theta_2) \\ &= r_1 r_2[(\cos \theta_1 \cos \theta_2 - \sin \theta_1 \sin \theta_2) \\ &\quad + i(\cos \theta_1 \sin \theta_2 + \cos \theta_2 \sin \theta_1)] \end{aligned}$$

Using the trigonometric identities for $\cos (\theta_1 + \theta_2)$ and $\sin (\theta_1 + \theta_2)$, we can write this latter result as

$$z_1 z_2 = r_1 r_2[\cos (\theta_1 + \theta_2) + i \sin (\theta_1 + \theta_2)]$$

EXAMPLES

1   Let $z_1 = 7(\cos 25° + i \sin 25°)$ and $z_2 = 3(\cos 35° + i \sin 35°)$. Find

a) $z_1 z_2$ in rectangular form
b) z_1^2 in polar form

SOLUTION

a)   The modulus of $z_1 z_2$ is $r_1 r_2 = 7(3) = 21$ and an argument of $z_1 z_2$ is $\theta_1 + \theta_2 = 25° + 35° = 60°$. Hence,

$$\begin{aligned} z_1 z_2 &= 21(\cos 60° + i \sin 60°) \\ &= 21 \left(\frac{1}{2} + i \frac{\sqrt{3}}{2} \right) \\ &= \frac{21}{2} + i \frac{21\sqrt{3}}{2} \end{aligned}$$

b)   The modulus of z_1^2 is $r_1^2 = 49$, and an argument is $2\theta_1 = 2(25°) = 50°$. Hence $z_1^2 = 49(\cos 50° + i \sin 50°)$.

2   Convert $z_1 = 1 + i$ and $z_2 = 2 - 2\sqrt{3}\,i$ to polar form, and then compute $z_1 z_2$ in polar form and in rectangular form.

SOLUTION.   (See Figure 21.) The modulus of z_1 is $r_1 = \sqrt{1 + 1} = \sqrt{2}$ and the modulus of z_2 is $r_2 = \sqrt{4 + 12} = 4$. An argument of z_1 is

$\theta_1 = \pi/4$, and an argument of z_2 is $\theta_2 = -\pi/3$. Hence,

$$z_1z_2 = 4\sqrt{2}\left(\cos\frac{-\pi}{12} + i\sin\frac{-\pi}{12}\right)$$

so that the rectangular form is

$$z_1z_2 = 4\sqrt{2}(0.9659 - i(0.2588))$$

Figure 21

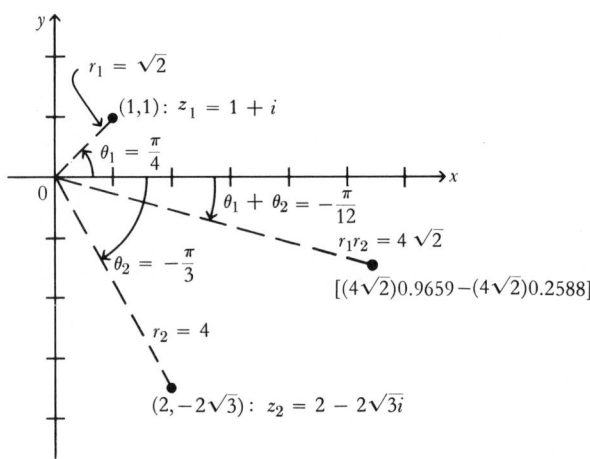

To find the quotient z_1/z_2 of two complex numbers $z_1 = 6 + 6\sqrt{3}\,i$ and $z_2 = 2\sqrt{2} + i2\sqrt{2}$, we can first plot z_1 and z_2 as shown in Figure 21. Two polar representation of z_1 and z_2 are $z_1 = 12[\cos(\pi/3) + i\sin(\pi/3)]$ and $z_2 = 4[\cos(\pi/4) + i\sin(\pi/4)]$. We are looking for a complex number $z_3 = r_3(\cos\theta_3 + i\sin\theta_3)$ such that $z_1 = z_2z_3$. Hence, if we use Theorem 1, we see that r_3 and θ_3 should be chosen so that

$$r_1(\cos\theta_1 + i\sin\theta_1) = r_2r_3[\cos(\theta_2 + \theta_3) + i\sin(\theta_2 + \theta_3)]$$

that is,

$$12\left(\cos\frac{\pi}{3} + i\sin\frac{\pi}{3}\right) = 4r_3\left[\cos\left(\frac{\pi}{4} + \theta_3\right) + i\sin\left(\frac{\pi}{4} + \theta_3\right)\right]$$

But two complex numbers are equal if and only if their moduli are equal and their arguments differ by a multiple of 2π. Thus,

$$12 = 4r_3 \quad \text{and} \quad \frac{\pi}{3} = \frac{\pi}{4} + \theta_3 + 2\pi k \qquad k \in I$$

that is,

$$r_3 = 3 \quad \text{and} \quad \theta_3 = \frac{\pi}{3} - \frac{\pi}{4} - 2\pi k \qquad k \in I$$

Since $\cos (\pi/3 - \pi/4 - 2\pi k) = \cos (\pi/3 - \pi/4)$ and $\sin (\pi/3 - \pi/4 - 2\pi k) = \sin (\pi/3 - \pi/4)$, the polar form of the quotient z_1/z_2 can be written as (Figure 22):

$$\frac{z_1}{z_2} = \frac{12}{4}\left[\cos\left(\frac{\pi}{3} - \frac{\pi}{4}\right) + i \sin\left(\frac{\pi}{3} - \frac{\pi}{4}\right)\right]$$

$$= 3\left(\cos\frac{\pi}{12} + i \sin\frac{\pi}{12}\right)$$

Figure 22

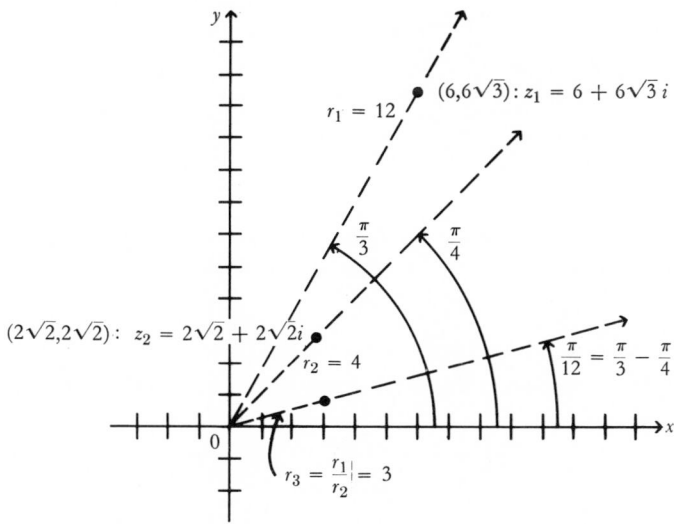

In general, we have the following result.

THEOREM 2

Let $z_1 = r_1(\cos\theta_1 + i\sin\theta_1)$ and $z_2 = r_2(\cos\theta_2 + i\sin\theta_2)$; then

$$\frac{z_1}{z_2} = \frac{r_1}{r_2}[\cos(\theta_1 - \theta_2) + i\sin(\theta_1 - \theta_2)] \qquad z_2 \neq 0$$

The proof of this theorem is left as an exercise for the student (see Problem 7).

EXAMPLES

1 Let $z_1 = 4(\cos 80° + i\sin 80°)$ and $z_2 = 2(\cos 50° + i\sin 50°)$. Find z_1/z_2 and express the result in rectangular form.

SOLUTION. Since $z_2 \neq 0$, we use Theorem 2 to get

$$\frac{z_1}{z_2} = \frac{4}{2}[\cos(80° - 50°) + i\sin(80° - 50°)]$$

$$= 2(\cos 30° + i\sin 30°)$$

$$= 2\left(\frac{\sqrt{3}}{2} + i\frac{1}{2}\right) = \sqrt{3} + i$$

2   Express $z_1 = -1 + i$ and $z_2 = -4i$ in polar form, and then compute z_1/z_2 in polar form. Write your answer in rectangular form also.

SOLUTION.   (See Figure 23.) The modulus of z_1 is $r_1 = \sqrt{2}$ and an argument is $3\pi/4$. (Why?) The modulus of z_2 is $r_2 = 4$, and an argument is $3\pi/2$. Using Theorem 2, we have

$$\frac{z_1}{z_2} = \frac{\sqrt{2}}{4}\left[\cos\left(\frac{3\pi}{4} - \frac{3\pi}{2}\right) + i \sin\left(\frac{3\pi}{4} - \frac{3\pi}{2}\right)\right]$$

$$= \frac{\sqrt{2}}{4}\left[\cos\left(-\frac{3\pi}{4}\right) + i \sin\left(-\frac{3\pi}{4}\right)\right]$$

$$= \frac{\sqrt{2}}{4}\left(\cos\frac{3\pi}{4} - i \sin\frac{3\pi}{4}\right)$$

$$= \frac{\sqrt{2}}{4}\left(-\frac{1}{\sqrt{2}} - i \frac{1}{\sqrt{2}}\right)$$

$$= -\frac{1}{4} - \frac{1}{4} i$$

Figure 23

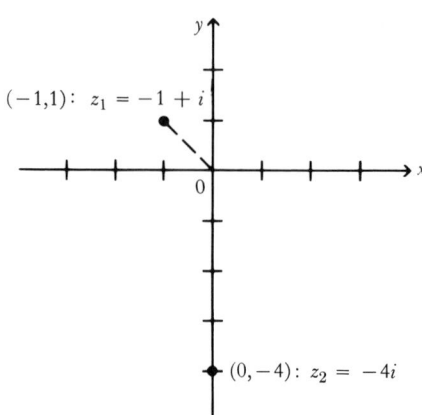

PROBLEM SET 2

1   Plot each of the rectangular coordinates and then convert to polar coordinates.

a) $(-1, \sqrt{3})$ b) $(-3, 0)$
c) $(4, 3)$ d) $(-6, 6\sqrt{3})$
e) $(5, 5)$ f) $(0, -2)$
g) $(-3, 3\sqrt{3})$ h) $(2\sqrt{3}, -2)$
i) $(-5, -5)$ j) $(-3, 5)$

2   Plot the polar points of the following pairs and convert the representation to rectangular form.

a) $(6, 30°)$ b) $(10, \pi/3)$
c) $(7, 120°)$ d) $(-4, -\pi/6)$

e) (4,90°)   f) (8,45°)
g) $(2\pi, -\pi/6)$ h) $(5,\pi/2)$
i) (4,210°)   j) (4,330°)

3   Let $z = x + iy$. Describe the following sets geometrically.
a) $\{z \| z | = 1\}$ b) $\{z \| z | = 2\}$
c) $\{z \| z - i | = 1\}$ d) $\{z \| z - 1 | = |z - 2|\}$

4   Prove that $|z| = \sqrt{z\bar{z}}$.

5   For each of the following complex numbers, find the modulus and the
argument. Express these numbers in polar form, and then represent
them graphically.
a) $-1 - i$ b) 7
c) $-2i$ d) $(1 - i)^2$
e) $(-\sqrt{3} - i)^3$ f) $3 + 4i$
g) $-\frac{1}{2} + (\sqrt{3}/2)i$ h) $\sqrt{3}/2 + \frac{1}{2}i$
i) $(1 - \sqrt{3}\,i)^3$

6   Represent each of the following complex numbers graphically, and then
express the number in the form of $a + bi$.
a) $z = 2(\cos 10° + i \sin 10°)$
b) $z = 3[\cos (-75°) + i \sin (-75°)]$
c) $z = 4(\cos 0° + i \sin 0°)$
d) $z = 2[\cos (\pi/4) + i \sin (\pi/4)]$
e) $z = 10[\cos (3\pi/4) + i \sin (3\pi/4)]$
f) $z = 2[\cos (\pi/2) + i \sin (\pi/2)]$
g) $z = 7[\cos (-3\pi/2) + i \sin (-3\pi/2)]$

7   Prove Theorem 2 by generalizing the example preceding the statement of Theorem 2.

8   Find $z_1 z_2$ and z_1/z_2 for each of the following numbers, and express the
answer in both polar and rectangular form.
a) $z_1 = 5(\cos 170° + i \sin 170°)$ and $z_2 = (\cos 55° + i \sin 55°)$
b) $z_1 = 2(\cos 50° + i \sin 50°)$ and $z_2 = 3(\cos 40° + i \sin 40°)$
c) $z_1 = 4[\cos (3\pi/4) + i \sin (3\pi/4)]$ and $z_2 = 2(\cos \pi + i \sin \pi)$

9   Convert $z_1 = -1 - i$ and $z_2 = -4 + 4\sqrt{3}\,i$ to polar form, and then
compute each of the following values in polar form. Convert the
answers to rectangular form.
a) $z_1 z_2$
b) z_1/z_2
c) $(z_1 z_2)^2$

10 Let $z_1 = \cos 30° + i \sin 30°$ and $z_2 = \cos 60° + i \sin 60°$. Find $z_1 z_2$
and z_2/z_1 and represent them graphically.

5   Roots of Complex Numbers

It was shown in Section 4.2 that if $z = r(\cos \theta + i \sin \theta)$, then $z^2 = r^2(\cos 2\theta + i \sin 2\theta)$. Now, $z^3 = z^2 \cdot z$, so that,

$$z^3 = r^2 \cdot r[\cos (2\theta + \theta) + i \sin (2\theta + \theta)]$$
$$= r^3(\cos 3\theta + i \sin 3\theta)$$

If we repeat the process once more, we get

$$z^4 = z^3 \cdot z = r^4(\cos 4\theta + i \sin 4\theta)$$

This scheme for repeated multiplication of complex numbers in polar form is generalized in the following theorem.

THEOREM 1   (DEMOIVRE'S THEOREM)

Let $z = r(\cos \theta + i \sin \theta)$. Then $z^n = r^n(\cos n\theta + i \sin n\theta)$ for n a positive integer.

PROOF.   We use mathematical induction to prove this theorem. Let S_n be the statement

$$[r(\cos \theta + i \sin \theta)]^n = r^n(\cos n\theta + i \sin n\theta)$$

i   The statement S_1 is true, since

$$r(\cos \theta + i \sin \theta) = r(\cos \theta + i \sin \theta)$$

ii   We must show that if S_n is true, then the statement S_{n+1} is also true. If S_n is true, that is, if $[r(\cos \theta + i \sin \theta)]^n = r^n(\cos n\theta + i \sin n\theta)$, then, after multiplying both sides by $r(\cos \theta + i \sin \theta)$, we get

$$[r(\cos \theta + i \sin \theta)]^{n+1}$$
$$= [r(\cos \theta + i \sin \theta)]^n[r(\cos \theta + i \sin \theta)]$$
$$= [r^n(\cos n\theta + i \sin n\theta)][r(\cos \theta + i \sin \theta)]$$
$$= r^{n+1}[\cos (n + 1)\theta + i \sin (n + 1)\theta]$$

which shows that S_{n+1} is true, so that S_n is true for any positive integer n; that is,

$$[r(\cos \theta + i \sin \theta)]^n = r^n(\cos n\theta + i \sin n\theta)$$

EXAMPLES

1   Use DeMoivre's theorem to determine each of the following values.

a) $[3(\cos 60° + i \sin 60°)]^4$ in rectangular form

b) $(1 + i)^{20}$ in rectangular form

SOLUTION

a)   Using DeMoivre's theorem, we have

$$[3(\cos 60° + i \sin 60°)]^4 = 3^4(\cos 240° + i \sin 240°)$$
$$= 81\left(-\frac{1}{2} - \frac{i\sqrt{3}}{2}\right) = -\frac{81}{2} - \frac{81\sqrt{3}}{2}i$$

b)   The complex number $1 + i$ can be expressed in the polar form as

$$\sqrt{2}\left(\cos\frac{\pi}{4} + i \sin\frac{\pi}{4}\right)$$

where the modulus is $\sqrt{2}$ and the argument is $\pi/4$. Using DeMoivre's theorem, we have

$$(1 + i)^{20} = \left[\sqrt{2}\left(\cos\frac{\pi}{4} + i \sin\frac{\pi}{4}\right)\right]^{20}$$
$$= 2^{10}(\cos 5\pi + i \sin 5\pi)$$
$$= 1024(-1 + 0i) = -1024$$

2   Use DeMoivre's theorem to express $\cos 2\theta$ and $\sin 2\theta$ in terms of $\sin \theta$ and $\cos \theta$.

SOLUTION.   By DeMoivre's theorem for $n = 2$, we have

$$\cos 2\theta + i \sin 2\theta = (\cos \theta + i \sin \theta)^2$$
$$= \cos^2 \theta + i2 \sin \theta \cos \theta - \sin^2 \theta$$
$$= (\cos^2 \theta - \sin^2 \theta) + i2 \sin \theta \cos \theta$$

Since the two complex numbers are equal, the real parts are equal; that is,

$$\cos 2\theta = \cos^2 \theta - \sin^2 \theta$$

The imaginary parts are also equal; that is,

$$\sin 2\theta = 2 \sin \theta \cos \theta$$

5.1   Roots

DeMoivre's theorem is useful in finding the n roots of a complex number, for if $w = R(\cos \phi + i \sin \phi)$ and $z = r(\cos \theta + i \sin \theta)$ is any solution of $z^n = w$, where n is a positive integer, then, by DeMoivre's theorem, it follows that

$$[r(\cos \theta + i \sin \theta)]^n = r^n(\cos n\theta + i \sin n\theta)$$
$$= R(\cos \phi + i \sin \phi)$$

so that

$$r^n = R$$

or, equivalently

$$r = \sqrt[n]{R} \qquad \text{(Notice that } R \geq 0.)$$

and

$$n\theta = \phi + 2k\pi \qquad (n\theta = \phi + 360°k \text{ if degrees are used)}$$

or, equivalently,

$$\theta = \frac{\phi}{n} + \frac{2k\pi}{n} \qquad \left(\theta = \frac{\phi}{n} + \frac{360°k}{n} \text{ if degrees are used} \right)$$

where $k = 0, \pm 1, \pm 2, \ldots$.
We will see in the examples below that those values of k from 0 to $n - 1$ give us all *distinct* n roots that exist.

EXAMPLES

1   Find the 4th roots of $1 + i$ in polar form.

SOLUTION.   As our first step, we determine the polar representation, $R(\cos \phi + i \sin \phi)$, of $1 + i$. Here, $R = \sqrt{2}$ and $\phi = \pi/4$. Finally, we obtain the roots $z = r(\cos \theta + i \sin \theta)$ by using the formulas for r and θ:

$$r = \sqrt[4]{\sqrt{2}} \qquad \text{and} \qquad \theta = \frac{\pi}{16} + \frac{2\pi k}{4} \qquad k = 0, 1, 2, 3, \ldots$$

so that the roots are

$$z_0 = \sqrt[8]{2} \left(\cos \frac{\pi}{16} + i \sin \frac{\pi}{16} \right) \qquad \text{for } k = 0$$

$$z_1 = \sqrt[8]{2} \left(\cos \frac{9\pi}{16} + i \sin \frac{9\pi}{16} \right) \qquad \text{for } k = 1$$

$$z_2 = \sqrt[8]{2} \left(\cos \frac{17\pi}{16} + i \sin \frac{17\pi}{16} \right) \qquad \text{for } k = 2$$

$$z_3 = \sqrt[8]{2} \left(\cos \frac{25\pi}{16} + i \sin \frac{25\pi}{16} \right) \qquad \text{for } k = 3$$

The fourth roots of $1 + i$ are equally spaced on the circumference of a circle of radius $\sqrt[8]{2}$ and differ by angles of $\pi/2$ radians (Figure 1). Notice that if we were to set $k = 4$, we would get

$$z_4 = \sqrt[8]{2} \left(\cos \frac{33\pi}{16} + i \sin \frac{33\pi}{16} \right)$$

Figure 1

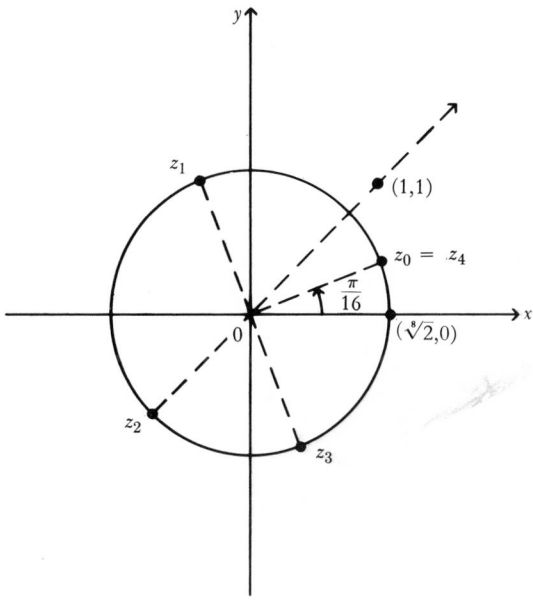

which is the same number as z_0. In general, if $k = 4, 5, 6, \ldots$, we would get a repetition of the roots which we have already found.

2   The solutions to $z^n = 1$ are called the *nth roots of unity*. Find the 5th roots of unity in polar form.

SOLUTION.   The number 1 can be written in polar form as $1 = 1(\cos 0 + i \sin 0)$. We obtain the five roots $z = r(\cos \theta + i \sin \theta)$ by using the formulas

$$r = \sqrt[5]{1} \qquad \text{and} \qquad \theta = \frac{0}{5} + \frac{2\pi k}{5} \qquad k = 0, 1, 2, 3, 4$$

so that the roots are

$$z_0 = 1(\cos 0 + i \sin 0) \qquad \text{for } k = 0$$

$$z_1 = 1\left(\cos \frac{2\pi}{5} + i \sin \frac{2\pi}{5}\right) \qquad \text{for } k = 1$$

$$z_2 = 1\left(\cos \frac{4\pi}{5} + i \sin \frac{4\pi}{5}\right) \qquad \text{for } k = 2$$

$$z_3 = 1\left(\cos \frac{6\pi}{5} + i \sin \frac{6\pi}{5}\right) \qquad \text{for } k = 3$$

$$z_4 = 1\left(\cos \frac{8\pi}{5} + i \sin \frac{8\pi}{5}\right) \qquad \text{for } k = 4$$

We observe that all the fifth roots of unity are on a unit circle and they are equally spaced at angles of $2\pi/5$ radians (Figure 2). Again, $k = 5$, 6, ... would give us a repetition of the roots which we have already found.

Figure 2

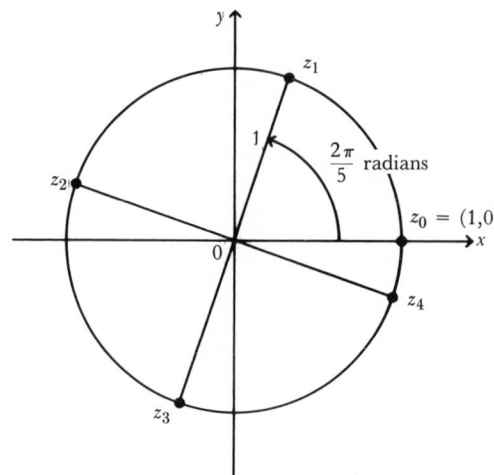

PROBLEM SET 3

1 Use DeMoivre's theorem to calculate each of the following powers. Express the result in the rectangular form $a + bi$.

a) $(\cos 30° + i \sin 30°)^7$ b) $(1 + i\sqrt{3})^5$
c) $(5 + 5i)^6$ d) $(\sqrt{3} - i)^4$
e) $(-\frac{1}{2} - i\sqrt{3}/2)^8$ f) $(\cos 15° + i \sin 15°)^8$
g) $(\sqrt{3} + i)^{30}$ h) $(1 + i)^{50}$
i) $(\sqrt{3} + i)^3/(1 - \sqrt{3} i)^3$
j) $[(1 + i)/\sqrt{2}]^{100}[(1 + i\sqrt{3})/2]^{30}$

2 Use DeMoivre's theorem to derive formulas for $\cos 3\theta$ and $\sin 3\theta$.

3 a) Find the 6th roots of unity.
   b) Describe the geometric position of the six 6th roots.

4 a) Find the 5th roots of -32.
   b) Describe the geometric positions of the five 5th roots.
   c) Find the sum of the five 5th roots.

5 We define $z = \sqrt{w}$ to be a number which satisfies $z^2 = w$. Write each of the following numbers in the form of $a + bi$.

a) $\sqrt{i}$ b) $\sqrt{i^5}$
c) $\sqrt{3 - 3i}$ d) $\sqrt{16i}$

6 Use DeMoivre's theorem, together with Theorem 2 of Section 4.2, to show that if $z = r(\cos \theta + i \sin \theta)$, then

$$z^{-n} = r^{-n}[\cos (-n\theta) + i \sin (-n\theta)]$$

where n is a positive integer.

7 Find all the roots in the following equations.

a) $z^3 = 8$ b) $z^2 = 1 - i$
c) $z^4 = -16$ d) $z^3 = i$

6 Complex Zeros of Polynomial Functions

We have seen (Chapter 3) that a polynomial function with real coefficients does not always have real number zeros. In particular, a quadratic polynomial function $f(x) = ax^2 + bx + c$, $a, b, c \in R$, $a \neq 0$, has real zeros if and only if the discriminant, $b^2 - 4ac$, is nonnegative. These real roots can be found by the quadratic formula

$$x = \frac{-b \pm \sqrt{b^2 - 4ac}}{2a}$$

If the zeros of the quadratic polynomial function are not real numbers, that is, if $b^2 - 4ac < 0$, the zeros are complex numbers and the quadratic formula can still be used. For example, the zeros of $f(x) = 2x^2 + x + 1$ can be found by using the quadratic formula; hence,

$$x = \frac{-1 \pm \sqrt{1 - 8}}{4} = \frac{-1 \pm \sqrt{-7}}{4} = -\frac{1 \pm \sqrt{7}\,i}{4}$$

The polynomial function $f(x) = x^3 - 6x^2 + 13x - 10$ can be factored as $f(x) = (x - 2)(x^2 - 4x + 5)$, so that after using the quadratic formula, we find that the zeros of f are 2, $2 - i$, and $2 + i$, and

$$f(x) = (x - 2)[(x - (2 - i)][(x - (2 + i)]$$

In general, all polynomial functions are factorable as the product of linear factors in the complex domain.

Notice that

$$2x^2 + x + 1 = 2\left(x - \frac{-1 + \sqrt{7}\,i}{4}\right)\left(x - \frac{-1 - \sqrt{7}\,i}{4}\right)$$

This result follows as a corollary of the *fundamental theorem of algebra*, whose proof depends upon methods generally considered beyond the scope of this text. We shall state the theorem without proof.

6.1   FUNDAMENTAL THEOREM OF ALGEBRA

If $f(x)$ is a polynomial of degree $n \geq 1$ with complex coefficients, then there is a complex number r such that $f(r) = 0$.

THEOREM 1   (THE FACTORIZATION THEOREM)

If $f(x) = a_n x^n + a_{n-1} x^{n-1} + \cdots + a_1 x + a_0$ and $a_n \neq 0$, n a positive integer, then

$$f(x) = a_n(x - r_1)(x - r_2) \ldots (x - r_n)$$

where the numbers r_j are complex numbers.

PROOF.   By the fundamental theorem of algebra, $f(x) = 0$ has a root r_1, so that by the factor theorem (see Chapter 3).

$$f(x) = (x - r_1)Q_1(x)$$

$Q_1(x)$ is a polynomial of degree $n - 1$, so that it has a zero r_2 if $n - 1 \geq 1$, and, as above,

$$Q_1(x) = (x - r_2)Q_2(x)$$

so that

$$f(x) = (x - r_1)(x - r_2)Q_2(x)$$

where $Q_2(x)$ has degree $n - 2$. Continuing the process, we get

$$f(x) = (x - r_1)(x - r_2) \ldots (x - r_n)Q_n(x)$$

where $Q_n(x)$ has degree 0, that is, $Q_n(x)$ is a constant. Multiplying out this expression for $f(x)$, it is seen that the coefficient of x^n is Q_n; hence $Q_n = a_n$ and the theorem is proved.

COROLLARY 2

If $f(x)$ is a polynomial function of degree n, $n \neq 0$, then $f(x) = 0$ has exactly n roots. (Not all roots are necessarily different.)

PROOF.   By the factorization theorem,

$$f(x) = a_n(x - r_1)(x - r_2) \ldots (x - r_n)$$

Clearly, the numbers $r_1, r_2, \ldots, r_n$ are roots of $f(x) = 0$. Moreover, if $f(r) = 0$ for $r \neq r_i$, $i = 1, \ldots, n$, then

$$f(x) = a_n(x - r_1)(x - r_2) \cdots (x - r_n)(x - r)$$

so that the degree of $f(x)$ is $n + 1$ (Why?), which contradicts our assumption that $f(x)$ is a polynomial of degree n.

Notice that the roots need not be distinct. For example, $x^2 - 4x + 4 = 0$ has two roots, both of which are equal to 2 and we say that $f(x) = x^2 - 4x + 4$ has $x = 2$ as a double root. In general, if

$$f(x) = (x - r)^s Q(x) \quad \text{and} \quad Q(r) \neq 0$$

we say that r is a zero of *multiplicity s*. For example $f(x) = (x - 1)^2 \times (x - 2)$ has $x = 1$ as a root of multiplicity 2 and $x = 2$ as a root of multiplicity 1.

THEOREM 3 (CONJUGATE ROOT THEOREM)

If a polynomial of degree n, $n \neq 0$, has *real* coefficients and $f(z_0) = 0$, where $z_0 = a + bi$, then $f(\overline{z_0}) = 0$.

PROOF. Let $f(z) = a_n z^n + a_{n-1} z^{n-1} + \cdots + a_1 z + a_0$ be a polynomial with real coefficients. Since $z_0 = a + bi$ is a zero of $f(z)$, then

$$f(z_0) = a_n z_0^n + a_{n-1} z_0^{n-1} + \cdots + a_1 z_0 + a_0 = 0$$

so that

$$\overline{f(z_0)} = \overline{a_n z_0^n + a_{n-1} z_0^{n-1} + \cdots + a_1 z_0 + a_0} = \overline{0} = 0$$

However,

$$\overline{a_n z_0^n + a_{n-1} z_0^{n-1} + \cdots + a_n z_0 + a_0}$$
$$= \overline{a_n z_0^n} + \overline{a_{n-1} z_0^{n-1}} \cdots + \overline{a_n z_0} + \overline{a_0}$$

because the conjugate of the sum of two complex numbers is the same as the sum of the conjugate of two complex numbers (see Problem set 1, Problem 4c). Also,

$$\overline{a_n z_0^n} = \overline{a_n} \overline{z_0}^n,$$

$$\overline{a_{n-1} a_0^{n-1}} = \overline{a_{n-1}} \overline{z_0}^{n-1}, \ldots, \overline{a_1 z_0} = \overline{a_1} \overline{z_0}$$

and

$$\overline{a_n} \overline{z_0}^n = \overline{a_n} \overline{z_0}^n,$$

$$\overline{a_{n-1} z_0}^{n-1} = \overline{a_{n-1}} \overline{z_0}^{n-1}, \ldots, \overline{a_1} \overline{z_0} = \overline{a_1} \overline{z_0}$$

(See Problem set 1, Problem 4d.) Since the conjugate of the real number is the real number itself, we have $\overline{a_0} = a_0$, $\overline{a_1} = a_1, \ldots, \overline{a_n} = a_n$.

Hence,

$$f(\overline{z_0}) = a_n\overline{z_0^n} + a_{n-1}\overline{z_0^{n-1}} + \cdots + a_1\overline{z_0} + a_0 = \overline{f(z_0)} = 0,$$

that is, $\overline{z_0}$ is also a zero of $f(z)$.

EXAMPLES

1   Form a polynomial $f(x)$ which has the following numbers as zeros:
$-\frac{1}{2}, 1 + i$, and 1 as a double zero.

SOLUTION.   Since $1 + i$ is a root of $f(x) = 0$, it follows from the conjugate root theorem that $1 - i$ is also a root; therefore,

$$f(x) = (x + \tfrac{1}{2})(x - 1)^2[x - (1 + i)][x - (1 - i)]$$

has the given roots. Simplifying the equation, we get

$$f(x) = x^5 - \tfrac{7}{2}x^4 + 5x^3 - \tfrac{5}{2}x^2 - x + 1$$

2   Determine the multiplicity of the zeros of the polynomial

$$f(x) = x^4 - 4x^3 + 5x^2 - 4x + 4$$

SOLUTION.   Using synthetic division, the polynomial can be factored as $x^4 - 4x^3 + 5x^2 - 4x + 4 = (x - 2)^2(x + i)(x - i)$, so that 2 is a double zero and i and $-i$ are each zeros of multiplicity 1.

PROBLEM SET 4

1   Show that the equation

$$\frac{1}{x - 3} + \frac{1}{x - 2} - \frac{x - 2}{x - 3} = 0$$

has no solutions. Why doesn't this contradict the fundamental theorem of algebra?

2   Determine whether the given numbers are zeros of the given polynomial functions. If they are, find their multiplicities.

a) $f(x) = x^4 - x^3 - 18x^2 + 52x - 40, x = 2$
b) $f(x) = 4x^6 + 4x^5 + 9x^4 + 8x^3 + 6x^2 + 4x + 1, x = i$
c) $f(x) = 9x^4 - 12x^3 + 13x^2 - 12x + 4, x = \tfrac{2}{3}$

3   Use the roots to write each of the following polynomial functions in factored form.

a) $\{(x, f(x)) \mid f(x) = 2x^2 - x - 2\}$
b) $\{(x, f(x)) \mid f(x) = x^2 - 3x - 3\}$

4 a) Given that $-1 + i$ is a zero of $f(x) = x^4 + 2x^3 - 4x - 4$, find all other zeros of $f(x)$.

b) Given that i is a double zero of $f(x) = 2x^6 + x^5 + 2x^3 - 6x^2 + x - 4$, find all other zeros of $f(x)$.

5 Find polynomials having the following numbers as their zeros.

a) $2, 3 - i$

b) $2, 2, 1 + i, 1 - i$

c) $1 - 3i, 1 - 3i, 1 + 3i, 1 + 3i$ d) $i, i, 0, 1, 2i$

e) $2, 2, \frac{1}{2}(-1 + i\sqrt{3})$

REVIEW PROBLEM SET

1 Perform the indicated operations and write the answer in the form $a + bi$.

a) $(3 - 2i) + (7 - 3i)$

b) $(3 - \sqrt{7}\,i)(3 + \sqrt{7}\,i)$

c) $(5 + 12i) + (-5 - 3i) + (1 + 2i)$

d) $(4 - i) - (7 - 3i) + (2 + i)$

e) $(5 + 3i)(3 - 5i)$

f) $(3 + 7i)/(2 - 3i)$

g) $(4 - \sqrt{3}\,i)/(2 + \sqrt{3}\,i)$

h) $(3 - 5i)/4i$

2 Solve each of the following for x and y, where $x, y \in R$.

a) $5x + 15i = 15 - yi$

b) $(2x + 3) + (y - 3)i = 0$

c) $-3 + 17i = x + 3yi$

d) $3x - 2i + 7 + 3yi = 0$

e) $x + iy = (3 - 2i)/(2 - 3i)$

f) $3x + 5yi = (1 + 3i)/(2 + i)$

g) $7 + 3yi = (2 + i)(3 - 2i)$

3 Suppose that $z = x + yi$. Under what conditions does $z^2 = \bar{z}^2$?

4 If $z = x + iy$ and $\bar{z} = -z$, show that the real part of z is zero.

5 Plot each of the following points in polar coordinates, and then find the rectangular coordinates that corresponds to each of them.

a) $(5, \pi/4)$

b) $(-2, -90°)$

c) $(\sqrt{2}, -135°)$

d) $(3, \pi)$

e) $(3, 270°)$

f) $(2, 4\pi/3)$

6 Find the modulus and an argument of each of the following complex numbers.

a) $z = 5 + 5i$

b) $z = \sqrt{3} + i$

c) $z = 6\sqrt{3} + 6i$

d) $z = 8i$

e) $z = 2 + 2i$

f) $z = -1 + \sqrt{3}\,i$

g) $z = 3 + 4i$

h) $z = (2 + 2\sqrt{3}\,i)^{10}$

7   Find $z_1 z_2$ and z_1/z_2 for each of the following pairs of complex numbers, giving the results in polar form and in rectangular form.

a) $z_1 = 5(\cos 170° + i \sin 170°)$ and $z_2 = (\cos 55° + i \sin 55°)$
b) $z_1 = 2(\cos 50° + i \sin 50°)$ and $z_2 = 3(\cos 40° + i \sin 40°)$
c) $z_1 = 6(\cos 230° + i \sin 230°)$ and $z_2 = 3(\cos 75° + i \sin 75°)$
d) $z_1 = 6(\cos 110° + i \sin 110°)$ and $z_2 = 2(\cos 212° + i \sin 212°)$
e) $z_1 = 14(\cos 305° + i \sin 305°)$ and $z_2 = 7(\cos 65° + i \sin 65°)$

8   Express each of the following powers in polar form and rectangular form.

a) $(\cos 60° + i \sin 60°)^5$ b) $(1 + i)^{40}$
c) $[\sqrt{2}/2 + i(\sqrt{2}/2)]^{100}$ d) $(\cos 0° + i \sin 0°)^{150}$
e) $(\sqrt{3} + i)^{30}$

9   Let $z = a + bi$. Show that each of the following equations are true.

a) $|(a + bi)/(a - bi)|^2 = 1$ b) $|(a + bi)^3/(a - bi)^2| = |z|$

10   Which of the following statements is true? If the statement is false, give a counterexample.

a) $z + \bar{z} = 0$ if and only if Re $z = 0$, where Re z denotes the real part of z.
b) $z + 1/z$ is real if and only if Im $z = 0$ or $|z| = 1$, where Im z denotes the imaginary part of z.
c)   If Im $z \neq 0$, then $z/(1 + z^2)$ is real if and only if $|z| = 1$.

11   Use DeMoivre's theorem to find expressions for $\cos 5\theta$ and $\sin 5\theta$.

12   Let $z = \cos (2\pi/5) + i \sin (2\pi/5)$. Show that

$$\left| \frac{(z^2 - z^3)}{(z^4 - z^5)} \right| = 1$$

13   Let $z = 10(\cos 17° + i \sin 17°)^{10}/(1 + i)^2$. Find Re z, Im z, and $|z|$.

14   Find the indicated roots in each of the following:

a) $\sqrt[4]{-8i}$ b) $\sqrt[3]{-64}$
c) $\sqrt[4]{1 + i}$ d) $\sqrt[4]{8 - 8i}$

15   Form an equation with integral coefficients which has the given roots:

a) -2 as a double root and, $-3, 3$
b) 2 and $(2 - i)$
c) $2, 3, -3, -4$
d) $1, 1, 3, -2, 5$
e) $i, 1 + i, 1 - i$

16   Show that the *sum* of the complex cube roots of 1 is 0.

CHAPTER 9

Analytic Geometry

9 ANALYTIC GEOMETRY

1 Introduction

In this chapter, we will continue to use the Cartesian coordinate system (see Chapter 1, Section 5) to relate the geometry of certain graphs to the algebraic representation of the graphs. We will investigate the *circle*,

Figure 1

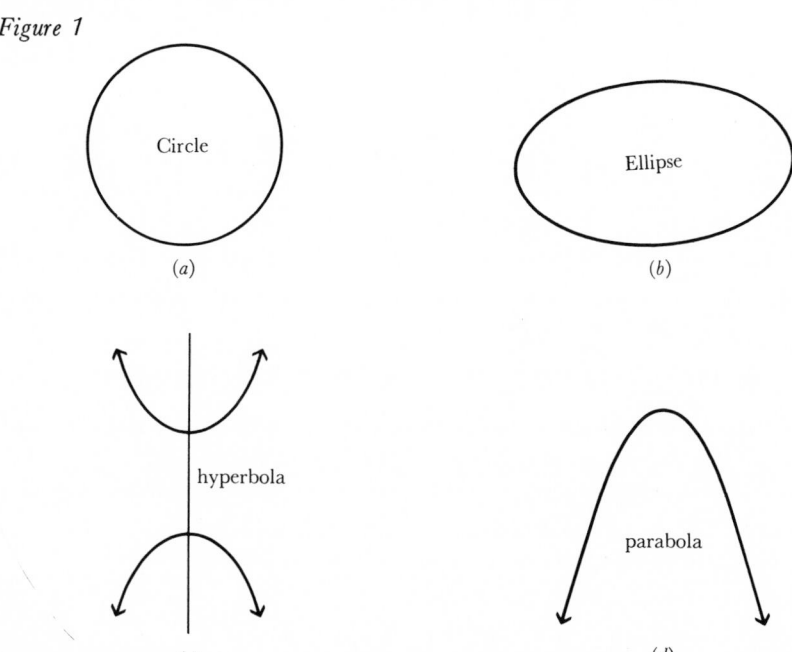

Circle

(a)

Ellipse

(b)

hyperbola

(c)

parabola

(d)

the *ellipse*, the *hyperbola*, and the *parabola* (Figure 1a, b, c, and d). [For convenience, we will use the notation $P = (a,b)$ to identify points in the plane rather than using the notation $P:(a,b)$.]

2   Circle

Geometrically, a *circle* can be defined in a plane as the set of all points which are at a fixed distance r, called the length of the *radius*, from a fixed point, called the *center C*. The length of a diameter of a circle is equal to $2r$. In Figure 1, P is a point of the circle, C is the center, and r is the length of the radius. $\overline{AB} = 2r$ is the length of a diameter. The distance formula can be used to write an equation that satisfies this geometric condition. This equation is the algebraic representation of a circle.

Figure 1

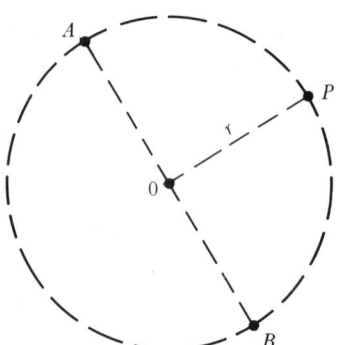

THEOREM 1   (CIRCLE EQUATION)

Let (h,k) be the center of a circle whose radius is r; then the equation of the circle is

$$(x - h)^2 + (y - k)^2 = r^2$$

PROOF.   Let $P = (x,y)$ represent *any* point on the circle whose center C is (h,k). Then, by the distance formula,

$$r = [(x - h)^2 + (y - k)^2]^{1/2}   \qquad \text{(Figure 2)}$$

Figure 2

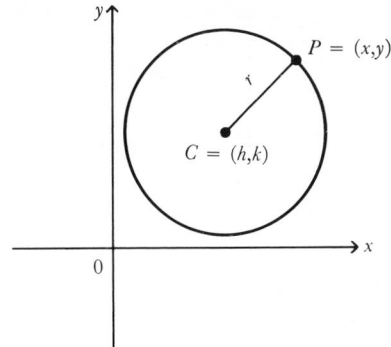

After squaring both sides of this equation, we get

(1) $$r^2 = (x - h)^2 + (y - k)^2$$

It remains to show that the points on the circle are the only points whose coordinates satisfy Equation (1). If $P = (x,y)$ is a point which satisfies Equation (1), we have

$$\sqrt{(x - h)^2 + (y - k)^2} = \sqrt{r^2} = r$$

so that P is r units from the center (h,k) and is a point on the circle.

Notice that the equation of the circle gives us an algebraic characterization which depends only on the center and the radius of the circle; hence, an equation of the form $(x - h)^2 + (y - k)^2 = r^2$ is a relation whose graph is a circle with center (h,k) and radius r. Using set notation, this means that a circle with center (h,k) of radius r can be considered as the relation $\{(x,y)|(x - h)^2 + (y - k)^2 = r^2\}$.

EXAMPLES

1   Find the equation of a circle if $P_1 = (3,7)$ and $P_2 = (-3,-1)$ are the end points of a diameter.

SOLUTION.   (See Figure 3.) The center of the circle, the midpoint of $\overline{P_1 P_2}$, can be determined by the formula $[(x_1 + x_2)/2, (y_1 + y_2)/2]$, (see Chapter 1, Problem set 5, Problem 13). Hence we have the center $C = (0,3)$. The radius is

$$r = \tfrac{1}{2}\overline{P_1 P_2} = \tfrac{1}{2}\sqrt{(3 + 3)^2 + (7 + 1)^2} = \tfrac{1}{2}\sqrt{36 + 64} = 5$$

Therefore, the equation of the circle is given by $x^2 + (y - 3)^2 = 25$.

Figure 3

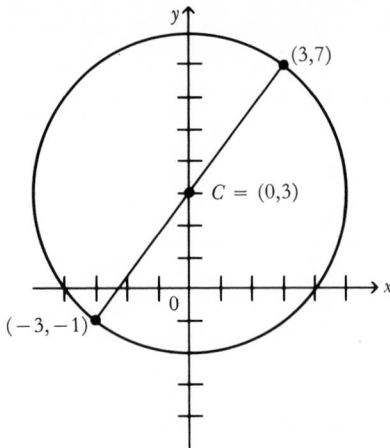

2   Find the center and the radius of the circle whose equation is
$x^2 + y^2 - 4x + 6y - 12 = 0$.

SOLUTION.   (See Figure 4.) First, we will rewrite the equation in the
standard form of Theorem 1. To do this, we "complete the square"
as follows.

$$(x^2 - 4x + \quad) + (y^2 + 6y + \quad) = 12$$
$$(x^2 - 4x + 4) + (y^2 + 6y + 9) = 12 + 4 + 9$$
$$(x - 2)^2 + (y + 3)^2 = 25$$

so that the graph is a circle with center at $(2, -3)$ and radius 5.

Figure 4

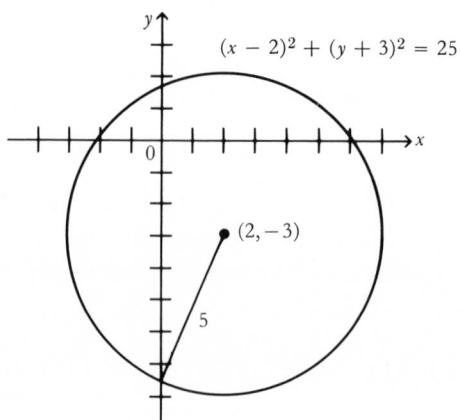

3 Find the equation of the circle that contains the three points
$P_1 = (5,4)$, $P_2 = (3,2)$, and $P_3 = (-3,0)$.

SOLUTION. (See Figure 5.) The equation of the circle is $(x - h)^2 + (y - k)^2 = r^2$. We must determine h, k, and r.

Figure 5

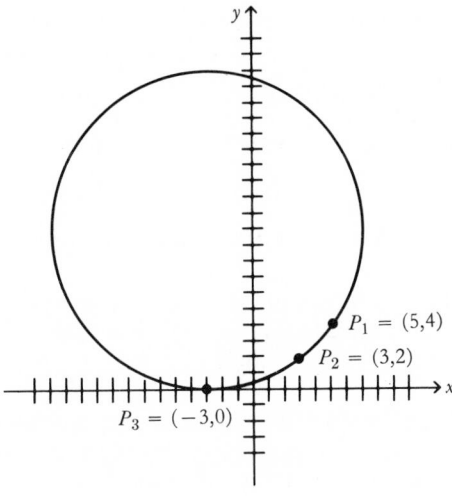

Since P_1 is on the circle, its coordinates satisfy the equation
$(5 - h)^2 + (4 - k)^2 = r^2$. Similarly, P_2 and P_3 are on the circle, so
that we have three equations for the three unknowns, and we proceed
to solve the system of equations

$$25 - 10h + h^2 + 16 - 8k + k^2 = r^2$$
$$9 - 6h + h^2 + 4 - 4k + k^2 = r^2$$
$$9 + 6h + h^2 \qquad\qquad + k^2 = r^2$$

simultaneously to get $h = -3$, $k = 10$, and $r = 10$. (Why?) Hence, the
equation of the circle is

$$(x + 3)^2 + (y - 10)^2 = 100.$$

PROBLEM SET 1

1 Find the center and radius of each of the following circles. Also, sketch
the circle in each case.

a) $(x - 3)^2 + (y - 1)^2 = 4$
b) $(x + 5)^2 + (y - 3)^2 = 9$
c) $(x - 1)^2 + (y + 2)^2 = 16$
d) $x^2 + y^2 + 4x - 6y = 5$

e) $x^2 + y^2 - 3x + 4y + 4 = 0$
f) $x^2 + y^2 - 6x + 8y - 25 = 0$
g) $x^2 + y^2 - 2x + 3y + 3 = 0$

2   Find the equation for each of the following circles.

a) The circle with radius 3 and center $(2, -1)$
b) The circle with center $(-3, -2)$ and radius 3
c) The circle that contains the points $(2, -6)$, $(6, 4)$, and $(-3, 1)$
d) The circle whose center lies on the line $x - 4y = 1$ and passes through the points $(3, 7)$ and $(5, 5)$

3   Find the equations of the circles of radius $\sqrt{10}$ that are tangent to $3x + y = 6$ at $(3, -3)$.

4   Prove that any circle with a center at the origin has an equation of the form $x^2 + y^2 = r^2$.

5   Use the graph of a circle to show that a circle is a relation which is not a function.

6   For each of the relations of Problem 1 indicate the domain and range.

7   Compare $y = \sqrt{9 - x^2}$, $y = -\sqrt{9 - x^2}$, and $x^2 + y^2 = 9$. Graph each of the three relations on different coordinate axes. Indicate the domain and range of each. Which, if any, of the three are functions? Are any of the three one-to-one? If any of the three is one-to-one, find the inverse.

8   Prove that any circle with center $(0,0)$ is symmetric with respect to the x axis, with respect to the y axis, and with respect to the origin.

9   Show that if the matrix

$$C = \begin{bmatrix} x - h & y - k \\ -(y - k) & x - h \end{bmatrix}$$

then det $(C) = r^2$ is the general equation of a circle. In this determinant form, find the equation of each of the following circles.

a) Radius of 1, center $(0,0)$
b) Radius of 1, center (a,b)
c) Radius of 1, with center on the line $y = x$
d) Radius of 1, with center on $y = x^2$

10 Find the equation of a circle of radius 2 that contains point $(3,4)$ and is tangent to $x^2 + y^2 = 25$.

11 Find the equation of a circle that contains point $(3, -2)$ with center on $2x - y + 2 = 0$ and the radius 5.

3 Translations

The circles $x^2 + y^2 = 9$ and $(x - 3)^2 + (y + 4)^2 = 9$ have the same radius (that is, 3) but different centers. $x^2 + y^2 = 9$ has center at $(0,0)$, and $(x - 3)^2 + (y + 4)^2 = 9$ has center at $(3,-4)$. In this section, we will investigate a method of changing the coordinate system, called a *translation*. With this method, equations such as $(x - 3)^2 + (y + 4)^2 = 9$ take on the simpler form $x^2 + y^2 = 9$ in the new coordinate system.

Figure 1

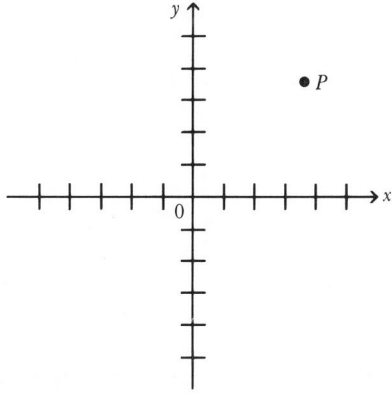

Suppose that P is a point in the xy plane (Figure 1). The coordinates of P depend on how the coordinate axes are placed in the plane. If the axes are positioned so that the origin coincides with P, then $P = (0,0)$ as shown in Figure 2.

Figure 2

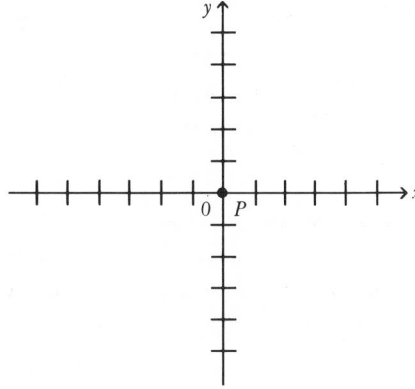

If another pair of axes are formed by "shifting" or "translating" the y axis 5 units to the left to get a $\bar{y}$ axis and the x axis 2 units up to get an

$\bar{x}$ axis, the coordinates of P in this new coordinate system, the $\overline{xy}$ system, are given by $(5,-2)$. (Why?) (Figure 3.) Also, $(5,0)$ in the xy system is $(10,-2)$ in the $\overline{xy}$ system, and $(0,0)$ in the $\overline{xy}$ system is $(-5,2)$ in the xy system. (Why?)

Figure 3

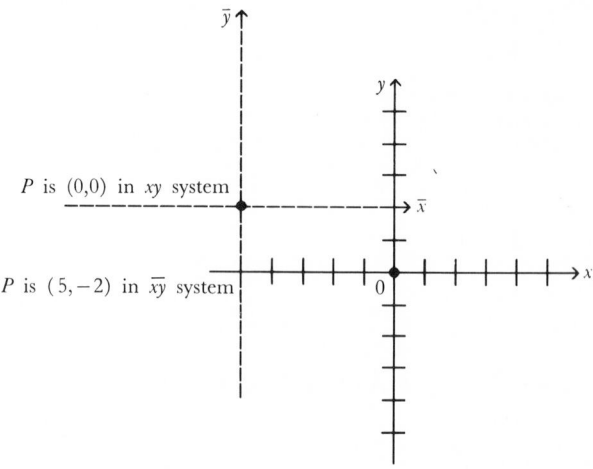

It is not difficult to see that a point in the plane has different coordinates depending on how the coordinate system has been established. In the example above, a "new" coordinate system was formed from a given coordinate system by "translating" the x axis 2 units up to get the $\bar{x}$ axis and by "translating" the y axis 5 units to the left to get the $\bar{y}$ axis. A translation of axes results in new coordinate axes which are parallel to the given axes.

Suppose that the xy coordinate axes have been translated to form the $\overline{xy}$ coordinate system, so that the origin $\overline{O}$ of the $\overline{xy}$ system has coordinates (h,k) in the xy system, as shown in Figure 4. $\overline{O} = (0,0)$ in the $\overline{xy}$ system; $\overline{O} = (h,k)$ in the xy system.

Assume that P is a point in the plane such that

$$P = (x,y) \qquad \text{in the } xy \text{ system}$$

whereas

$$P = (\bar{x},\bar{y}) \qquad \text{in the } \overline{xy} \text{ system.}$$

From our knowledge of vectors, we know that if $\mathbf{i}$ and $\mathbf{j}$ are the basis vectors in the xy system,

$$\mathbf{OP} = x\mathbf{i} + y\mathbf{j}$$
$$\mathbf{O\overline{O}} = h\mathbf{i} + k\mathbf{j}$$

and

$$\overline{\mathbf{OP}} = \bar{x}\mathbf{i} + \bar{y}\mathbf{j} \qquad \text{(Why?)}$$

Figure 4

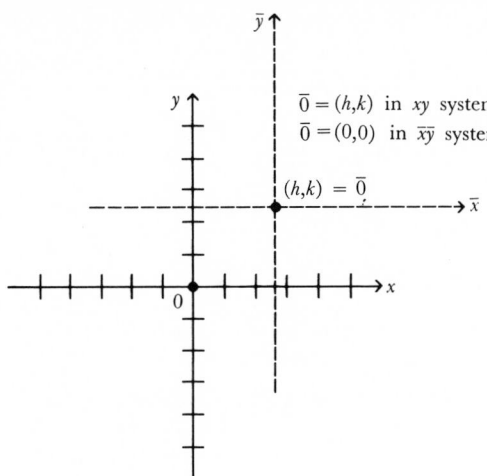

but, equivalently,

$$\mathbf{O\bar{O}} + \mathbf{\bar{O}P} = \mathbf{OP} \qquad \text{(Why?)}$$

so that

$$(h\mathbf{i} + k\mathbf{j}) + (\bar{x}\mathbf{i} + \bar{y}\mathbf{j}) = x\mathbf{i} + y\mathbf{j} \qquad \text{(Figure 5)}$$

Figure 5

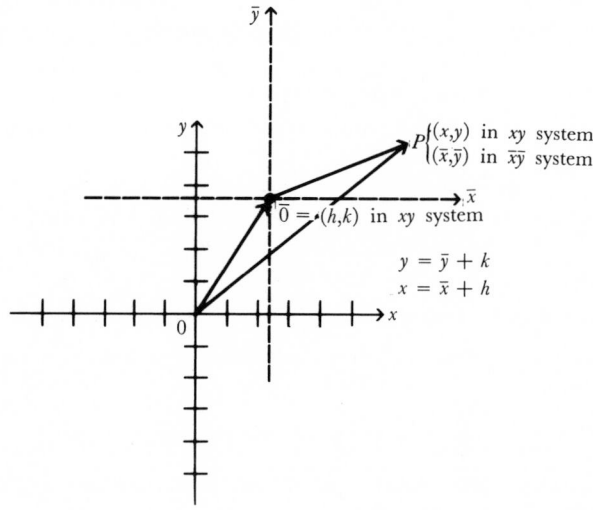

Hence,

$$(h + \bar{x})\mathbf{i} + (k + \bar{y})\mathbf{j} = x\mathbf{i} + y\mathbf{j}$$

that is,

$$(h + \bar{x}, k + \bar{y}) = (x, y)$$

from which we conclude that

$$x = \bar{x} + h \qquad \text{and} \qquad y = \bar{y} + k$$

or, equivalently,

$$\bar{x} = x - h \qquad \text{and} \qquad \bar{y} = y - k$$

Hence, we have proved the following theorem.

THEOREM 1   (TRANSLATION EQUATIONS)

Suppose that the coordinate axes xy are translated to coordinate axes $\bar{x}\bar{y}$, so that the origin $\bar{O}$ of the $\bar{x}\bar{y}$ system has coordinates (h,k) in the xy system. If P has coordinates (x,y) in the xy system and coordinates $(\bar{x},\bar{y})$ in the $\bar{x}\bar{y}$ system, then

$$x = \bar{x} + h \qquad \text{and} \qquad y = \bar{y} + k$$

or, equivalently,

$$\bar{x} = x - h \qquad \text{and} \qquad \bar{y} = y - k$$

EXAMPLES

1   Translate the xy axes to form the $\bar{x}\bar{y}$ axes, so that the origin $\bar{O}$ in the $\bar{x}\bar{y}$ system corresponds to $(4,-3)$ in the xy system. If $P_1 = (2,1)$, $P_2 = (0,1)$, $P_3 = (-2,3)$, and $P_4 = (-3,5)$ are given in the xy system, find their representation in the $\bar{x}\bar{y}$ system.

SOLUTION.   (See Figure 6.) From Theorem 1, we have $\bar{x} = x - h$ and $\bar{y} = y - k$. In this situation $h = 4$ and $k = -3$; hence, for $(2,1)$,

$$\bar{x} = 2 - 4 = -2 \qquad \text{and} \qquad \bar{y} = 1 - (-3) = 4$$

Figure 6

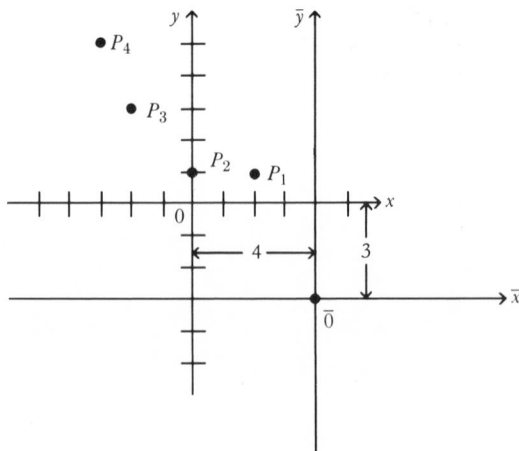

so that $(2,1)$ in the xy system is represented by $(-2,4)$ in the $\bar{x}\bar{y}$ system. For $(0,1)$,

$$\bar{x} = 0 - 4 = -4 \qquad \text{and} \qquad \bar{y} = 1 - (-3) = 4$$

so that $(0,1)$ in the xy system is represented by $(-4,4)$ in the $\bar{x}\bar{y}$ system.
For $(-2,3)$, $\bar{x} = -2 - 4 = -6$ and $\bar{y} = 3 - (-3) = 6$, so that $(-2,3)$ in the xy system is represented by $(-6,6)$ in the $\bar{x}\bar{y}$ system.
For $(-3,5)$, $\bar{x} = -3 - 4 = -7$ and $\bar{y} = 5 - (-3) = 8$, so that $(-3,5)$ in the xy system is represented by $(-7,8)$ in the $\bar{x}\bar{y}$ system.

2 Transform the equation $x^2 + y^2 + 6x - 8y - 11 = 0$ to the form $\bar{x}^2 + \bar{y}^2 = r^2$, using Theorem 1 with $h = -3$ and $k = 4$.

SOLUTION. (See Figure 7.) We have $h = -3$, and $k = 4$. Thus, $x = \bar{x} - 3$ and $y = \bar{y} + 4$. Upon substituting these values of x and y into the given equation, we obtain

$$(\bar{x} - 3)^2 + (\bar{y} + 4)^2 + 6(\bar{x} - 3) - 8(\bar{y} + 4) - 11 = 0$$

so that

$$\bar{x}^2 - 6\bar{x} + 9 + \bar{y}^2 + 8\bar{y} + 16 + 6\bar{x} - 18 - 8\bar{y} - 32 - 11 = 0$$

After simplifying this equation, we obtain $\bar{x}^2 + \bar{y}^2 = 36$.

Figure 7

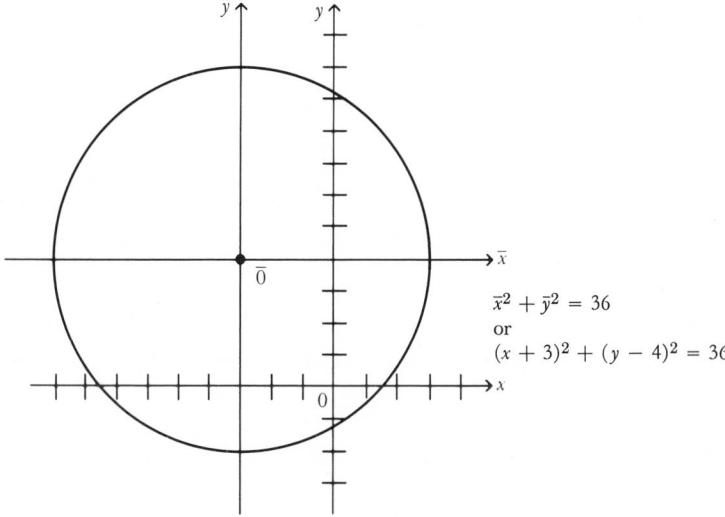

$\bar{x}^2 + \bar{y}^2 = 36$
or
$(x + 3)^2 + (y - 4)^2 = 36$

3 Find a translation of axes that reduces the equation $x^2 + y^2 - 4x + 2y - 4 = 0$ to the form $\bar{x}^2 + \bar{y}^2 = r^2$.

Solution.   (See Figure 8.) By completing the square for $x^2 + y^2 -4x + 2y - 4 = 0$, we get the equation of the circle,

$$(x - 2)^2 + (y + 1)^2 = 9$$

so that if we let $\bar{x} = x - 2$ and $\bar{y} = y + 1$, we get the equation of the circle in the simple form

$$\bar{x}^2 + \bar{y}^2 = 9$$

Figure 8

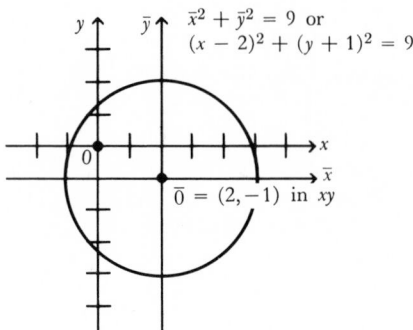

$\bar{x}^2 + \bar{y}^2 = 9$ or
$(x - 2)^2 + (y + 1)^2 = 9$

$\bar{0} = (2, -1)$ in xy

PROBLEM SET 2

1 What are the xy coordinates of the point whose $\bar{x}\bar{y}$ coordinates are:

a) $(3, -4)$ b) $(2, 2)$ c) $(5, 7)$
d) $(3, -5)$ e) $(0, 0)$ f) $(1, -3)$

   i   If $\bar{x} = x + 1$ and $\bar{y} = y - 3$
   ii If the translation is the one that takes $(5, 6)$ in the xy system to $(-1, 3)$ in the $\bar{x}\bar{y}$ system

2 What are the $\bar{x}\bar{y}$ coordinates of the point whose xy coordinates are:

a) $(2, -7)$ b) $(-5, 3)$ c) $(-3, 4)$
d) $(\frac{7}{4}, -\frac{13}{4})$ e) $(-7, -5)$ f) $(3, -7)$

   i   If $\bar{x} = x + 1$ and $\bar{y} = y - 3$
   ii If the translation is the one that takes $(3, 4)$ in the xy system to $(0, 0)$ in the $\bar{x}\bar{y}$ system

3 If $\bar{x} = x - 1$ and $\bar{y} = y + 2$, show that

$$\{(x, y)\,|\,y = 2x + 1\} = \{(\bar{x}, \bar{y})\,|\,\bar{y} = 2\bar{x} + 5\}$$

4 We say that a quantity is *invariant* under a process if the quantity remains the same after the process has been carried out. Prove that each of the following is invariant under a translation.

a) The distance between $P_1 = (x_1, y_1)$ and $P_2 = (x_2, y_2)$
b) The area of a triangle whose base is b and whose height is h
c) The slope of a line joining $P_1 = (x_1, y_1)$ and $P_2 = (x_2, y_2)$

5 Find the translation of axes that will reduce each of the following equations to the form $\bar{x}^2 + \bar{y}^2 = r^2$

a) $2x^2 + 2y^2 + 16x - 7y = 0$
b) $3x^2 + 3y^2 + 7x - 5y + 3 = 0$
c) $x^2 + y^2 - 8x - 10y + 40 = 0$

6 Suppose that the coordinate axes xy are translated, so that the origin of the $\bar{x}\bar{y}$ coordinate system is the point whose coordinates are the indicated point. Write each of the following equations in terms of $\bar{x}$ and $\bar{y}$.

a) $3x - 4y + 13 = 0, \ (-2,3)$
b) $-2x + 3y + 5 = 0, \ (3,4)$
c) $x^2 - 2x + y^2 - 4y - 16 = 0, \ (1,-1)$
d) $3x^2 + 3y^2 - 9x - 7y - 36 = 0, \ (1,0)$

4 Ellipse

With the tool of translations available, let us study the *ellipse*. The planets follow an elliptical orbit about the sun, and satellites follow a very nearly elliptical orbit about the earth.

Geometrically, an *ellipse* can be defined in a plane as the set of all points each of which has the property that the sum of its distances from two fixed points, called *foci*, is a constant. In Figure 1, F_1 and F_2 are the foci, P_1, P_2, and P_3 are points of the conic, and

$$d_1 + c_1 = d_2 + c_2 = d_3 + c_3 = k$$

Figure 1

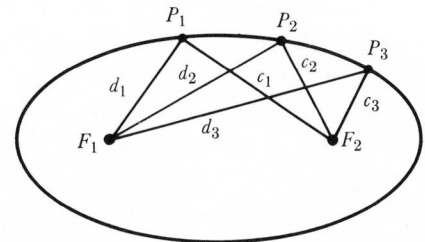

is the constant of the ellipse. The midpoint of line segment $\overline{F_1F_2}$ is called the *center of the ellipse.*

The ellipse is symmetric with respect to each of two perpendicular lines that intersect at its center (Figure 2). The four points of intersection of the lines of symmetry and the ellipse are called *vertices* of the ellipse;

Figure 2

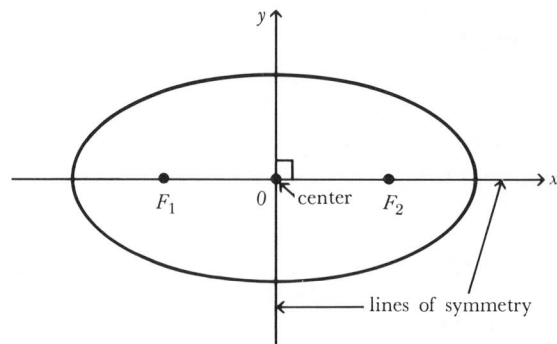

the longer line segment determined by the vertices is called the *major axis,* whereas the length of the shorter line segment determined by the vertices is called the *minor axis.* In Figure 3, V_1, V_2, V_3, and V_4 are the vertices, $\overline{V_1V_2}$ is the major axis, $\overline{V_3V_4}$ is the minor axis, and O is the center.

Figure 3

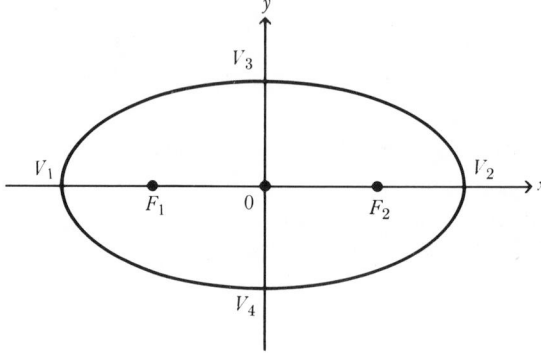

In order to express the geometric description of an ellipse in analytic terms, let us choose the coordinate system so that the coordinates of the foci are $(-c,0)$ and $(c,0)$, where $c > 0$. Also, we will assume that the constant which is equal to the sum of the distances between a point on the ellipse and the foci is $2a$ (Figure 4). (This constant is written in the form $2a$ so that the equation of the ellipse will have a simpler form.)

Figure 4

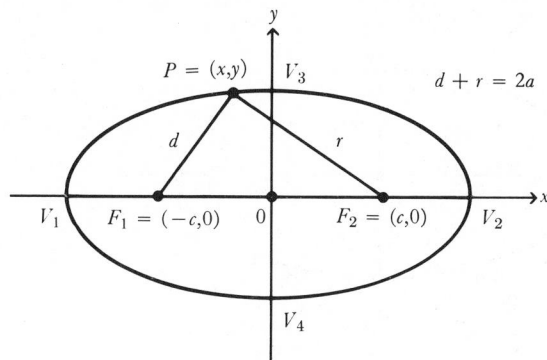

Notice that the major axis lies on the x axis; the minor axis lies on the y axis; the center of the ellipse is $(0,0)$.

It is not difficult to show that the major axis, that is, the line segment determined by $\overline{V_1V_2}$, is $2a$. $(\overline{F_1O} + \overline{OV_2}) + (\overline{OV_2} - \overline{OF_2}) = 2a$, since V_2 is a point on the ellipse; therefore, $c + \overline{OV_2} + \overline{OV_2} - c = 2\overline{OV_2} = 2a$, so that $\overline{OV_2} = a$. By symmetry, $\overline{OV_1} = a$; hence, $\overline{V_1V_2} = 2a$.

Next, we will show the relationship between the length of the major and the length of the minor axis. Let the distance $\overline{V_3V_4} = 2b$ (Figure 5). Since V_3 is a point on the ellipse, $\overline{V_3F_1} + \overline{V_3F_2} = 2a$. By symmetry, $\overline{V_3F_1} = \overline{V_3F_2}$, so that $\overline{V_3F_2} = a$. From the right triangle, $\triangle OF_2V_3$, we get $a^2 = b^2 + c^2$, from which we conclude that $b < a$, so that the major axis is longer than the minor axis.

Figure 5

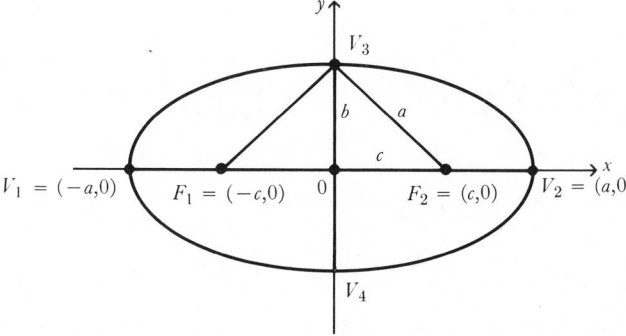

To summarize the important distances associated with the ellipse, we have, as shown in Figure 6,

1   c = distance from center to a focus

Figure 6

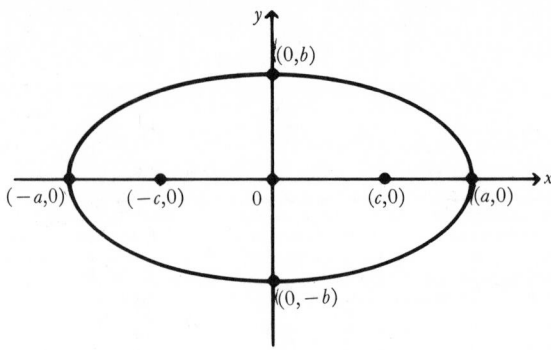

2   b = one-half the minor axis

3   a = one-half the major axis

Now the equation of the ellipse will be derived in the following theorem.

THEOREM 1   (ELLIPSE EQUATION)

An equation for the ellipse with foci at $F_2 = (c,0)$ and $F_1 = (-c,0)$ is

$$\frac{x^2}{a^2} + \frac{y^2}{b^2} = 1$$

where $b^2 = a^2 - c^2$, $a > b$, $2a$ is the length of the major axis, and $2b$ is the length of the minor axis.

PROOF.   Assume that $P = (x,y)$ is any point on the ellipse (Figure 7).

Figure 7

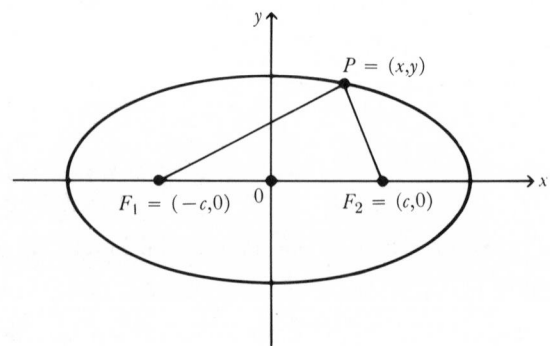

Then $\overline{PF_1} + \overline{PF_2} = 2a$, so that

$$\sqrt{(x+c)^2 + y^2} + \sqrt{(x-c)^2 + y^2} = 2a$$

that is,

$$\sqrt{(x+c)^2 + y^2} = 2a - \sqrt{(x-c)^2 + y^2}$$

Squaring both sides, we get

$$x^2 + 2xc + c^2 + y^2 = 4a^2 - 4a\sqrt{(x-c)^2 + y^2} \\ + x^2 - 2cx + c^2 + y^2$$

so that

$$4cx - 4a^2 = -4a\sqrt{(x-c)^2 + y^2}$$

that is,

$$cx - a^2 = -a\sqrt{(x-c)^2 + y^2}$$

Squaring both sides again, we get

$$c^2x^2 - 2a^2cx + a^4 = a^2(x^2 - 2cx + c^2 + y^2)$$

so that

$$a^4 - a^2c^2 = (a^2 - c^2)x^2 + a^2y^2$$

that is,

$$(a^2 - c^2)x^2 + a^2y^2 = a^2(a^2 - c^2)$$

Hence,

$$\frac{x^2}{a^2} + \frac{y^2}{a^2 - c^2} = 1$$

Since $a^2 - c^2 = b^2$, we have $x^2/a^2 + y^2/b^2 = 1$. The graph of the ellipse is shown in Figure 8.

Figure 8

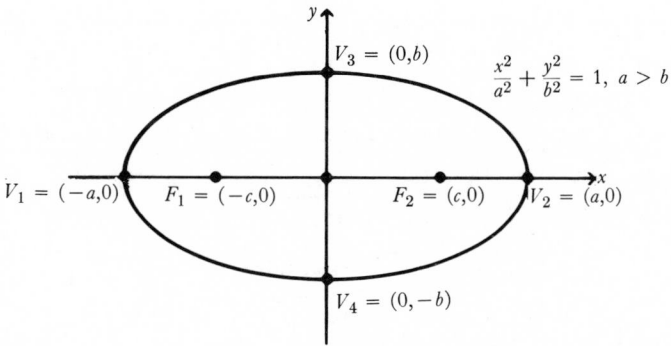

$V_3 = (0,b)$

$\dfrac{x^2}{a^2} + \dfrac{y^2}{b^2} = 1, \ a > b$

$V_1 = (-a,0)$ $F_1 = (-c,0)$ $F_2 = (c,0)$ $V_2 = (a,0)$

$V_4 = (0,-b)$

EXAMPLES

1   Given the equation of the ellipse $x^2 + 9y^2 = 9$, find the vertices and the foci, and sketch the graph.

SOLUTION.   (See Figure 9.) After dividing both sides by 9, we get the equation

$$\frac{x^2}{9} + \frac{y^2}{1} = 1$$

This equation is of the form $x^2/a^2 + y^2/b^2 = 1$, with $a^2 = 9$ and $b^2 = 1$. Thus, the graph is an ellipse whose vertices are $(3,0)$, $(-3,0)$, $(0,1)$, and $(0,-1)$; and, since $c^2 = a^2 - b^2 = 9 - 1 = 8$, we have $c = 2\sqrt{2}$, so that the coordinates of the foci are $(2\sqrt{2}, 0)$ and $(-2\sqrt{2},0)$.

Figure 9

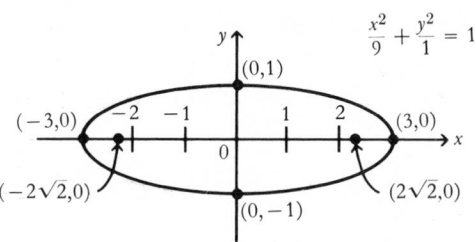

2   Find the equation of the ellipse with foci $(2,0)$ and $(-2,0)$ and vertices $(3,0)$ and $(-3,0)$ Also sketch the graph of the ellipse.

SOLUTION.   (See Figure 10.) The ellipse has its center at the origin and its foci on the x axis; therefore, its equation is of the form $x^2/a^2 +$

Figure 10

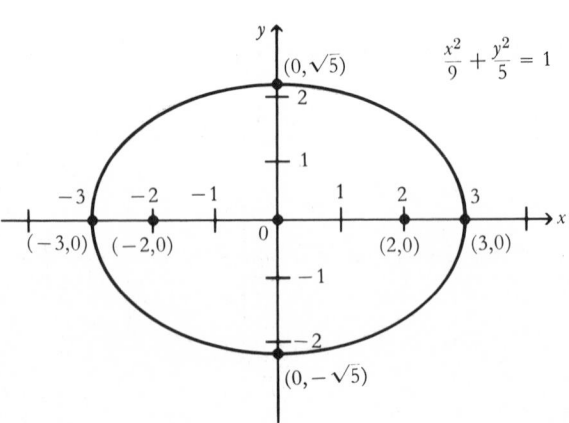

$y^2/b^2 = 1$, with $b^2 = 9 - 4 = 5$, so that $b = \sqrt{5}$; thus, the ellipse has an equation of the form

$$\frac{x^2}{9} + \frac{y^2}{5} = 1$$

Since we denoted a to be half of the major axis and b to be half of the minor axis, the equation of the ellipse takes the form $x^2/a^2 + y^2/b^2 = 1$. Its major axis happens to be along the x axis if $a > b$; also, its foci are on the x axis.

If the foci of an ellipse centered at the origin are on the y axis and $2a$ is the sum of the distances to the foci from each point on the ellipse, then, by symmetry, its equation will become $x^2/b^2 + y^2/a^2 = 1$, and, since $a > b$, we still have $c^2 = a^2 - b^2$. The graph is shown in Figure 11.

Figure 11

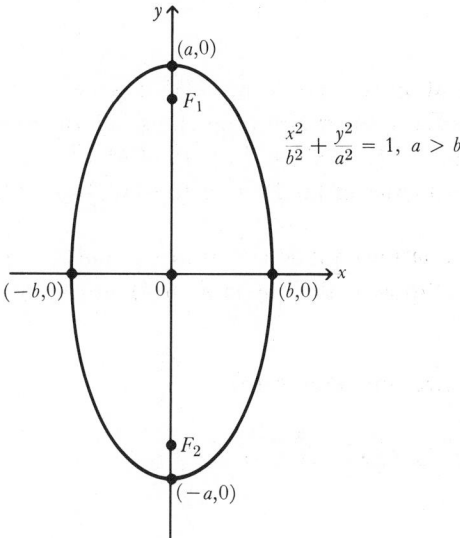

$$\frac{x^2}{b^2} + \frac{y^2}{a^2} = 1, \ a > b$$

EXAMPLE

Given the equation of the ellipse $4x^2 + y^2 = 4$; find the vertices and the foci, and sketch the graph.

SOLUTION.   (See Figure 12.) After dividing both sides by 4, we get the equation

$$\frac{x^2}{1} + \frac{y^2}{4} = 1$$

Figure 12

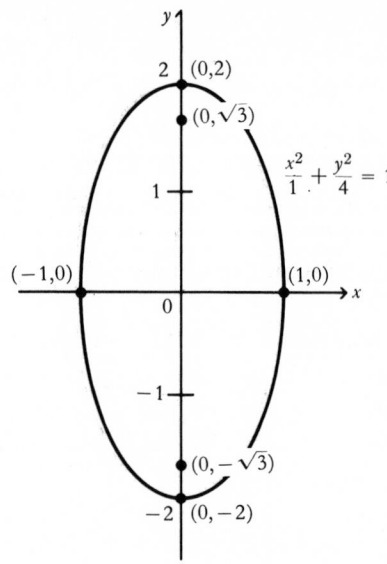

This equation is of the form $x^2/b^2 + y^2/a^2 = 1$, with $b^2 = 1$ and $a^2 = 4$. Thus, the graph is an ellipse whose vertices are $(0,2)$, $(0,-2)$, $(1,0)$, and $(-1,0)$. Since $c^2 = a^2 - b^2$, $c^2 = 4 - 1 = 3$ or $c = \sqrt{3}$. The coordinates of the foci are $(0,-\sqrt{3})$ and $(0,\sqrt{3})$.

When we use the translation equations $\bar{x} = x - h$ and $\bar{y} = y - k$, then the equations of the ellipses with centers at (h,k) in the xy coordinate system are as follows:

If the major axis is horizontal (Figure 13):

$$\frac{(x-h)^2}{a^2} + \frac{(y-k)^2}{b^2} = 1 \qquad a > b$$

Figure 13

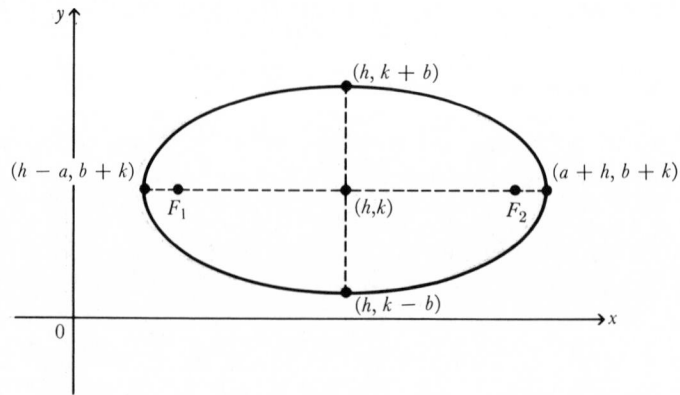

If the major axis is vertical (Figure 14):

$$\frac{(x - h)^2}{b^2} + \frac{(y - k)^2}{a^2} = 1 \qquad a > b$$

Figure 14

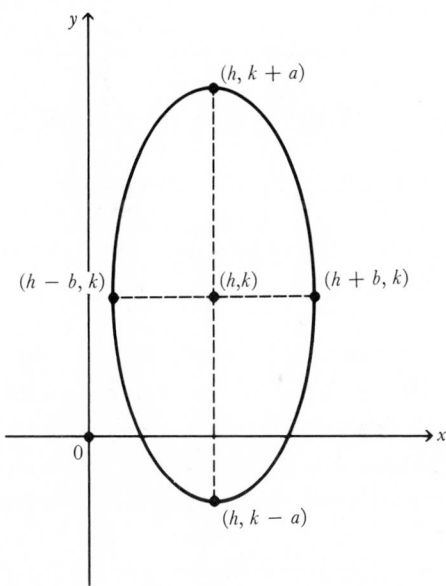

(h, k + a)

(h − b, k)   (h,k)   (h + b, k)

0   →x

(h, k − a)

EXAMPLES

1 Given the equation of the ellipse $4x^2 + 9y^2 + 16x - 18y - 11 = 0$, find the coordinates of the center, the coordinates of the vertices, and the coordinates of the foci. Also sketch the graph.

SOLUTION.   (See Figure 15.) First, complete the square to get

$$4(x^2 + 4x + 4) + 9(y^2 - 2y + 1) = 11 + 16 + 9$$

so that

$$4(x + 2)^2 + 9(y - 1)^2 = 36$$

or, equivalently,

$$\frac{(x + 2)^2}{9} + \frac{(y - 1)^2}{4} = 1$$

If we let $\bar{x} = x + 2$ and $\bar{y} = y - 1$, then $\bar{x}^2/9 + \bar{y}^2/4 = 1$. The center is $(-2,1)$.

Figure 15

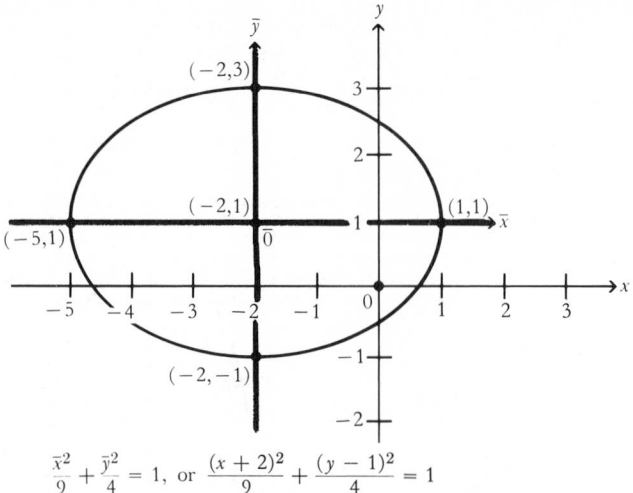

$$\frac{\bar{x}^2}{9} + \frac{\bar{y}^2}{4} = 1, \text{ or } \frac{(x+2)^2}{9} + \frac{(y-1)^2}{4} = 1$$

$a^2 = 9$ and $b^2 = 4$, so that $a = 3$ and $b = 2$. The coordinates of the vertices are $(1,1)$, $(-5,1)$, $(-2,-1)$, and $(-2,3)$, since the major axis is parallel to the x axis. $c^2 = a^2 - b^2 = 9 - 4 = 5$; therefore, $c = \sqrt{5}$, so that the coordinates of the foci are $(-2 + \sqrt{5}, 1)$ and $(-2 - \sqrt{5}, 1)$.

2   Given the equation of the ellipse $9x^2 + 4y^2 - 18x + 16y - 11 = 0$, find the coordinates of the center, the coordinates of the vertices, and the coordinates of the foci. Also sketch the graph.

SOLUTION.   (See Figure 16.) First, complete the square to get

$$9(x^2 - 2x + 1) + 4(y^2 + 4y + 4) = 11 + 9 + 16$$

Hence,

$$9(x - 1)^2 + 4(y + 2)^2 = 36$$

that is,

$$\frac{(x-1)^2}{4} + \frac{(y+2)^2}{9} = 1$$

If we let $\bar{x} = x - 1$ and $\bar{y} = y + 2$, we get $\bar{x}^2/4 + \bar{y}^2/9 = 1$; the center is $(1,-2)$ in the xy system.

$a^2 = 9$ and $b^2 = 4$; therefore, $a = 3$ and $b = 2$, and the coordinates of the vertices are $(1,1)$, $(1,-5)$, $(-1,-2)$, and $(3,-2)$, since the major axis is parallel to the y axis. $c^2 = a^2 - b^2 = 9 - 4 = 5$; therefore, $c = \sqrt{5}$ and the coordinates of the foci are $(1, -2 + \sqrt{5})$ and $(1, -2 - \sqrt{5})$.

Figure 16

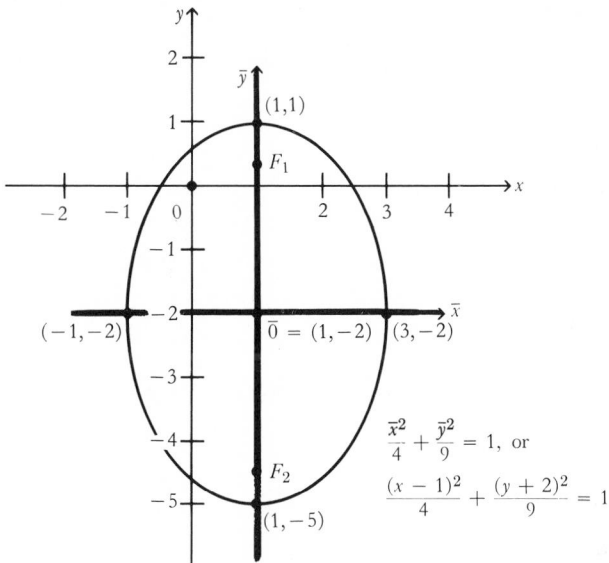

$$\frac{\bar{x}^2}{4} + \frac{\bar{y}^2}{9} = 1, \text{ or}$$

$$\frac{(x-1)^2}{4} + \frac{(y+2)^2}{9} = 1$$

3 Write the equation of the ellipse whose vertices are $(-2,-3)$, $(-2,5)$, $(-7,1)$, and $(3,1)$ and sketch its graph.

SOLUTION. First, plot the given vertices as shown in Figure 17. These four points are the ends of the major axis and the minor axis; the major axis is parallel to the x axis and is 10 units long (Why?), and the minor axis is parallel to the y axis and is 8 units long. (Why?) Thus, $a = 5$ and $b = 4$. In this case, the center is at $(-2,1)$ (Why?), so that $h = -2$ and $k = 1$; hence, the equation becomes

$$\frac{\bar{x}^2}{25} + \frac{\bar{y}^2}{16} = 1 \qquad \text{where } \bar{x} = x + 2 \text{ and } \bar{y} = y - 1$$

Figure 17

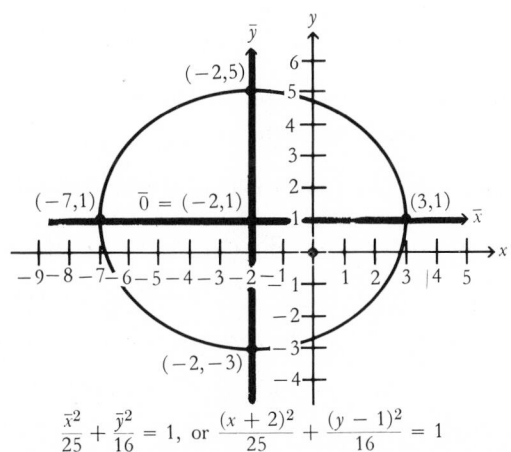

$$\frac{\bar{x}^2}{25} + \frac{\bar{y}^2}{16} = 1, \text{ or} \quad \frac{(x+2)^2}{25} + \frac{(y-1)^2}{16} = 1$$

so that

$$\frac{(x+2)^2}{25} + \frac{(v-1)^2}{16} = 1$$

PROBLEM SET 3

1 For each of the following ellipses find the coordinates of the vertices and the coordinates of the foci, and sketch the graph.

a) $4x^2 + 9y^2 = 36$ b) $x^2/16 + y^2/9 = 1$
c) $y^2/25 + x^2/16 = 1$ d) $y^2/16 + x^2/4 = 1$
e) $25x^2 + 9y^2 = 1$ f) $4x^2 + 16y^2 = 64$

2 For each of the following ellipses find the coordinates of the center, the coordinates of the vertices, and the coordinates of the foci, and sketch the graph.

a) $3(x-1)^2 + 4(y+2)^2 = 192$
b) $x^2 + 4y^2 - 2x - 16y + 13 = 0$
c) $9x^2 + 4y^2 + 18x - 16y - 11 = 0$
d) $25(x-3)^2 + 4(y-1)^2 = 100$
e) $4x^2 + 9y^2 - 24x + 36y + 36 = 0$
f) $16(x+2)^2 + 25(y-1)^2 = 400$

3 Find the equations of the ellipse whose vertices are:

a) $(1,-2)$, $(5,-2)$, $(3,-7)$, and $(3,3)$
b) $(0,-1)$, $(12,-1)$, $(6,-4)$, and $(6,2)$
c) $(1,1)$, $(5,1)$, $(3,6)$, and $(3,-4)$

4 Find the equation of the ellipse:

a) With vertices $(-5,0)$ and $(5,0)$ and containing the point $(4,\tfrac{12}{5})$
b) With foci $(1,4)$ and $(3,4)$ and with major axis of length 4
c) With center at $(0,0)$, axes parallel to coordinate axes, and containing the points $(8\sqrt{6}/5,1)$ and $(2,5\sqrt{3}/2)$
d) With center at $(-3,1)$, major axis parallel to the y axis and 5 units long, and minor axis 1 unit long.

5 Use the graph of an ellipse to show that the equation of an ellipse is a relation which is not a function.

6 For each of the relations of Problem 1, indicate the domain and range.

7 Discuss the symmetry of an ellipse of the form $x^2/a^2 + y^2/b^2 = 1$.

8 Compare the graphs of $y = \sqrt{1 - x^2/4}$, $y = -\sqrt{1 - x^2/4}$, and $y^2 = 1 - x^2/4$. Which of the three equations defines a function?

9 Consider the equation of the ellipse $x^2/a^2 + y^2/b^2 = 1$. Describe the graph of the ellipse if $a = b$.

10 We have the matrix

$$E = \begin{bmatrix} \left(\dfrac{x-h}{a}\right) & \left(\dfrac{y-k}{b}\right) \\ -\left(\dfrac{y-k}{b}\right) & \left(\dfrac{x-h}{a}\right) \end{bmatrix}$$

Show that the equation det $(E) = 1$ is the general equation for an ellipse.

5 Hyperbola

The *hyperbola* will be developed in a manner similar to that in which the ellipse was developed.

Geometrically, a hyperbola can be defined in a plane as the set of points each of which has the property that the absolute value of the difference of the distances from the point to two distinct fixed points, called *foci*, is equal to a constant.

The line determined by the foci is a line of symmetry; the midpoint of the line segment determined by the foci is the *center* of the hyperbola; the two points of intersection of the hyperbola with the line of symmetry are called the *vertices* of the hyperbola; the line segment determined by the vertices is called the transverse axis. In Figure 1 F_1 and F_2 are the foci, V_1 and V_2 are the vertices, C is the center, V_1V_2 is the transverse axis, and

$$|d_2 - c_2| = |d_1 - c_1| = k$$

is the constant of the hyperbola.

Figure 1

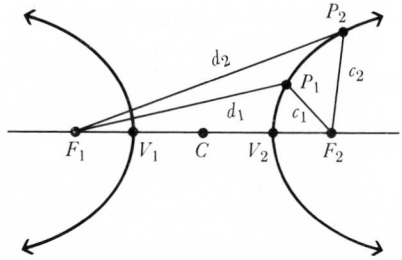

We will determine the equation of the hyperbola by choosing the co-ordinate system so that the foci are $(c,0)$ and $(-c,0)$, with $c > 0$, and we will assume the constant difference to be $2a$. Thus, if $P = (x,y)$ is a point on the hyperbola, we have $|\overline{PF_1} - \overline{PF_2}| = 2a$ as shown in Figure 2.

Figure 2

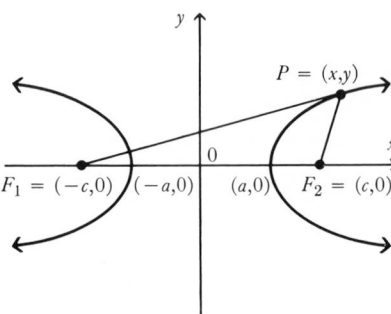

By using the distance formula, we get

$$|\sqrt{(x+c)^2 + y^2} - \sqrt{(x-c)^2 + y^2}| = 2a$$

hence,

$$\sqrt{(x+c)^2 + y^2} - \sqrt{(x-c)^2 + y^2} = \pm 2a$$

so that

$$\sqrt{(x+c)^2 + y^2} = \pm 2a + \sqrt{(x-c)^2 + y^2}$$

After squaring both sides, we get

$$x^2 + 2cx + c^2 + y^2 = 4a^2 \pm 4a\sqrt{(x-c)^2 + y^2}$$
$$+ x^2 - 2cx + c^2 + y^2$$

or, equivalently,

$$4cx - 4a^2 = \pm 4a\sqrt{(x-c)^2 + y^2}$$

so that

$$cx - a^2 = \pm a\sqrt{(x-c)^2 + y^2}$$

Again, square both sides to get

$$c^2x^2 - 2a^2cx + a^4 = a^2(x^2 - 2cx + c^2 + y^2)$$

so that

$$(c^2 - a^2)x^2 - a^2y^2 = a^2c^2 - a^4 = a^2(c^2 - a^2)$$

or, equivalently,

$$\frac{x^2}{a^2} - \frac{y^2}{c^2 - a^2} = 1$$

If we let $b^2 = c^2 - a^2$, the equation of the hyperbola becomes

$$\frac{x^2}{a^2} - \frac{y^2}{b^2} = 1$$

Notice that by letting $y = 0$, we get $(a,0)$ and $(-a,0)$, the vertices of the hyperbola. Also notice that $a^2 + b^2 = c^2$ because we defined $b^2 = c^2 - a^2$.

We have just proved the following theorem.

THEOREM 1 (HYPERBOLA EQUATION)

The equation of the hyperbola with foci $(c,0)$ and $(-c,0)$ and constant distance $2a$ is

$$\frac{x^2}{a^2} - \frac{y^2}{b^2} = 1 \qquad \text{where} \quad b^2 = c^2 - a^2$$

5.1 Properties of the Hyperbola

The graph of the hyperbola $x^2/a^2 - y^2/b^2 = 1$ is symmetric with respect to the x axis and the y axis. (Why?)

The x intercepts of the hyperbola $x^2/a^2 - y^2/b^2 = 1$ are found by letting $y = 0$ and solving for x to get $(-a,0)$ and $(a,0)$. If $x = 0$, then we have $y^2 = -b^2$. But such a y is not a real number (Why?); hence, we conclude that the hyperbola does not intersect the y axis.

If we write $x^2/a^2 - y^2/b^2 = 1$ as $y^2 = (b^2/a^2)(x^2 - a^2)$, then

$$y = \frac{\pm bx}{a} \sqrt{1 - \frac{a^2}{x^2}}$$

Now, $1 - a^2/x^2$ approaches 1 as $|x|$ gets very large, so that the larger x is in absolute value, the closer the graph of the hyperbola is to the lines whose equations are given by $y = \pm bx/a$. These lines are called the *asymptotes of the hyperbola*. The asymptotes are not part of the hyperbola; they are easy to draw if we construct the rectangle of dimensions $2a$ and $2b$, as in Figure 3.

Figure 3

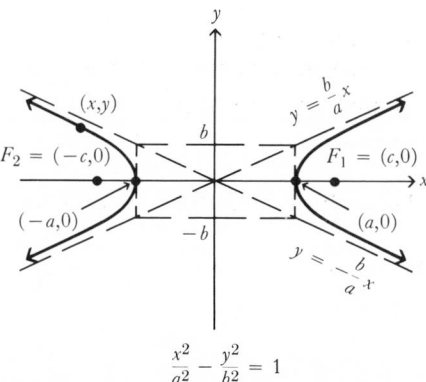

$$\frac{x^2}{a^2} - \frac{y^2}{b^2} = 1$$

EXAMPLES

1   Given the equation of the hyperbola $x^2/16 - y^2/9 = 1$, find the co-ordinates of the foci, the coordinates of the vertices, and the equations of the asymptotes. Also sketch the graph.

SOLUTION.   From Theorem 1, we have, since $a = 4$ and $b = 3$, $c = \sqrt{4^2 + 3^2} = 5$, so that the coordinates of the foci are $(5,0)$ and $(-5,0)$; the coordinates of the vertices are $(4,0)$ and $(-4,0)$. The equations of the asymptotes are given by $y = \pm\frac{3}{4}x$, and the graph is shown in Figure 4.

Figure 4

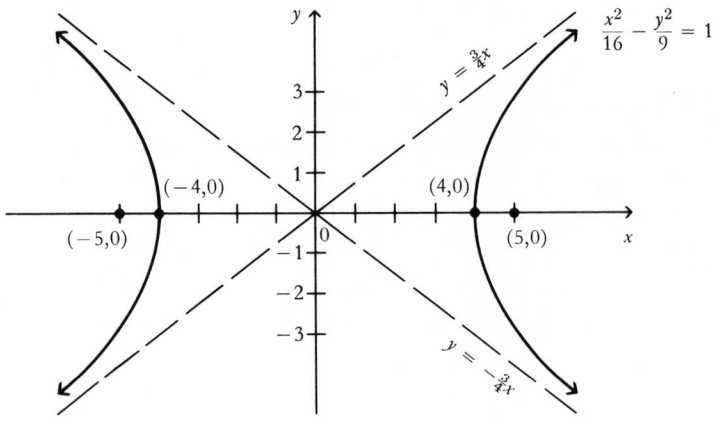

2   Given the hyperbola $25x^2 - 16y^2 = 400$, find the coordinates of the vertices, the coordinates of the foci, and the equations of the asymptotes. Also sketch the graph.

SOLUTION.   Divide both sides of the equation by 400 to get

$$\frac{x^2}{16} - \frac{y^2}{25} = 1$$

The vertices are $(4,0)$ and $(-4,0)$. Since $c^2 = a^2 + b^2 = 4^2 + 5^2 = 41$, $c = \sqrt{41}$, so that the foci are $(-\sqrt{41},0)$ and $(\sqrt{41},0)$. The equations of the asymptotes are given by $y = \pm bx/a = \pm\frac{5}{4}x$ and the graph is shown in Figure 5.

The equations of the hyperbola with center $(0,0)$ are as follows:

If its transverse axis is on the x axis:

$$\frac{x^2}{a^2} - \frac{y^2}{b^2} = 1$$

Figure 5

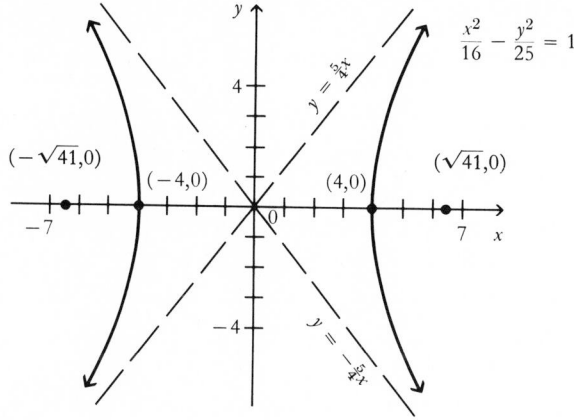

$$\frac{x^2}{16} - \frac{y^2}{25} = 1$$

If its transverse axis is on the y axis (by symmetry):

$$\frac{y^2}{a^2} - \frac{x^2}{b^2} = 1$$

As with the ellipse, if the center of the hyperbola is translated so that the point (h,k) is the center, the forms of the equation are as follows:

If its transverse axis is parallel to the x axis (Figure 6):

$$\frac{(x - h)^2}{a^2} - \frac{(y - k)^2}{b^2} = 1$$

Figure 6

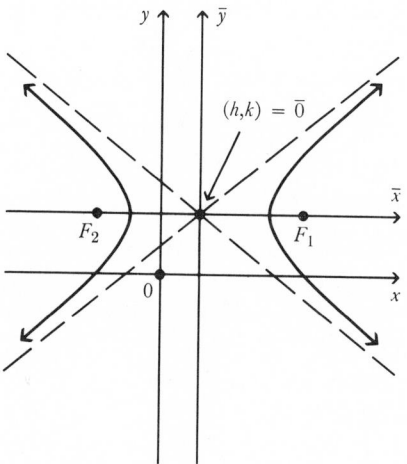

If its transverse axis is parallel to the y axis (Figure 7):

$$\frac{(y-k)^2}{a^2} - \frac{(x-h)^2}{b^2} = 1$$

Figure 7

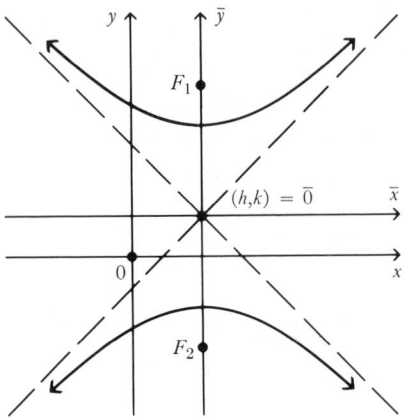

EXAMPLES

1 Given the equation of the hyperbola $4x^2 - y^2 - 8x + 2y + 7 = 0$, find the coordinates of the center, the coordinates of the foci, the coordinates of the vertices, and the equations of the asymptotes. Also sketch the graph.

SOLUTION.   (See Figure 8.) First, complete the square to get

$$4(x^2 - 2x + 1) - (y^2 - 2y + 1) = -7 + 4 - 1$$

that is,

$$4(x - 1)^2 - (y - 1)^2 = -4$$

so that

$$\frac{(y-1)^2}{4} - \frac{(x-1)^2}{1} = 1$$

Hence, the center $(h,k) = (1,1)$. The coordinates of the foci are $(1, 1 + \sqrt{5})$ and $(1, 1 - \sqrt{5})$, since $c^2 = 2^2 + 1^2 = 5$. The coordinates of the vertices are $(1,-1)$ and $(1,3)$ (Why?), since $a = 2$ and the transverse axis is $x = 1$.

$y - k = \pm(a/b)(x - h)$ gives the asymptotes $y - 1 = \pm 2(x - 1)$.

Figure 8

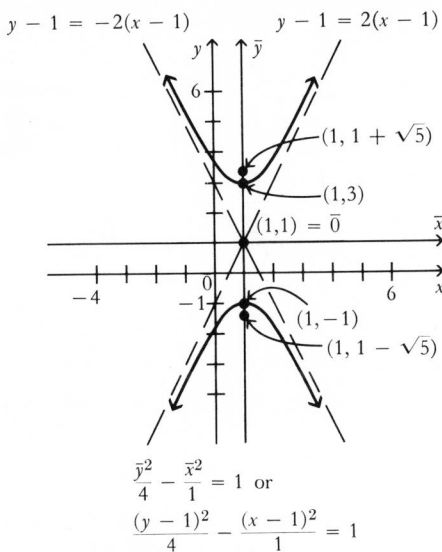

$$y - 1 = -2(x - 1) \qquad y - 1 = 2(x - 1)$$

$(1, 1 + \sqrt{5})$

$(1,3)$

$(1,1) = \bar{0}$

$(1,-1)$

$(1, 1 - \sqrt{5})$

$$\frac{\bar{y}^2}{4} - \frac{\bar{x}^2}{1} = 1 \quad \text{or}$$

$$\frac{(y-1)^2}{4} - \frac{(x-1)^2}{1} = 1$$

2   Find the equation of the hyperbola whose foci are the points $(-\frac{9}{2},3)$ and $(\frac{1}{2},3)$ and whose vertices are the points $(0,3)$ and $(-4,3)$; also, sketch the graph.

SOLUTION.   (See Figure 9.) First, plot these points on the coordinate axes; the transverse axis is parallel to the x axis. The center is $[(-\frac{9}{2} + \frac{1}{2})/2, (3 + 3)/2] = (-2,3)$; $a = 2$ and $c = \frac{5}{2}$. Since

Figure 9

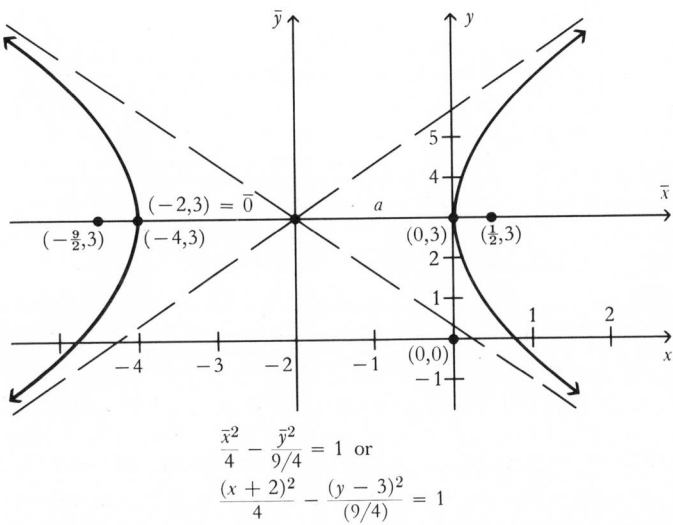

$(-2,3) = \bar{0}$

$(-\frac{9}{2},3)$ $(-4,3)$

$(0,3)$ $(\frac{1}{2},3)$

$(0,0)$

$$\frac{\bar{x}^2}{4} - \frac{\bar{y}^2}{9/4} = 1 \quad \text{or}$$

$$\frac{(x+2)^2}{4} - \frac{(y-3)^2}{(9/4)} = 1$$

$$b^2 = c^2 - a^2 = \frac{25}{4} - 4 = \frac{9}{4}, b = \frac{3}{2}.$$ Hence, the equation is

$$\frac{\bar{x}^2}{4} - \frac{\bar{y}^2}{\frac{9}{4}} = 1 \qquad \text{with } \bar{x} = x + 2 \text{ and } \bar{y} = y - 3$$

or, equivalently,

$$\frac{(x + 2)^2}{4} - \frac{(y - 3)^2}{\frac{9}{4}} = 1$$

PROBLEM SET 4

1 For each of the following hyperbolas find the coordinates of the vertices, the coordinates of the foci, and the equations of the asymptotes, and sketch the graph.

a) $36x^2 - 9y^2 = 1$ b) $16y^2 - 4x^2 = 48$
c) $y^2 - x^2 = 9$ d) $x^2/49 - y^2/36 = 1$
e) $x^2 - 9y^2 = 9$ f) $9x^2 - y^2 = 9$

2 For each of the following hyperbolas find the coordinates of the center, the coordinates of the vertices, the coordinates of the foci, and the equations of the asymptotes, and sketch the graph.

a) $4x^2 - y^2 + 8x - 2y + 6 = 0$
b) $(x - 5)^2/25 - (y - 4)^2/4 = 1$
c) $(x + 2)^2/16 - (y - 3)^2/9 = 1$
d) $(y - 2)^2/16 - (x + 3)^2/25 = 1$
e) $4x^2 - 3y^2 - 32x + 6y + 73 = 0$
f) $4x^2 - 9y^2 - 32x + 36y + 27 = 0$

3 Find the equation of the hyperbola with vertices at $(-1,4)$ and $(-1,6)$ and foci at $(-1,3)$ and $(-1,7)$.

4 Find the equation of the hyperbola with vertices at $(-16,0)$ and $(16,0)$ and asymptotes $y = \pm\frac{5}{4}x$.

5 The line segment with end points on a hyperbola that contains a focus and is perpendicular to the transverse axis is called a *focal chord*, or *latus rectum*, of the hyperbola. Show that the length of the focal chord of the hyperbola $x^2/a^2 - y^2/b^2 = 1$ is $2b^2/a$.

6 Find the equation of the hyperbola in each of the following cases:
a) Center at $(2,3)$, a focus at $(2,5)$, and a focal chord of length 6
b) Center at $(-2,1)$, a focus at $(-2,6)$, and a focal chord of length $\frac{32}{3}$

7 a) Use the graph of the hyperbola to determine the symmetry.
b) Use the graph to show that the equation of the hyperbola is not a function.

8 Find the domain and range of each of the relations of Problem 1.

9 Write the general equation for a hyperbola in determinant form if the transverse axis is parallel to the x axis.

6 Parabola

Geometrically, a *parabola* can be defined in a plane as the set of points, each of which is equidistant from a given point called the *focus* and from a given line called the *directrix*. In Figure 1, P_1, P_2, and P_3 are on the parabola; hence,

$$d_1 = c_1 \qquad d_2 = c_2 \qquad d_3 = c_3$$

Figure 1

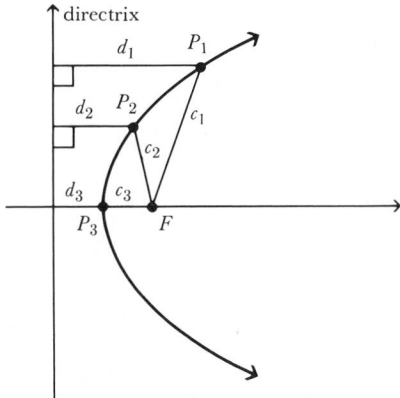

It is not difficult to derive the equation for a parabola from this geometric description.

THEOREM 1 (PARABOLA EQUATION)

Let $P = (x,y)$ be any point on a parabola with focus $(c,0)$ and directrix $x = -c$; then its equation is $y^2 = 4cx$, where $c > 0$ (Figure 2).

Figure 2

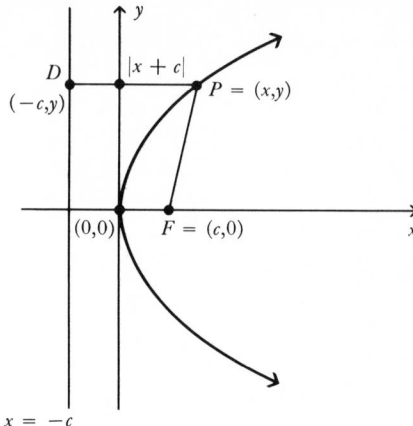

PROOF.   Since $P = (x,y)$ is equidistant from the focus and directrix, we can write $\overline{PF} = \overline{PD}$ so that

$$\sqrt{(x - c)^2 + y^2} = |x + c|$$

After squaring both sides, we get

$$(x - c)^2 + y^2 = (x + c)^2$$

so that

$$x^2 - 2cx + c^2 + y^2 = x^2 + 2cx + c^2$$

that is,

$$y^2 = 4cx$$

The line passing through the focus of the parabola perpendicular to the directrix is called the *axis of symmetry;* the point on the axis of symmetry midway between the directrix and focus is called the *center,* or *vertex,* of the parabola; the line segment with endpoints on the parabola perpendicular to the axis at the focus is called the *focal chord,* or *latus rectum,* of the parabola. In Figure 3, V is the vertex, F is the focus, and segment $\overline{AB}$ is the focal chord.

Notice that the graph of $y^2 = 4cx$ has the x axis as its axis of symmetry. Also, no point of the graph lies to the left of the y axis, for, if $x < 0$, we have $y^2 < 0$ (Why?) and y cannot be real. The directrix is parallel to the y axis, and the focus is a point to its right. This case, which might be described by saying that the parabola "opens to the right," is one of

Figure 3

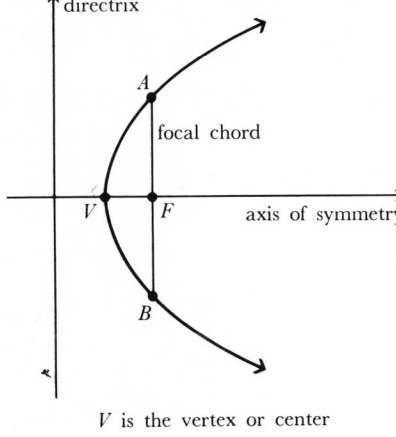

V is the vertex or center
F is the focus
Segment *AB* is the focal chord

four possible cases which could have been developed here. These cases
are as follows (assume $c > 0$ in all cases):

CASE 1. $y^2 = 4cx$. The focus is on the x axis, the directrix is parallel to
the y axis, and the vertex is $(0,0)$. The parabola opens to the right
(Figure 4).

Figure 4

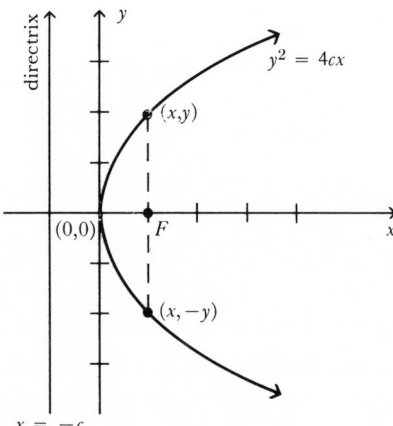

CASE 2. $y^2 = -4cx$. The focus is on the x axis, the directrix is parallel
to the y axis, and the vertex is $(0,0)$. The parabola opens to the left
(Figure 5).

Figure 5

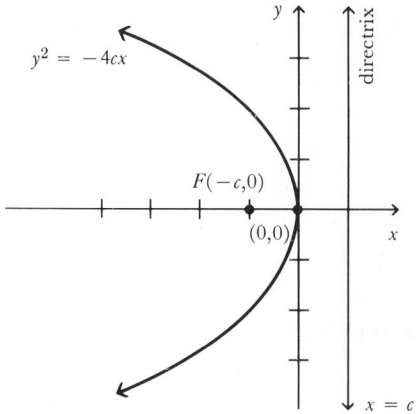

CASE 3. $x^2 = 4cy$. The focus is on the y axis, the directrix is parallel to the x axis, and the vertex is $(0,0)$. The parabola opens upward.

Figure 6

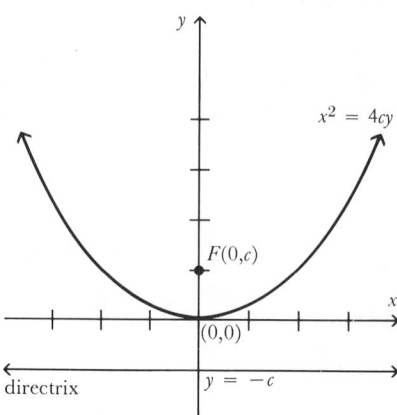

CASE 4. $x^2 = -4cy$. The focus is on the y axis, the directrix is parallel to the x axis, and the vertex is $(0,0)$. The parabola opens downward (Figure 7).

EXAMPLES

1   Find the focus and directrix of $x^2 = 12y$ and sketch the graph.

SOLUTION.   This is an example of Case 3 above. The graph is symmetric with respect to the y axis because $(-x,y)$ lies on the graph

Figure 7

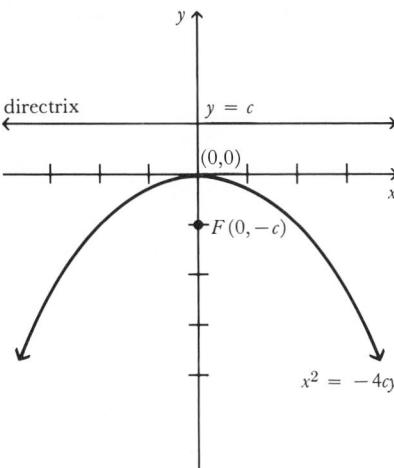

whenever (x,y) lies on the graph. Since x^2 in $x^2 = 12y$ is always non-negative, $y \geq 0$, so that the parabola opens upward. Since $4c = 12$, $c = 3$; therefore, the focus is $(0,3)$, and the equation of the directrix is $y = -3$ (Figure 8).

Figure 8

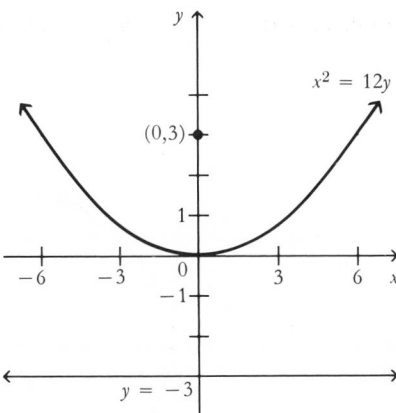

2 A parabola with its vertex at the origin has its focus at $(6,0)$. Find its equation and sketch the graph.

SOLUTION. Since the focus is $(6,0)$, the directrix is the line $x = -6$. The axis of symmetry in this case is the x axis; hence, its equation is

$y^2 = 4cx$. Since $c = 6$, the equation is $y^2 = 24x$. This is an example of Case 1. The graph is shown in Figure 9.

Figure 9

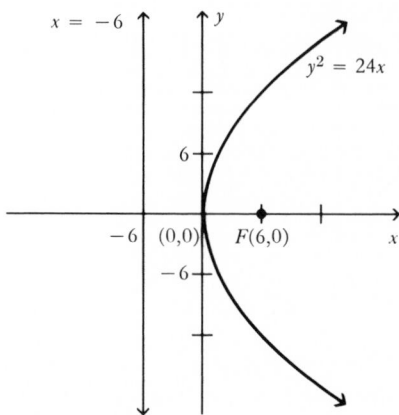

If the vertex of a parabola is translated to the point (h,k), then the equation of the parabola can take any one of the following forms (assume $c > 0$ in all cases):

1    $(y - k)^2 = 4c(x - h)$. The vertex of the parabola is the point (h,k) and the directrix is the line $x = h - c$ (Figure 10).

Figure 10

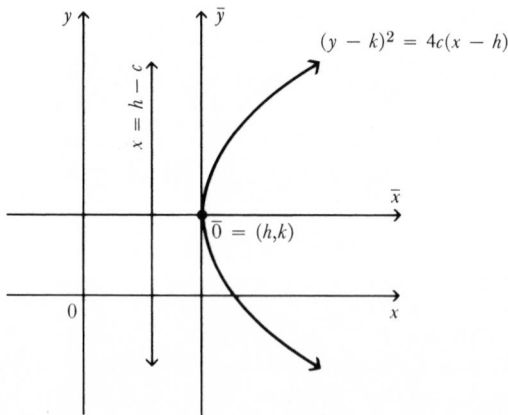

2    $(y - k)^2 = -4c(x - h)$. The vertex of the parabola is the point (h,k), and the directrix is the line $x = h + c$ (Figure 11).

Figure 11

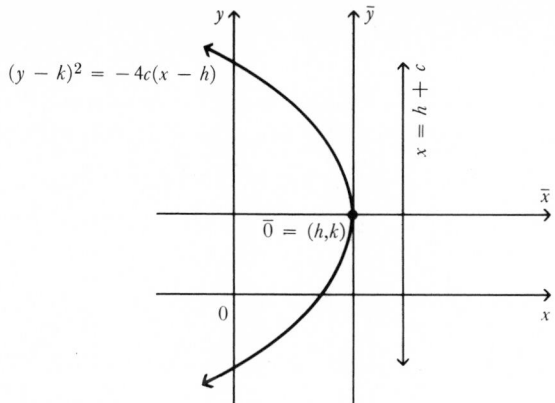

$(y - k)^2 = -4c(x - h)$

$\bar{0} = (h,k)$

3 $(x - h)^2 = 4c(y - k)$. The vertex of the parabola is the point (h,k), and the directrix is the line $y = k - c$ (Figure 12).

Figure 12

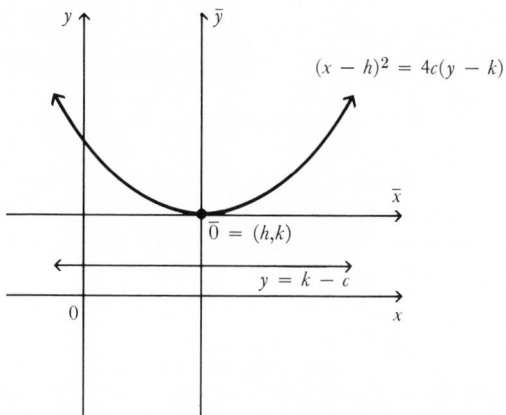

$(x - h)^2 = 4c(y - k)$

$\bar{0} = (h,k)$

$y = k - c$

4 $(x - h)^2 = -4c(y - k)$. The vertex of the parabola is the point (h,k), and the directrix is the line $y = k + c$ (Figure 13).

EXAMPLES

1 For the parabola $y^2 + 2y - 8x - 3 = 0$, find the vertex, the focus, the equation of the directrix, and the length of the focal chord. Also sketch the graph.

SOLUTION. (See Figure 14.) First, complete the square in $y^2 + 2y - 8x - 3$ to get $y^2 + 2y + 1 = 8x + 3 + 1$. Hence, $(y + 1)^2 = 8x + 4 = 4(2x + 1)$; that is, $(y + 1)^2 = 8(x + \frac{1}{2})$ or, equivalently,

Figure 13

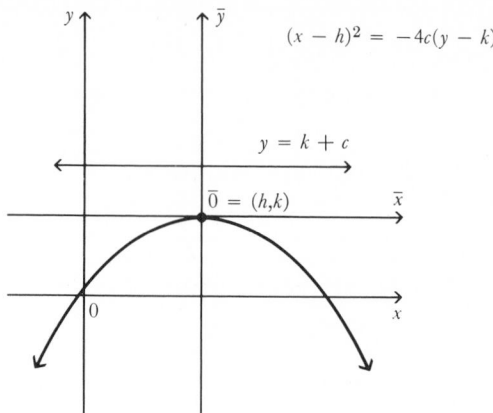

$\bar{y}^2 = 8\bar{x}$, where $\bar{y} = y + 1$ and $\bar{x} = x + \frac{1}{2}$; therefore, the vertex is $(-\frac{1}{2}, -1)$. Since $4c = 8$, it follows that $c = 2$; hence, we have the focus at $(-\frac{1}{2} + 2, -1) = (\frac{3}{2}, -1)$. The equation of the directrix is $x = -\frac{1}{2} - 2 = -\frac{5}{2}$. The length of the focal chord is 8.

Figure 14

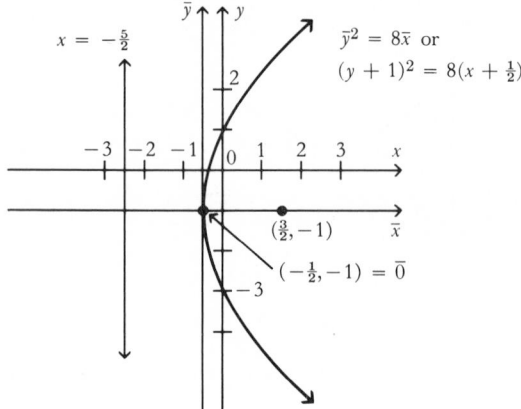

2   Consider the equation of the parabola $x^2 + 2x + 4y - 7 = 0$. Find the vertex, the focus, and the equation of the directrix. Also sketch the graph.

SOLUTION.   (See Figure 15.) After completing the square, we have

$$x^2 + 2x + 1 = -4y + 7 + 1 = -4y + 8$$

that is,

$$(x + 1)^2 = -4(y - 2)$$

Figure 15

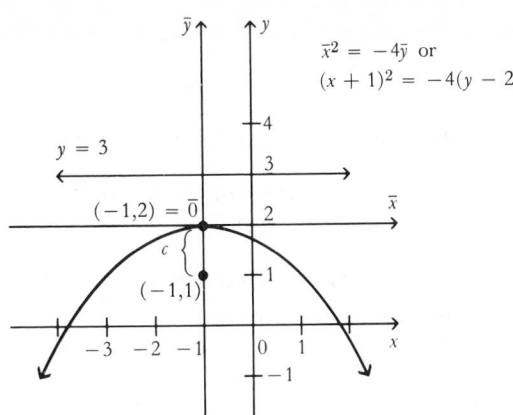

$\bar{x}^2 = -4\bar{y}$ or
$(x + 1)^2 = -4(y - 2)$

Thus, the vertex is $(-1,2)$, and the parabola opens downward because of the negative sign. Since $4c = 4$, $c = 1$ and the focus is $(-1,1)$; the equation of the directrix is $y = 2 + 1 = 3$.

PROBLEM SET 5

1 For each of the following parabolas find the vertex, the focus, the equation of the directrix, and the length of the focal chord, and sketch the graph.

a) $y^2 = 8x$
b) $x^2 + 2y = 0$
c) $x^2 - 4y = 0$
d) $y^2 + 4x = 0$
e) $y^2 + 5x = 0$
f) $(y + 3)^2 = 4(x + 1)$
g) $(x - 2)^2 = -6(y - 1)$
h) $(x + 3)^2 = y + 2$
i) $y^2 + 2x + 2y + 7 = 0$
j) $x^2 + 4x + 5y - 11 = 0$
k) $x^2 - 2x - 4y + 5 = 0$

2 Find the equation of the parabola in each of the following cases:

a) Vertex at $(1,2)$ and focus at $(3,2)$
b) Focus at $(0,4)$ and directrix $x = 2$
c) Vertex at $(3,4)$ and directrix $x = 1$
d) Vertex at $(2,-5)$ and directrix $y = 3$

3 Find the equation of the parabola whose axis is parallel to the y axis, with vertex $(1,3)$ and containing the point $(5,7)$.

4 Find the equation of the parabola with focus $(-3,-5)$ and directrix $x = 5$.

5 If the vertex of a parabola is translated to the point (h,k), then the equation of the parabola can take on the following forms, where $c > 0$.

a) $(y - k)^2 = 4c(x - h)$
b) $(y - k)^2 = -4c(x - h)$
c) $(x - h)^2 = 4c(y - k)$
d) $(x - h)^2 = -4c(y - k)$

Sketch the graph of a specific parabola for each of the above cases.

6   Use the graphs of parabolas to determine the cases when parabolas are functions. If a parabola is a function, is it one-to-one? Explain.

7   Discuss the symmetry of the parabola.

8   Find the domain and range for each of the relations in Problem 1.

9   Find the equation of the line through the points on the parabola $y^2 = 3x$ whose ordinates are 2 and 3.

10 For each of the four cases in which the vertex is $(0,0)$, write the equation of the parabola in determinant form.

7 Conics

We have developed analytically the equations of the circle, the ellipse, the hyperbola, and the parabola, and we have also discussed their properties. In our approach, we derived the equations using the geometric properties. In this section, we will give a general approach that simultaneously applies to the ellipse, the hyperbola, and the parabola. These three graphs are called *conics* because they are determined by the intersections of planes with cones of two nappes (Figure 1a, b, and c).

Figure 1

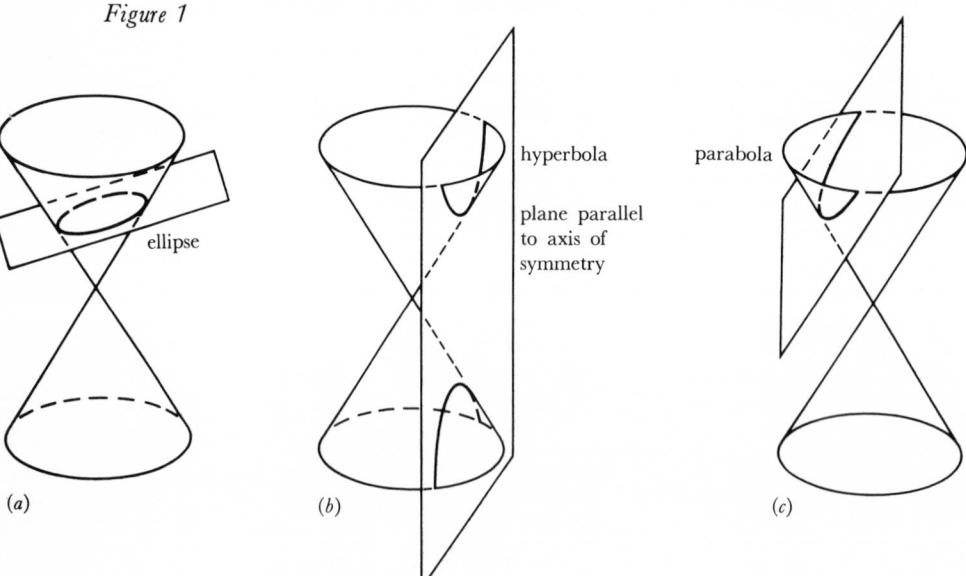

ellipse

hyperbola

plane parallel to axis of symmetry

parabola

(a)   (b)   (c)

In general, a conic is determined by a given point F, called the *focus*, a given line d, associated with F but not containing F, called the *directrix*, and a positive constant number e.

7.1 Definition

Assume that e is a positive constant (*eccentricity*), F is a fixed point (*focus*), and $\overline{PD}$ is the distance between point P and a given line d (*directrix*). Then, a conic is a set of points C where

$$C = \left\{ P \,\middle|\, P = (x,y) \quad \text{where} \quad \frac{\overline{FP}}{\overline{PD}} = e \right\} \quad \square$$

Figure 2

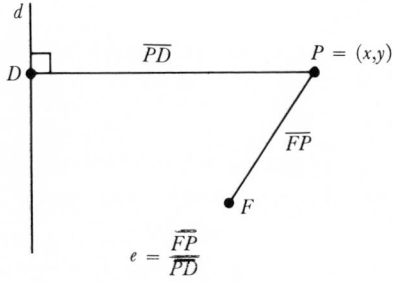

$$e = \frac{\overline{FP}}{\overline{PD}}$$

EXAMPLES

1   Assume that the eccentricity $e = 1$, the focus is $(-2,0)$, and the directrix is $x = 3$. Find the equation of the conic and sketch the conic.

SOLUTION.   (See Figure 3.) If $P = (x,y)$ is a point of the conic, then $r_1/r_2 = 1$ (Why?); that is, $r_1 = r_2$ or, equivalently, $r_1^2 = r_2^2$. By the

Figure 3

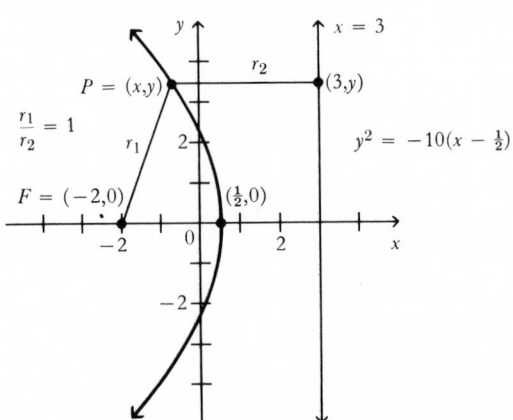

distance formula, $(x + 2)^2 + y^2 = (x - 3)^2$; that is, the conic is the parabola $y^2 = -10(x - \frac{1}{2})$.

2   Find the equation of the conic that has eccentricity $\frac{2}{3}$ and has the point $(4,0)$ as a focus for which the corresponding directrix is the y axis.

SOLUTION.   (See Figure 4.) By Definition 7.1, we have $e = r_1/r_2 = \frac{2}{3}$ or, equivalently, $3r_1 = 2r_2$. But, $r_1^2 = (x - 4)^2 + y^2$ and $r_2^2 = x^2$, so that $9r_1^2 = 4r_2^2$; that is,

$$9(x^2 - 8x + 16 + y^2) = 4x^2$$

so that

$$5x^2 - 72x + 9y^2 + 144 = 0$$

Figure 4

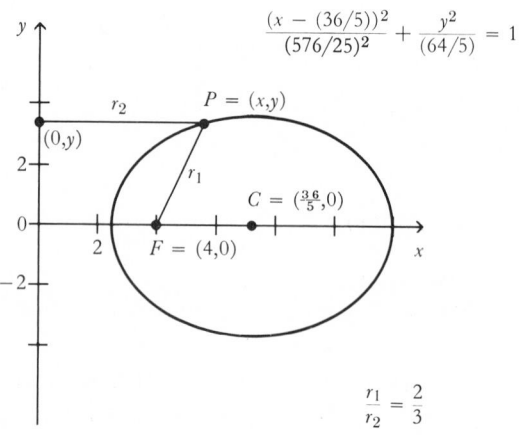

$$\frac{(x - (36/5))^2}{(576/25)^2} + \frac{y^2}{(64/5)} = 1$$

$$\frac{r_1}{r_2} = \frac{2}{3}$$

However, upon completing the square,

$$5[x^2 - \tfrac{72}{5}x + (\tfrac{36}{5})^2] + 9y^2 = -144 + \frac{(36)^2}{5}$$

that is,

$$5(x - \tfrac{36}{5})^2 + 9y^2 = \tfrac{576}{5}$$

Hence, the conic is the ellipse

$$\frac{(x - \tfrac{36}{5})^2}{(\tfrac{576}{25})} + \frac{y^2}{(\tfrac{64}{5})} = 1$$

3 Find the equation of the conic with focus $(2,0)$, directrix $x = 0$, and eccentricity 2.

SOLUTION. (See Figure 5.) Since $e = r_1/r_2 = 2$, $r_1 = 2r_2$; that is, $r_1^2 = 4r_2^2$, so that $(x - 2)^2 + y^2 = 4x^2$ (Why?) or, equivalently, $3x^2 + 4x - y^2 = 4$. After completing the square, we get $3(x + \frac{2}{3})^2 - y^2 = \frac{16}{3}$ or, equivalently, the hyperbola

$$\frac{(x + \frac{2}{3})^2}{(\frac{16}{9})} - \frac{y^2}{(\frac{16}{3})} = 1$$

Figure 5

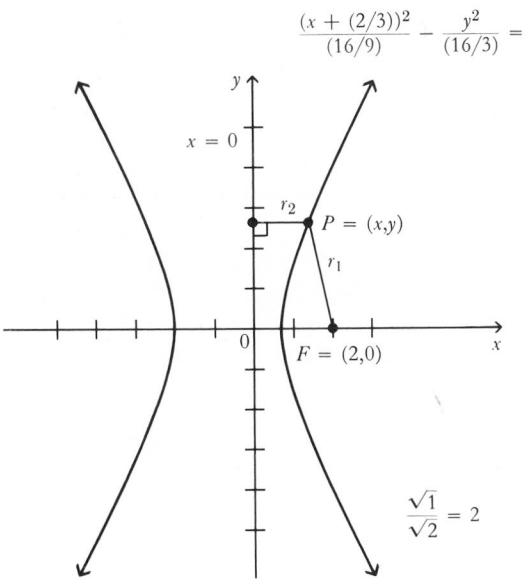

$$\frac{(x + (2/3))^2}{(16/9)} - \frac{y^2}{(16/3)} = 1$$

$x = 0$

r_2

$P = (x,y)$

r_1

$F = (2,0)$

$\dfrac{\sqrt{1}}{\sqrt{2}} = 2$

From the geometric definition of a *parabola* (see Section 6), it can be seen that the eccentricity $e = 1$ (see Example 1 above). Also, it can be shown that if $e < 1$, the conic is an ellipse (see Example 2 above), and if $e > 1$, the conic is a hyperbola (see Example 3 above).

Finally, we state without proof the following theorem.

THEOREM 1

For ellipses and hyperbolas of the form

$$\frac{(x - h)^2}{a^2} \pm \frac{(y - k)^2}{b^2} = 1$$

where $c^2 = a^2 - b^2$ for the ellipse and $c^2 = a^2 + b^2$ for the hyperbola. The eccentricity $e = c/a$.

EXAMPLES

1   Assume that the equation of the directrix is $x = a^2/c$. Verify that for the hyperbola $x^2/a^2 - y^2/b^2 = 1$, $e = c/a$.

PROOF.   Consider the graph of the hyperbola $x^2/a^2 - y^2/b^2 = 1$ in Figure 6. One of the foci is $(c,0)$, where $c = \sqrt{a^2 + b^2}$. (Why?) Let $r_1 = \overline{PF_1}$ and $r_2 = \overline{PD}$. Using the distance formula, we have

$$r_1^2 = (x - c)^2 + y^2 = x^2 - 2cx + c^2 + y^2$$

Figure 6

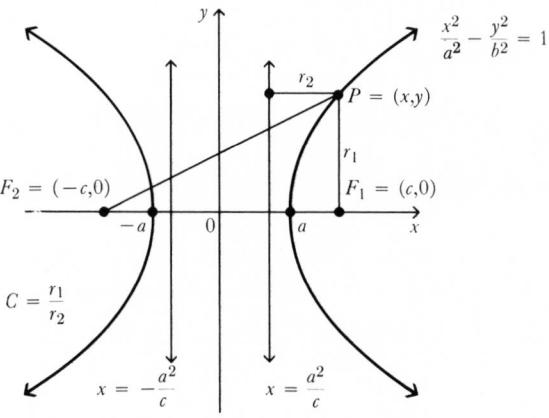

However,

$$y^2 = \frac{b^2 x^2}{a^2} - b^2$$

so that

$$r_1^2 = x^2 - 2cx + c^2 + \frac{b^2 x^2}{a^2} - b^2$$

$$= \left(\frac{a^2 + b^2}{a^2}\right) x^2 - 2cx + c^2 - b^2$$

Since $a^2 + b^2 = c^2$, $c^2 - b^2 = a^2$, so that

$$r_1^2 = \frac{c^2}{a^2} x^2 - 2cx + a^2$$

$$= \frac{c^2}{a^2}\left(x^2 - \frac{2a^2}{c} x + \frac{a^4}{c^2}\right)$$

$$= \frac{c^2}{a^2}\left(x - \frac{a^2}{c}\right)^2$$

Therefore,

$$r_1 = \frac{c}{a}\left|x - \frac{a^2}{c}\right|$$

Also,

$$r_2 = \overline{PD} = \left|x - \frac{a^2}{c}\right| \qquad \text{(Why?)}$$

Hence,

$$e = \frac{r_1}{r_2} = \frac{(c/a)|x - a^2/c|}{|x - a^2/c|} = \frac{c}{a}$$

so that Theorem 1 holds for the hyperbola.

2 Find the eccentricity of the ellipse whose equation is $4x^2 + 9y^2 = 36$.

SOLUTION. (See Figure 7.) $4x^2 + 9y^2 = 36$ in standard form is $x^2/9 + y^2/4 = 1$. This is an equation of the ellipse where $a = 3$ and $b = 2$; hence,

$$c = \sqrt{a^2 - b^2} = \sqrt{9 - 4} = \sqrt{5}$$

Figure 7

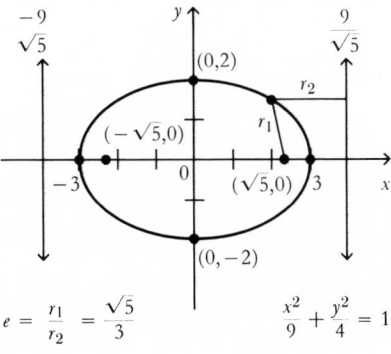

Therefore, by Theorem 1, the eccentricity is

$$e = \frac{c}{a} = \frac{\sqrt{5}}{3}$$

3 Find the equation of the parabola which has focus $(1,3)$ and directrix $y = -2$, and graph the parabola.

SOLUTION.   (See Figure 8.) The eccentricity is 1, so that $r_1^2 = r_2^2$ (Why?); that is,

$$(x - 1)^2 + (y - 3)^2 = (y + 2)^2$$

Hence,

$$(x - 1)^2 = 4(\tfrac{5}{2})(y - \tfrac{1}{2}).$$

Figure 8

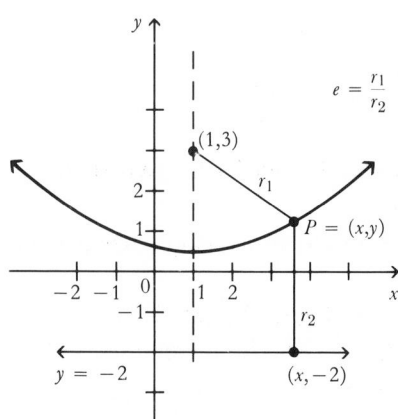

PROBLEM SET 6

1   Find the eccentricity and the equations of the directrices for each of the following conics.

a) $25x^2 + 16y^2 = 400$ b) $x^2 + 2y^2 = 1$
c) $x^2 + 3y^2 = 4$ d) $y^2 - 8y + 3x + 5 = 0$
e) $9x^2 - 16y^2 + 144 = 0$ f) $4x^2 - 4y^2 + 1 = 0$
g) $3x^2 - 5x + y^2 + 22y = 1$ h) $x^2 + 16x - y + 7 = 0$

2   Use Definition 7.1 to determine the equation of each of the following conics. Also sketch the graph.

a)   Focus at (3,0), directrix $y = \tfrac{5}{3}$, and eccentricity $e = 3/\sqrt{5}$
b)   Focus at (5,0), directrix $x = \tfrac{16}{5}$, and eccentricity $e = \tfrac{5}{4}$
c)   Focus at (3,0), directrix $x = \tfrac{25}{3}$, and eccentricity $e = \tfrac{3}{5}$
d)   Focus at (1,2), directrix $y = -2$, and eccentricity $e = \tfrac{1}{2}$
e)   Focus at (2,0), directrix $x = 4$, and eccentricity $e = 1$.

3   Given the equation $25x^2 - 4y^2 + 50x - 12y + 116 = 0$, find the center, the foci, the vertices, the equations of the asymptotes, and the eccentricity. Also sketch the graph.

4   We know that the eccentricity $e = c/a < 1$ for the ellipse $x^2/a^2 + y^2/b^2 = 1$, where $c^2 = a^2 - b^2$. Now, as e becomes closer and closer to zero in value, $c/a = e$ approaches zero; hence c^2 approaches zero or a approaches b in value. (Why?) What is the shape of an ellipse in which a and b are close in value? What if $a = b$? Does this give an indication of how to define a conic with eccentricity $e = 0$? Use sketches and examples to answer these questions.

REVIEW PROBLEM SET

1 Find the equation of the parabola which satisfies each of the following conditions.

   a) Focus $(-4,0)$ and directrix $y = 3$
   b) Focus $(0,3)$ and directrix $x = \frac{5}{2}$
   c) Focus $(1,-\frac{5}{2})$ and directrix $y = -4$
   d) Focus $(3,0)$, containing point $(2,3)$ with the axis of symmetry the x axis and opens to the right.

2 Find the equation of the ellipse satisfying the given conditions and sketch the graph in each case.

   a) Vertices $(-5,0)$ and $(5,0)$ and foci $(-3,0)$ and $(3,0)$
   b) Foci $(-1,0)$ and $(1,0)$ and length of minor axis $2\sqrt{2}$
   c) Foci $(0,-6)$ and $(0,6)$ and eccentricity $e = \frac{1}{2}$
   d) Vertices $(-5,0)$ and $(5,0)$ and eccentricity $e = \frac{3}{5}$.

3 Do the ellipses $2x^2 + 3y^2 = 18$ and $9x^2 + 16y^2 = 36$ intersect? Explain.

4 The end points of the base of a triangle are $(-2,0)$ and $(2,0)$ and the sum of the lengths of the other two sides is 6. Find the equation of the set of all points which are possible vertices.

5 Find the points on the parabola $y^2 + 20x = 0$ for which the sum of two focal radii is equal in length to the latus rectum. (*Note:* the focal radii are the line segments with one end point on the parabola and the other end point the focus.)

6 Find the equation of the line containing the points on the parabola $y^2 = 8x$ whose y coordinates are 2 and 8, respectively.

7 Find the equation of each of the following ellipses.

   a) Focus $(2,0)$, eccentricity $e = \frac{2}{3}$, and directrix $2x - 9 = 0$
   b) Focus $(0,-4)$, eccentricity $e = \frac{2}{3}$, and directrix $y + 9 = 0$
   c) Vertex $(10,0)$, center $(0,0)$, and eccentricity $e = \frac{3}{5}$
   d) Center $(0,0)$, vertex $(0,3)$, and eccentricity $e = \frac{2}{5}$

8 A square with sides parallel to the coordinate axes is inscribed in the ellipse $9x^2 + 16y^2 = 100$. Find the coordinates of its vertices and its area.

9 Find the equation of the hyperbola in each of the following cases and sketch the graph.

a) Vertices $(-2,0)$ and $(2,0)$ and foci $(-3,0)$ and $(3,0)$

b) Foci $(-10,0)$ and $(10,0)$ and eccentricity $e = \frac{5}{4}$

c) Vertices $(-15,0)$ and $(15,0)$ and asymptotes $5y = \pm 4x$

d) Contains the point $(5,9)$ and asymptotes $y = \pm x$.

10 Consider the equation $(b^2 - k)x^2 + (a^2 - k)y^2 = 1$, where $a \geq b$.

a) For what choices of k is the graph an ellipse?

b) For what choices of k is the graph a hyperbola?

c) For what choices of k is the graph a circle?

11 Show that the hyperbolas whose equations are $x^2/4 - y^2/9 = 1$ and $y^2/9 - x^2/4 = 1$ have the same set of asymptotes, and sketch them on the same coordinate system.

12 Show that if a point P is equidistant from the y axis and the point $(6,0)$, then its coordinates (x,y) must satisfy the equation $y^2 = 12(x - 3)$. Is the converse true?

13 Let d_1 be the distance from the point $P = (x,y)$ to the point $A = (1,0)$, and d_2 be the distance from the point $P = (x,y)$ to the point $B = (9,0)$. Derive the equation that the point must satisfy if $d_1 + d_2 = 4$.

14 Let d_1 be the distance from the point $P = (x,y)$ to the point $A = (-10,0)$ and d_2 be the distance from the point $P = (x,y)$ to the point $B = (10,0)$. Show that if $d_1 - d_2 = 12$, then the coordinates of P must satisfy the equation $x^2/36 - y^2/64 = 1$. Is it true that every point P whose coordinates satisfy this equation has $d_1 - d_2 = 12$?

15 Write the equation of an ellipse whose center is at the origin, whose axes of symmetry are on the coordinate axes, and whose major axis is three times the minor axis and contains the point $(3,1)$.

16 The Earth moves in an elliptical orbit with eccentricity 0.017, major axis 185.8 million miles, and the sun at one focus. How close does the Earth come to the Sun when it is positioned on the major axis?

Appendixes

APPENDIX A

Tables

TABLE I COMMON LOGARITHMS

n	0	1	2	3	4	5	6	7	8	9
10	0000	0043	0086	0128	0170	0212	0253	0294	0334	0374
11	0414	0453	0492	0531	0569	0607	0645	0682	0719	0755
12	0792	0828	0864	0899	0934	0969	1004	1038	1072	1106
13	1139	1173	1206	1239	1271	1303	1335	1367	1399	1430
14	1461	1492	1523	1553	1584	1614	1644	1673	1703	1732
15	1761	1790	1818	1847	1875	1903	1931	1959	1987	2014
16	2041	2068	2095	2122	2148	2175	2201	2227	2253	2279
17	2304	2330	2355	2380	2405	2430	2455	2480	2504	2529
18	2553	2577	2601	2625	2648	2672	2695	2718	2742	2765
19	2788	2810	2833	2856	2878	2900	2923	2945	2967	2989
20	3010	3032	3054	3075	3096	3118	3139	3160	3181	3201
21	3222	3243	3263	3284	3304	3324	3345	3365	3385	3404
22	3424	3444	3464	3483	3502	3522	3541	3560	3579	3598
23	3617	3636	3655	3674	3692	3711	3729	3747	3766	3784
24	3802	3820	3838	3856	3874	3892	3909	3927	3945	3962
25	3979	3997	4014	4031	4048	4065	4082	4099	4116	4133
26	4150	4166	4183	4200	4216	4232	4249	4265	4281	4298
27	4314	4330	4346	4362	4378	4393	4409	4425	4440	4456
28	4472	4487	4502	4518	4533	4548	4564	4579	4594	4609
29	4624	4639	4654	4669	4683	4698	4713	4728	4742	4757
30	4771	4786	4800	4814	4829	4843	4857	4871	4886	4900
31	4914	4928	4942	4955	4969	4983	4997	5011	5024	5038
32	5051	5065	5079	5092	5105	5119	5132	5145	5159	5172
33	5185	5198	5211	5224	5237	5250	5263	5276	5289	5302
34	5315	5328	5340	5353	5366	5378	5391	5403	5416	5428

TABLE I   COMMON LOGARITHMS — Cont.

n	0	1	2	3	4	5	6	7	8	9
35	5441	5453	5465	5478	5490	5502	5514	5527	5539	5551
36	5563	5575	5587	5599	5611	5623	5635	5647	5658	5670
37	5682	5694	5705	5717	5729	5740	5752	5763	5775	5786
38	5798	5809	5821	5832	5843	5855	5866	5877	5888	5899
39	5911	5922	5933	5944	5955	5966	5977	5988	5999	6010
40	6021	6031	6042	6053	6064	6075	6085	6096	6107	6117
41	6128	6138	6149	6160	6170	6180	6191	6201	6212	6222
42	6232	6243	6253	6263	6274	6284	6294	6304	6314	6325
43	6335	6345	6355	6365	6375	6385	6395	6405	6415	6425
44	6435	6444	6454	6464	6474	6484	6493	6503	6513	6522
45	6532	6542	6551	6561	6571	6580	6590	6599	6609	6618
46	6628	6637	6646	6656	6665	6675	6684	6693	6702	6712
47	6721	6730	6739	6749	6758	6767	6776	6785	6794	6803
48	6812	6821	6830	6839	6848	6857	6866	6875	6884	6893
49	6902	6911	6920	6928	6937	6946	6955	6964	6972	6981
50	6990	6998	7007	7016	7024	7033	7042	7050	7059	7067
51	7076	7084	7093	7101	7110	7118	7126	7135	7143	7152
52	7160	7168	7177	7185	7193	7202	7210	7218	7226	7235
53	7243	7251	7259	7267	7275	7284	7292	7300	7308	7316
54	7324	7332	7340	7348	7356	7364	7372	7380	7388	7396
55	7404	7412	7419	7427	7435	7443	7451	7459	7466	7474
56	7482	7490	7497	7505	7513	7520	7528	7536	7543	7551
57	7559	7566	7574	7582	7589	7597	7604	7612	7619	7627
58	7634	7642	7649	7657	7664	7672	7679	7686	7694	7701
59	7709	7716	7723	7731	7738	7745	7752	7760	7767	7774
60	7782	7789	7796	7803	7810	7818	7825	7832	7839	7846
61	7853	7860	7868	7875	7882	7889	7896	7903	7910	7917
62	7924	7931	7938	7945	7952	7959	7966	7973	7980	7987
63	7993	8000	8007	8014	8021	8028	8035	8041	8048	8055
64	8062	8069	8075	8082	8089	8096	8102	8109	8116	8122
65	8129	8136	8142	8149	8156	8162	8169	8176	8182	8189
66	8195	8202	8209	8215	8222	8228	8235	8241	8248	8254
67	8261	8267	8274	8280	8287	8293	8299	8306	8312	8319
68	8325	8331	8338	8344	8351	8357	8363	8370	8376	8382
69	8388	8395	8401	8407	8414	8420	8426	8432	8439	8445
70	8451	8457	8463	8470	8476	8482	8488	8494	8500	8506
71	8513	8519	8525	8531	8537	8543	8549	8555	8561	8567
72	8673	8579	8585	8591	8597	8603	8609	8615	8621	8627
73	8633	8639	8645	8651	8657	8663	8669	8675	8681	8686
74	8692	8698	8704	8710	8716	8722	8727	8733	8739	8745
75	8751	8756	8762	8768	8774	8779	8785	8791	8797	8802
76	8808	8814	8820	8825	8831	8837	8842	8848	8854	8859
77	8865	8871	8876	8882	8887	8893	8899	8904	8910	8915
78	8921	8927	8932	8938	8943	8949	8954	8960	8965	8971
79	8976	8982	8987	8993	8998	9004	9009	9015	9020	9025
80	9031	9036	9042	9047	9053	9058	9063	9069	9074	9079
81	9085	9090	9096	9101	9106	9112	9117	9122	9128	9133
82	9138	9143	9149	9154	9159	9165	9170	9175	9180	9186
83	9191	9196	9201	9206	9212	9217	9222	9227	9232	9238
84	9243	9248	9253	9258	9263	9269	9274	9279	9284	9289

TABLE I   **COMMON LOGARITHMS** — Cont.

n	0	1	2	3	4	5	6	7	8	9
85	9294	9299	9304	9309	9315	9320	9325	9330	9335	9340
86	9345	9350	9355	9360	9365	9370	9375	9380	9385	9390
87	9395	9400	9405	9410	9415	9420	9425	9430	9435	9440
88	9445	9450	9455	9460	9465	9469	9474	9479	9484	9489
89	9494	9499	9504	9509	9513	9518	9523	9528	9533	9538
90	9542	9547	9552	9557	9562	9566	9571	9576	9581	9586
91	9590	9595	9600	9605	9609	9614	9619	9624	9628	9633
92	9638	9643	9647	9652	9657	9661	9666	9671	9675	9680
93	9685	9689	9694	9699	9703	9708	9713	9717	9722	9727
94	9731	9736	9741	9745	9750	9754	9759	9763	9768	9773
95	9777	9782	9786	9791	9795	9800	9805	9809	9814	9818
96	9823	9827	9832	9836	9841	9845	9850	9854	9859	9863
97	9868	9872	9877	9881	9886	9890	9894	9899	9903	9908
98	9912	9917	9921	9926	9930	9934	9939	9943	9948	9952
99	9956	9961	9965	9969	9974	9978	9983	9987	9991	9996

TABLE II   NATURAL LOGARITHMS

t	0.00	0.01	0.02	0.03	0.04	0.05	0.06	0.07	0.08	0.09
1.0	0.0000	0.0100	0.0198	0.0296	0.0392	0.0488	0.0583	0.0677	0.0770	0.0862
1.1	0.0953	0.1044	0.1133	0.1222	0.1310	0.1398	0.1484	0.1570	0.1655	0.1740
1.2	0.1823	0.1906	0.1989	0.2070	0.2151	0.2231	0.2311	0.2390	0.2469	0.2546
1.3	0.2624	0.2700	0.2776	0.2852	0.2927	0.3001	0.3075	0.3148	0.3221	0.3293
1.4	0.3365	0.3436	0.3507	0.3577	0.3646	0.3716	0.3784	0.3853	0.3920	0.3988
1.5	0.4055	0.4121	0.4187	0.4253	0.4318	0.4383	0.4447	0.4511	0.4574	0.4637
1.6	0.4700	0.4762	0.4824	0.4886	0.4947	0.5008	0.5068	0.5128	0.5188	0.5247
1.7	0.5306	0.5365	0.5423	0.5481	0.5539	0.5596	0.5653	0.5710	0.5766	0.5822
1.8	0.5878	0.5933	0.5988	0.6043	0.6098	0.6152	0.6206	0.6259	0.6313	0.6366
1.9	0.6419	0.6471	0.6523	0.6575	0.6627	0.6678	0.6729	0.6780	0.6831	0.6881
2.0	0.6931	0.6981	0.7031	0.7080	0.7130	0.7178	0.7227	0.7275	0.7324	0.7372
2.1	0.7419	0.7467	0.7514	0.7561	0.7608	0.7655	0.7701	0.7747	0.7793	0.7839
2.2	0.7885	0.7930	0.7975	0.8020	0.8065	0.8109	0.8154	0.8198	0.8242	0.8286
2.3	0.8329	0.8372	0.8416	0.8459	0.8502	0.8544	0.8587	0.8629	0.8671	0.8713
2.4	0.8755	0.8796	0.8838	0.8879	0.8920	0.8961	0.9002	0.9042	0.9083	0.9123
2.5	0.9163	0.9203	0.9243	0.9282	0.9322	0.9361	0.9400	0.9439	0.9478	0.9517
2.6	0.9555	0.9594	0.9632	0.9670	0.9708	0.9746	0.9783	0.9821	0.9858	0.9895
2.7	0.9933	0.9969	1.0006	1.0043	1.0080	1.0116	1.0152	0.0188	1.0225	1.0260
2.8	1.0296	1.0332	1.0367	1.0403	1.0438	1.0473	1.0508	1.0543	1.0578	1.0613
2.9	1.0647	1.0682	1.0716	1.0750	1.0784	1.0818	1.0852	1.0886	1.0919	1.0953
3.0	1.0986	1.1019	1.1053	1.1086	1.1119	1.1151	1.1184	1.1217	1.1249	1.1282
3.1	1.1314	1.1346	1.1378	1.1410	1.1442	1.1474	1.1506	1.1537	1.1569	1.1600
3.2	1.1632	1.1663	1.1694	1.1725	1.1756	1.1787	1.1817	1.1848	1.1878	1.1909
3.3	1.1939	1.1970	1.2000	1.2030	1.2060	1.2090	1.2119	1.2149	1.2179	1.2208
3.4	1.2238	1.2267	1.2296	1.2326	1.2355	1.2384	1.2413	1.2442	1.2470	1.2499
3.5	1.2528	1.2556	1.2585	1.2613	1.2641	1.2669	1.2698	1.2726	1.2754	1.2782
3.6	1.2809	1.2837	1.2865	1.2892	1.2920	1.2947	1.2975	1.3002	1.3029	1.3056
3.7	1.3083	1.3110	1.3137	1.3164	1.3191	1.3218	1.3244	1.3271	1.3297	1.3324
3.8	1.3350	1.3376	1.3403	1.3429	1.3455	1.3481	1.3507	1.3533	1.3558	1.3584
3.9	1.3610	1.3635	1.3661	1.3686	1.3712	1.3737	1.3762	1.3788	1.3813	1.3838
4.0	1.3863	1.3888	1.3913	1.3938	1.3962	1.3987	1.4012	1.4036	1.4061	1.4085
4.1	1.4110	1.4134	1.4159	1.4183	1.4207	1.4231	1.4255	1.4279	1.4303	1.4327
4.2	1.4351	1.4375	1.4398	1.4422	1.4446	1.4469	1.4493	1.4516	1.4540	1.4563
4.3	1.4586	1.4609	1.4633	1.4656	1.4679	1.4702	1.4725	1.4748	1.4770	1.4793
4.4	1.4816	1.4839	1.4861	1.4884	1.4907	1.4929	1.4952	1.4974	1.4996	1.5019
4.5	1.5041	1.5063	1.5085	1.5107	1.5129	1.5151	1.5173	1.5195	1.5217	1.5239
4.6	1.5261	1.5282	1.5304	1.5326	1.5347	1.5369	1.5390	1.5412	1.5433	1.5454
4.7	1.5476	1.5497	1.5518	1.5539	1.5560	1.5581	1.5602	1.5623	1.5644	1.5665
4.8	1.5686	1.5707	1.5728	1.5748	1.5769	1.5790	1.5810	1.5831	1.5851	1.5872
4.9	1.5892	1.5913	1.5933	1.5953	1.5974	1.5994	1.6014	1.6034	1.6054	1.6074
5.0	1.6094	1.6114	1.6134	1.6154	1.6174	1.6194	1.6214	1.6233	1.6253	1.6273
5.1	1.6292	1.6312	1.6332	1.6351	1.6371	1.6390	1.6409	1.6429	1.6448	1.6467
5.2	1.6487	1.6506	1.6525	1.6544	1.6563	1.6582	1.6601	1.6620	1.6639	1.6658
5.3	1.6677	1.6696	1.6715	1.6734	1.6752	1.6771	1.6790	1.6808	1.6827	1.6845
5.4	1.6864	1.6882	1.6901	1.6919	1.6938	1.6956	1.6974	1.6993	1.7011	1.7029
5.5	1.7047	1.7066	1.7084	1.7102	1.7120	1.7138	1.7156	1.7174	1.7192	1.7210
5.6	1.7228	1.7246	1.7263	1.7281	1.7299	1.7317	1.7334	1.7352	1.7370	1.7387
5.7	1.7405	1.7422	1.7440	1.7457	1.7475	1.7492	1.7509	1.7527	1.7544	1.7561
5.8	1.7579	1.7596	1.7613	1.7630	1.7647	1.7664	1.7682	1.7699	1.7716	1.7733
5.9	1.7750	1.7766	1.7783	1.7800	1.7817	1.7834	1.7851	1.7867	1.7884	1.7901

TABLE II   **NATURAL LOGARITHMS** — Cont.

t	0.00	0.01	0.02	0.03	0.04	0.05	0.06	0.07	0.08	0.09
6.0	1.7918	1.7934	1.7951	1.7967	1.7984	1.8001	1.8017	1.8034	1.8050	1.8066
6.1	1.8083	1.8099	1.8116	1.8132	1.8148	1.8165	1.8181	1.8197	1.8213	1.8229
6.2	1.8245	1.8262	1.8278	1.8294	1.8310	1.8326	1.8342	1.8358	1.8374	1.8390
6.3	1.8406	1.8421	1.8437	1.8453	1.8469	1.8485	1.8500	1.8516	1.8532	1.8547
6.4	1.8563	1.8579	1.8594	1.8610	1.8625	1.8641	1.8656	1.8672	1.8687	1.8703
6.5	1.8718	1.8733	1.8749	1.8764	1.8779	1.8795	1.8810	1.8825	1.8840	1.8856
6.6	1.8871	1.8886	1.8901	1.8916	1.8931	1.8946	1.8961	1.8976	1.8991	1.9006
6.7	1.9021	1.9036	1.9051	1.9066	1.9081	1.9095	1.9110	1.9125	1.9140	1.9155
6.8	1.9169	1.9184	1.9199	1.9213	1.9228	1.9242	1.9257	1.9272	1.9286	1.9301
6.9	1.9315	1.9330	1.9344	1.9359	1.9373	1.9387	1.9402	1.9416	1.9430	1.9445
7.0	1.9459	1.9473	1.9488	1.9502	1.9516	1.9530	1.9544	1.9559	1.9573	1.9587
7.1	1.9601	1.9615	1.9629	1.9643	1.9657	1.9671	1.9685	1.9699	1.9713	1.9727
7.2	1.9741	1.9755	1.9769	1.9782	1.9796	1.9810	1.9824	1.9838	1.9851	1.9865
7.3	1.9879	1.9892	1.9906	1.9920	1.9933	1.9947	1.9961	1.9974	1.9988	2.0001
7.4	2.0015	2.0028	2.0042	2.0055	2.0069	2.0082	2.0096	2.0109	2.0122	2.0136
7.5	2.0149	2.0162	2.0176	2.0189	2.0202	2.0215	2.0229	2.0242	2.0255	2.0268
7.6	2.0282	2.0295	2.0308	2.0321	2.0334	2.0347	2.0360	2.0373	2.0386	2.0399
7.7	2.0412	2.0425	2.0438	2.0451	2.0464	2.0477	2.0490	2.0503	2.0516	2.0528
7.8	2.0541	2.0554	2.0567	2.0580	2.0592	2.0605	2.0618	2.0631	2.0643	2.0665
7.9	2.0669	2.0681	2.0694	2.0707	2.0719	2.0732	2.0744	2.0757	2.0769	2.0782
8.0	2.0794	2.0807	2.0819	2.0832	2.0844	2.0857	2.0869	2.0882	2.0894	2.0906
8.1	2.0919	2.0931	2.0943	2.0956	2.0968	2.0980	2.0992	2.1005	2.1017	2.1029
8.2	2.1041	2.1054	2.1066	2.1078	2.1090	2.1102	2.1114	2.1126	2.1138	2.1150
8.3	2.1163	2.1175	2.1187	2.1199	2.1211	2.1223	2.1235	2.1247	2.1258	2.1270
8.4	2.1282	2.1294	2.1306	2.1318	2.1330	2.1342	2.1353	2.1365	2.1377	2.1389
8.5	2.1401	2.1412	2.1424	2.1436	2.1448	2.1459	2.1471	2.1483	2.1494	2.1506
8.6	2.1518	2.1529	2.1541	2.1552	2.1564	2.1576	2.1587	2.1599	2.1610	2.1622
8.7	2.1633	2.1645	2.1656	2.1668	2.1679	2.1691	2.1702	2.1713	2.1725	2.1736
8.8	2.1748	2.1759	2.1770	2.1782	2.1793	2.1804	2.1815	2.1827	2.1838	2.1849
8.9	2.1861	2.1872	2.1883	2.1894	2.1905	2.1917	2.1928	2.1939	2.1950	2.1961
9.0	2.1972	2.1983	2.1994	2.2006	2.2017	2.2028	2.2039	2.2050	2.2061	2.2072
9.1	2.2083	2.2094	2.2105	2.2116	2.2127	2.2138	2.2148	2.2159	2.2170	2.2181
9.2	2.2192	2.2203	2.2214	2.2225	2.2235	2.2246	2.2257	2.2268	2.2279	2.2289
9.3	2.2300	2.2311	2.2322	2.2332	2.2343	2.2354	2.2364	2.2375	2.2386	2.2396
9.4	2.2407	2.2418	2.2428	2.2439	2.2450	2.2460	2.2471	2.2481	2.2492	2.2502
9.5	2.2513	2.2523	2.2534	2.2544	2.2555	2.2565	2.2576	2.2586	2.2597	2.2607
9.6	2.2618	2.2628	2.2638	2.2649	2.2659	2.2670	2.2680	2.2690	2.2701	2.2711
9.7	2.2721	2.2732	2.2742	2.2752	2.2762	2.2773	2.2783	2.2793	2.2803	2.2814
9.8	2.2824	2.2834	2.2844	2.2854	2.2865	2.2875	2.2885	2.2895	2.2905	2.2915
9.9	2.2925	2.2935	2.2946	2.2956	2.2966	2.2976	2.2986	2.2996	2.3006	2.3016

TABLE III   VALUES OF CIRCULAR FUNCTIONS

t	$\sin t$	$\cos t$	$\tan t$	$\cot t$	$\sec t$	$\csc t$
.00	.0000	1.0000	.0000	—	1.000	—
.01	.0100	1.0000	.0100	99.997	1.000	100.00
.02	.0200	.9998	.0200	49.993	1.000	50.00
.03	.0300	.9996	.0300	33.323	1.000	33.34
.04	.0400	.9992	.0400	24.987	1.001	25.01
.05	.0500	.9988	.0500	19.983	1.001	20.01
.06	.0600	.9982	.0601	16.647	1.002	16.68
.07	.0699	.9976	.0701	14.262	1.002	14.30
.08	.0799	.9968	.0802	12.473	1.003	12.51
.09	.0899	.9960	.0902	11.081	1.004	11.13
.10	.0998	.9950	.1003	9.967	1.005	10.02
.11	.1098	.9940	.1104	9.054	1.006	9.109
.12	.1197	.9928	.1206	8.293	1.007	8.353
.13	.1296	.9916	.1307	7.649	1.009	7.714
.14	.1395	.9902	.1409	7.096	1.010	7.166
.15	.1494	.9888	.1511	6.617	1.011	6.692
.16	.1593	.9872	.1614	6.197	1.013	6.277
.17	.1692	.9856	.1717	5.826	1.015	5.911
.18	.1790	.9838	.1820	5.495	1.016	5.586
.19	.1889	.9820	.1923	5.200	1.018	5.295
.20	.1987	.9801	.2027	4.933	1.020	5.033
.21	.2085	.9780	.2131	4.692	1.022	4.797
.22	.2182	.9759	.2236	4.472	1.025	4.582
.23	.2280	.9737	.2341	4.271	1.027	4.386
.24	.2377	.9713	.2447	4.086	1.030	4.207
.25	.2474	.9689	.2553	3.916	1.032	4.042
.26	.2571	.9664	.2660	3.759	1.035	3,890
.27	.2667	.9638	.2768	3.613	1.038	3.749
.28	.2764	.9611	.2876	3.478	1.041	3.619
.29	.2860	.9582	.2984	3.351	1.044	3.497
.30	.2955	.9553	.3093	3.233	1.047	3.384
.31	.3051	.9523	.3203	3.122	1.050	3.278
.32	.3146	.9492	.3314	3.018	1.053	3.179
.33	.3240	.9460	.3425	2.920	1.057	3.086
.34	.3335	.9428	.3537	2.827	1.061	2.999
.35	.3429	.9394	.3650	2.740	1.065	2.916
.36	.3523	.9359	.3764	2.657	1.068	2.839
.37	.3616	.9323	.3879	2.578	1.073	2.765
.38	.3709	.9287	.3994	2.504	1.077	2.696
.39	.3802	.9249	.4111	2.433	1.081	2.630
.40	.3894	.9211	.4228	2.365	1.086	2.568
.41	.3986	.9171	.4346	2.301	1.090	2.509
.42	.4078	.9131	.4466	2.239	1.095	2.452
.43	.4169	.9090	.4586	2.180	1.100	2.399
.44	.4259	.9048	.4708	2.124	1.105	2.348
.45	.4350	.9004	.4831	2.070	1.111	2.299
.46	.4439	.8961	.4954	2.018	1.116	2.253
.47	.4529	.8916	.5080	1.969	1.122	2.208
.48	.4618	.8870	.5206	1.921	1.127	2.166
.49	.4706	.8823	.5334	1.875	1.133	2.125

TABLE III   VALUES OF CIRCULAR FUNCTIONS — Cont.

t	$\sin t$	$\cos t$	$\tan t$	$\cot t$	$\sec t$	$\csc t$
.50	.4794	.8776	.5463	1.830	1.139	2.086
.51	.4882	.8727	.5594	1.788	1.146	2.048
.52	.4969	.8678	.5726	1.747	1.152	2.013
$\dfrac{\pi}{6}$	.5000	.8660	.5774	1.732	1.155	2.000
.53	.5055	.8628	.5859	1.707	1.159	1.978
.54	.5141	.8577	.5994	1.668	1.166	1.945
.55	.5227	.8525	.6131	1.631	1.173	1.913
.56	.5312	.8473	.6269	1.595	1.180	1.883
.57	.5396	.8419	.6410	1.560	1.188	1.853
.58	.5480	.8365	.6552	1.526	1.196	1.825
.59	.5564	.8309	.6696	1.494	1.203	1.797
.60	.5646	.8253	.6841	1.462	1.212	1.771
.61	.5729	.8196	.6989	1.431	1.220	1.746
.62	.5810	.8139	.7139	1.401	1.229	1.721
.63	.5891	.8080	.7291	1.372	1.238	1.697
.64	.5972	.8021	.7445	1.343	1.247	1.674
.65	.6052	.7961	.7602	1.315	1.256	1.652
.66	.6131	.7900	.7761	1.288	1.266	1.631
.67	.6210	.7838	.7923	1.262	1.276	1.610
.68	.6288	.7776	.8087	1.237	1.286	1.590
.69	.6365	.7712	.8253	1.212	1.297	1.571
.70	.6442	.7648	.8423	1.187	1.307	1.552
.71	.6518	.7584	.8595	1.163	1.319	1.534
.72	.6594	.7518	.8771	1.140	1.330	1.517
.73	.6669	.7452	.8949	1.117	1.342	1.500
.74	.6743	.7385	.9131	1.095	1.354	1.483
.75	.6816	.7317	.9316	1.073	1.367	1.467
.76	.6889	.7248	.9505	1.052	1.380	1.452
.77	.6961	.7179	.9697	1.031	1.393	1.437
.78	.7033	.7109	.9893	1.011	1.407	1.422
$\dfrac{\pi}{4}$	.7071	.7071	1.000	1.000	1.414	1.414
.79	.7104	.7038	1.009	.9908	1.421	1.408
.80	.7174	.6967	1.030	.9712	1.435	1.394
.81	.7243	.6895	1.050	.9520	1.450	1.381
.82	.7311	.6822	1.072	.9331	1.466	1.368
.83	.7379	.6749	1.093	.9146	1.482	1.355
.84	.7446	.6675	1.116	.8964	1.498	1.343
.85	.7513	.6600	1.138	.8785	1.515	1.331
.86	.7578	.6524	1.162	.8609	1.533	1.320
.87	.7643	.6448	1.185	.8437	1.551	1.308
.88	.7707	.6372	1.210	.8267	1.569	1.297
.89	.7771	.6294	1.235	.8100	1.589	1.287
.90	.7833	.6216	1.260	.7936	1.609	1.277
.91	.7895	.6137	1.286	.7774	1.629	1.267
.92	.7956	.6058	1.313	.7615	1.651	1.257
.93	.8016	.5978	1.341	.7458	1.673	1.247
.94	.8076	.5898	1.369	.7303	1.696	1.238

TABLE III   **VALUES OF CIRCULAR FUNCTIONS** — Cont.

t	$\sin t$	$\cos t$	$\tan t$	$\cot t$	$\sec t$	$\csc t$
.95	.8134	.5817	1.398	.7151	1.719	1.229
.96	.8192	.5735	1.428	.7001	1.744	1.221
.97	.8249	.5653	1.459	.6853	1.769	1.212
.98	.8305	.5570	1.491	.6707	1.795	1.204
.99	.8360	.5487	1.524	.6563	1.823	1.196
1.00	.8415	.5403	1.557	.6421	1.851	1.188
1.01	.8468	.5319	1.592	.6281	1.880	1.181
1.02	.8521	.5234	1.628	.6142	1.911	1.174
1.03	.8573	.5148	1.665	.6005	1.942	1.166
1.04	.8624	.5062	1.704	.5870	1.975	1.160
$\dfrac{\pi}{3}$	.8660	.5000	1.732	.5774	2.000	1.155
1.05	.8674	.4976	1.743	.5736	2.010	1.153
1.06	.8724	.4889	1.784	.5604	2.046	1.146
1.07	.8772	.4801	1.827	.5473	2.083	1.140
1.08	.8820	.4713	1.871	.5344	2.122	1.134
1.09	.8866	.4625	1.917	.5216	2.162	1.128
1.10	.8912	.4536	1.965	.5090	2.205	1.122
1.11	.8957	.4447	2.014	.4964	2.249	1.116
1.12	.9001	.4357	2.066	.4840	2.295	1.111
1.13	.9044	.4267	2.120	.4718	2.344	1.106
1.14	.9086	.4176	2.176	.4596	2.395	1.101
1.15	.9128	.4085	2.234	.4475	2.448	1.096
1.16	.9168	.3993	2.296	.4356	2.504	1.091
1.17	.9208	.3902	2.360	.4237	2.563	1.086
1.18	.9246	.3809	2.427	.4120	2.625	1.082
1.19	.9284	.3717	2.498	.4003	2.691	1.077
1.20	.9320	.3624	2.572	.3888	2.760	1.073
1.21	.9356	.3530	2.650	.3773	2.833	1.069
1.22	.9391	.3436	2.733	.3659	2.910	1.065
1.23	.9425	.3342	2.820	.3546	2.992	1.061
1.24	.9458	.3248	2.912	.3434	3.079	1.057
1.25	.9490	.3153	3.010	.3323	3.171	1.054
1.26	.9521	.3058	3.113	.3212	3.270	1.050
1.27	.9551	.2963	3.224	.3102	3.375	1.047
1.28	.9580	.2867	3.341	.2993	3.488	1.044
1.29	.9608	.2771	3.467	.2884	3.609	1.041
1.30	.9636	.2675	3.602	.2776	3.738	1.038
1.31	.9662	.2579	3.747	.2669	3.878	1.035
1.32	.9687	.2482	3.903	.2562	4.029	1.032
1.33	.9711	.2385	4.072	.2456	4.193	1.030
1.34	.9735	.2288	4.256	.2350	4.372	1.027
1.35	.9757	.2190	4.455	.2245	4.566	1.025
1.36	.9779	.2092	4.673	.2140	4.779	1.023
1.37	.9799	.1994	4.913	.2035	5.014	1.021
1.38	.9819	.1896	5.177	.1931	5.273	1.018
1.39	.9837	.1798	5.471	.1828	5.561	1.017
1.40	.9854	.1700	5.798	.1725	5.883	1.015
1.41	.9871	.1601	6.165	.1622	6.246	1.013
1.42	.9887	.1502	6.581	.1519	6.657	1.011
1.43	.9901	.1403	7.055	.1417	7.126	1.010
1.44	.9915	.1304	7.602	.1315	7.667	1.009

TABLE III   **VALUES OF CIRCULAR FUNCTIONS** — Cont.

t	$\sin t$	$\cos t$	$\tan t$	$\cot t$	$\sec t$	$\csc t$
1.45	.9927	.1205	8.238	.1214	8.299	1.007
1.46	.9939	.1106	8.989	.1113	9.044	1.006
1.47	.9949	.1006	9.887	.1011	9.938	1.005
1.48	.9959	.0907	10.983	.0910	11.029	1.004
1.49	.9967	.0807	12.350	.0810	12.390	1.003
1.50	.9975	.0707	14.101	.0709	14.137	1.003
1.51	.9982	.0608	16.428	.0609	16.458	1.002
1.52	.9987	.0508	19.670	.0508	19.695	1.001
1.53	.9992	.0408	24.498	.0408	24.519	1.001
1.54	.9995	.0308	32.461	.0308	32.476	1.000
1.55	.9998	.0208	48.078	.0208	18.089	1.000
1.56	.9999	.0108	92.620	.0108	92.626	1.000
1.57	1.0000	.0008	1255.8	.0008	1255.8	1.000
$\dfrac{\pi}{2}$	1.0000	.0000	—	.0000	—	1.000
1.58	1.0000	−.0092	−108.65	−.0092	−108.65	1.000
1.59	.9998	−.0192	−52.067	−.0192	−52.08	1.000
1.60	.9996	−.0292	−34.233	−.0292	−34.25	1.000

TABLE IV   VALUES OF TRIGONOMETRIC FUNCTIONS

Degrees	Radians	Sin	Csc	Tan	Cot	Sec	Cos		
0° 0′	.0000	.0000	——	.0000	——	1.000	1.0000	1.5708	90° 0′
10′	029	029	343.8	029	343.8	000	000	679	50′
20′	058	058	171.9	058	171.9	000	000	650	40′
30′	.0087	.0087	114.6	.0087	114.6	1.000	1.0000	1.5621	30′
40′	116	116	85.95	116	85.94	000	0.9999	592	20′
50′	145	145	68.76	145	68.75	000	999	563	10′
1° 0′	.0175	.0175	57.30	.0175	57.29	1.000	.9998	1.5533	89° 0′
10′	204	204	49.11	204	49.10	000	998	504	50′
20′	233	233	42.98	233	42.96	000	997	475	40′
30′	.0262	.0262	38.20	.0262	38.19	1.000	.9997	1.5446	30′
40′	291	291	34.38	291	34.37	000	996	417	20′
50′	320	320	31.26	320	31.24	001	995	388	10′
2° 0′	.0349	.0349	28.65	.0349	28.64	1.001	.9994	1.5359	88° 0′
10′	378	378	26.45	378	26.43	001	993	330	50′
20′	407	407	24.56	407	24.54	001	992	301	40′
30′	.0436	.0436	22.93	.0437	22.90	1.001	.9990	1.5272	30′
40′	465	465	21.49	466	21.47	001	989	243	20′
50′	495	494	20.23	495	20.21	001	988	213	10′
3° 0′	.0524	.0523	19.11	.0524	19.08	1.001	.9986	1.5184	87° 0′
10′	553	552	18.10	553	18.07	002	985	155	50′
20′	582	581	17.20	582	17.17	002	983	126	40′
30′	.0611	.0610	16.38	.0612	16.35	1.002	.9981	1.5097	30′
40′	640	640	15.64	641	15.60	002	980	068	20′
50′	669	669	14.96	670	14.92	002	978	039	10′
4° 0′	.0698	.0698	14.34	.0699	14.30	1.002	.9976	1.5010	86° 0′
10′	727	727	13.76	729	13.73	003	974	1.4981	50′
20′	756	756	13.23	758	13.20	003	971	952	40′
30′	.0785	.0785	12.75	.0787	12.71	1.003	.9969	1.4923	30′
40′	814	814	12.29	816	12.25	003	967	893	20′
50′	844	843	11.87	846	11.83	004	964	864	10′
5° 0′	.0873	.0872	11.47	.0875	11.43	1.004	.9962	1.4835	85° 0′
10′	902	901	11.10	904	11.06	004	959	806	50′
20′	931	929	10.76	934	10.71	004	957	777	40′
30′	.0960	.0958	10.43	.0963	10.39	1.005	.9954	1.4748	30′
40′	989	.0987	10.13	.0992	10.08	005	951	719	20′
50′	.1018	.1016	9.839	.1022	9.788	005	948	690	10′
6° 0′	.1047	.1045	9.567	.1051	9.514	1.006	.9945	1.4661	84° 0′
10′	076	074	9.309	080	9.255	006	942	632	50′
20′	105	103	9.065	110	9.010	006	939	603	40′
30′	.1134	.1132	8.834	.1139	8.777	1.006	.9936	1.4573	30′
40′	164	161	8.614	169	8.556	007	932	544	20′
50′	193	190	8.405	198	8.345	007	929	515	10′
7° 0′	.1222	.1219	8.206	.1228	8.144	1.008	.9925	1.4486	83° 0′
10′	251	248	8.016	257	7.953	008	922	457	50′
20′	280	276	7.834	287	7.770	008	918	428	40′
30′	.1309	.1305	7.661	.1317	7.596	1.009	.9914	1.4399	30′
40′	338	334	7.496	346	7.429	009	911	370	20′
50′	367	363	7.337	376	7.269	009	907	341	10′
8° 0′	.1396	.1392	7.185	.1405	7.115	1.010	.9903	1.4312	82° 0′
		Cos	Sec	Cot	Tan	Csc	Sin	Radians	Degrees

TABLE IV VALUES OF TRIGONOMETRIC FUNCTIONS — Cont.

Degrees	Radians	Sin	Csc	Tan	Cot	Sec	Cos		
8° 0′	.1396	.1392	7.185	.1405	7.115	1.010	.9903	1.4312	82° 0′
10′	425	421	7.040	435	6.968	010	899	283	50′
20′	454	449	6.900	465	6.827	011	894	254	40′
30′	.1484	.1478	6.765	.1495	6.691	1.011	.8980	1.4224	30′
40′	513	507	6.636	524	6.561	012	886	195	20′
50′	542	536	6.512	554	6.435	012	881	166	10′
9° 0′	.1571	.1564	6.392	.1584	6.314	1.012	.9877	1.4137	81° 0′
10′	600	593	277	614	197	013	872	108	50′
20′	629	622	166	644	6.084	013	868	079	40′
30′	.1658	.1650	6.059	.1673	5.976	1.014	.9863	1.4050	30′
40′	687	679	5.955	703	871	014	858	1.4021	20′
50′	716	708	855	733	769	015	853	1.3992	10′
10° 0′	.1745	.1736	5.759	.1763	5.671	1.015	.9848	1.3963	80° 0′
10′	774	765	665	793	576	016	843	934	50′
20′	804	794	575	823	485	016	838	904	40′
30′	.1833	.1822	5.487	.1853	5.396	1.017	.9833	1.3875	30′
40′	862	851	403	883	309	018	827	846	20′
50′	891	880	320	914	226	018	822	817	10′
11° 0′	.1920	.1908	5.241	.1944	5.145	1.019	.9816	1.3788	79° 0′
10′	949	937	164	.1974	5.066	019	811	759	50′
20′	978	965	089	.2004	4.989	020	805	730	40′
30′	.2007	.1994	5.016	.2035	4.915	1.020	.9799	1.3701	30′
40′	036	.2022	4.945	065	843	021	793	672	20′
50′	065	051	876	095	773	022	787	643	10′
12° 0′	.2094	.2079	4.810	.2126	4.705	1.022	.9781	1.3614	78° 0′
10′	123	108	745	156	638	023	775	584	50′
20′	153	136	682	186	574	024	769	555	40′
30′	.2182	.2164	4.620	.2217	4.511	1.024	.9763	1.3526	30′
40′	211	193	560	247	449	025	757	497	20′
50′	240	221	502	278	390	026	750	468	10′
13° 0′	.2269	.2250	4.445	.2309	4.331	1.026	.9744	1.3439	77° 0′
10′	298	278	390	339	275	027	737	410	50′
20′	327	306	336	370	219	028	730	381	40′
30′	.2356	.2334	4.284	.2401	4.165	1.028	.9724	1.3352	30′
40′	385	363	232	432	113	029	717	323	20′
50′	414	391	182	462	061	030	710	294	10′
14° 0′	.2443	.2419	4.134	.2493	4.011	1.031	.9703	1.3265	76° 0′
10′	473	447	086	524	3.962	031	696	235	50′
20′	502	476	4.039	555	914	032	698	206	40′
30′	.2531	.2504	3.994	.2586	3.867	1.033	.9681	1.3177	30′
40′	560	532	950	617	821	034	674	148	20′
50′	589	560	906	648	776	034	667	119	10′
15° 0′	.2618	.2588	3.864	.2679	3.732	1.035	.9659	1.3090	75° 0′
10′	647	616	822	711	689	036	652	061	50′
20′	676	644	782	742	647	037	644	032	40′
30′	.2705	.2672	3.742	.2773	3.606	1.038	.9636	1.3003	30′
40′	734	700	703	805	566	039	628	1.2974	20′
50′	763	728	665	836	526	039	621	945	10′
16° 0′	.2793	.2756	3.628	.2867	3.487	1.040	.9613	1.2915	74° 0′
		Cos	Sec	Cot	Tan	Csc	Sin	Radians	Degrees

TABLE IV   VALUES OF TRIGONOMETRIC FUNCTIONS — Cont.

Degrees	Radians	Sin	Csc	Tan	Cot	Sec	Cos		
16° 0'	.2793	.2756	3.628	.2867	3.487	1.040	.9613	1.2915	74° 0'
10'	822	784	592	899	450	041	605	886	50'
20'	851	812	556	931	412	042	596	857	40'
30'	.2880	.2840	3.521	.2962	3.376	1.043	.9588	1.2828	30'
40'	909	868	487	.2994	340	044	580	799	20'
50'	938	896	453	3026	305	045	572	770	10'
17° 0'	.2967	.2924	3.420	.3057	3.271	1.046	.9563	1.2741	73° 0'
10'	996	952	388	089	237	047	555	712	50'
20'	.3025	.2979	357	121	204	048	546	683	40'
30'	.3054	.3007	3.326	.3153	3.172	1.048	.9537	1.2654	30'
40'	083	035	295	185	140	049	528	625	20'
50'	113	062	265	217	108	050	520	595	10'
18° 0'	.3142	.3090	3.236	.3249	3.078	1.051	.9511	1.2566	72° 0'
10'	171	118	207	281	047	052	502	537	50'
20'	200	145	179	314	3.018	053	492	508	40'
30'	.3229	.3173	3.152	.3346	2.989	1.054	.9483	1.2479	30'
40'	258	201	124	378	960	056	474	450	20'
50'	287	228	098	411	932	057	465	421	10'
19° 0'	.3316	.3256	3.072	.3443	2.904	1.058	.9455	1.2392	71° 0'
10'	345	283	046	476	877	059	446	363	50'
20'	374	311	3.021	508	850	060	436	334	40'
30'	.3403	.3338	2.996	.3541	2.824	1.061	.9426	1.2305	30'
40'	432	365	971	574	798	062	417	275	20'
50'	462	393	947	607	773	063	407	246	10'
20° 0'	.3491	.3420	2.924	.3640	2.747	1.064	.9397	1.2217	70° 0'
10'	520	448	901	673	723	065	387	188	50'
20'	549	475	878	706	699	066	377	159	40'
30'	.3578	.3502	2.855	.3739	2.675	1.068	.9367	1.2130	30'
40'	607	529	833	772	651	069	356	101	20'
50'	636	557	812	805	628	070	346	072	10'
21° 0'	.3665	.3584	2.790	.3839	2.605	1.071	.9336	1.2043	69° 0'
10'	694	611	769	872	583	072	325	1.2014	50'
20'	723	638	749	906	560	074	315	1.1985	40'
30'	.3752	.3665	2.729	.3939	2.539	1.075	.9304	1.1956	30'
40'	782	692	709	.3973	517	076	293	926	20'
50'	811	719	689	.4006	496	077	283	897	10'
22° 0'	.3840	.3746	2.669	.4040	2.475	1.079	.9272	1.1868	68° 0'
10'	869	773	650	074	455	080	261	839	50'
20'	898	800	632	108	434	081	250	810	40'
30'	.3927	.3827	2.613	.4142	2.414	1.082	.9239	1.1781	30'
40'	956	854	595	176	394	084	228	752	20'
50'	985	881	577	210	375	085	216	723	10'
23° 0'	.4014	.3907	2.559	.4245	2.356	1.086	.9205	1.1694	67° 0'
10'	043	934	542	279	337	088	194	665	50'
20'	072	961	525	314	318	089	182	636	40'
30'	.4102	.3987	2.508	.4348	2.300	1.090	.9171	1.1606	30'
40'	131	.4014	491	383	282	092	159	577	20'
50'	160	041	475	417	264	093	147	548	10'
24° 0'	.4189	.4067	2.459	.4452	2.246	1.095	.9135	1.1519	66° 0'
	Cos	Sec	Cot	Tan	Csc	Sin	Radians	Degrees	

TABLE IV   **VALUES OF TRIGONOMETRIC FUNCTIONS** — Cont.

Degrees	Radians	Sin	Csc	Tan	Cot	Sec	Cos		
24° 0′	.4189	.4067	2.459	.4452	2.246	1.095	.9135	1.1519	66° 0′
10′	218	094	443	487	229	096	124	490	50′
20′	247	120	427	522	211	097	112	461	40′
30′	.4276	.4147	2.411	.4557	2.194	1.099	.9100	1.1432	30′
40′	305	173	396	592	177	100	088	403	20′
50′	334	200	381	628	161	102	075	374	10′
25° 0′	.4363	.4226	2.366	.4663	2.145	1.103	.9063	1.1345	65° 0′
10′	392	253	352	699	128	105	051	316	50′
20′	422	279	337	734	112	106	038	286	40′
30′	.4451	.4305	2.323	.4770	2.097	1.108	.9026	1.1257	30′
40′	480	331	309	806	081	109	013	228	20′
50′	509	358	295	841	066	111	.9001	199	10′
26° 0′	.4538	.4384	2.281	.4877	2.050	1.113	.8988	1.1170	64° 0′
10′	567	410	268	913	035	114	975	141	50′
20′	596	436	254	950	020	116	962	112	40′
30′	.4625	.4462	2.241	.4986	2.006	1.117	.8949	1.1083	30′
40′	654	488	228	.5022	1.991	119	936	054	20′
50′	683	514	215	059	977	121	923	1.1025	10′
27° 0′	.4712	.4540	2.203	.5095	1.963	1.122	.8910	1.0996	63° 0′
10′	741	566	190	132	949	124	897	966	50′
20′	771	592	178	169	935	126	884	937	40′
30′	.4800	.4617	2.166	.5206	1.921	1.127	.8870	1.0908	30′
40′	829	643	154	243	907	129	857	879	20′
50′	858	669	142	280	894	131	843	850	10′
28° 0′	.4887	.4695	2.130	.5317	1.881	1.133	.8829	1.0821	62° 0′
10′	916	720	118	354	868	134	.816	792	50′
20′	945	746	107	392	855	136	802	763	40′
30′	.4974	.4772	2.096	.5430	1.842	1.138	.8788	1.0734	30′
40′	.5003	797	085	467	829	140	774	705	20′
50′	032	823	074	505	816	142	760	676	10′
29° 0′	.5061	.4848	2.063	.5543	1.804	1.143	.8746	1.0647	61° 0′
10′	091	874	052	581	792	145	732	617	50′
20′	120	899	041	619	780	147	718	588	40′
30′	.5149	.4924	2.031	.5658	1.767	1.149	.8704	1.0559	30′
40′	178	950	020	696	756	151	689	530	20′
50′	207	.4975	010	735	744	153	675	501	10′
30° 0′	.5236	.5000	2.000	.5774	1.732	1.155	.8660	1.0472	60° 0′
10′	265	025	1.990	812	720	157	646	443	50′
20′	294	050	980	851	709	159	631	414	40′
30′	.5323	.5075	1.970	.5890	1.698	1.161	.8616	1.0385	30′
40′	352	100	961	930	686	163	601	356	20′
50′	381	125	951	.5969	675	165	587	327	10′
31° 0′	.5411	.5150	1.942	.6009	1.664	1.167	.8572	1.0297	59° 0′
10′	440	175	932	048	653	169	557	268	50′
20′	469	200	923	088	643	171	542	239	40′
30′	.5498	.5225	1.914	.6128	1.632	1.173	.8526	1.0210	30′
40′	527	250	905	168	621	175	511	181	20′
50′	556	275	896	208	611	177	496	152	10′
32° 0′	.5585	.5299	1.887	.6249	1.600	1.179	.8480	1.0123	58° 0′
		Cos	Sec	Cot	Tan	Csc	Sin	Radians	Degrees

TABLE IV   **VALUES OF TRIGONOMETRIC FUNCTIONS** — Cont.

Degrees	Radians	Sin	Csc	Tan	Cot	Sec	Cos		
32° 0′	.5585	.5299	1.887	.6249	1.600	1.179	.8480	1.0123	58° 0′
10′	614	324	878	289	590	181	465	094	50′
20′	643	348	870	330	580	184	450	065	40′
30′	.5672	.5373	1.861	.6371	1.570	1.186	.8434	1.0036	30′
40′	701	398	853	412	560	188	418	1.0007	20′
50′	730	422	844	453	550	190	403	.9977	10′
33° 0′	.5760	.5446	1.836	.6494	1.540	1.192	.8387	.9948	57° 0′
10′	789	471	828	536	530	195	371	919	50′
20′	818	495	820	577	520	197	355	890	40′
30′	.5847	.5519	1.812	.6619	1.511	1.199	.8339	.9861	30′
40′	876	544	804	661	501	202	323	832	20′
50′	905	568	796	703	1.492	204	307	803	10′
34° 0′	.5934	.5592	1.788	.6745	1.483	1.206	.8290	.9774	56° 0′
10′	963	616	781	787	473	209	274	745	50′
20′	992	640	773	830	464	211	258	716	40′
30′	.6021	.5664	1.766	.6873	1.455	1.213	.8241	.9687	30′
40′	050	688	758	916	446	216	225	657	20′
50′	080	712	751	.6959	437	218	208	628	10′
35° 0′	.6109	.5736	1.743	.7002	1.428	1.221	.8192	.9599	55° 0′
10′	138	760	736	046	419	223	175	570	50′
20′	167	783	729	089	411	226	158	541	40′
30′	.6196	.5807	1.722	.7133	1.402	1.228	.8141	.9512	30′
40′	225	831	715	177	393	231	124	483	20′
50′	254	854	708	221	385	233	107	454	10′
36° 0′	.6283	.5878	1.701	.7265	1.376	1.236	.8090	.9425	54° 0′
10′	312	901	695	310	368	239	073	396	50′
20′	341	925	688	355	360	241	056	367	40′
30′	.6370	.5948	1.681	.7400	1.351	1.244	.8039	.9338	30′
40′	400	972	675	445	343	247	021	308	20′
50′	429	.5995	668	490	335	249	.8004	279	10′
37° 0′	.6458	.6018	1.662	.7536	1.327	1.252	.7986	.9250	53° 0′
10′	487	041	655	581	319	255	969	221	50′
20′	516	065	649	627	311	258	951	192	40′
30′	.6545	.6088	1.643	.7673	1.303	1.260	.7934	.9163	30′
40′	574	111	636	720	295	263	916	134	20′
50′	603	134	630	766	288	266	898	105	10′
38° 0′	.6632	.6157	1.624	.7813	1.280	1.269	.7880	.9076	52° 0′
10′	661	180	618	860	272	272	862	047	50′
20′	690	202	612	907	265	275	844	.9018	40′
30′	.6720	.6225	1.606	.7954	1.257	1.278	.7826	.8988	30′
40′	749	248	601	.8002	250	281	808	959	20′
50′	778	271	595	050	242	284	790	930	10′
39° 0′	.6807	.6293	1.589	.8098	1.235	1.287	.7771	.8901	51° 0′
10′	836	316	583	146	228	290	753	872	50′
20′	865	338	578	195	220	293	735	843	40′
30′	.6894	.6361	1.572	.8243	1.213	1.296	.7716	.8814	30′
40′	923	383	567	292	206	299	698	785	20′
50′	952	406	561	342	199	302	679	756	10′
40° 0′	.6981	.6428	1.556	.8391	1.192	1.305	.7660	.8727	50° 0′
		Cos	Sec	Cot	Tan	Csc	Sin	Radians	Degrees

TABLE IV   VALUES OF TRIGONOMETRIC FUNCTIONS — Cont.

Degrees	Radians	Sin	Csc	Tan	Cot	Sec	Cos		
40° 0′	.6981	.6428	1.556	.8391	1.192	1.305	.7660	.8727	50° 0′
10′	.7010	450	550	441	185	309	642	698	50′
20′	039	472	545	491	178	312	623	668	40′
30′	.7069	.6494	1.540	.8541	1.171	1.315	.7604	.8639	30′
40′	098	517	535	591	164	318	585	610	20′
50′	127	539	529	642	157	322	566	581	10′
41° 0′	.7156	.6561	1.524	.8693	1.150	1.325	.7547	.8552	49° 0′
10′	185	583	519	744	144	328	528	523	50′
20′	214	604	514	796	137	332	509	494	40′
30′	.7243	.6626	1.509	.8847	1.130	1.335	.7490	.8465	30′
40′	272	648	504	899	124	339	470	436	20′
50′	301	670	499	.8952	117	342	451	407	10′
42° 0′	.7330	.6691	1.494	.9004	1.111	1.346	.7431	.8378	48° 0′
10′	359	713	490	057	104	349	412	348	50′
20′	389	734	485	110	098	353	392	319	40′
30′	.7418	.6756	1.480	.9163	1.091	1.356	.7373	.8290	30′
40′	447	777	476	217	085	360	353	261	20′
50′	476	799	471	271	079	364	333	232	10′
43° 0′	.7505	.6820	1.466	.9325	1.072	1.367	.7314	.8203	47° 0′
10′	534	841	462	380	066	371	294	174	50′
20′	563	862	457	435	060	375	274	145	40′
30′	.7592	.6884	1.453	.9490	1.054	1.379	.7254	.8116	30′
40′	621	905	448	545	048	382	234	087	20′
50′	650	926	444	601	042	386	214	058	10′
44° 0′	.7679	.6947	1.440	.9657	1.036	1.390	.7193	.8029	46° 0′
10′	709	967	435	713	030	394	173	.7999	50′
20′	738	.6988	431	770	024	398	153	970	40′
30′	.7707	.7009	1.427	.9827	1.018	1.402	.7133	.7941	30′
40′	796	030	423	884	012	406	112	912	20′
50′	825	050	418	.9942	006	410	092	883	10′
45° 0′	.7854	.7071	1.414	1.000	1.000	1.414	.7071	.7854	45° 0′
		Cos	Sec	Cot	Tan	Csc	Sin	Radians	Degrees

TABLE V   POWERS AND ROOTS

Number	Square	Square Root	Cube	Cube Root	Number	Square	Square Root	Cube	Cube Root
1	1	1.000	1	1.000	51	2,601	7.141	132,651	3.708
2	4	1.414	8	1.260	52	2,704	7.211	140,608	3.733
3	9	1.732	27	1.442	53	2,809	7.280	148,877	3.756
4	16	2.000	64	1.587	54	2,916	7.348	157,464	3.780
5	25	2.236	125	1.710	55	3,025	7.416	166,375	3.803
6	36	2.449	216	1.817	56	3,136	7.483	175,616	3.826
7	49	2.646	343	1.913	57	3,249	7.550	185,193	3.849
8	64	2.828	512	2.000	58	3,364	7.616	195,112	3.871
9	81	3.000	729	2.080	59	3,481	7.681	205,379	3.893
10	100	3.162	1,000	2.154	60	3,600	7.746	216,000	3.915
11	121	3.317	1,331	2.224	61	3,721	7.810	226,981	3.936
12	144	3.464	1,728	2.289	62	3,844	7.874	238,328	3.958
13	169	3.606	2,197	2.351	63	3,969	7.937	250,047	3.979
14	196	3.742	2,744	2.410	64	4,096	8.000	262,144	4.000
15	225	3.873	3,375	2.466	65	4,225	8.062	274,625	4.021
16	256	4.000	4,096	2.520	66	4,356	8.124	287,496	4.041
17	289	4.123	4,913	2.571	67	4,489	8.185	300,763	4.062
18	324	4.243	5,832	2.621	68	4,624	8.246	314,432	4.082
19	361	4.359	6,859	2.668	69	4,761	8.307	328,509	4.102
20	400	4.472	8,000	2.714	70	4,900	8.367	343,000	4.121
21	441	4.583	9,261	2.759	71	5,041	8.426	357,911	4.141
22	484	4.690	10,648	2.802	72	5,184	8.485	373,248	4.160
23	529	4.796	12,167	2.844	73	5,329	8.544	389,017	4.179
24	576	4.899	13,824	2.884	74	5,476	8.602	405,224	4.198
25	625	5.000	15,625	2.924	75	5,625	8.660	421,875	4.217
26	676	5.099	17,576	2.962	76	5,776	8.718	438,976	4.236
27	729	5.196	19,683	3.000	77	5,929	8.775	456,533	4.254
28	784	5.292	21,952	3.037	78	6,084	8.832	474,552	4.273
29	841	5.385	24,389	3.072	79	6,241	8.888	493,039	4.291
30	900	5.477	27,000	3.107	80	6,400	8.944	512,000	4.309
31	961	5.568	29,791	3.141	81	6,561	9.000	531,441	4.327
32	1,024	5.657	32,768	3.175	82	6,724	9.055	551,368	4.344
33	1,089	5.745	35,937	3.208	83	6,889	9.110	571,787	4.362
34	1,156	5.831	39,304	3.240	84	7,056	9.165	592,704	4.380
35	1,225	5.916	42,875	3.271	85	7,225	9.220	614,125	4.397
36	1,296	6.000	46,656	3.302	86	7,396	9.274	636,056	4.414
37	1,369	6.083	50,653	3.332	87	7,569	9.327	658,503	4.431
38	1,444	6.164	54,872	3.362	88	7,744	9.381	681,472	4.448
39	1,521	6.245	59,319	3.391	89	7,921	9.434	704,969	4.465
40	1,600	6.325	64,000	3.420	90	8,100	9.487	729,000	4.481
41	1,681	6.403	68,921	3.448	91	8,281	9.539	753,571	4.498
42	1,764	6.481	74,088	3.476	92	8,464	9.592	778,688	4.514
43	1,849	6.557	79,507	3.503	93	8,649	9.644	804,357	4.531
44	1,936	6.633	85,184	3.530	94	8,836	9.695	830,584	4.547
45	2,025	6.708	91,125	3.557	95	9,025	9.747	857,375	4.563
46	2,116	6.782	97,336	3.583	96	9,216	9.798	884,736	4.579
47	2,209	6.856	103,823	3.609	97	9,409	9.849	912,673	4.595
48	2,304	6.928	110,592	3.634	98	9,604	9.899	941,192	4.610
49	2,401	7.000	117,649	3.659	99	9,801	9.950	970,299	4.626
50	2,500	7.071	125,000	3.684	100	10,000	10.000	1,000,000	4.642

APPENDIX B

Field Axioms for Real Numbers

The set of real numbers R with the operations of addition and multiplication satisfy the following axioms.

Axiom 1. The Closure Laws

If a and b are real numbers, then

i) $a + b$ is a real number and

ii) $a \cdot b$ is a real number.

Axiom 2. The Commutative Laws

If a and b are real numbers, then

i) $a + b = b + a$ and

ii) $a \cdot b = b \cdot a$.

Axiom 3. The Associative Laws

If a, b, and c are real numbers, then

i) $(a + b) + c = a + (b + c)$ and

ii) $(a \cdot b) \cdot c = a \cdot (b \cdot c)$.

Axiom 4.   The Identity Elements

i)   There exists a real number zero, denoted by 0, such that for any real number a

$$a + 0 = 0 + a = a$$

ii)   There exists a real number one, denoted by 1, where zero is different from one, such that for any real number a

$$a \cdot 1 = 1 \cdot a = a.$$

Axiom 5.   The Inverse Elements

i)   For each real number a, there exists a real number, the *additive inverse* of a, denoted by $-a$ such that

$$a + (-a) = (-a) + a = 0$$

ii)   For each real number a where $a \neq 0$, there exists a real number, the *multiplicative inverse or reciprocal*, denoted by $1/a$ or a^{-1} such that

$$a \cdot \frac{1}{a} = \frac{1}{a} \cdot a = 1$$

Axiom 6.   The Distributive Laws

If a, b and c are real numbers, then

i) $a(b + c) = ab + ac$ and

ii) $(b + c)a = ba + ca.$

Any set of elements containing at least two elements with two operations that satisfy these six axioms is called a *field*.

APPENDIX C

Trigonometric and Circular Identities

1. $\sin^2 t + \cos^2 t = 1$

2. $\sin(-t) = -\sin t$

3. $\cos(-t) = \cos t$

4. $\tan t = \dfrac{\sin t}{\cos t}$

5. $\cot t = \dfrac{\cos t}{\sin t}$

6. $\sec t = \dfrac{1}{\cos t}$

7. $\csc t = \dfrac{1}{\sin t}$

8. $\tan t \cot t = 1$

9. $\sec^2 t = 1 + \tan^2 t$

10. $\csc^2 t = 1 + \cot^2 t$

11. $\cos (t + s) = \cos t \cos s - \sin t \sin s$

12. $\cos (t - s) = \cos t \cos s + \sin t \sin s$

13. $\cos \left(\dfrac{\pi}{2} - t \right) = \sin t$

14. $\sin \left(\dfrac{\pi}{2} - t \right) = \cos t$

15. $\sin (t + s) = \sin t \cos s + \cos t \sin s$

16. $\sin (t - s) = \sin t \cos s - \cos t \sin s$

17. $\tan (t + s) = \dfrac{\tan t + \tan s}{1 - \tan t \tan s}$

18. $\tan (t - s) = \dfrac{\tan t - \tan s}{1 + \tan t \tan s}$

19. $\cos 2t = \cos^2 t - \sin^2 t$

20. $\cos 2t = 2 \cos^2 t - 1$

21. $\cos 2t = 1 - 2 \sin^2 t$

22. $\sin 2t = 2 \sin t \cos t$

23. $\tan 2t = \dfrac{2 \tan t}{1 - \tan^2 t}$

24. $\cos^2 t = \dfrac{1 + \cos 2t}{2}$

25. $\sin^2 t = \dfrac{1 - \cos 2t}{2}$

ANSWERS TO SELECTED PROBLEMS

CHAPTER 1

PROBLEM SET 1, PAGE 11

1. (a) T (b) F (c) F (d) F (e) F (f) T (g) F (h) T (i) T (j) F (k) F
(l) T

3. (a) $\emptyset$ (b) {4,7} (c) {3,4,5,6,7} (d) {3,4,5,6,7} (e) {7,3,5}

6. (a) 1 (b) 2 (c) 4 (d) 8 (e) 16
Yes, if a set has n elements, then 2^n subsets can be formed.

7. (a) disjoint (b) First set is a proper subset of second. (c) overlap
(d) Second set is proper subset of first. (e) equal

10. (i) = 4 (ii) = 1, 2 (iii) = 5 (iv) = 1, 2 (v) = 3

11.

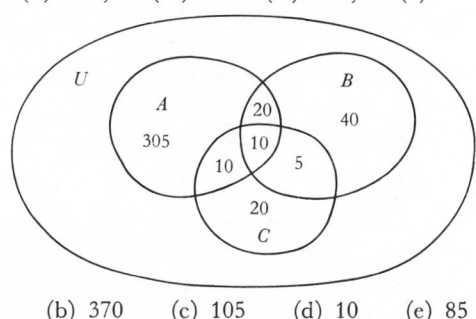

(a) 390   (b) 370   (c) 105   (d) 10   (e) 85

PROBLEM SET 2, PAGE 23

1. (a) $1 \leftrightarrow a$ (b) $1 \leftrightarrow -1$ (c) Impossible   (d) $7 \leftrightarrow 8$ (f) $1 \leftrightarrow 0$

$\quad\quad\quad 2 \leftrightarrow c \quad\quad\quad\quad 2 \leftrightarrow -2 \quad\quad\quad\quad\quad\quad\quad\quad\quad\quad\quad\quad 8 \leftrightarrow 9 \quad\quad\quad 2 \leftrightarrow -1$

$\quad\quad\quad 3 \leftrightarrow d \quad\quad\quad\quad\quad \vdots \quad\quad \vdots \quad\quad\quad\quad\quad\quad\quad\quad\quad 9 \leftrightarrow 91 \quad\quad 3 \leftrightarrow 1$

$\quad\quad\quad 4 \leftrightarrow e \quad\quad\quad\quad n \leftrightarrow -n \quad\quad\quad\quad\quad\quad\quad\quad\quad\quad\quad\quad\quad\quad\quad 4 \leftrightarrow -2$

$\quad\quad\quad 6 \leftrightarrow f \quad\quad\quad\quad\quad\quad\quad\quad\quad\quad\quad\quad\quad\quad\quad\quad\quad\quad\quad\quad\quad\quad\quad\quad 5 \leftrightarrow 2$

$\quad\quad\quad\quad\quad\quad\quad\quad\quad\quad\quad\quad\quad\quad\quad\quad\quad\quad\quad\quad\quad\quad\quad\quad\quad\quad\quad\quad\quad\quad\quad\quad \vdots \quad\quad \vdots$

3. (a) $-5 = -\frac{5}{1} = -5.0$ (b) $0 = \frac{0}{1} = 0.0$ (c) $0.2 = \frac{1}{5} = 0.20$

$\quad$ (d) $5\frac{7}{15} = \frac{82}{15} = 5.46\overline{6}$ (e) $3.464646 = \frac{343}{99}$ (f) $\frac{2}{9} = 0.2\overline{2}$ (g) $\frac{4}{13} = 0.30\overline{76154}$

$\quad$ (h) $33\% = \frac{33}{100} = 0.330$ (i) $0.499\overline{9} = \frac{1}{2}$ (j) $7.3621621 = \frac{1362}{185}$

5. (a) $\emptyset$ (b) all integers except 0   (c) $\emptyset$ (d) $\emptyset$ (e) Q

PROBLEM SET 3, PAGE 36

1. (a) *Trichotomy:* If a is a real number then one and only one of the following conditions must hold: either $a > 0$ or $-a > 0$ or $a = 0$.

$\quad$ *Positive number axiom:* If $a > 0$ and $b > 0$, then $a + b > 0$ (positive number set is closed under addition) and $ab > 0$ (positive number set is closed under multiplication).

3. (a) $-x < 0$ if x is a positive number.   (b) $-x > 0$ if x is a negative number.

5. (a) False; let $a = -2$.   (b) True; Theorem 3.   (c) False; let $a = 2$ and $b = -5$.

$\quad$ (d) False; trichotomy.   (e) True; let $a = 1$ and $b = 5$.   (f) True; Theorem 2.

$\quad$ (g) True; Theorem 4.   (h) True; Definition 3.3.   (i) True; Theorem 4 applied twice.   (j) True; transitive.   (k) True; Theorem 4.   (l) True; since $a \not< 2$ implies that $a \geq 2$ which in turn implies $a^2 \geq 4$.

7. (a)   (b)

$\quad$ (c)   (d)

$\quad$ (e)   (f)

$\quad$ (g)   (h)

11. (a) $\{x | x > \frac{2}{11}\} = (\frac{2}{11}, \infty)$

$\quad$ (b) $\{x | x \geq \frac{9}{4}\} = [\frac{9}{4}, \infty)$

$\quad$ (c) $\{x | x \leq -\frac{1}{2}\} = (-\infty, -\frac{1}{2}]$

$\quad$ (d) $\{x | 5 \leq 3x < 17\} = [\frac{5}{3}, \frac{17}{3})$

$\quad$ (e) $\{x | \frac{3}{5} \leq x \leq \frac{11}{3}\} = [\frac{3}{5}, \frac{11}{3}]$

$\quad$ (f) $\{x | x > 3\} = (3, \infty)$

$\quad$ (g) $\{x | -\frac{1}{2} \leq x < \frac{3}{2}\} = [-\frac{1}{2}, \frac{3}{2})$

15. (a) $A^C = (3,\infty)$ (b) $B^C = (-\infty,3) \cup (4,\infty)$ (c) $C^C = [-3,3]$
(d) $D^C = (-\infty,0)$

PROBLEM SET 4, PAGE 48

1. (a) 7   (b) 1   (c) 7   (d) -1 (e) 12   (f) 12   (g) 16   (h) $\frac{3}{4}$ (i) 25   (j) -7
3. (a) $x \geq 0$ (b) $x \leq 2$ (c) $x \geq 0$ (d) $x = \pm 1$ (e) $x \neq 0$
5. (a) 1   (b) $x \geq 0$ (c) $x > 0$ and simultaneously $y > 0$; $x < 0$ and simultaneously
$y < 0$; $x = 0$; $y = 0$.   (d) $x = y$ or $x = -y$
7. (a) $(-\infty,-1) \cup (1,\infty)$

（b) $(-2,2)$

（c) $(-1,4)$

（d) $(-2,4)$

（e) $(-\infty,-7) \cup [3,\infty)$

（f) $(-2,-1)$

（g) $(-\infty,\frac{3}{10}) \cup (\frac{11}{30},\infty)$

（h) $(\frac{39999}{70000}, \frac{40001}{70000})$

（i) $(-\infty,-3)$

（j) $[\frac{1}{4},\frac{3}{4}]$

（k) $(\frac{1}{6},\frac{1}{4})$

9. (a) R (b) $[4,\infty)$ (c) $(\frac{1}{2},\infty)$ (d) $\emptyset$
11. (a) $[0,8]$ (b) $\emptyset$

PROBLEM SET 5, PAGE 60

1. $S \times T = \{(2,a),(2,b),(4,a),(4,b),(6,a),(6,b)\}$
$S \times S = \{(2,2),(2,4),(2,6),(4,2),(4,4),(4,6),(6,2),(6,4),(6,6)\}$
$T \times T = \{(a,a),(a,b),(b,a),(b,b)\}$
$T \times S = \{(a,2),(b,2),(a,4),(b,4),(a,6),(b,6)\}$
(a) disjoint; note that $S \times T \neq T \times S$
(b) $(S \times T) \cup (T \times S) = \{(2,a),(2,b),(4,a),(4,b),(6,a),(6,b),(a,a),(a,b),(b,a),(b,b)\}$

3. (a) $A \times B = B \times A$ implies that $A = B$ since
$A \times B = \{(1,2),(1,1),(2,2),(2,1)\} = B \times A$
(b) $A = B$ implies $A \times B = B \times A$, since $A \times A = A \times A$

5. $A \times B = \{(-2,-1),(-2,3),(-2,4),(0,1),(0,3),(0,4),(1,-1),(1,3),(1,4)\}$

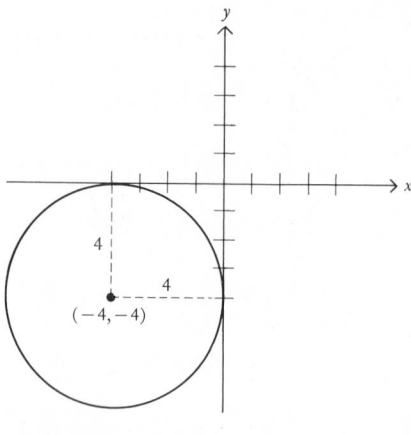

Any point (x,y) must satisfy $x^2 + y^2 = 1$.

7. (a) $(1,0),(2,0),(3,0),(4,0),(5,0)$ (b) Any point on the x-axis is of the form $(x,0)$.

9. (a) radius is 4   (b) no

11. (a) $\dfrac{\sqrt{41}}{2}$ (b) $\sqrt{13}$ (c) $\sqrt{153}$ (d)

13. (a) $\overline{P_1 P_3} = \dfrac{\sqrt{(a-c)^2 + (b-d)^2}}{2}$

$\overline{P_2 P_3} = \dfrac{\sqrt{(c-a)^2 + (d-b)^2}}{2}$

(b) equal   (c) P_3 is the midpoint of segment P_1P_2.
(d) $P_1 = (1,0)$, $P_2 = (-1,0)$, then $P_3 = (0,0)$.

REVIEW PROBLEM SET, PAGE 62

1. (a) I_P (b) R (c) F or Q (d) I (e) F (f) R (g) F (h) L or F (i) $\emptyset$
(j) F or L

3. (a) {all women}   (b) {all integers}   (c) {all states}

5. $\frac{1}{9} \cdot \frac{1}{3} = \frac{1}{27} = 0.03\overline{7037}$; $\frac{1}{9} + \frac{1}{3} = \frac{4}{9} = 0.44\overline{4}$

7. (a) $A \times B = \{(a,x),(a,y),(b,x),(b,y),(c,x),(c,y)\}$
(b) $B \times A = \{(x,a),(y,a),(x,b),(y,b),(x,c),(y,c)\}$

9. I_P represents the set of positive integers.
(a) $\{x|x = 15K, K \in I_P\}$.   (b) $\{x|x = 6K, K \in I_P\}$.   (c) $\{x|x = 36K, K \in I_P\}$.

11. (a) F; let $a = -2$ and $b = -1$ (b) F; let $a = 1$ and $b = 3$ (c) T   (d) T
(e) T   (f) F; let $a = \frac{1}{2}$ and $b = \frac{5}{6}$ (g) F; let $a = 3$ and $b = 4$
(h) F; let $a = -2$ and $b = -1$

13. (a) T   (b) F; let $x = \frac{5}{12}$ (c) T   (d) T   (e) T   (f) F; let $x = 2$ and $y = 1$

15. (a) $(-\infty, \frac{7}{2}] \cup [\frac{13}{2}, \infty)$

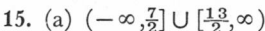

(b) $(-\infty, -3) \cup (\frac{7}{3}, \infty)$

(c) $\{3\}$

(d) $(-1, 5)$

(e) R

(f) $(-2, 7)$

(g) R

(h) $(\frac{1}{2}, 1)$

17. The equation whose center is $(-2, 3)$ has a radius of 5, and its equation is $(x - 2)^2 + (y - 3)^2 = 25$.

CHAPTER 2

PROBLEM SET 1, PAGE 73

1. (a) and (d) are relations

3. (a)

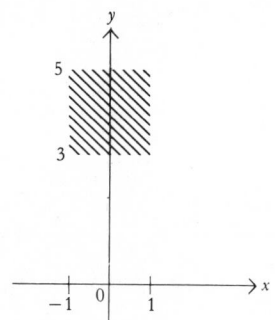

(b)

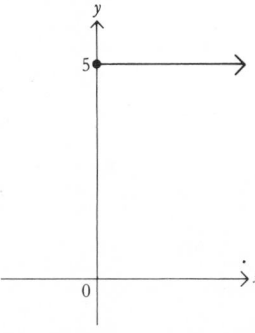

(c)

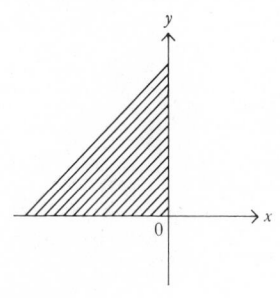

(d)

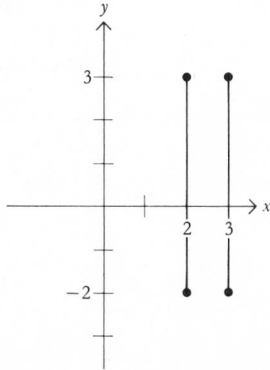

(e)

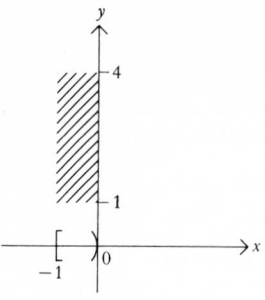

5. (a) $\{(x,y)|y = 2x + 1\}$
Dom $= R$, Range $= R$

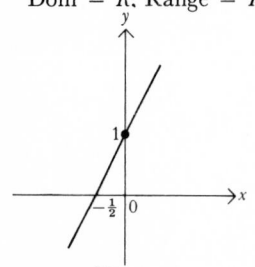

(b) $\{(x,y)|y = -2\}$
Dom $= R$, Range $= \{-2\}$

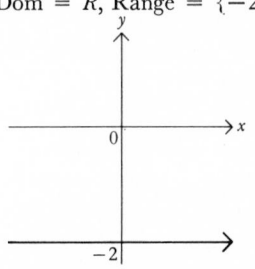

(c) $\{(x,y)|y^2 = x\}$
Dom $= [0, \infty)$ Range $= R$

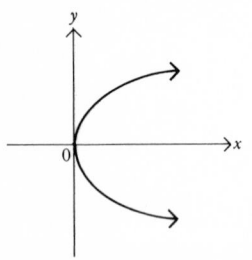

(d) $\{(x,y)|2x + 2y = 3\}$
Dom $= R$, Range $= R$

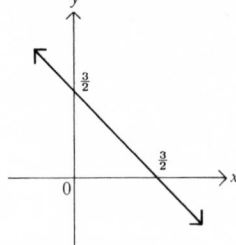

(e) $\{(x,y)|y < 2x + 1\}$
Dom $= R$, Range $= R$

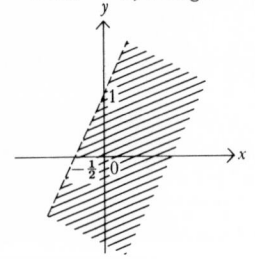

(f) $\{(x,y)|x^2 = y^2\}$
Dom $= R$, Range $= R$

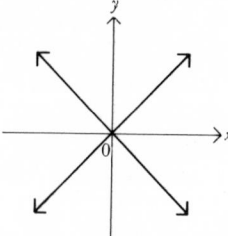

(g) $\{(x,y)|x = 7\}$
Dom $= \{7\}$, Range $= R$

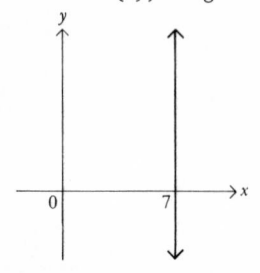

(h) $\{(x,y)|x^2 + y^2 = 1\}$
Dom $=$ Range $= [-1,1]$

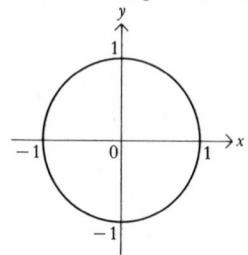

(i) $\{(x,y)|y = |x + 1|\}$

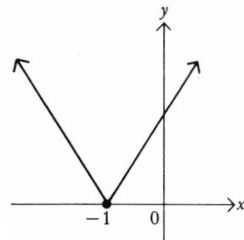

(j) $\{(x,y)||x| + |y| = 1\}$

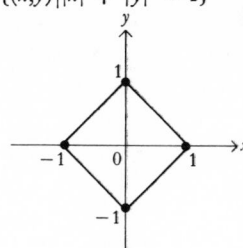

7. (1,1), (2,1), (1,2), (2,2)

PROBLEM SET 2, PAGE 87

1. (a) yes

3. (a) $f(2) = 3, f(-3) = 2, f(a + b) = |a + b + 1|$
   (b) $3 \to 9; \; -1 \to 1;$ and $1 \to 1$ (c) $a = \pm 4$

5. (a) $x \mapsto f(x)$
      $-3 \mapsto 2$
      $-2 \mapsto 2$
      $0 \mapsto 2$
      $1 \mapsto 2$
      $x \mapsto 2$
      $f = \{(x,2)|x \in R\}$

  (b) $x \mapsto f(x)$
      $1 \mapsto 8$
      $2 \mapsto 11$
      $0 \mapsto 5$
      $x \mapsto 3x + 5$
      $f = \{(x,y)|y = 3x + 5\}$

  (c) $x \mapsto f(x)$
      $1 \mapsto \frac{3}{2}$
      $2 \mapsto 3$
      $3 \mapsto \frac{11}{2}$
      $x \mapsto (x^2/2) + 1$
      $f = \{(x + y)|y = (x^2/2) + 1\}$

  (d) $x \mapsto f(x)$
      $1 \mapsto 4$
      $2 \mapsto 12$
      $0 \mapsto 2$
      $x \mapsto 3x^2 - x + 2$
      $f = \{(x + y)|y = 3x^2 - x + 2\}$

  (e) $x \to f(x)$
      $1 \to 1$
      $2 \to \frac{1}{4}$
      $x \to 1/x^2$
      $f = \{(x + y)|y = 1/x^2\}$

7. (a) $r = c/2\pi$ (b) $d = \sqrt{14}\,w$ (c) $V = 4x(7 - x)(5 - x)$

9. (a) $(f + g)(x) = x^2 + x + 5$
   (b) $(f - g)(x) = -x^2 + x - 9$
   (c) $(f \cdot g)(x) = (x - 2)(x^2 + 7) = x^3 - 2x^2 + 7x - 14$
   (d) $\left(\dfrac{f}{g}\right)(x) = \dfrac{x - 2}{x^2 + 7}$

11. The "new" graph would be the same as the "old" graph, only translated by 3 units upward.

PROBLEM SET 3, PAGE 94

1. (a) x-axis, y-axis, origin

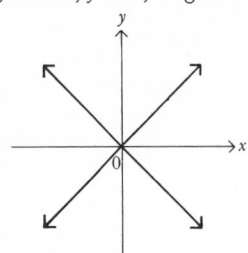

(b) y-axis

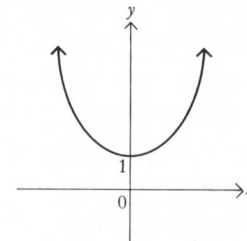

(c) x-axis

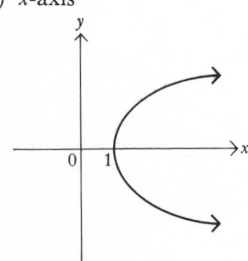

(d) x-axis, y-axis, origin

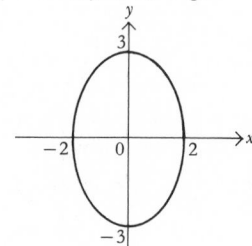

(e) x-axis

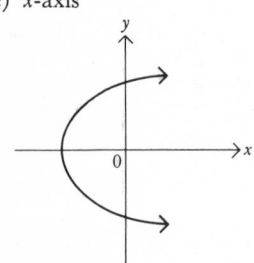

(f) y-axis

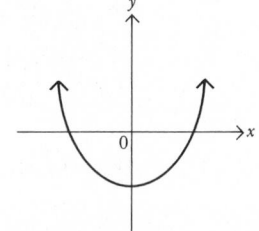

3. Because if it were, then it would have more than one y-value corresponding to each x-value.

5. Consider $x^2 + y^2 = 4$.

7. All symmetric with respect to the origin.

PROBLEM SET 4, PAGE 102

1. Increasing in the interval [1,9].

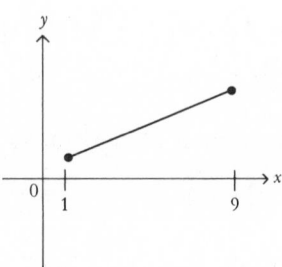

3. (a) find $f(a)$ and $f(-a)$ (b) odd

5. (a) even   (b) even   (c) even   (d) even

7. (a) Dom = Range = R;
increasing on R;
f is neither even nor odd; no symmetry.

(b) Dom = Range = R;
odd;
symmetry w.r.t. origin increasing on R.

(c) Dom = R, Range = $[0,\infty)$;
increasing on $[1,\infty)$;
decreasing on $(-\infty,1]$;
f is neither even nor odd; no symmetry.

(d) Dom = $\{x \mid x \neq \pm 1\}$;
Range = $\{x \mid x \neq 0\}$;
even;
symmetry w.r.t. y-axis;
increasing on $(-\infty,-1)$ and $(-1,0)$;
decreasing on $[0,1]$ and $[1,\infty)$.

(e) Dom = R, Range = I
f is neither increasing nor decreasing;
symmetric w.r.t. origin

(f) Dom = Range = R;
Decreasing on R;
f is neither even nor odd;
no symmetry.

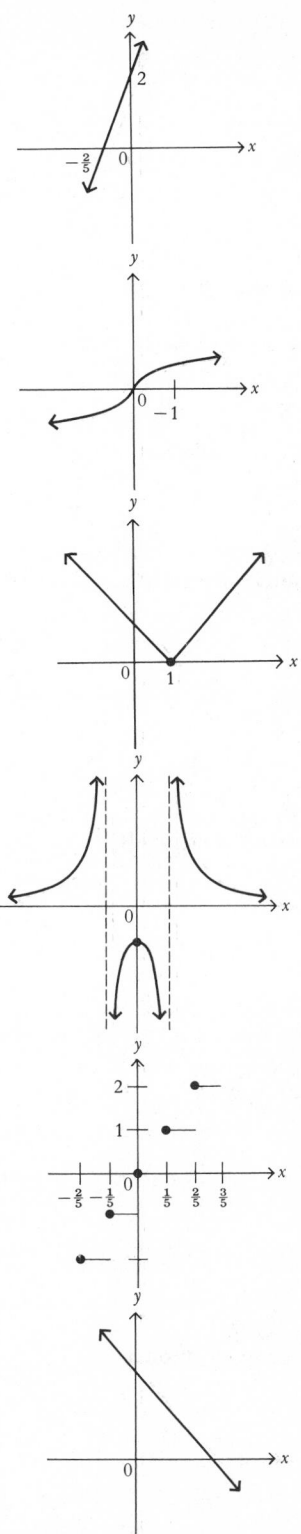

(g) Dom = {0}; Range = {0}

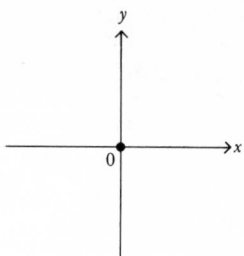

(h) Dom = R; Range = $[3,\infty)$
even;
symmetry w.r.t. y-axis;
increasing on $[0,\infty)$;
decreasing on $(-\infty,0]$.

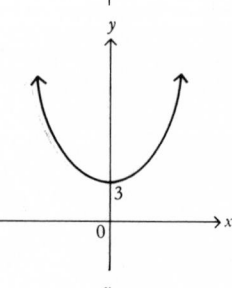

9. (a) $\frac{1}{2}, \frac{1}{3}, \frac{1}{4}, \frac{1}{5}, \frac{1}{6}$
Range: subset of rationals

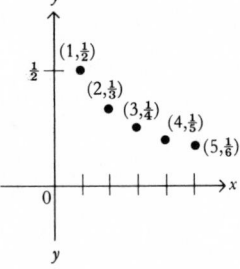

(b) $1, \frac{2}{5}, \frac{1}{5}, \frac{2}{17}, \frac{2}{26}$
Range: subset of rationals

(c) $0, 2, 0, 2, 0$
Range = {0,2}

(d) $\frac{1}{2}, \frac{1}{6}, \frac{1}{12}, \frac{1}{20}, \frac{1}{30}$
Range: subset of rationals

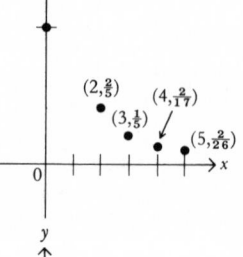

PROBLEM SET 5, PAGE 107

1. (a) 2   (b) 5   (c) 4   (d) 2   (e) 3   (f) 6   (g) 5   (h) 5   (i) 2   (j) 3
3. (a) $k = -\frac{7}{2}$ (b) Try $g(x) = x$
5. (a) even   (b) even   (c) odd   (d) even
7. (a) $V = 16\pi h$ (b) $h = 2t + 4$ (c) $V = 32\pi(t + 2)$

PROBLEM SET 6, PAGE 116

2. (a)   (b)

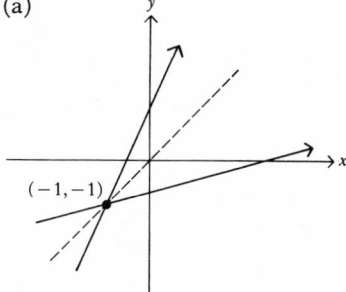   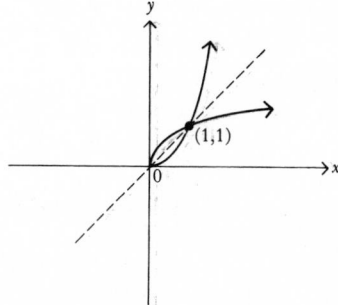

3. (a) no inverse   (b) $f(x)^{-1} = \sqrt[5]{x}$ (c) no inverse   (d) $f^{-1}(x) = (1 - x)/2x$
5. Yes, consider $f(x) = -x$
7. $f^{-1}(x) = \dfrac{x - 2}{-5}$
9. Look at the graph.

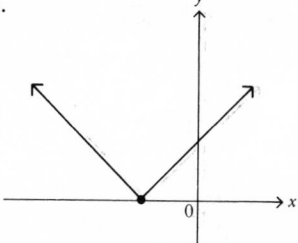

11. (a) No inverse

(b) $f^{-1}(x) = \dfrac{x - 5}{7}$ (c) $f^{-1}(x) = \dfrac{3}{x}$

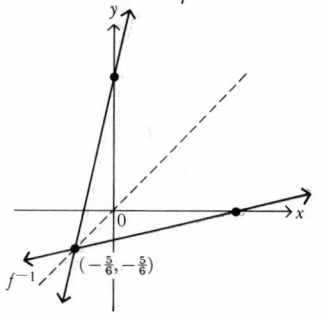   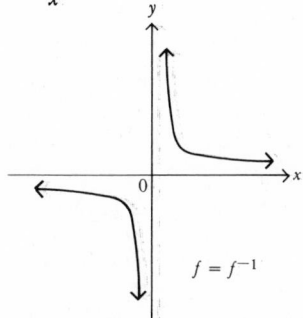

(d) No inverse

(e) $f^{-1}(x) = \dfrac{x-1}{-3}$

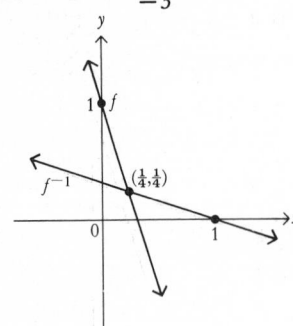

(f) $f^{-1}(x) = \sqrt[3]{x-5}$

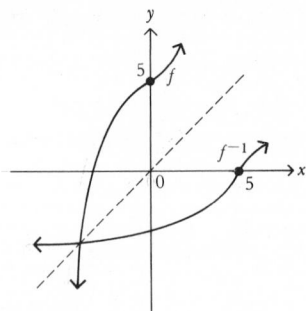

(g) $f^{-1}(x) = \sqrt{x-2}$

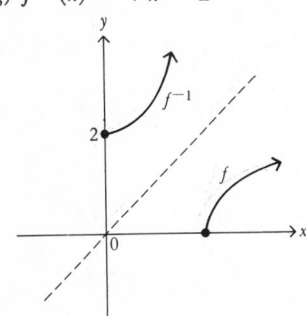

(h) No inverse

15. (a) Symmetric w.r.t. origin

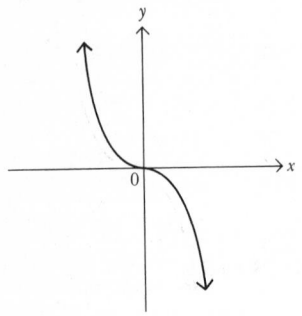

(b) Symmetric w.r.t. origin

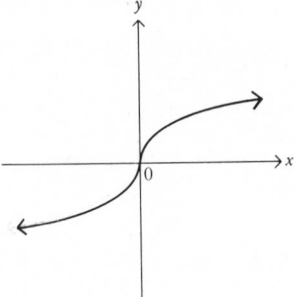

(c) Symmetric w.r.t. y-axis

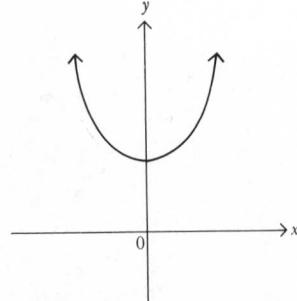

(d) Symmetric w.r.t. x-axis, y-axis, and origin

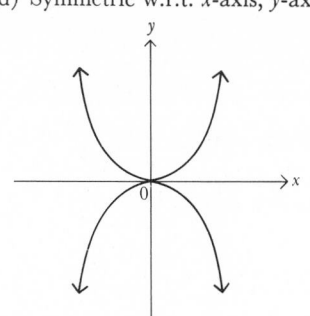

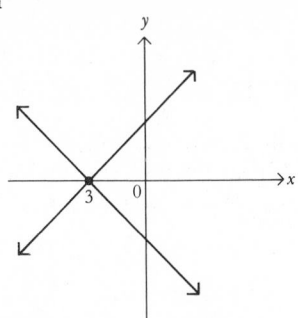

(e) No symmetry

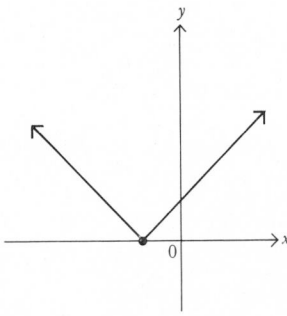

(f) Symmetric w.r.t. x-axis.

REVIEW PROBLEM SET, PAGE 117

1. (a) Function; Dom = Range = R
   (b) Function; Dom = R; Range = $(-\infty, 25)$
   (c) Relation; Dom = $\{1,2,6\}$, Range = $\{2,3,5,7\}$
   (d) Relation; Dom = Range = R

3. Dom = $\{1,2,3,4,5\}$; Range = $\{1,2,3,4,5\}$; $f(3) = 1, f(1) = 5, f(5) = 3$.

5.

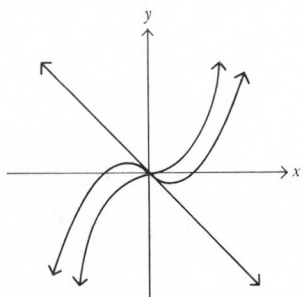

7. (a) $\{-10,4\}$ (b) $(1,3)$ (c) $(\frac{15}{2},\infty)$ (d) 2 (e) $g^{-1}(x) = (x + 3)/2$

9. (a) odd (b) odd (c) even (d) even

11. $y = \sqrt{36 - x^2}$, $A = x\sqrt{36 - x^2}$

13. $f^{-1}(x) = \dfrac{x + 13}{7}$, $g^{-1}(x) = \dfrac{x - 7}{3}$

CHAPTER 3

PROBLEM SET 1, PAGE 137

1. (a) $f(x) = (-5)x^2 + 7x + \pi$, degree 2   (b) no   (c) $f(x) = 5^{-1}$, degree 0
   (d) no   (e) $f(x) = 5x^3 + (-3^{1/2})x^2 + 2x + (-7)$, degree 3
3. (a) $f(x) = 3x - 2$ (b) $f(x) = -2x + 1$ (c) $f(x) = -2$ (d) $f(x) = -\frac{3}{2}x - \frac{11}{2}$
   (e) $f(x) = \frac{2}{3}x - 3$
5. (b) $\dfrac{x}{4} + \dfrac{y}{-6} = 1$

9. (a) $f(x) = \frac{5}{2}x - \frac{7}{2}$ (b) $b = \dfrac{m-1}{2}$, $f(x) = mx + \left(\dfrac{m-1}{2}\right)$

   (c) $b = 0, f(x) = x$
11. (a) $(-8,-19)$ (b) $(-1,\frac{3}{2})$ (c) $(4,-\frac{19}{4})$ (d) $(3,5)$ (e) $(\frac{25}{4},\frac{19}{2})$
15. (a) Not a function, Domain $= \{k\}$, Range $= R$.

PROBLEM SET 2, PAGE 151

1. (a) $\{(3,5)\}$ (b) $\{(3,1)\}$ (c) $\{(\frac{23}{4},\frac{13}{2})\}$ (d) $\emptyset$ (e) $R \times R$ (f) $\{(-\frac{2}{3},-\frac{7}{3})\}$
3. (a) A is 3×3 matrix
   (b) $a_{11} = -4$, $a_{12} = 0$, $a_{13} = 1$
   $a_{21} = 2$, $a_{22} = 3$, $a_{23} = -1$
   $a_{31} = 5$, $a_{32} = 2$, $a_{33} = 8$
5. (a) $\{(1,1,0)\}$ (b) $\{(\frac{39}{21},0,-\frac{12}{21})\}$ (c) dependent   (d) $\{(3,-1,-2)\}$
   (e) dependent   (f) dependent

PROBLEM SET 3, PAGE 161

1. (a) 17   (b) -19 (c) 63   (d) 135   (e) 0   (f) $\frac{69}{2}$
5. (a) 0   (b) -3 (c) -20 (d) 0   (e) 3
9. (a) Watch $= \$75$, chain $= \$25$, ring $= \$125$ (b) First number $= 6$, second
   number $= 9$.

PROBLEM SET 4, PAGE 176

1.

	Dom	Range	Extreme	x-intercept	y-intercept	Axis of Symmetry
(a)	R	$[-3,\infty)$	$(0,-3)$	$(\pm\sqrt{3/2}, 0)$	$(0,-3)$	$x = 0$
(b)	R	$[-1,\infty)$	$(-1,-1)$	$(0,0)$ and $(-2,0)$	$(0,0)$	$x = -1$
(c)	R	$(-\infty,-\frac{3}{4}]$	$(-\frac{1}{2},-\frac{3}{4})$	none	$(0,-1)$	$x = -\frac{1}{2}$
(d)	R	$[0,\infty)$	$(5,0)$	$(5,0)$	$(0,25)$	$x = 5$
(e)	R	$[-\frac{17}{4},\infty)$	$(-\frac{5}{2},-\frac{17}{4})$	$\left(\dfrac{-5 \pm \sqrt{17}}{2}, 0\right)$	$(0,2)$	$x = -\frac{5}{2}$
(f)	R	$(-\infty,-1]$	$(0,-1)$	none	$(0,-1)$	$x = 0$
(g)	R	$[-\frac{9}{8},\infty)$	$(\frac{3}{4},-\frac{9}{8})$	$(0,0)$, $(\frac{3}{2},0)$	$(0,0)$	$x = \frac{3}{4}$
(h)	R	$(-\infty,0]$	$(-1,0)$	$(-1,0)$	$(0,-1)$	$x = -1$
(l)	R	$[\frac{35}{12},\infty)$	$(-\frac{1}{6},\frac{35}{12})$	none	$(0,3)$	$x = -\frac{1}{6}$
(k)	R	$(-\infty,\frac{21}{4})$	$(\frac{1}{2},\frac{21}{4})$	$\left(\dfrac{-1 \pm \sqrt{21}}{-2}, 0\right)$	$(0,5)$	$x = \frac{1}{2}$

5. (a) R (b) $(-\infty,-\frac{1}{2})\cup(1,\infty)$ (c) $\emptyset$ (d) $[-4,-2]$ (e) $\emptyset$ (f) $(-\infty,\frac{3}{2})\cup(2,\infty)$

(g) $\left(\dfrac{5-\sqrt{13}}{6},\dfrac{5+\sqrt{13}}{6}\right)$ (h) $(-\frac{3}{2},3)$

7. (a) $(\frac{1}{2},-3)$ (b) $(-\infty,\frac{1}{3})$ (c) 2 (d) $(-3,\frac{3}{2})$ (e) $(-\infty,1)$ (f) R (g) $[-3,1]$

(h) $(-4,4)$

PROBLEM SET 5, PAGE 187

1. (a) $\{-\frac{2}{3}\}$ (b) $\left\{\dfrac{5-i\sqrt{3}}{14},\dfrac{5+i\sqrt{13}}{14}\right\}$ (c) $\{-1,-i,i\}$ (d) $\{0,1,3,-2,\pi\}$

(e) $\{1-\sqrt{3},1+\sqrt{3}\}$

7.

	x-intercept	y-intercept
(a)	$(0,0)$, $(-1,0)$	$(0,0)$
(b)	$(1,0)$, $\left(\dfrac{-1\pm\sqrt{5}}{2},0\right)$	$(0,4)$
(c)	$(2,0)$, $(-5,0)$, $(4,0)$	$(0,-6)$
(d)	$(1,0)$, $\left(\dfrac{1\pm\sqrt{105}}{4},0\right)$	$(0,13)$
(e)	no x-intercept	$(0,5)$
(f)	$(2,0)$	$(0,16)$
(g)	$(0,0)$, $(1,0)$, $(2,0)$, $(-1,0)$	$(0,0)$

REVIEW PROBLEM SET, PAGE 189

1. (a) degree 3; 4, 0, 2, 6   (b) degree 3; 2, 5, 7, -3
   (c) degree 5; 7, -4, 3, 2, -5, -7 (d) degree 7; 2, 0, 0, 0, 0, 0, 0, -3

3.

	m	x-intercept	y-intercept
(a)	$\frac{3}{5}$	$(-\frac{35}{9},0)$	$(0,\frac{7}{3})$
(b)	$-\frac{5}{3}$	$(3,0)$	$(0,5)$
(c)	$-\frac{7}{5}$	$(\frac{13}{7},0)$	$(0,\frac{13}{5})$
(d)	0	none	$(0,5)$
(e)	undefined	$(-3,0)$	none
(f)	$-\frac{5}{3}$	$(\frac{11}{5},0)$	$(0,\frac{11}{3})$

5. (a) $[-\frac{1}{2},\frac{4}{3}]$ (b) $(-\infty,\frac{1}{2})\cup(\frac{3}{4},\infty)$ (c) $(\frac{3}{7},\frac{1}{2})$

7. yes, $f(x_1)>f(x_2)$, $f(x_1)=f(x_2)$

9. (a) F (b) F (c) F (d) T

11. Yes

13. $(-3,-5)$

15. (a) $t=0$ or $t=\frac{11}{2}$ (b) 121

17. (a) $Q(x)=3x^2+11x+29$, $f(r)=55$
    (b) $Q(x)=5x^3+3x^2+14x+19$, $f(r)=55$
    (c) $Q(x)=2x^2+2x+1$, $f(r)=-19$
    (d) $Q(x)=x^6+2x^5+4x^4+8x^3+16x^2+32x+64$, $f(r)=123$

19. (a) $\frac{25}{48}$ (b) $k\geq-\frac{1}{3}$

21. (a) $\{(\frac{1}{2},0,3)\}$ (b) dependent (c) dependent (d) $\{(-\frac{4}{5},-\frac{9}{5},-\frac{13}{5})\}$

23. (a) $\{1,2,3\}$ (b) $\{-\frac{1}{2},\frac{1}{3},\frac{1}{2},\frac{3}{4}\}$ (c) $\{\frac{1}{2},3,\pm\sqrt{3}\}$

25. (b) $y = -\frac{1}{3}x + \frac{19}{3}$

CHAPTER 4

PROBLEM SET 1, PAGE 200

1. (a) 25 (b) 243 (c) $\frac{1}{3}$ (d) $-\frac{1}{25}$ (e) $1/3^{11}$ (f) $x^{23/20}$ (g) $x\sqrt[3]{x}$ (h) $2\sqrt[3]{3}$
(i) $3(1+\sqrt{3})$ (j) $4/x\sqrt[8]{x}$

3. (a) 2^{24} (b) $\frac{9}{64}$ (c) $1/x^4$ (d) $1/x^{13}$ (e) 8 (f) 9 (g) 9 (h) $\frac{1}{4}$

5. (a) $\sqrt{2}$ (b) $5(\sqrt{3}+\sqrt{2})$ (c) $\dfrac{5(\sqrt{x}-1)}{x-1}$ (d) $\dfrac{6+\sqrt{15}}{3}$ (e) $\dfrac{\sqrt{3}}{9}$

(f) $x + \sqrt{x^2 - 1}$ (g) $\dfrac{6 + 3\sqrt{6} - 3\sqrt{10} + 2\sqrt{3} + 3\sqrt{2} - \sqrt{30}}{12}$

7. (a) $x^{2n} - 2x^n - 24$ (b) $x^{2n+2} - 3y^{n-1}x^{n+1} + 3y^{n-2}x^{n+1} - 9y^{2n-3}$

(c) $x^n + 14x^{n/2} + 49$ (d) $7\sqrt{6}$ (e) $\dfrac{-39}{5}\dfrac{\sqrt{5x}}{x}$ (f) $\sqrt[3]{x}$ (g) $\dfrac{x^2\sqrt{6}}{4}$ (h) $|x|$

9.

	Domain	Range	Even or Odd	Increasing or Decreasing
(a)	$[0,\infty)$	$[0,\infty)$	no	increasing
(b)	$(-\infty,1]$	$[0,\infty)$	no	decreasing
(c)	R	$[1,\infty)$	even	increasing
(d)	$(-\infty,0]$	$[0,\infty)$	no	decreasing
(e)	$[0,\infty)$	$[0,\infty)$	no	increasing

PROBLEM SET 2, PAGE 204

1.

	Domain	Range	Increasing or Decreasing	Inverse
(a)	R	$(0,\infty)$	increasing	yes
(b)	R	$\{1\}$	neither	no
(c)	R	$(0,\infty)$	increasing	yes
(d)	R	$(0,\infty)$	increasing	yes
(e)	R	$(0,\infty)$	decreasing	yes
(f)	R	$(0,\infty)$	decreasing	yes
(g)	R	$(0,\infty)$	increasing	yes
(h)	R	$(0,\infty)$	decreasing	yes
(i)	R	$(0,\infty)$	increasing	yes
(j)	R	$(-\infty,0]$	decreasing	yes

3. For $b = 1$, f is neither increasing nor decreasing. For $0 < b < 1$, f is decreasing. For $b > 1$, f is increasing.

5. $f(x) = 5^x$ is an increasing function, while $f(x) = -5^x$ is a decreasing function

7. (a) 3^{25} (b) 5^9 (c) 3^{5x} (d) 5^{3x} (e) 5

9. (a) 2,997,000 (b) 1

PROBLEM SET 3, PAGE 208

1.

	Domain	Range	Increasing or Decreasing	Inverse
(a)	$(0,\infty)$	R	increasing	$f^{-1}(x) = 2^x$
(b)	$(0,\infty)$	R	increasing	$f^{-1}(x) = 5^x$
(c)	$(0,\infty)$	R	decreasing	$f^{-1}(x) = (\tfrac{1}{2})^x$
(d)	$(0,\infty)$	R	increasing	$f^{-1}(x) = 4^x$
(e)	$(0,\infty)$	R	increasing	$f^{-1}(x) = \pi^x$

7. (a) $0 < x < 1$ (b) $x > 1$ (c) $x = 1$ (d) $\log_{10} x_1 < \log_{10} x_2$

PROBLEM SET 4, PAGE 211

2. (a) 0.6020 (b) 1.2552 (c) 3 (d) 0.0602 (e) 3.4771 (f) 0.6990 (g) 1.7781
   (h) -0.3010 (i) -0.4771 (j) 0

5. (a) $\{7\}$ (b) $\{\tfrac{1}{9}\}$ (c) $\emptyset$ (d) $\{3,4\}$ (e) $\{-2\}$ (f) $\left\{\dfrac{-11 + \sqrt{217}}{12}\right\}$ (g) $\{7\}$

PROBLEM SET 5, PAGE 220

1. (a) $0.1761 - 2$ (b) $0.1895 + 3$ (c) $0.3625 - 3$ (d) $0.9007 + 2$
   (e) $0.5228 + 1$ (f) $0.2304 + 1$ (g) $0.1367 - 6$ (h) $0.1367 + 6$
   (i) $0.2864 - 2$ (j) 0.0954 (k) 4.9216 (l) 0.5583

5. (a) $\tfrac{8451}{3010}$ (b) $\tfrac{6990}{4343}$ (c) $\tfrac{12304}{30629}$ (d) $\tfrac{4000}{511}$

7. (a) 1,808,000 (b) 15.65 min.

9. $A = 1270$ (b) 11.7

PROBLEM SET 6, PAGE 230

7. (a) 273 (b) 1 (c) 15 (d) 273 (e) 1 (f) 6 (g) 455 (h) n (i) 15

9. (a) $x^{20} + 20ax^{18} + 180a^2x^{16} + 960a^3x^{14}$ (b) $64a^6 - 192\dfrac{a^5}{b} + 240\dfrac{a^4}{b^2} - 160\dfrac{a^3}{b^3}$

(c) $\left(\dfrac{x}{2}\right)^{7/2} + 14\left(\dfrac{x}{2}\right)^3 y + 84\left(\dfrac{x}{2}\right)^{5/2} y^2 + 280x^2 y^3$

(d) $\dfrac{1}{a^{11}} + \dfrac{11x}{2a^{10}} + \dfrac{55x^2}{4a^9} + \dfrac{165x^3}{8a^8}$ (e) $a^8 - 16a^{21/2}x^2 + 112a^9 x^4 - 448a^{15/2} x^6$

11. (a) $\tfrac{455}{4096}x^{24}a^3$ (b) $-8064y^{10}z^5$ (c) $-\tfrac{1792}{9}x^{12}a^6$ (d) $924x^6 a^3$ (e) $\tfrac{84}{729}a^3 x^{12}$
    (f) $2880x^2 y^4$

PROBLEM SET 7, PAGE 235

1. (a) 15 (b) 8381 (c) 15 (d) 160 (e) $\tfrac{5}{6}$ (f) $\tfrac{211}{30}$ (g) 30 (h) 95 (i) 500
   (j) $\tfrac{25}{4}$

3. (a) $\displaystyle\sum_{k=0}^{4}(3k+1)$ (b) $\displaystyle\sum_{k=0}^{5} 1/2^k$ (c) $\displaystyle\sum_{k=1}^{4}(\tfrac{3}{5})^k$ (d) $\displaystyle\sum_{k=0}^{3}\dfrac{k+1}{5k+6}$

5. (a) $\tfrac{3}{2}$ (b) 3 (c) $\tfrac{5}{4}$ (d) 8

REVIEW PROBLEM SET, PAGE 236

1. (a) a^{2n+4} (b) 2^{6n+2} (c) x^4 (d) $1/x^3$ (e) $2\sqrt{x}$ (f) $\dfrac{x^{17/12}}{\sqrt[3]{2}\cdot\sqrt[4]{3}}$

3. (a) 11 (b) 9 (c) 3 (d) 4 (e) 4

5. Domain $= R$, Range $= (0,\infty)$

7. (a) $\frac{3}{2}$ (b) $-\frac{6}{5}$ (c) $-1, \log_3 2 - 1$ (d) $-2, \log_2 6 - 2$

9. (a) 1.32 (b) 2.52 (c) 0.92 (d) $\sqrt[3]{2.76}$ (e) 1.64 (f) 0.14 (g) 4.10
   (h) -0.06

11. (a) Domain $= R$, Range $= (0,\infty)$, $f^{-1}(x) = \log_5 x$
   (b) Domain $= (0,\infty)$, Range $= R$, $f^{-1}(x) = 5^x$
   (c) Domain $= (-\infty,0) \cup (0,\infty)$, Range $= R$, $f^{-1}(x) = \sqrt{5^x/2}$
   (d) Domain $= (-\frac{3}{5},\infty)$, Range $= R$, $f^{-1}(x) = (5^x - 3)/5$

13. (a) $\log 7$ (b) $-\log 6$ (c) $9 \log x$

17. $\sqrt{10}$

19. 10

21. $\log_{3/4} (91/100)$

23. (a) 5^{x^2+1} (b) $\log_3 x$ (c) $2^{2x} + 3.2^x - 2$ (d) $\log_2 (x^2 + x + 1)$

25. (a) $81x^4 + 108x^3 y + 54x^2 y^2 + 12xy^3 + y^4$
   (b) $243x^5 + 405x^{9/2} + 270x^4 + 90x^{7/2} + 15x^3 + x^{5/2}$
   (c) $8x^3 + \dfrac{12x^2}{y} + \dfrac{6x}{y^2} + \dfrac{1}{y^3}$
   (d) $x^8 - 8x^6 + 28x^4 - 56x^2 + 70 - 56x^{-2} + 28x^{-4} - 8x^{-6} + x^{-8}$
   (e) $729y^6 + 486y^{9/2} + 135y^3 + 20y^{3/2} + \frac{15}{9} + \frac{18}{81}y^{-3/2} + \frac{1}{729}y^{-3}$
   (f) $x^{27} - 9x^{47/2} + 36x^{20} - 84x^{33/2} + 126x^{13} - 126x^{19/2} + 84x^3 - 36x^{5/2}$
   $+ 9x^{-1} - x^{-9/2}$

27. 7.41

29. (a) 95 (b) 140 (c) 160 (d) 1246 (e) 3276 (f) $\frac{17}{315}$

CHAPTER 5

PROBLEM SET 1, PAGE 253

1.

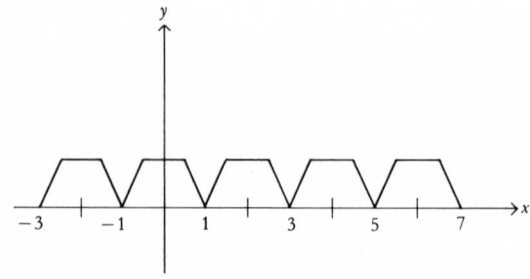

3. (a) $f(1)$ (b) $f(4)$ (c) $f(3)$ (d) $f(5.5)$ (e) $f(4.85)$

4. All are periodic with period a.

5. (a) IV (b) III (c) IV (d) III (e) III (f) I (g) II (h) II (i) IV

6. $P\left(\dfrac{\pi}{6}\right) = \left(\dfrac{\sqrt{3}}{2}, \dfrac{1}{2}\right)$, $P\left(\dfrac{5\pi}{6}\right) = \left(-\dfrac{\sqrt{3}}{2}, \dfrac{1}{2}\right)$, $P\left(\dfrac{7\pi}{6}\right) = \left(-\dfrac{\sqrt{3}}{2}, -\dfrac{1}{2}\right)$,

$P\left(\dfrac{11\pi}{6}\right) = \left(\dfrac{\sqrt{3}}{2}, -\dfrac{1}{2}\right)$

7. (a) $(0,-1)$ (b) $(0,1)$ (c) $(0,1)$ (d) $(-1,0)$ (e) $\left(-\dfrac{\sqrt{2}}{2}, -\dfrac{\sqrt{2}}{2}\right)$

(f) $\left(\dfrac{\sqrt{3}}{2}, \dfrac{1}{2}\right)$ (g) $\left(-\dfrac{1}{2}, \dfrac{\sqrt{3}}{2}\right)$ (h) $\left(-\dfrac{\sqrt{2}}{2}, -\dfrac{\sqrt{2}}{2}\right)$

9. (a) 3 (b) -3 (c) 0

PROBLEM SET 2, PAGE 261

3. (a) $a = 5$, $\cos t = \frac{3}{5}$, $\sin t = \frac{4}{5}$ (b) $\sin t > 0$ and $\cos t < 0$

(c) $\dfrac{\sqrt{11}}{6}$ (d) $\dfrac{\sqrt{91}}{10}$ (e) 1 (f) $-\dfrac{a^4 + 6a^2 b^2 + b^4}{(a^2 + b^2)^2}$

4. (a) $\dfrac{\pi}{2}$ (b) $\dfrac{2\pi}{3}$ (c) 4π (d) 2π

5. (a) $f\left(\dfrac{15\pi}{6}\right) = 0$ and $g\left(\dfrac{15\pi}{6}\right) = 1$ (b) $f\left(-\dfrac{11\pi}{6}\right) = \dfrac{\sqrt{3}}{2}$ and $g\left(-\dfrac{11\pi}{6}\right) = \dfrac{1}{2}$

(c) $f\left(-\dfrac{11\pi}{6}\right) = 0$ and $g\left(-\dfrac{11\pi}{6}\right) = 1$ (d) $f\left(\dfrac{89\pi}{6}\right) = -\dfrac{\sqrt{3}}{2}$ and

$g\left(\dfrac{89\pi}{6}\right) = \dfrac{1}{2}$

8. Both are periodic.

9. $(g \circ f)(x) = 2 \sin x$ whereas $(f \circ g)(x) = \sin 2x$

10. (a) $(g \circ f)(x) = 3 \cos x$, $(f \circ g)(x) = \cos 3x$, $(f \circ f)(x) = \cos (\cos x)$

(b) The domain of $g \circ f$ is R and the range is $[-3,3]$. The domain of $f \circ g$ is R and the range is $[-1,1]$.

(c) All are even

PROBLEM SET 3, PAGE 271

1. (a) $-\sin \pi/4$ or $\sin 7\pi/4$ (b) $\cos 2.56$ or $\cos 3.72$ (c) $\sin 0.97$ (d) $\cos 1.72$

(e) $-\sin 2.9$ or $\sin 3.38$ (f) $\cos \pi$ (g) $-\sin 2\pi/3$ or $\sin 4\pi/3$ (h) $\cos 1.111$

(i) $\cos 1.588$ (j) $-\sin 4.232$ or $\sin 2.048$ (k) $\cos 2.4$ or $\cos 3.88$ (l) $\cos 7\pi/6$

2. (a) $-\sin \pi/4$ (b) $-\cos 0.58$ (c) $\sin 0.97$ (d) $-\cos 1.42$ (e) $-\sin 0.24$

(f) $-\cos 0$ (g) $-\sin \pi/3$ (h) $\cos 1.111$ (i) $-\cos 1.552$ (j) $\sin 1.092$

(k) $-\cos 0.74$ (l) $-\cos \pi/6$

3. (a) $-\sqrt{2}/2$ (b) -0.8365 (c) 0.8249 (d) -0.1502 (e) -0.2377 (f) -1

(g) $-\sqrt{3}/2$ (h) 0.4438 (i) -0.0188 (j) 0.8875 (k) -0.7385 (l) $-\sqrt{3}/2$

5.

t	$\dfrac{\pi}{2} \rightarrow \pi$	$\pi \rightarrow \dfrac{3\pi}{2}$	$\dfrac{3\pi}{2} \rightarrow 2\pi$
$\cos t$	Decreases from $0 \rightarrow -1$	Increases from $-1 \rightarrow 0$	Increases from $0 \rightarrow 1$
$\sin t$	Decreases from $1 \rightarrow 0$	Decreases from $0 \rightarrow -1$	Increases from $-1 \rightarrow 0$

PROBLEM SET 4, PAGE 282

1. (a)

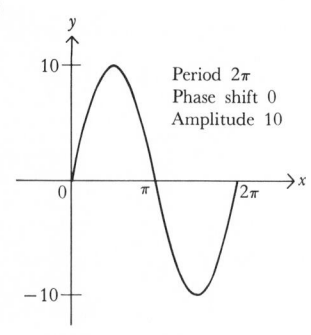

Period 2π
Phase shift 0
Amplitude 10

(b)

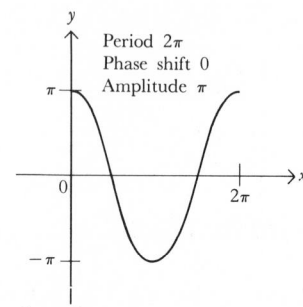

Period 2π
Phase shift 0
Amplitude π

(c)

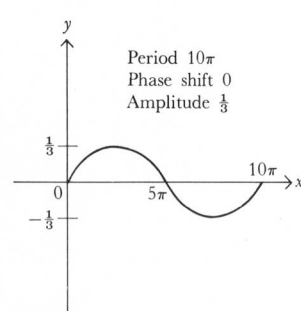

Period 10π
Phase shift 0
Amplitude $\frac{1}{3}$

(d) $3 \cos(-2x) = 3 \cos 2x$

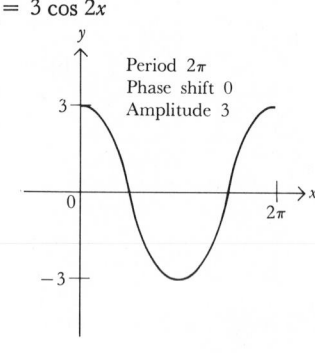

Period 2π
Phase shift 0
Amplitude 3

(f) $4 \sin(-x/2) = -4 \sin(x/2)$

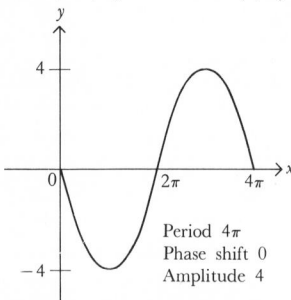

Period 4π
Phase shift 0
Amplitude 4

2. (a)

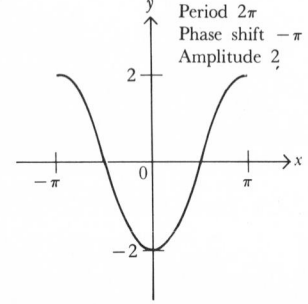

Period 2π
Phase shift $-\pi$
Amplitude 2

(b)

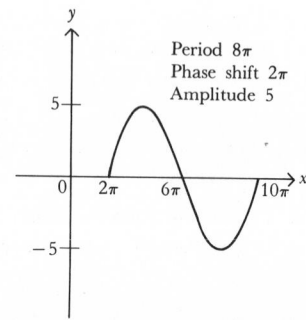

Period 8π
Phase shift 2π
Amplitude 5

(c)

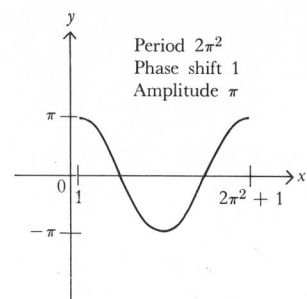

Period $2\pi^2$
Phase shift 1
Amplitude π

(e)

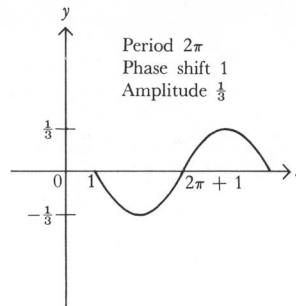

Period 2π
Phase shift 1
Amplitude $\frac{1}{3}$

(h)

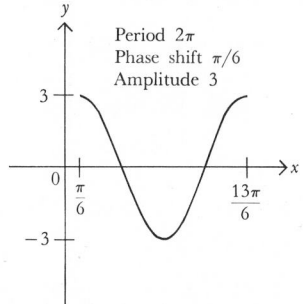

Period 2π
Phase shift $\pi/6$
Amplitude 3

3. The cosine is an even function.

PROBLEM SET 5, PAGE 288

1. (a) $\dfrac{\pi}{2}$ (b) 0 (c) $\dfrac{\pi}{4}$ (d) $\dfrac{\pi}{2}$ (e) $\dfrac{\pi}{3}$ (f) $\dfrac{5\pi}{6}$ (g) $-\dfrac{\pi}{4}$ (h) π (i) $-\dfrac{\pi}{2}$ (j) $\dfrac{\pi}{2}$

(k) 0.212 (l) 0.535

2. (a) $\dfrac{\sqrt{7}}{4}$ (b) $\dfrac{12}{37}$ (c) $-\dfrac{7}{25}$ (d) 0 (e) $\dfrac{\pi}{2}$ (f) $\dfrac{7}{12}$ (g) $\dfrac{\sqrt{2}}{2}$ (h) $-\dfrac{\pi}{4}$ (i) $-\dfrac{\pi}{2}$

(j) $\dfrac{\pi}{3}$

3. (a) $x \in \left[-\dfrac{\pi}{2}, \dfrac{\pi}{2}\right]$ (b) $x \in [-1,1]$ (c) $x \in [0,\pi]$ (d) $x \in [-1,1]$

5. (a) odd (b) neither

7. $f(x) = \sin^{-1} x$ is symmetric w.r.t. the origin.

8. (a)

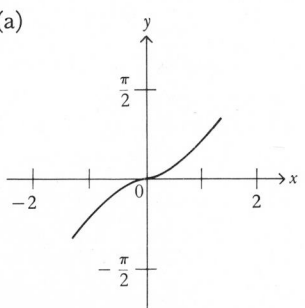

(c)

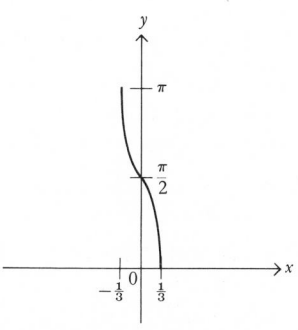

PROBLEM SET 6, PAGE 302

2. (a) -2 (b) -1 (c) $\sqrt{3}$ (d) $\sqrt{2}$ (e) $-\dfrac{2\sqrt{3}}{3}$ (f) $\sqrt{3}$

3. $\sin x = \frac{3}{5}$, $\csc x = \frac{5}{3}$, $\cos x = \frac{4}{5}$, $\sec x = \frac{5}{4}$, $\tan x = \frac{3}{4}$, $\cot x = \frac{4}{3}$, or $\sin x = \frac{3}{5}$,
   $\csc x = \frac{5}{3}$, $\cos x = -\frac{4}{5}$, $\sec x = -\frac{5}{4}$, $\tan x = -\frac{3}{4}$, $\cot x = -\frac{4}{3}$

4. (a) -1.704 (b) -1.003 (c) -1.526 (d) -1.183 (e) -1.051

5.

	$\tan x$	$\cot x$	$\sec x$	$\csc x$
i	$\left\{x \middle| x \neq \dfrac{\pi}{2} + n\pi\right\}$	$\{x \mid x \neq n\pi\}$	$\left\{x \middle| x \neq \dfrac{\pi}{2} + n\pi\right\}$	$\{x \mid x \neq n\pi\}$
ii	R	R	$(-\infty, -1] \cup [1, \infty)$	$(-\infty, -1] \cup [1, \infty)$
iii	odd (sym-origin)	odd (sym-origin)	even (sym-y axis)	odd (sym-origin)
iv	no	no	no	no
v	no	no	no	no
vi	π	π	2π	2π

7. (a)

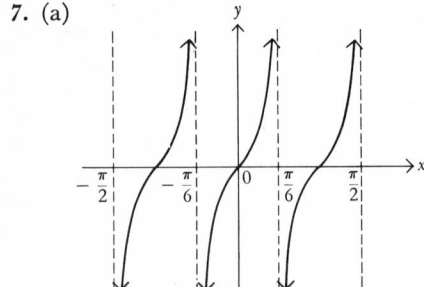

(b)

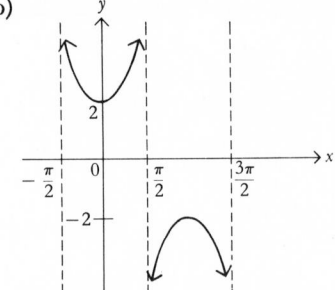

(c)

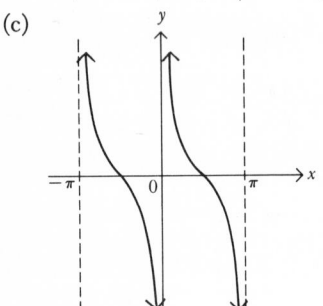

(h)

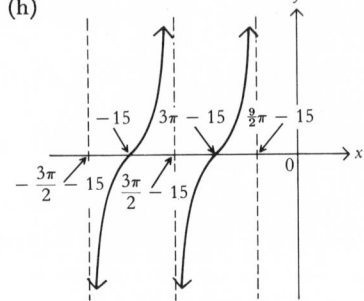

9. (e) $\tan^{-1}\left(\dfrac{\sqrt{3}}{3}\right) = \dfrac{\pi}{6}$, $\arctan(-1) = -\dfrac{\pi}{4}$, $\tan^{-1}\left(\cos\dfrac{\pi}{2}\right) = 0$

(f)

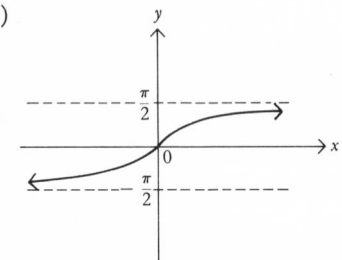

11. (a) x (b) $1/\sqrt{x^2 + 1}$

REVIEW PROBLEM SET, PAGE 304

1. (a) 4   (b) -4 (c) -4 (d) 0

3. (a) $\{2,3,4\}$ (b) yes, 3   (c) 2

5. (a) $\left\{t \middle| t = \dfrac{\pi}{4} + 2k\pi,\ k \in I\right\} \cup \left\{t \middle| t = \dfrac{5\pi}{4} + 2k\pi,\ k \in I\right\}$

  (b) $\left\{t \middle| t = \dfrac{3\pi}{4} + 2k\pi,\ k \in I\right\} \cup \left\{t \middle| t = \dfrac{7\pi}{4} + 2k\pi,\ k \in I\right\}$

7. (a) 0.2482   (b) 0.7446   (c) 0.7291   (d) 11.081   (e) 0.0208   (f) 1.629
  (g) 1.697   (h) -0.7139 (i) 0.3436   (j) 0.9284

9.

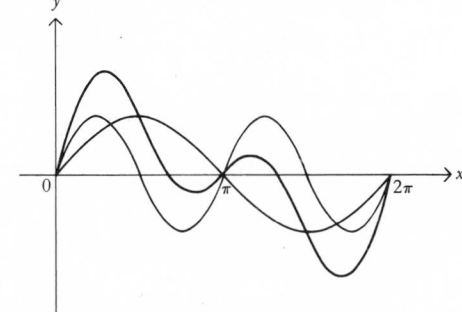

11. (a) $\frac{1}{2}$ (b) $\sqrt{3}$ (c) $\pi/4$ (d) $-\sqrt{3}/2$ (e) $\sqrt{2}/2$ (f) $x + 1$ (g) x (h) $1/2x$
  (i) 0.753   (j) 1.32   (k) $(1 + x^2)$ (l) 1.1

CHAPTER 6

PROBLEM SET 1, PAGE 320

1. (a) $2\pi/9$ (b) $-630°$ (c) $37\pi/15$ (d) $-19\pi/36$ (e) $1260°$ (f) $11\pi/6$
  (g) $-\pi/6$ (h) $330°$ (i) $46.98°/\pi$ (j) $-1517.4°/\pi$

2. (a) $\dfrac{3\pi}{2}$ in.   (b) $\dfrac{8\pi}{5}$ in.   (c) $\dfrac{5\pi}{3}$ in.   (d) $\dfrac{55\pi}{4}$ in.   (e) $\dfrac{7\pi^2}{180}$ in.

3. (a) $\dfrac{48\pi}{11}$ sq in.   (b) π sq in.   (c) $\dfrac{121\pi}{8}$ sq in.   (d) $\dfrac{2401\pi}{18}$ sq in.   (e) 8π sq in.

5. $\sin 60° = \sqrt{3}/2$, $\cos 60° = \frac{1}{2}$, $\tan 60° = \sqrt{3}$, $\csc 60° = 2\sqrt{3}/3$, $\sec 60° = 2$,
  $\cot 60° = \sqrt{3}/3$. No, same terminal side.

6. (a) $\sin \theta = 0$, $\cos \theta = -1$, $\tan \theta = 0$, $\sec \theta = -1$, $\csc \theta$ and $\cot \theta$ are undefined.
  (c) $\sin \theta = -10/\sqrt{149}$, $\cos \theta = 7/\sqrt{149}$, $\tan \theta = -\frac{10}{7}$, $\csc \theta = -\sqrt{149}/10$,
  $\sec \theta = \sqrt{149}/7$, $\cot \theta = -\frac{7}{10}$
  (e) $\theta = 120°$ (f) $x = \pm\sqrt{105}$ (g) $\sin \theta = \pm\sqrt{11}/6$, $\tan \theta = \pm\sqrt{11}/5$,
  $\csc \theta = \pm 6\sqrt{11}/11$, $\sec \theta = \frac{6}{5}$, $\cot \theta = \pm 5\sqrt{11}/11$

PROBLEM SET 2, PAGE 327

1.

θ measure		sin θ	cos θ	tan θ	cot θ	sec θ	csc θ
Degree	Radian						
0°	0	0	1	0	undef.	1	undef.
30°	$\dfrac{\pi}{6}$	$\dfrac{1}{2}$	$\dfrac{\sqrt{3}}{2}$	$\dfrac{\sqrt{3}}{3}$	$\sqrt{3}$	$\dfrac{2\sqrt{3}}{3}$	2
45°	$\dfrac{\pi}{4}$	$\dfrac{\sqrt{2}}{2}$	$\dfrac{\sqrt{2}}{2}$	1	1	$\sqrt{2}$	$\sqrt{2}$
60°	$\dfrac{\pi}{3}$	$\dfrac{\sqrt{3}}{2}$	$\dfrac{1}{2}$	$\sqrt{3}$	$\dfrac{\sqrt{3}}{3}$	2	$\dfrac{2\sqrt{3}}{3}$
90°	$\dfrac{\pi}{2}$	1	0	undef.	0	undef.	1
135°	$\dfrac{3\pi}{4}$	$\dfrac{\sqrt{2}}{2}$	$-\dfrac{\sqrt{2}}{2}$	−1	−1	$-\sqrt{2}$	$-\sqrt{2}$
150°	$\dfrac{5\pi}{6}$	$\dfrac{1}{2}$	$-\dfrac{\sqrt{3}}{2}$	$-\dfrac{\sqrt{3}}{3}$	$-\sqrt{3}$	$-\dfrac{2\sqrt{3}}{3}$	2
180°	π	0	−1	0	undef.	−1	undef.

3. (a) All are positive   (b) sin θ and csc θ are positive and the rest are negative
(c) tan θ and cot θ are positive and the rest are negative   (d) cos θ and sec θ are
positive and the rest are negative

6. (a) $-\sqrt{3}/2$ (b) −2 (c) $\sqrt{2}/2$ (d) $\sqrt{3}$ (e) $\frac{1}{2}$ (f) −2

7. (a) $-\sin 21°$ (b) $-\cos 55°$ (c) $-\tan 35°$ (d) $-\csc 40°$ (e) $-\sin 37°45'$
(f) $-\sec 80°$ (g) $-\cot 78°$

PROBLEM SET 3, PAGE 334

3. (a) 1 (b) 1 (c) $\cos^4 t + \sin^4 t - \cos^2 t \sin^2 t$ (d) 1

5. (a) $\frac{24}{25}$ (b) $\frac{7}{25}$ (c) $\frac{117}{125}, -\frac{44}{125}$

7. (a) $\dfrac{\sqrt{2 - \sqrt{2}}}{2}$ (b) $\dfrac{\sqrt{2 + \sqrt{3}}}{2}$ (c) $\dfrac{\sqrt{6} + \sqrt{2}}{4}$ (d) $\dfrac{\sqrt{2 - \sqrt{2}}}{2}$

(e) $\dfrac{\sqrt{2 + \sqrt{3}}}{2}$

10. (a) $-\frac{1}{2}$ (b) 1 (c) $\dfrac{\sqrt{3}}{2}$ (d) $-\dfrac{\sqrt{3}}{2}$ (e) $-\dfrac{\sqrt{3}}{2}$ (f) $\dfrac{\sqrt{2 + \sqrt{3}}}{2}$

13. (a) $\dfrac{1 + 2\sin t \cos t}{\sin t \cos^3 t}$ (c) $\cos^2 t$ (e) $\dfrac{\sin^2 x}{\cos^2 x}$ (g) $-\dfrac{\sin t}{\cos t}$

15. (a) $\cos \theta$ (c) $\cot \theta$ (e) $-\cos \theta$ (g) $\sec \theta$ (i) $\sin \theta$ (k) $-\sin \theta$ (m) $\cos \theta$

PROBLEM SET 4, PAGE 341

1. (a) $\left\{ t \,\middle|\, t = \dfrac{\pi}{4} + 2\pi k, \ k \in I \right\} \cup \left\{ t \,\middle|\, t = \dfrac{3\pi}{4} + 2\pi k, \ k \in I \right\}$

(c) $\left\{t | t = \dfrac{\pi}{3} + 2\pi k,\ k \in I\right\} \cup \left\{t | t = \dfrac{5\pi}{3} + 2\pi k,\ k \in I\right\}$

(e) $\{t | t = 2\pi k,\ k \in I\}$

(g) $\{t | t = 0.775 + 2\pi k,\ k \in I\} \cup \{t | t = 2.365 + 2\pi k,\ k \in I\}$

(i) $\{t | t = k\pi,\ k \in I\}$

2. (a) $\left\{x | x = \dfrac{\pi}{4} + 2\pi k,\ k \in I\right\} \cup \left\{x | x = \dfrac{5\pi}{4} + 2\pi k,\ k \in I\right\}$

(c) $\left\{x | x = \dfrac{\pi}{6} + 2\pi k,\ k \in I\right\} \cup \left\{x | x = \dfrac{7\pi}{6} + 2\pi k,\ k \in I\right\}$

3. $x = \dfrac{3\pi}{8},\ y = \dfrac{\pi}{8}$

4. (a) $0.64,\ 2.5,\ 3\pi/2$ (c) $0,\ \pi,\ \pi/6,\ 5\pi/6$ (e) $7\pi/6,\ 11\pi/6,\ \pi/2$ (g) $2\pi/3,\ 4\pi/3$
(i) No solution

5. (a) $240°,\ 300°$ (c) $60°,\ 90°,\ 270°,\ 300°$ (e) $45°,\ 225°$ (g) $90°,\ 120°,\ 240°,\ 270°$
(i) $60°,\ 120°,\ 240°,\ 300°$

PROBLEM SET 5, PAGE 352

1. (a) $c = \sqrt{34},\ \beta = 30°58',\ \alpha = 59°2'$ (c) $\alpha = 47°,\ b = 15.85,\ c = 23.24$
(e) $\alpha = 75°,\ a = 29.86,\ c = 30.91$ (g) $\alpha = \beta = 45°,\ c = a\sqrt{2}$

2. (a) Two triangles: $\beta = 54°30',\ \alpha = 80°30',\ a = 21.4$ or $\beta = 125°30',\ \alpha = 9°30',$
    $a = 3.55$
(b) No triangle   (c) $\alpha = 30°,\ \beta = 85°,\ b = 20.77$

3. (a) $2\sqrt{79}$ (b) $26°\ 23'$ (c) $\alpha = 34°3',\ \beta = 101°28',\ \gamma = 44°29'$

5. 3864 ft

7. 3.095 ft

11. $36°50'$

13. 97 ft

REVIEW PROBLEM SET, PAGE 354

1. (a) $300°$ (c) $56°15'$ (e) $390°$ (g) $480°$ (i) $612°$ (k) $1485°$

2. (a) $29\pi/18$ (c) $3\pi/4$ (e) $19\pi/18$ (g) $41\pi/9$ (i) $\pi/15$

3. (a) $\dfrac{35\pi}{12}$ length   (c) $\dfrac{350\pi}{9}$ length   (e) $\dfrac{6\pi}{5}$ length

(a) $\dfrac{245\pi}{24}$ area   (c) $\dfrac{1752\pi}{9}$ area   (e) $\dfrac{18\pi}{5}$ area

5. (a) $\sin(-330°) = \tfrac{1}{2},\ \cos(-330°) = \sqrt{3}/2,\ \tan(-330°) = \sqrt{3}/3$
(c) $\sin 180° = 0,\ \cos(180°) = -1,\ \tan 180° = 0$
(e) $\sin 210° = -\tfrac{1}{2},\ \cos 210° = -\sqrt{3}/2,\ \tan 210° = \sqrt{3}/3$
(g) $\sin(-120°) = -\sqrt{3}/2,\ \cos(-120°) = -\tfrac{1}{2},\ \tan(-120°) = \sqrt{3}$
(i) $\sin = (-45°) = -\sqrt{2}/2,\ \cos(-45°) = \sqrt{2}/2,\ \tan(-45°) = -1$

9. (a) $-\tfrac{4}{7}$ (b) $\pm\sqrt{33}/7$ (c) $\pm4\sqrt{33}/33$ (d) $\pm\sqrt{33}/4$ (e) $\pm7\sqrt{33}/33$

13. (a) $\pi/4,\ 3\pi/4$ (c) $0,\ 2\pi/3,\ 4\pi/3$ (e) $3\pi/4,\ 7\pi/4,\ \pi/3,\ 4\pi/3$ (g) $0,\ \pi/6,\ \pi,\ 7\pi/6$

15. (a) $\dfrac{\sqrt{2 - \sqrt{3}}}{2}$ (c) $2 + \sqrt{3}$

17. (i) is false, the rest are true

19. (a) $c = \sqrt{74 - 35\sqrt{3}}$ (c) $\gamma = 60°$, $a = 10\sqrt{6}/3$, $b = 11.15$ (e) $\gamma = 48°36'$
and $\alpha = 101°24'$ or $\gamma = 131°24'$ and $\alpha = 18°36'$ (g) $\gamma = 54°17'$ and
$\beta = 10°43'$ (i) $b = 6.7$, $c = 7.8$

CHAPTER 7

PROBLEM SET 1, PAGE 376

3. No

6. (a) $\langle 0,20 \rangle$ (b) $\langle -9,8 \rangle$ (c) $\langle 8,16 \rangle$ (d) $\langle 4,12 \rangle$ (e) $\langle 12,-4 \rangle$ (f) $\langle -12,-8 \rangle$

7. (a) $-5\mathbf{i} - 2\mathbf{j}$ and $|\bar{\mathbf{u}}| = \sqrt{29}$ (b) $-5\mathbf{i} - 3\mathbf{j}$ and $|\bar{\mathbf{u}}| = \sqrt{34}$
(c) $5\mathbf{i} - 11\mathbf{j}$ and $|\bar{\mathbf{u}}| = \sqrt{146}$ (d) $4\mathbf{i} - 5\mathbf{j}$ and $|\bar{\mathbf{u}}| = \sqrt{41}$
(e) $-6\mathbf{i} - 6\mathbf{j}$ and $|\bar{\mathbf{u}}| = 6\sqrt{2}$ (f) $4\mathbf{i} + 2\mathbf{j}$ and $|\bar{\mathbf{u}}| = 2\sqrt{5}$

8. (a) $(\frac{10}{3},2)$ (b) $\left(\dfrac{28}{\sqrt{130}} - 6, \ \dfrac{36}{\sqrt{130}} - 10 \right)$

9. (a) Vectors with terminal points on the line $y = -2x$
(b) Vectors with terminal points on the line segment between $(0,2)$ and $(3,4)$
(c) Line $y = -\frac{1}{5}x + \frac{14}{5}$

PROBLEM SET 2, PAGE 381

1. (a) -6, $109°30'$ (b) 6, $53°10'$ (c) -1, $108°30'$ (d) 0, $90°$

3. (a) $\sqrt{13}$ (b) 3 (c) $-6\sqrt{34}/17$

5. (a) $(16|\bar{\mathbf{u}}|^2 + 25|\bar{\mathbf{v}}|^2)^{1/2}$ (b) $\sqrt{2}\,|\bar{\mathbf{u}}|\,|\bar{\mathbf{v}}|$ (c) $(4|\bar{\mathbf{u}}|^2 + 9|\bar{\mathbf{v}}|^2)^{1/2}$ (d) $|\bar{\mathbf{u}}|$

PROBLEM SET 3, PAGE 393

1. (a) $\dfrac{\sqrt{3}}{2}\mathbf{i} + \frac{1}{2}\mathbf{j}$ (b) $-\frac{1}{2}\mathbf{i} + \dfrac{\sqrt{3}}{2}\mathbf{j}$

(c) $2\sqrt{3}\,\mathbf{i} + 2\mathbf{j}$, $\left(\dfrac{-7\sqrt{3} - 5}{2} \right)\mathbf{i} + \left(\dfrac{-7 + 5\sqrt{3}}{2} \right)\mathbf{j}$, $4\mathbf{i} - 4\sqrt{3}\,\mathbf{j}$,

$\left(\dfrac{\sqrt{3} + 1}{2} \right)\mathbf{i} + \left(\dfrac{1 - \sqrt{3}}{2} \right)\mathbf{j}$ (d) yes, $-30°$ rotation

2. (a) $180°$ (b) $-\mathbf{j}$ (c) $225°$ rotation

8. (a) $\langle 3t + 1, -t + 4 \rangle$ (b) $\langle t,3 \rangle$ (c) $\langle 2,t \rangle$ (d) $\langle t, -3t - 1 \rangle$ (e) $\langle t, -\frac{1}{2}t + \frac{5}{2} \rangle$

REVIEW PROBLEM SET, PAGE 394

1. (a) $\frac{1}{2}$ (b) 2 (c) -1 (d) $\frac{3}{4}$

3. (a) 0   (b) 40   (c) 50   (d) 50   (e) 55   (f) 125   (g) 60   (h) 275

5. One possible solution is $s = 1, t = 4, r = -1$

6. (a) $-\frac{1}{2}i + \frac{\sqrt{3}}{2}j$ (b) $-i$ (c) $\frac{\sqrt{2}}{2}i - \frac{\sqrt{2}}{2}j$ (d) $-0.1736i + 0.9848j$

9. (a) $\langle 5\sqrt{3}/2, \frac{5}{2}\rangle$ (b) $\langle 3\sqrt{2}, 3\sqrt{2}\rangle$ (c) $\langle 4, 4\sqrt{3}\rangle$

11. (a) $\langle -3, 2\rangle$ (b) $\langle 2, \frac{17}{3}\rangle$ (c) $\langle \frac{17}{2}, \frac{37}{2}\rangle$ (d) $\langle -\frac{1}{4}, -\frac{25}{8}\rangle$

12. (a) 10   (b) 60   (c) 132   (d) 124   (e) -24 (f) -97 (g) 9

17. $x = \dfrac{-|\overline{u}|}{|\overline{v}| \cos \theta}$ where θ is the angle between $\overline{u}$ and $\overline{v}$.

22. (a) $\frac{1}{2}i + \frac{\sqrt{3}}{2}j$ (b) $60°$ (c) $-\frac{\sqrt{3}}{2}i + \frac{1}{2}j$ (d) $\left(\dfrac{5\sqrt{3}+2}{2}\right)i + \left(\dfrac{2\sqrt{3}-5}{2}\right)j$

CHAPTER 8

PROBLEM SET 1, PAGE 404

1. (a) $6 - 5i$ (b) $33 - 13i$ (c) $5 - 27i$ (d) $\frac{8}{5} - \frac{1}{5}i$ (e) $7 - 17i$ (f) $-i$
   (g) $\dfrac{25 + 3\sqrt{2}}{34} + \dfrac{(15 - 5\sqrt{2})}{34}i$ (h) 11   (i) $-\frac{6}{7}i$ (j) $18 + 24i$ (k) $\frac{4}{25} - \frac{3}{25}i$
   (l) $-4 + 5i$ (m) $-\frac{3}{5} - \frac{7}{5}i$ (n) $\frac{12}{13} - \frac{8}{13}i$ (o) $2 - \frac{35}{4}i$ (p) $\frac{3}{13} - \frac{11}{13}i$
   (q) $-\frac{3}{5}i$ (r) $-143 - 24i$ (s) $25 - 8i$ (t) $-4i$ (u) -4 (v) $-1 + 3i$
   (w) $-\frac{3}{13} + \frac{29}{13}i$

3.

	$\overline{z}$	Re z	Im z	$1/z$
(a)	$2 - \sqrt{3}\,i$	2	$\sqrt{3}$	$\dfrac{2}{7} - \dfrac{\sqrt{3}}{7}i$
(b)	$1 + \frac{1}{2}i$	1	$-\frac{1}{2}$	$\frac{4}{5} + \frac{2}{5}i$
(c)	$\dfrac{3 + 2\sqrt{3}}{2} + \left(\dfrac{3\sqrt{3} - 8}{4}\right)i$	$\dfrac{3 + 2\sqrt{3}}{2}$	$\dfrac{3\sqrt{3} - 8}{4}$	$(24 + 16\sqrt{3}) - (12\sqrt{3} - 32)i$
(d)	$-2i$	0	-2	$-\frac{1}{2}i$

5. Use the fact that Re $(W_1 + W_2) =$ Re $W_1 +$ Re W_2, where W_1 and W_2 are complex numbers.

7. (a) $13 - 8i$ (b) $13 + 10i$ (c) $5 - 6i$ (d) $5 + 8i$

PROBLEM SET 2, PAGE 424

3. (a) $\{z \mid |z| = 1\}$ is a circle with center at the origin 0 and of radius 1.
   (b) $\{z \mid |z| = 2\}$ is a circle with center at the origin 0 and of radius 2.
   (c) $\{z \mid |z - i| = 1\}$ is a circle with center at the point $(0,1)$ and of radius 1.
   (d) $\{z \mid |z - 1| = |z - 2|\}$ is the set of points on the line $x = \frac{3}{2}$.

5.

	Modulus	Argument	Polar form
(a)	$\sqrt{2}$	$\dfrac{5\pi}{4}$	$z = \sqrt{2}\left(\cos\dfrac{5\pi}{4} + i\sin\dfrac{5\pi}{4}\right)$
(b)	7	0	$z = 7(\cos 0 + i\sin 0)$
(c)	2	$\dfrac{3\pi}{2}$	$z = 2\left(\cos\dfrac{3\pi}{2} + i\sin\dfrac{3\pi}{2}\right)$
(d)	2	$\dfrac{3\pi}{2}$	$z = 2\left(\cos\dfrac{3\pi}{2} + i\sin\dfrac{3\pi}{2}\right)$
(e)	8	$\dfrac{7\pi}{6}$	$z = 8\left(\cos\dfrac{7\pi}{6} + i\sin\dfrac{7\pi}{6}\right)$
(f)	5	$53°8'$	$z = 5(\cos 53°8' + i\sin 53°8')$
(g)	1	$\dfrac{2\pi}{3}$	$z = 1\left(\cos\dfrac{2\pi}{3} + i\sin\dfrac{2\pi}{3}\right)$
(h)	1	$30°$	$z = 1(\cos 30° + i\sin 30°)$
(i)	8	$330°$	$z = 8(\cos 330° + i\sin 330°)$

9. $z_1 = -1 - i = \sqrt{2}\left(\cos\dfrac{5\pi}{4} + i\sin\dfrac{5\pi}{4}\right) = \sqrt{2}\,(\cos 225° + i\sin 225°)$

$z_2 = -4 + 4\sqrt{3}\,i = 8\left(\cos\dfrac{2\pi}{3} + i\sin\dfrac{2\pi}{3}\right) = 8(\cos 120° + i\sin 120°)$

(a) $z_1 z_2 = 8\sqrt{2}\,(\cos 345° + i\sin 345°) = 8\sqrt{2}\,(0.9659 - i(0.2588))$

(b) $\dfrac{z_1}{z_2} = \dfrac{\sqrt{2}}{8}\,(\cos 105° + i\sin 105°) = \dfrac{\sqrt{2}}{8}\,(-0.2588 + i(0.9659))$

(c) $(z_1 z_2)^2 = 128(\cos 690° + i\sin 690°) = 64\sqrt{3} + i64$

PROBLEM SET 3, PAGE 430

1. (a) $-\dfrac{\sqrt{3}}{2} - \dfrac{1}{2}i$ (b) $16 - 16\sqrt{3}\,i$ (c) $-(2^3)(5^6)i$ (d) $-8 - 8\sqrt{3}\,i$

(e) $-\dfrac{1}{2} + \dfrac{\sqrt{3}}{2}i$ (f) $-\dfrac{1}{2} + \dfrac{\sqrt{3}}{2}i$ (g) 2^{30} (h) $2^{25}i$ (i) $-i$ (j) -1

3. (a) $k = 0,\ z_0 = \cos 0 + i\sin 0 = 1 + 0i$

$k = 1,\ z_1 = \cos\dfrac{\pi}{3} + i\sin\dfrac{\pi}{3} = \dfrac{1}{2} + \dfrac{\sqrt{3}}{2}i$

$k = 2,\ z_2 = \cos\dfrac{2\pi}{3} + i\sin\dfrac{2\pi}{3} = -\dfrac{1}{2} + \dfrac{\sqrt{3}}{2}i$

$k = 3,\ z_3 = \cos\pi + i\sin\pi = -1 + 0i$

$k = 4,\ z_4 = \cos\dfrac{4\pi}{3} + i\sin\dfrac{4\pi}{3} = -\dfrac{1}{2} - \dfrac{\sqrt{3}}{2}i$

$k = 5,\ z_5 = \cos\dfrac{5\pi}{3} + i\sin\dfrac{5\pi}{3} = \dfrac{1}{2} - \dfrac{\sqrt{3}}{2}i$

5. (a) $\sqrt{i} = \dfrac{\sqrt{2}}{2} + \dfrac{\sqrt{2}}{2}i$ (b) $\sqrt{i^5} = -\dfrac{\sqrt{2}}{2} + \dfrac{\sqrt{2}}{2}i$

(c) $\sqrt{3 - 3i} = \sqrt{3\sqrt{2}}\,(0.9238 + 0.3826i)$ (d) $\sqrt{16i} = 2\sqrt{2} + 2\sqrt{2}\,i$

7. The roots will be expressed in polar form.

(a) $z_k = 8^{1/3}\left(\cos\left(\dfrac{0}{3} + \dfrac{2\pi k}{3}\right) + i\sin\left(\dfrac{0}{3} + \dfrac{2\pi k}{3}\right)\right)$, $k = 0, 1, 2$

$z_0 = 2(\cos 0 + i\sin 0)$

$z_1 = 2\left(\cos\dfrac{2\pi}{3} + i\sin\dfrac{2\pi}{3}\right)$

$z_2 = 2\left(\cos\dfrac{4\pi}{3} + i\sin\dfrac{4\pi}{3}\right)$

(b) $z_k = 2^{1/4}\left(\cos\left(\dfrac{7\pi}{8} + \dfrac{2\pi k}{2}\right) + i\sin\left(\dfrac{7\pi}{8} + \dfrac{2\pi k}{2}\right)\right)$, $k = 0, 1$

$z_0 = 2^{1/4}\left(\cos\dfrac{7\pi}{8} + i\sin\dfrac{7\pi}{8}\right)$

$z_1 = 2^{1/4}\left(\cos\dfrac{15\pi}{8} + i\sin\dfrac{15\pi}{8}\right)$

(c) $z_k = (16)^{1/4}\left(\cos\left(\dfrac{\pi}{4} + \dfrac{2\pi k}{4}\right) + i\sin\left(\dfrac{\pi}{4} + \dfrac{2\pi k}{4}\right)\right)$, $k = 0, 1, 2, 3$

$z_0 = 2\left(\cos\dfrac{\pi}{4} + i\sin\dfrac{\pi}{4}\right)$

$z_1 = 2\left(\cos\dfrac{\pi}{4} + i\sin\dfrac{3\pi}{4}\right)$

$z_2 = 2\left(\cos\dfrac{5\pi}{4} + i\sin\dfrac{5\pi}{4}\right)$

$z_3 = 2\left(\cos\dfrac{7\pi}{4} + i\sin\dfrac{7\pi}{4}\right)$

(d) $z_k = 1^{1/3}\left(\cos\left(\dfrac{\pi}{6} + \dfrac{2\pi k}{3}\right) + i\sin\left(\dfrac{\pi}{6} + \dfrac{2\pi k}{3}\right)\right)$, $k = 0, 1, 2$

$z_0 = \left(\cos\dfrac{\pi}{6} + i\sin\dfrac{\pi}{6}\right)$

$z_1 = \left(\cos\dfrac{5\pi}{6} + i\sin\dfrac{5\pi}{6}\right)$

$z_2 = \left(\cos\dfrac{9\pi}{6} + i\sin\dfrac{9\pi}{6}\right)$

PROBLEM SET 4, PAGE 434

1. This does not contradict the fundamental theorem of algebra, since the equation is not a polynomial equation.

3. (a) $f(x) = \left(x - \dfrac{1 - \sqrt{17}}{4}\right)\left(x - \dfrac{1 + \sqrt{17}}{4}\right)$

(b) $f(x) = \left(x - \dfrac{3 + \sqrt{21}}{2}\right)\left(x - \dfrac{3 - \sqrt{21}}{2}\right)$

5. (a) $f(x) = x^4 - 5x^3 + 7x^2 - 5x + 6$
(b) $f(x) = x^4 - 6x^3 + 14x^2 - 14x + 8$
(c) $f(x) = x^4 - 2x^3 + 20x^2 - 20x + 100$
(d) $f(x) = x^8 - x^7 + 6x^6 - 6x^5 + 9x^4 - 9x^3 + 4x^2 - 4x$
(e) $f(x) = x^4 - 3x^3 + x^2 + 4$

REVIEW PROBLEM SET, PAGE 435

1. (a) $10 - 5i$ (b) 16 (c) $1 + 11i$ (d) $-1 + 3i$ (e) $30 - 16i$ (f) $-\frac{15}{13} + \frac{23}{13}i$
   (g) $\frac{5}{7} - ((6\sqrt{3})/7)i$ (h) $-\frac{5}{4} - \frac{3}{4}i$

3. Either x or y is equal to 0 or both are equal to 0.

5. (a) $((5\sqrt{2}/2),(5\sqrt{2}/2))$ (b) $(0,-2)$ (c) $(-1,-1)$ (d) $(-3,0)$ (e) $(0,-3)$
   (f) $(-1,-\sqrt{3})$

7. (a) Polar form: $z_1 z_2 = 5(\cos 225° + i \sin 225°)$, $z_1/z_2 = 5(\cos 115° + i \sin 115°)$
       Rectangular form: $z_1 z_2 = -(5\sqrt{2}/2) - (5\sqrt{2}/2)i$, $z_1/z_2 = -2.1130 + 4.5315i$
   (b) Polar form: $z_1 z_2 = 6(\cos 90° + i \sin 90°)$, $z_1/z_2 = \frac{2}{3}(\cos 10° + i \sin 10°)$
       Rectangular form: $z_1 z_2 = 6i$, $z_1/z_2 = \frac{2}{3}(0.9848 + 0.1736i)$
   (c) Polar form: $z_1 z_2 = 18(\cos 305° + i \sin 305°)$, $z_1/z_2 = 2(\cos 155° + i \sin 155°)$
       Rectangular form: $z_1 z_2 = 18(0.5735 - 0.8191i)$, $z_1/z_2 = 2(-0.9063 + 0.4226i)$
   (d) Polar form: $z_1 z_2 = 12(\cos 322° + i \sin 322°)$, $z_1/z_2 = 3(\cos 102° - i \sin 102°)$
       Rectangular form: $z_1 z_2 = 12(0.7880 - 0.6156i)$, $z_1/z_2 = 3(-0.2079 - 0.9781i)$
   (e) Polar form: $z_1 z_2 = 98(\cos 370° + i \sin 370°)$, $z_1/z_2 = 2(\cos 240° + i \sin 240°)$
       Rectangular form: $z_1 z_2 = 98(0.9848 + 0.1736i)$, $z_1/z_2 = 2(-\frac{1}{2} - (\sqrt{3}/2)i)$

8. (a) $\frac{1}{2} - (\sqrt{3}/2)i$ (b) 2^{20} (c) -1 (d) 1 (c) -2^{30}

11. $\cos 5\theta = \cos^5 \theta - 8 \sin^2 \theta \cos^3 \theta + 5 \sin^4 \theta \cos \theta$
    $\sin 5\theta = 5 \sin \theta \cos^4 \theta - 8 \sin^3 \theta \cos^2 \theta + \sin^5 \theta$

13. $\operatorname{Re} z = 5 \cos 80°$, $\operatorname{Im} z = 5 \sin 80°$, $|z| = 5$

15. (a) $f(x) = x^4 + 4x^3 - 5x^2 - 36x - 36$ (b) $f(x) = x^3 - 6x^2 + 13x - 10$
    (c) $f(x) = x^4 + 2x^3 - 17x^2 - 18x + 72$
    (d) $f(x) = x^5 - 8x^4 + 12x^3 + 26x^2 - 61x + 30$
    (e) $f(x) = x^4 - 2x^3 + 3x^2 - 2x + 2$

CHAPTER 9

PROBLEM SET 1, PAGE 443

1.

	Center	Radius
(a)	$(3,1)$	2
(b)	$(-5,3)$	3
(c)	$(1,-2)$	4
(d)	$(-2,3)$	$3\sqrt{2}$
(e)	$(\frac{3}{2},-2)$	$\frac{3}{2}$
(f)	$(3,-4)$	$5\sqrt{2}$
(g)	$(1,-\frac{3}{2})$	$\frac{1}{2}$

3. $(x - 6)^2 + (y + 2)^2 = 10$ or $x^2 + (y + 4)^2 = 10$

5. The graph of $x^2 + y^2 = r^2$ is not a function, since every value of x is associated with more than one value of y.

7. $y = \sqrt{9 - x^2}$ is a function with domain $[-3,3]$ and range $[0,3]$. It is not one-to-one. $y = -\sqrt{9 - x^2}$ is a function with domain $[-3,3]$ and range $[-3,0]$. It is not one-to-one. $x^2 + y^2 = 9$ is not a function, with the domain of the relation $[-3,3]$ and the range $[-3,3]$.

9. $(x - h)^2 + (y - k)^2 = r^2$

(a) $C = \begin{bmatrix} x & y \\ -y & x \end{bmatrix}$, $\det C = x^2 + y^2 = 1$

(b) $C = \begin{bmatrix} x - a & y - b \\ -(y - b) & x - a \end{bmatrix}$, $\det C = (x - a)^2 + (y - b)^2 = 1$

(c) $C = \begin{bmatrix} x - h & y - h \\ -(y - h) & x - h \end{bmatrix}$, $\det C = (x - h)^2 + (y - h)^2 = 1$

(d) $C = \begin{bmatrix} x - h & y - h^2 \\ -(y - h^2) & x - h \end{bmatrix}$, $\det C = (x - h)^2 + (y - h^2)^2 = 1$

11. $(x + 2)^2 + (y + 2)^2 = 25$ or $x^2 + (y - 2)^2 = 25$

PROBLEM SET 2, PAGE 450

1. i) (a) $(2,-1)$ (b) $(1,5)$ (c) $(4,10)$ (d) $(2,-2)$ (e) $(-1,3)$ (f) $(0,0)$
   ii) (a) $(9,-1)$ (b) $(8,5)$ (c) $(11,10)$ (d) $(9,-2)$ (e) $(6,3)$ (f) $(7,0)$

3. $\{(x,y) \mid y = 2x + 1\} = \{(\bar{x},\bar{y}) \mid \bar{y} - 2 = 2(\bar{x} + 1) + 1\}$

5. (a) $\bar{x} = x + 4$, $\bar{y} = y - \frac{7}{4}$ (b) $\bar{x} = x + \frac{7}{6}$, $\bar{y} = y - \frac{5}{6}$
   (c) $\bar{x} = x - 4$, $\bar{y} = y - 5$

PROBLEM SET 3, PAGE 462

1.

	Vertices	Foci
(a)	$(3,0)$, $(-3,0)$, $(0,2)$, $(0,-2)$	$(\sqrt{5},0)$, $(-\sqrt{5},0)$
(b)	$(4,0)$, $(-4,0)$, $(0,3)$, $(0,-3)$	$(\sqrt{7},0)$, $(-\sqrt{7},0)$
(c)	$(0,5)$, $(0,-5)$, $(4,0)$, $(-4,0)$	$(0,3)$, $(0,-3)$
(d)	$(0,4)$, $(0,-4)$, $(2,0)$, $(-2,0)$	$(0,2\sqrt{3})$, $(0,-2\sqrt{3})$
(e)	$(\frac{1}{5},0)$, $(-\frac{1}{5},0)$, $(0,\frac{1}{3})$, $(0,-\frac{1}{3})$	$(0,\frac{4}{5})$, $(0,-\frac{4}{5})$
(f)	$(4,0)$, $(-4,0)$, $(0,2)$, $(0,-2)$	$(2\sqrt{3},0)$, $(-2\sqrt{3},0)$

3. (a) $25(x - 3)^2 + 4(y + 2)^2 = 100$ (b) $9(x - 6)^2 + 36(y + 1)^2 = 324$
   (c) $25(x - 3)^2 + 4(y - 1)^2 = 100$

5. $ax^2 + by^2 = 1$, since every value of x is associated with more than one value of y.

7. $x^2/a^2 + y^2/b^2 = 1$ is symmetric with respect to x-axis, y-axis, and the origin.

9. $x^2/a^2 + y^2/a^2 = 1$ is equivalent to $x^2 + y^2 = a^2$ and the graph is a circle.

PROBLEM SET 4, PAGE 470

1.

	Vertices	Foci	Asymptotes
(a)	$(\frac{1}{6},0)$, $(-\frac{1}{6},0)$	$(\sqrt{5}/6,0)$, $(-\sqrt{5}/6,0)$	$y = \pm 2x$
(b)	$(0,\sqrt{3})$, $(0,-\sqrt{3})$	$(0,\sqrt{15})$, $(0,-\sqrt{15})$	$y = \pm\frac{1}{2}x$
(c)	$(0,3)$, $(0,-3)$	$(0,3\sqrt{2})$, $(0,-3\sqrt{2})$	$y = \pm x$
(d)	$(7,0)$, $(-7,0)$	$(-\sqrt{85},0)$, $(\sqrt{85},0)$	$y = \pm\frac{6}{7}x$
(e)	$(3,0)$, $(-3,0)$	$(\sqrt{10},0)$, $(-\sqrt{10},0)$	$y = \pm\frac{1}{3}x$
(f)	$(1,0)$, $(-1,0)$	$(\sqrt{10},0)$, $(-\sqrt{10},0)$	$y = \pm 3x$

3. $35(y - 5)^2 - (x + 1)^2 = 35$

4. $\dfrac{x^2}{256} - \dfrac{y^2}{400} = 1$

7. (a) The graph of the hyperbola is symmetric with respect to x-axis, y-axis, and the origin.

  (b) The hyperbola $x^2/a^2 - y^2/b^2 = 1$ is not a function, since every value of x is associated with more than one value of y.

9. $H = \begin{bmatrix} \dfrac{x - h}{a} & \dfrac{y - k}{b} \\ -\dfrac{(y - k)}{b} & \dfrac{x - h}{a} \end{bmatrix}$ and $\det H = 1$

PROBLEM SET 5, PAGE 479

1.

	Vertex	Focus	Directrix	Focal chord
(a)	$(0,0)$	$(2,0)$	$x = -2$	8
(b)	$(0,0)$	$(0,-\frac{1}{2})$	$y = \frac{1}{2}$	2
(c)	$(0,0)$	$(0,1)$	$y = -1$	4
(d)	$(0,0)$	$(-1,0)$	$x = 1$	4
(e)	$(0,0)$	$(-\frac{5}{4},0)$	$x = \frac{5}{4}$	5
(f)	$(-1,-3)$	$(0,-3)$	$x = -2$	4
(g)	$(2,1)$	$(2,\frac{5}{2})$	$y = -\frac{1}{2}$	6
(h)	$(-3,-2)$	$(-3,-\frac{7}{4})$	$y = -\frac{9}{4}$	1
(i)	$(-3,-1)$	$(-\frac{7}{3},-1)$	$y = -\frac{5}{2}$	2
(j)	$(-2,3)$	$(-2,\frac{7}{4})$	$y = \frac{17}{4}$	5
(k)	$(1,1)$	$(1,2)$	$y = 0$	4

3. $4(y - 3) = (x - 1)^2$

5. (a) $\bar{y}^2 = 4c\bar{x}$ open to right (b) $\bar{y}^2 = -4c\bar{x}$ open to left
  (c) $\bar{x}^2 = 4c\bar{y}$ open upward (d) $\bar{x}^2 = -4c\bar{y}$ open downward

7. The parabola $y^2 = 4cx$ is symmetric with respect to the x-axis. Check the symmetry for other cases.

9. $5y - 3x - 6 = 0$

PROBLEM SET 6, PAGE 486

1.

	Eccentricity	Directrix
(a)	$e = \frac{3}{5}$	$y = \pm\frac{16}{3}$
(b)	$e = \sqrt{2}/2$	$y = \pm\sqrt{2}$
(c)	$e = \sqrt{\frac{2}{3}}$	$x = \pm\sqrt{6}$
(d)	$e = 1$	$x = \frac{53}{12}$
(e)	$e = \frac{5}{4}$	$y = \pm\frac{9}{5}$
(f)	$e = \sqrt{2}$	$y = \pm\sqrt{2}/4$
(g)	$e = \sqrt{\frac{1489}{12}}$	$x = \frac{1}{2}\sqrt{\frac{1489}{2}}$
(h)	$e = 1$	$y = -\frac{283}{4}$

3. Center $= (-1, -\frac{3}{2})$

  Foci $= (-1, -\frac{3}{2} - \sqrt{29}), (-1, -\frac{3}{2} + \sqrt{29})$

  Vertices $= (-1, -\frac{13}{2}), (-1, \frac{7}{2})$

  Asymptotes $y + \frac{3}{2} = \pm\frac{5}{2}(x + 1)$

  Eccentricity $e = \sqrt{29}/5$

REVIEW PROBLEM SET, PAGE 487

1. (a) $(x + 4)^2 = -6(y - \frac{3}{2})$ (b) $(y - 3)^2 = -5(x - \frac{5}{4})$

  (c) $(x - 1)^2 = 3(y + \frac{13}{4})$ (d) $y^2 = (10 - 2\sqrt{10})\left(x - \left(\dfrac{5 - \sqrt{10}}{2}\right)\right)$

3. No

5. $(-5,10), (-5,-10)$

7. (a) $5x^2 + 9y^2 = 45$ (b) $36x^2 + 20y^2 = 720$ (c) $64x^2 + 100y^2 = 6400$
  (d) $25x^2 + 21y^2 = 189$

9. (a) $5x^2 - 4y^2 = 20$ (b) $(x^2/64) - (y^2/36) = 1$ (c) $(x^2/225) - (y^2/144) = 1$
  (d) $y^2 - x^2 = 56$

11. Asymptotes $y = \pm\frac{3}{2}x$

13. $3(x - 5)^2 - y^2 = 12$

15. $9x^2 + y^2 = 82$

INDEX

Abscissa, 53
Absolute value, 39
  equality, 39
  definition, 39
  complex number, 407
  inequalities, 43
  functions, 84
  properties, 39
Acute angles, 325
Addition formula
  of cosine, 329
  of tangent, 333
  of sine, 330
Addition of two functions, 84
Algebra
  fundamental theorem, 432
  of functions, 84
Ambiguous case in the solution of
    triangles, 347
Amplitude, 279
Analytic geometry, 439
Analytic representation of vectors, 368
Angles

initial side, 310
  measure, degree, radian, 311
  negative, 310
  sides, 310
  standard position, 315
  terminal side, 310
  vertex, 310
Arccosine function, 286
Arccotangent function, 304
Arc length along a circle, 313
Arcsine function, 284
Arctangent function, 303
Area of a circular sector, 313
Argument of a complex number, 417
Associative laws
  of real numbers, 507
  of complex numbers, 401
Asymptotes
  of tangent functions, 296
  of a hyperbola, 465
Augmented matrix of a system of linear
    equations, 145
Auxiliary graphs, 295

Axioms of real numbers, 507
Axis
  major, 452
  minor, 452
  of symmetry of parabola, 472
  polar, 410
  transverse, 463

Base, 196
  e, 218
  logarithmic, 212
  of an exponential function, 202
  ten, 218
Binomial
  coefficients, 226
  expansion, 226
  theorem, 226

Cartesian coordinates system, 52
Cartesian product, 51
Center
  of a circle, 440
  of an ellipse, 452
Characteristic of logarithm, 213
Circle, 440
  area of a sector, 440
  equation in cartesian coordinates, 440
  unit, 59
Circular function, 255
  definition, 255
  graph, 272
  period, 257
  properties, 256
Closure of complex number, 401
Coefficient of a polynomial, 123
Combination $\binom{n}{k}$, 227
Commutative law
  of complex numbers, 401
  of real numbers, 507
Complement of a set, 33
Completing the square, 164
Complex numbers, 399
  absolute value, 407
  addition, 400
  argument, 417
  conjugate, 402
  division, 402
  equality, 400
  form, 404
  geometric representation, 406
  imaginary part, 400
  multiplication, 400

polar form, 417
real part, 400
roots, 427
subtraction, 402
Complex zeros, 431
Composite functions, 104
  definition, 105
Conics, 480
  definition, 481
Conjugate of a complex number, 402
Conjugate root theorem, 433
Conversion
  cartesian form to polar form, 413
  polar form to cartesian form, 413
Coordinates
  of points of the number line, 22
  of points of the plane, 53
  of polar, 410
Cosecant, 289
  circular function, 289
  graph, 300
  trigonometric function, 323
Cosine
  circular function, 255
  evaluation, 256
  graph, of function, 272
  inverse of, 283
  properties, 263
  trigonometric function, 316
Cosine, law of, 349
Cotangent
  circular function, 289
  graph, 299
  inverse, 299
  period (see problem 12c), 335
  trigonometric function, 316
Cramer's rule, 157
Cut point method, 173
Cycle of a periodic function, 275

Decreasing functions, 95
Definition, recursive, 225
Degree as angle measure, 311
Degree of a polynomial, 123
DeMoivre's theorem, 426
Dependent system of linear equation, 141
Determinant, 152
  cofactor of an element, 153
  definition, 153
  expansion, 153
  function, 153
  properties, 154

use in solutions of system, 157
value of, 157
Difference
  formula of cosines, 329
  formula of sines, 330
  formula of tangents (ff11a), 335
  quotient, 83
Directrix, 471
  of an ellipse, 481
  of a hyperbola, 481
  of a parabola, 471
Discriminant of a quadratic equation,
  166
Disjoint sets, 5
Distance formula, 56
Distributive laws
  of complex numbers, 401
  of real numbers, 508
Dividend, 179
Division, 178
  of complex numbers, 402
  of polynomials, 178
  of two functions, 84
Divisor, 179
Domain
  of an exponential function, 202
  of a function, 75
  of a logarithmic function, 207
  of a relation, 68
  of cosecant function, 290
  of cosine function, 272
  of cotangent function, 290
  of secant function, 289
  of sine function, 272
  of tangent function, 289
Dot product of vectors, 377
Double angle formula
  for cosine function, 331
  for sine function, 331
  for tangent function, 335

e, 218
Eccentricity of a conic, 481
Echelon form of a matrix, 148
Element of a set, 4
Elimination method, 142
Ellipse, 440
  center, 452
  definition, 451
  directrices, 481
  eccentricity, 481
  foci, 451
  vertices, 452

Empty set, 4
Entries of a matrix, 144
Equality
  of ordered pairs, 50
  of complex numbers, 400
  of sets, 5
  of vectors, 369
Equations
  exponential, 201
  linear, 139
  logarithmic, 211
  quadratic, 163
  systems of, 143
  theory of, 431
  trigonometric, 337
Even functions, 97
Expansion
  binomial, 226
  of a determinant, 153
Equivalent systems of linear equations,
  143
Exponents, 195
  definition, 196
  properties, 196
  law of rational, 198
  zero, 196
Exponential function, 202
  definition, 202
  graph of, 203
  inverse, 205
Exponential equation, 201
Extreme values, 168

Factor
  method of solution, 164
  of a polynomial, 432
Factor theorem, 181
Factorial, 226
Factorization theorem, 432
Field, 508
Finite sets, 4
First degree equation, 125
Focal length of a parabola, 470
Foci, 451
Focus
  of a conic, 481
  of an ellipse, 451
  of a hyperbola, 463
  of a parabola, 471
Functions, 76
  absolute value, 99
  algebra, 84
  circular, 255

composite, 105
complex, 405
constant, 125
cosecant, 289
cosine, 255
cotangent, 289
decreasing, 96
definition, 127
determinant, 153
exponential, 202
even, 97
graph, 89
greatest integer, 99
identity, 99
image, 81
increasing, 96
inverse, 109, 285
linear, 125
logarithmic, 205
mapping, 80
notation, 80
odd, 97
one-to-one, 111
periodic, 246
polynomial, 123
quadratic, 163
secant, 289
sequence, 101
sine, 255
trigonometric, 309
value of, 82
Fundamental period
    of cosine function, 257
    of cotangent function, 335
    of tangent function, 335
    of sine function, 257
Fundamental theorem of algebra, 432

Geometric series, 233
Geometry of lines, 133
Geometric representation of complex
        number, 406
Graph, 68
    of absolute value function, 99
    of auxiliary graph, 295
    of cosecant function, 289
    of cosine function, 255
    of cotangent function, 289
    of exponential function, 202
    of greatest integer function, 99
    of inverse function, 113
    of inverse cosine function, 287
    of inverse sine function, 286

of linear function, 125
of polynomial of degree greater than
        two, 183
of quadratic function, 166
of secant function, 289
of sequence function, 272, 276
of tangent function, 289
of sine function, 255
Graphical addition of ordinates, 86

Horizontal axis, 52
Hyperbola, 463, 480
    asymptotes, 465
    center, 463
    definition, 463
    directrices, 481
    eccentricity, 481
    foci, 463
    latus rectum (see Problem 5), 470
    transverse axis, 463
    vertices, 463

Identities
    circular, 328
    trigonometric, 328
    trigonometric (summary), 510
Identity
    element, 508
    function, 99
Image of a function, 81
Imaginary
    axis, 406
    part of complex number, 400
Increasing function, 96
Inconsistent system of linear equation,
        140
Index of summation, 232
Induction, mathematical, 221
Inequalities, 34
    linear, 34
    quadratic, 171
Infinite series, 233
Infinite set, 4
Inner product of vectors, 377
Integers, 14
    negative, 14
    positive, 14
Intercept of a graph, 131
Intercept form of a line, 131
Intervals
    bounded, 30
    unbounded, 32
Interpolation, linear, 215

Intersection of sets, 8
Inverse
    additive, 508
    additive of a complex number, 402
    multiplicative, 508
    of a circular function, sine, and
        cosine, 283
    of a cotangent function, 299
    of an exponential function, 205
    of a function, 109
    of a tangent function, 303
Irrational numbers, 18

Latus rectum
    of a hyperbola, 470
    of a parabola, 472
Law of cosines, 349
Law of sines, 344
Length of an arc, 313
Less than, 25
Limit, 234
Line segment, 22, 309
Linear equation
    point — slope form, 131
    slope — intercept form, 131
Linear function, 124
    definition, 125
Linear inequalities, 34
Linear interpolation, 215
Linear systems, 139
    Cramer's rule, 157, 159
    dependent, 140
    elimination method, 142
    inconsistent, 140
Linear transformation, 385
Logarithmic functions, 205
    definition, 205
    properties, 209
Logarithms
    base e, 212, 218
    base 10, 212
    change of base, 219
    characteristic, 213
    common, 212
    computations with, 212
    mantissa, 213
    properties, 209
    standard form, 213

Magnitude of a vector, 363, 369
Major axis of an ellipse, 452
Mantissa, 213

Mapping, 80
Mathematical induction, 221
    principle of, 222
Matrix (Matrices), 144
    augmented, 145
    column, 144
    determinant, 153
    entry, 144
    row, 144
    row-reduced echelon form, 148
    size, 144

Maximum value of quadratic function,
    168
Measure of an angle, 311
Midpoint, 61
Minimum value of quadratic function,
    168
Minor axis of an ellipse, 452
Modulus of complex number, 407
Multiplication
    associative law of, 401, 507
    closure under, 401, 507
    commutative law of, 401, 507
Multiplicative identity, 402, 508
Multiplicative inverse, 402, 508

n factorial, 226
nth roots, 427
Negative angles, 310
Negative numbers, 24
Null set, 4
Number(s)
    complex, 399
    counting, 3
    integers, 14
    irrational, 18
    negative, 24
    positive, 24
    rational, 14
    real, 19
Number line, 22

Odd function, 97
One-to-one
    correspondence, 19
    function, 111
Ordered pairs, 50
    as functions, 76
    as relations, 68
    as vectors, 368
    in Cartesian product, 50

Order relation
  definition, 25
  notation, 30
  positive number axiom, 25
  properties, 26
  transitive, 26
  trichotomy, 25
Ordinate, 53
Origin
  of Cartesian coordinate system, 52
  on a number line, 22
Orthogonality, 378
Overlapping sets, 5

Parabola, 168, 471
  axis of symmetry, 169, 472
  definition, 471
  directrix, 471
  eccentricity, 483
  focal chord, 472
  focal radii, 487
  focus, 471
  latus rectum, 472
  vertex, 472
Parallel lines, 133
Partial sums, 233
Period
  fundamental, 246
  of a function, 246
  of circular functions, 257, 292, 335
  of the wrapping function, 246
Perpendicular lines, 134
Phase shift, 279
Point-slope form of linear equations, 131
Polar axis, 410
Polar coordinates, 409
Polar form of complex numbers, 417
Pole, 410
Polynomial(s)
  coefficients, 123
  conjugate root theorem, 433
  constant function, 125
  continuity of function, 183
  definition of function, 123
  degree, 123
  division, 178
  factor theorem, 181
  factorization theorem, 432
  fundamental theorem of algebra, 432
  rational root theorem, 186
  rational zeros, 186
  remainder theorem, 181
  zeros, 178, 431

Position vector, 368
Positive angle, 310
Positive numbers, 24
Positive number axiom, 25
Powers of complex numbers, 426
Product
  Cartesian, 50
  dot, 377
  inner, 377
Projection, scalar, 377
Proper subset, 5
Pythagorean theorem, 18

Quadrants, 55
Quadratic equations, 163
  completing the square, 164
  factor method solution, 164
Quadratic formula, 165
Quadratic functions, 163, 165
Quadratic inequalities, 171
  cut point method, 173
Quotient, 179

Radian measure of an angle, 311
Radical, 197
Radius of a circle, 440
Radius vector, 368
Range
  of an exponential function, 202
  of a function, 75
  of a logarithmic function, 207
  of a relation, 68
  of cosecant function, 290
  of cosine function, 256
  of cotangent function, 290
  of secant function, 290
  of sine function, 256
  of tangent function, 290
Rational numbers, 14
Rational root theorem, 186
Rationalizing the denominator, 199
Ray, 309
Real line, 22
Real numbers, 19
  field axioms, 507
Real part of complex number, 400
Recursive definition of powers, 225
Reference angle, 324
Reference number, 264
Reflection across $y = x$, 113
Relations, 67
  definition, 68
Remainder theorem, 181

Repeating decimal, 16
Right triangle trigonometry, 342
Roots
  nth, of complex numbers, 427
  rational, of polynomials, 186
Rotation(s), 382
Row operations, 148
Row-reduced echelon matrix, 148

Scalar, 365
Scalar projection, 377
Scientific notation, 213
Secant
  circular function, 289
  trigonometric function, 323
Sequence, 101
Series
  geometric, 233
  infinite, 233
Set(s), 3
  complement, 33
  description, 4
  disjoint, 5
  element, 4
  empty, 4
  equal, 5
  finite, 4
  intersection, 8
  infinite, 4
  null, 4
  operations, 7
  overlapping, 5
  proper subset, 5
  relations, 5
  subsets, 5
  union, 7
  universal, 6
Set builder notation, 4
Sigma notation, 232
Sine
  circular function, 255
  evaluation, 263
  function properties, 256
  graph, of function, 272
  inverse of, 284
  trigonometric function, 316
Sines, law of, 344
Size of a matrix, 144
Slope, 127
  -intercept form of line, 131
Solution
  of linear inequalities, 34
  of linear systems, 139

of quadratic equations, 163
of quadratic inequalities, 171
Standard form of logarithm, 213
Standard position of an angle, 315
Subset(s), 5
Sums, finite, 232
Symmetry of graphs, 89
Synthetic division, 179

Tangent
  circular function, 289
  inverse, 303
  period, 335
  trigonometric function, 316
Terminal side of an angle, 310
Terminating decimals, 16
Transitive property of order, 26
Translation of axes, 445, 448
Transverse diameter, 463
Triangle inequality, 47
Triangle trigonometry, 342
Trichotomy, 25
Trigonometric equations, 337
Trigonometric form of a complex
    number, 417
Trigonometric functions, 309
Trigonometric identities, 328

Union of sets, 7
Unit circle, 59, 244
Unit vector, 372
Universal set, 6

Value
  absolute, 38
  of a determinant, 153
Vector(s)
  analytic representation, 368
  basis, 372
  dot product, 377
  geometric representation, 361
  inner product, 377
  magnitude, 363, 369
  normalized, 372
  orthogonal, 378
  position, 368
  radius, 368
  scalar, 365
  scalar projection, 377
  unit, 372
  zero, 363
Venn diagrams, 6

Vertex
  of a hyperbola, 463
  of a parabola, 472
  of an angle, 310
  of an ellipse, 452
Vertical
  asymptote, 296
  axis, 52

Wrapping function, 244

Zero(s)
  factorial, 226
  of a polynomial, 178, 431
  rational, 186
  vector, 363